PRAEGER ADVANCED GEOGRAPHIES

EDITED BY S. H. BEAVER

A REGIONAL GEOGRAPHY OF WESTERN EUROPE

A REGIONAL GEOGRAPHY OF
WESTERN EUROPE

THIRD EDITION

BY

F. J. MONKHOUSE

FREDERICK A. PRAEGER, *Publishers*

New York · Washington

BOOKS THAT MATTER

Published in the United States of America in 1967
by Frederick A. Praeger, Inc., Publishers
111 Fourth Avenue, New York, N.Y. 10003

*This is a revised and enlarged edition of the book first
published in the United States in 1959 by John Wiley and Sons, Inc.*

© F. J. Monkhouse 1959; 1964; 1967

Library of Congress Catalog Card Number: 67-25038

Printed in Great Britain

PREFACE

I n his introduction to *Great Britain: Essays in Regional Geography* edited by the late Professor A. G. Ogilvie, Sir John Russell wrote: 'The purpose of regional geography is to describe the regions of a country as they are and to discover the causes that have made them what they are'. It is in pursuing such an aim that the geographer feels that his subject has gone some way to attain a coherence of content which systematic studies, though of course essential and affording satisfying specialisation, sometimes seem to lack.

I must say at once that I do not seek to defend my apparent definition of western Europe as comprising France (less Corsica) and the Benelux countries. This is a matter of editorial apportionment, since other parts which one might reasonably expect to include in western Europe were for practical reasons allocated to colleagues. Nor does this work offer a regional study of each of these four sovereign states as individuals, but is based on major structural and physical units (outlined in Chapter 1) which inevitably disregard man-made frontiers. Thus 'Maritime Flanders' includes the contiguous portions of France, Belgium and the Netherlands, while 'the Ardennes' and 'the Scarplands and Vales of Lorraine' each comprise parts of Belgium, France and Luxembourg.

I fully realise the magnitude of my task and the shortcomings of the result. Much of the satisfaction which I derived some years ago from making a survey of the Kempenland, a small unit-area in north-eastern Belgium, came from visiting this area and studying its features in the field. Ideally I should have treated each of the other regions and sub-regions in similar detail, but life, space and the editor's patience are all too short. I have indeed been fortunate in visiting most parts of western Europe, though in a necessarily more superficial way than the Kempenland; I have stood on top of Mont Blanc and at the bottom of one of the deepest Belgian collieries, I have walked over the heathlands of the eastern Netherlands and across the mistral-swept Rhône delta, and for several summers I have towed my caravan across Europe, halting where we pleased. But I am still conscious of the gaps, the defects, in my personal acquaintance with the west European landscape.

There have been other difficulties. Paradoxically one of these is

v

the wealth of available material, for few parts of the world have been so thoroughly studied and described by geographers. The classic *Tableau de la Géographie de la France* of Paul Vidal de la Blache, published at the beginning of this century, has been succeeded by numerous monographs, many of them elegant, accurate and methodical pieces of work. Belgian and Dutch geographers have also been active, and my footnotes, frequent as they are, can refer to but a small proportion of the vast literature. Of statistical information too there is an embarrassing wealth; even the Grand Duchy of Luxembourg, of much the same size as Derbyshire, publishes an *Annuaire Statistique* exceeding five hundred pages. A major problem therefore has been to preserve some balance in the detailed descriptions, in the presentation of facts. Another difficulty results from the dynamic quality of western Europe, for the post-war years have experienced changes with which it is virtually impossible to keep pace; much of what is here written will inevitably have been modified before this book appears.

In this part of the world one or more alternative forms of place-names are frequently found. Briefly, the policy adopted in this text has been to adopt the official form sanctioned by the particular country, in French, Dutch, or Flemish as the case may be. A few exceptions involve names which have been anglicised or for which there is an accepted form for English readers. It would be sheer pedantry to use the official forms for Antwerp, Bruges, Brussels, Lyons, Marseilles, Picardy and the Scheldt; for these and a few other cases the official name is indexed with cross-reference to the form actually used.

I am happy to express my thanks to numerous friends. Professor S. H. Beaver, who is General Editor of these *Geographies for Advanced Study* and who first suggested that I should undertake this task, has given freely of his help at all stages, and I owe more than I can readily say to his exceptional critical ability. My colleagues in the Department of Geography at Southampton have throughout contributed suggestions and advice. During the course of the work much assistance and hospitality has been received in the four countries from Government departments (notably the statistical offices listed on p. 689), communal authorities, industrial firms and private individuals too numerous to list; to them I collectively convey my sincere thanks.

The heavy labour of typing the manuscript was carried out by Miss D. M. Cross, Miss H. Tranmer and Miss B. Wotton of the staff of the University of Southampton. The maps and diagrams were drawn with infinite care and patience by Mr. A. Carson Clark, cartographer in the Department of Geography at Southampton. The aerial photographs used as half-tone illustrations were obtained through the courtesy of Miss M. D. Roberts, Assistant Librarian of the vast *Aerofilms* collection, and Mr. R. H. Austin of *Sabena Belgian World Air Lines*.

F. J. M.

Southampton,
December 1957

The opportunity of a new edition has enabled a further most important statistical revision to be carried out. The first volumes of the French Census of 1962 are now available, published in 1963 for the *Ministère de l'Intérieur*; population statistics which in earlier impressions related to 1954 have now been replaced by those for 1962. Most of the other statistics and factual material have been brought up to the years 1961–2. Several maps have been redrawn. I am most grateful to my colleague Dr. I. B. Thompson for much assistance in this revision. Monsieur J. Tilmont, *Inspecteur de Géographie de l'Enseignement Moyen et Normal* (Brussels), has kindly sent me a note of a number of minor modifications, suggested by the committee of the Council of Europe concerned with geography text-books, of which I have been happy to take advantage.

F. J. M.

Southampton,
1964

The production of a third edition has enabled further extensive revision to be carried out, in an effort to bring up-to-date the description of this dynamic region. Most statistics have been revised to 1963–5, with the notable exception of French population figures, for which the Census of 1962 remains the most recent source. Several maps and plates have been replaced. The Bibliography has been revised and extended, and within the limitations of space a large number of footnotes has been added, a reflection of the vast amount of recent material available. I am again most grateful to my colleague Dr. I. B. Thompson for great assistance in this revision.

F. J. M.

Southampton,
1966

CONTENTS

ix

LIST OF PLATES

ACKNOWLEDGEMENTS

For permission to reproduce photographs we are indebted to the following:
Aerofilms for Plates II, IV, XLIII, XLIV; Cliché Combier à Mâcon for Plate
LVI; Compagnie Aérienne Française for Plates XXX, XXXI, XXXIII, XXXIV,
XXXV, XXXVI, XXXVII, XXXVIII, XXXIX, XL, XLI, XLII, XLV, XLVI, XLVII, XLVIII, XLIX,
LI, LII, LVII, LVIII, LX; Documentation Française Photothèque for Plates
XIX, XXVIII, XXXII, LV; K.L.M. for Plates I, III, V, VI, VII, VIII, X, XI, XII, XIII,
XVI, XVII, XVIII, XXVI; Photo Alix for Plates LXIII, LXIV; Photographie Aérienne
Aéro-Photo for Plates XXIX, L, LXII; Jean Roubier for Plate LIII; Sabena for
Plates IX, XIV, XX, XXI, XXII, XXIII, XXIV, XXV, XXVII, LIV; S. A. des Charbonnages
Winterslag for Plate XV, Swissair-Photo A.-G. Zürich for Plates LIX, LXI.

MAPS AND DIAGRAMS

MAPS AND DIAGRAMS

CHAPTER 1

INTRODUCTION

Western Europe is rich in regional names which can be used by the geographer to facilitate his analysis and description of unit-areas with a marked individuality. Many of these were former administrative units. In Belgium names such as *Brabant, Hesbaye* and *Flandre* (*Vlaanderen* in Flemish) have been used for centuries ; some, such as Brabant, survive as the names of present-day provinces, others, like Hesbaye, no longer have this administrative significance but are still used to refer to specific parts of the country. In the Netherlands the names *Friesland, Groningen* and *Limburg* have been in use for centuries, and still denote present-day provinces.

It is in France that these wider regional names survive in such numbers, shorn of any administrative significance. About forty feudal units retained their identity as '*gouvernements*' under the *ancien régime* until the outbreak of the French Revolution (Fig. 1), when they were swept away and replaced by eighty-three highly centralised *départements*, since increased in number to ninety. Many of these provincial names are still in common usage ; two examples will illustrate this point. *Provence* is derived from the name *Provincia*, a Roman state with its capital at Aix. Even when the province was annexed to the French kingdom towards the end of the fifteenth century, it retained much administrative autonomy, together with its own language and legal system. But in 1791 the *gouvernement* was split up into the *départements* of Bouches-du-Rhône, Basses-Alpes and Var. Though Provence administratively vanished, the name now affords a convenient term of reference to the Mediterranean littoral between the Rhône and the High Alps. *Languedoc* affords a second example, a name derived from a thirteenth-century linguistic term, the *langue d'oc* of southern France, contrasting with the *langue d'oïl* of the centre and north of the country. The name was later applied in a more limited sense to one of the ancient provinces and is now used to refer to the Mediterranean coastlands between the rivers Rhône and Aude, extending inland to the scarp of the Cévennes, that is, the *départements* of Ardèche, Gard and Hérault.[1]

Within these larger divisions may be demarcated a considerable number of more detailed units known as *pays*. These are of great diversity and their names are of varied origin. Some are derived

[1] This more limited district is strictly known as *Bas-Languedoc* (see pp. 426-8).

from feudal administrative units or families (*Valois*, *Vexin*), others from prominent physical features (*Pays des Buttes*, *Gâtinais*, *Champagne humide*), from a near-by urban focus (*Bordelais*, *Soissonnais*, *Laonnais*), or from types of land-use (*Landes*, *Boischaut*, *Ségalas*, *pays noir*). The origin of many is lost in antiquity, while others have been coined in quite recent times. Most are, however, based on distinctive and characteristic features of geology, relief and land-use which distinguish them from their neighbours, and for that reason the regional geographer can make good use of them.

FIG. 1.—THE ANCIENT PROVINCES OF FRANCE.

S indicates the Saarland, which was incorporated into West Germany on January 1st, 1957; L the Grand Duchy of Luxembourg; and N the Netherlands.

Based on (i) W. R. Shepherd, *Historical Atlas* (1930), p. 146; and (ii) R. L. Poole, *Historical Atlas of Modern Europe* (1902), plate 58.

It was as long ago as 1746 that the Abbé Guettard published a map of the '*zones concentriques*' of the Paris Basin, a revised edition of which, with accompanying '*texte descriptif*' contributed by Monnet, appeared in 1780. This stressed that the surface of the earth '. . . *n'est point formée d'un mélange confus de matières, mais que ces*

matières y sont distinguées les unes des autres et y observent tel ordre,
que pendant une certaine étendue de pays, on trouve que telle ou telle
matière en forme le fond. . . . *De là naît naturellement la division des*
terrains que nous distinguons sous les noms, par exemple, de pays à
craie, et de pays à coquilles, etc. . . .' [1] There were several other early
attempts to discuss and to demarcate the regional units of various
parts of France.[2] It was P. Vidal de la Blache, one of the greatest of
French geographers, who developed the concept of regional studies
to become one of the most fundamental aspects of modern geography.
In 1888 he wrote an article entitled 'Des divisions fondamentales du
sol français',[3] which in the words of Gallois was '. . . *destiné aux*
maîtres chargés de l'enseignement de la géographie'. In 1903 appeared
Vidal de la Blache's great work, *Tableau de la Géographie de la France,*
forming the first volume of the monumental *Histoire de France*
illustrée. After an introductory survey of the '*Personnalité géo-*
graphique de la France', he went on to a detailed description of each
of the main regions. This work stimulated, on the one hand, detailed
monographs which dealt with individual unit-areas ; early examples
include *La Picardie*, by A. Demangeon (1905), and *La Basse-Bretagne*,
by C. Vallaux (1907). Gallois himself produced in 1908 a detailed
'*Etude sur la Région Parisienne' (op. cit.*), in the form of a systematic
description of Beauce, Hurepoix, Gâtinais, Puisaye and the rest. On
the other hand, several general 'regional geographies of France'
appeared, more or less based on Vidal de la Blache. In 1909, for
example, Joseph Fèvre and Henri Hauser published an attractive
geography of France entitled *Régions et pays de France*, in which
under twelve main divisions many hundred of *pays* were described.
They say as introduction : '*Le point de départ d'une division naturelle*
de la France est dans la distinction des "*pays*", *dont les noms, familiers*
aux habitants, ont victorieusement persisté à côté des dénominations
administratives anciennes ou récentes' (pp. 6-7).

Rarely do the *pays* conform to any administrative unit, which
does make it difficult to obtain relevant statistical information. In
1943 the *Service National des Statistiques* inaugurated an official
enquiry '. . . *pour objet la détermination d'ensembles territoriaux*
homogènes, régions, contrées ou pays naturels, susceptibles, pour
l'étude et la présentation statistique, de remplacer le cadre adminis-
tratif traditionnel ou tout au moins de se juxtaposer à lui'. After
the war the newly formed *Institut National de la Statistique et des*
Etudes Economiques set up a *Commission Centrale*, including several

---

[1] Quoted by L. Gallois, *Régions naturelles et noms de pays: étude sur la*
Région Parisienne (1908), pp. 8-9.

[2] These are conveniently summarised by L. Gallois, *op. cit.*, chapter 1 (pp.
8-34), 'La Notion de région naturelle'.

[3] *Bulletin littéraire* (1888–9), vol. ii, pp. 1-7, and 49-57.

distinguished French geographers, among them E. de Martonne. They produced in 1948 an impressive volume entitled *Régions Géographiques de la France*, with a detailed folding-map classifying no less than 520 unit-areas grouped into four orders of magnitude. Each is precisely defined in terms of its constituent *départements*, *cantons* or *communes*, and its area and population are given. Thus although the basis of division is the *pays*, the exact boundaries provide a basis for statistical plotting.

While France is exceptional in the number of these *pays*-names, the result of her physical diversity, Belgian regional geographers have not been backward in their utilisation of such units. In 1913 M. Leriche [1] defined the natural regions of the country, and in 1927 P. L. Michotte discussed the basis of *régions géographiques*. [2] A. Demangeon, in the second volume (1927) of the *Géographie universelle*, 'Belgique-Pays Bas-Luxembourg', delineated such regions as '*Le pays Lorrain*', '*Le pays industriel*', '*Les pays du Rhin et de la Meuse*'. J. Halkin, in his attractive *Atlas classique* (1934), divided Belgium into a number of distinct unit-regions, indicated on Fig. 2. Again, in 1940 Mlle M. A. Lefèvre produced a map, with accompanying text, defining the geographical regions. [3] Many studies have also been written of individual regions. [4] A notable contribution was by R. Blanchard, who produced in 1906 a masterly study of Flanders, [5] which cut across frontiers and dealt with the French, Belgian and Dutch portions as a homogeneous whole.

Belgium is administratively divided into nine provinces, forty-one *arrondissements*, 211 cantons and a large number of communes, officially used as the basis of most statistical returns on various scales. It is significant, however, that the *Institut National de Statistique* distinguishes and utilises ten *régions climatologiques* and fourteen *régions agricoles*. [6] The latter is the basis of their triennial publication *La Statistique agricole* and is shown on a '*Carte formée des régions agricoles*' published in 1951; regions include, for example, '*Polders et Dunes*', '*Région limoneuse*' and '*Haute Ardenne*'. Statistics of

[1] M. Leriche, 'Les Régions naturelles de la Belgique', in *Revue Université de Bruxelles* (1913–14), vol. 19, pp. 185-218.

[2] P. L. Michotte, 'Cartes-types des régions géographiques de Belgique', in *B.S.R. Belge G.* (1926), vol. 50, pp. 301-7.

[3] M. A. Lefèvre, 'Carte des régions géographiques belges', in *B.S. Belge Et. G.* (1940), vol. 10, pp. 49-74.

[4] See M. E. Dumont and L. de Smet, *Bibliographie géographique de la Belgique* (1954), an impressive volume of 450 pages with a large number of entries.

[5] R. Blanchard, *La Flandre: étude géographique de la Plaine Flamande en France, Belgique et Hollande* (1906).

[6] Cf. S. W. E. Vince, 'The Agricultural Regions of Belgium', *London Essays in Geography* (1951), pp. 255-87. By using intersecting isopleths of crop densities, he produced twenty-seven sub-regions within ten main regions.

agricultural distributions and production are tabulated for each unit. In the Netherlands, despite its less varied landscape, *pays*-names are to be found. The *Betuwe* or 'good-land' of the clay-floored

FIG. 2.—THE REGIONS OF BELGIUM.

The abbreviations are as follows: **A,** Antwerp district; **B,** Brussels district; **G,** Gent district; **V,** Verviers district. The area denoted as '*Région Mixte*' comprises a number of small districts—in the west '*Petit Brabant*', in the centre the '*Campine brabançonne*', and in the east the '*Hageland*'.

Based on J. Halkin, *Atlas classique* (1934), plate 18.

flood-plain between the Maas and the Lek contrasts with the sandy heathland of the *Veluwe* or 'bad-land'. The *Bon Pays* (*Gutland*) of the scarplands of southern Luxembourg differ markedly from the *Oesling* (the Ardennes plateau) of the north.[1]

In the regional analyses which follow, reference is made to many hundreds of *pays* in western Europe.

The physical elements of western Europe must form the basis of any logical pattern of regional division, and at first glance three main

[1] G. Baeckeroot, *Oesling et Gutland* (1942).

categories of relief regions can be distinguished (Fig. 3). The ancient uplands include Armorica, the Central Massif, the Vosges and the Ardennes. The younger fold-ranges of the Jura and the French Alps lie in the south-east along the Swiss and Italian frontiers, and the Pyrenees border Spain. The residual lowlands—coastal plains, basins and valleys, border the North Sea and the English Channel on the north, the Bay of Biscay on the west, and the Mediterranean Sea on the south, and form re-entrants within the uplands.

The Uplands.—The ancient uplands have experienced through long periods of geological time a complex series of geomorphological vicissitudes: alternations of folding, peneplanation, *en bloc* uplift and renewed denudation. Widespread earth-movements of Carbo-Permian times were responsible for their basic structures. The Palaeozoic and still older rocks were folded to form a series of vast ranges across central Europe, sometimes given the general name of *Altaides*, which once extended from south-western Ireland to southern Russia. The trends of folding in the west are referred to as *Armorican*, after the Breton name *Ar-Mor*, 'the country of the sea'; the structural lines run at first from west to east, gradually changing in central France until their direction is almost from north-west to south-east. Further east the trend is south-west to north-east (*Variscan*), as in the Ardennes and Vosges. A most complex structural 'apex' occurred in the south of the Central Massif of France where these fold-systems met. The name *Hercynian* is sometimes applied collectively to all these Carbo-Permian fold-systems.

They were slowly reduced to peneplains by a lengthly period of denudation in Permian and Triassic times, to be covered during the prolonged Mesozoic and Tertiary marine transgressions by limestones, sandstones and clays. Renewed denudation, followed by *en masse* movements, produced a series of upland blocks projecting from the surrounding sedimentary plains. During the Alpine orogeny of mid-Tertiary times, these uplands formed stable bastions against the fold-movements from the south, and in fact helped as 'outer horsts' to determine the alignment of the newer mountain ranges. In addition, the blocks suffered at that time renewed *en masse* movement with tilting and considerable faulting; in some areas volcanic activity was associated with the disturbances. Since then denudation has modified the surface features still further. Thus they each comprise a massif of Pre-Cambrian and Palaeozoic rocks— slate, schist, sandstone, quartzite, limestone, together with intrusive masses of granite and with some superficial products of volcanic activity. Smaller areas of newer rocks are preserved in basins and depressions within the uplands or on their margins.

In the north-west is *Armorica*, a triangular peninsula projecting into the Atlantic Ocean. Its geological definition appears clearly on Fig. 103, but, it must be admitted, in respect of its eastern boundary more clearly on this map than on the ground. Although geologically

FIG. 3.—THE MAJOR REGIONS OF WESTERN EUROPE.
The 'upland' and 'mountain' regions are distinguished by a stipple.

there is such a profound change from the ancient rocks of Armorica to the limestones of the lowlands of northern France, there is no corresponding change in landscape and land-use; the characteristic *bocage* of small fields of pasture interspersed with hedgerows, copses and orchards extends well to the east. In this case it is necessary to be arbitrary, and to define a boundary which simply follows the geological division.

The *Central Massif of France* is enclosed by the thousand-foot contour and occupies roughly a sixth of the area of the country. It stands prominently above the surrounding lowlands, with a markedly steep drop along its uptilted eastern and south-eastern margins to the trough of the Saône-Rhône valley and the Mediterranean coast-lands.

The *Vosges* rise along the western side of the rift-valley of the Rhine. The western boundary is difficult to define, since the upland mass slopes gradually into the scarp-lands of Lorraine; one can choose the line of the low Muschelkalk hills which form the eastern boundary of the Keuper and Lias Clays of Lorraine.

Finally, the *Ardennes* form the western section of a group of uplands lying across the basin of the Rhine, known collectively as 'the Middle Rhine Highlands'. The Ardennes are situated for the most part in south-eastern Belgium, although a small portion extends into France as far west as Hirson, and they also comprise the northern third of the Grand Duchy of Luxembourg.

These Hercynian uplands may be regarded as the structural nuclei of western Europe, and form four major regions which are described in Chapters 17 to 20.

The Fold Ranges.—The mountainous region of south-eastern France, between Lake Geneva and the Mediterranean Sea, forms part of the fold-system of the *Alps*. The frontiers of France, Switzerland and Italy meet in fact at a pinnacle on the summit-ridge of Mont Dolent, in the north-east of the Mont Blanc massif (Fig. 136). From here the Franco-Italian frontier runs southward along the main watershed between the tributaries of the Rhône and of the Po, leaving many lofty mountain groups within France.

The Alps are primarily the result of mid-Tertiary earth-movements which upfolded vast thicknesses of Mesozoic and Tertiary sediments, accumulated in the geosyncline between the Hercynian foreland of Europe and the plateau-continent of Africa. The direction, nature and degree of this folding depended both on the compressive forces affecting the geosyncline and the position of the rigid horsts of the Hercynian continent. The outer margins of this folded zone were affected only superficially, and are now represented by the sweeping curve of the limestone Fore-Alps which lie between the Rhône valley and the main High Alps further east. They are also represented by the hill-ranges of the *Jura*, extending in an arc for 150 miles from the southern end of the Rhine rift-valley to the Rhône valley east of Lyons. The frontier between France and Switzerland crosses these uplands obliquely from Basel to Geneva, leaving the south-western Jura in France.

A third system of fold-mountains comprises the *Pyrenees*, the crest-line of which for the most part demarcates the Franco-Spanish frontier. These complex mountains, rising abruptly above the Basin of Aquitaine, form a comparatively narrow series of ranges, and though not as lofty as the highest Alpine peaks, they are remarkably continuous and afford few well-defined passes. Structurally they owe their origin mainly to the Tertiary orogeny, but the particular fold-movements occurred rather earlier than those of mid-Tertiary times which were mainly responsible for the Alpine ranges.

The Lowlands.—The basins, coastal plains and valleys which comprise the lowland areas of western Europe are more easily defined after these seven upland and mountain regions have been demarcated. It is possible to describe them in terms of the major river basins (Fig. 4). The main continental water-parting runs north-eastward from the eastern Pyrenees, along the south-eastern edge of the Central Massif to the Plateau de Langres, and so to the 'Belfort Gate' and the Rhine at Basel. To the south and east of this line most of the drainage finds its way through the Saône-Rhône system to the Mediterranean. To the west and north are the basins of the Garonne, Loire, Seine, Scheldt (*Schelde*, *Escaut*), Meuse (*Maas*) and Rhine (*Rhin*, *Rhein*, *Rijn*).

It is not, however, really practicable to describe each of these river basins as individual units. This is partly because they come into such close juxtaposition and their watersheds interlock in a most complex manner, partly because their basins naturally include areas of the uplands already defined. It is more convenient to distinguish seven separate lowland areas; though differing in scale from the extensive lowlands of northern France to the restricted Plain of Alsace, each has an undoubted individuality.

In the north, occupying the Netherlands, two-thirds of Belgium, and part of the extreme north of France, are the *North Sea Lowlands*, bounded on the south by the chalk ridge of Artois, and on the south-east by the line of the Sambre-Meuse valley. Then to the south lie the extensive *Lowlands of Northern France*, a structural depression enclosed by the Ardennes, the Central Massif and Armorica, and filled with varied sedimentary rocks. The heart, the focus of these lowlands, as indeed of France itself, is Paris, and the term Paris Basin is commonly applied. The major problem is where to draw the boundaries on the west with Armorica (where as has been shown it is necessary to be arbitrary) and on the east. Here the lowlands merge into the *Scarplands and Vales of Lorraine*, another region with an undoubted individuality, not limited to France but continued northward into the *Bon Pays* of Luxembourg and the *Côtes Lorraines* of south-eastern Belgium. The compromise effected in drawing the boundary utilises the watershed between the Meuse, which has cut a long south-north furrow through the edge of the

Corallian escarpment, and the almost parallel Aire, the most westerly of the Seine's family of rivers.

There is a broad gap, the 'sill' (*seuil*) of Poitou, between Armorica and the Central Massif, through which the lowlands of northern France are continuous with those of *Aquitaine*. The last is an undulating triangular lowland, about one-seventh of the area of

FIG. 4.—THE MAJOR DRAINAGE BASINS OF WESTERN EUROPE.

France, occupied by a fan of rivers flowing from both the Central Massif and the Pyrenees, and focusing on the Gironde estuary.

The coastal plain of southern France, between the uplands and the Mediterranean Sea, is sometimes known as the *Midi*. From the point of view of structure and relief it exhibits great diversity, but on to this the climate has imposed a unifying stamp reflected both in the landscape and the way of life. To the north the Midi is continued by the *Rhône-Saône Valley*, '*le couloir entre les montagnes*', forming a lowland re-entrant far into central France. Indeed, another low 'gateway', the '*Porte de Bourgogne*' or '*Trouée de Belfort*', leads from the upper Saône valley into the Rhineland. The valley of the Rhine from Basel to Mainz consists of a rift-valley bordered by the Vosges and the Black Forest. The *Plain of Alsace*, varying in width from ten to twenty-five miles, lies on the western side of the great river which for about ninety miles forms the international frontier.

In this way, then, fourteen major physical regions, each with a marked individuality, have been defined (Fig. 3), and are used as a basis for presenting a systematic survey of the regional geography of France and the Benelux countries.

NOTE : FRENCH PLANNING REGIONS

It is interesting to note that in the creation of planning regions (*Circonscription d'Action Régionale*), statistics for which are published in the *Annuaire Statistique de la France* from 1964, the *Institut National de la Statistique et des Etudes Economiques* has returned to many of the old provincial names. The regions are as follows :

Name	Headquarters	Name	Headquarters
Région parisienne	Paris	*Bretagne*	Rennes
Champagne	Reims	*Limousin*	Limoges
Picardie	Lille	*Auvergne*	Clermont-Ferrand
Haute-Normandie	Rouen	*Poitou-Charente*	Poitiers
Centre	Orléans	*Aquitaine*	Bordeaux
Nord	Lille	*Midi-Pyrénées*	Toulouse
Lorraine	Nancy	*Bourgogne*	Dijon
Alsace	Strasbourg	*Rhône-Alpes*	Lyons
Franche-Comté	Dijon	*Languedoc*	Montpellier
Basse-Normandie	Rouen	*Provence: Côte*	Marseilles
Pays de la Loire	Nantes	*d'Azur : Corse*	

PART I

THE LOWLANDS

CHAPTER 2

THE NORTH SEA LOWLANDS: GENERAL FEATURES

For long periods of geological time the North Sea and its margins have been an area of depression and of resultant sedimentation.[1] The structural boundary of this depression on the south is formed by the Palaeozoic rocks of the 'massif of Brabant', separating it from the syncline of the Paris Basin further south (Fig. 5). The 'floor' of the depression is essentially the surface of the peneplain of Hercynian Europe, including horst-like masses which contain coal-bearing rocks at various, though considerable, depths. The filling-in of this depression by sedimentation has proceeded since Permian times. The many deep borings put down by the Dutch and Belgian geological survey departments have reached Permian and Lower Carboniferous rocks in the south-east of the Netherlands and in north-east Belgium, although further north these lie at vast depths as yet unproven.[2] Triassic and Jurassic rocks have been found at depth beneath the surface of the Kempenland and parts of the southern Netherlands, but they do not occur on the surface, as they do on the outer margins of the Paris Basin.

In Upper Cretaceous times a widespread marine transgression spread far beyond the North Sea depression, during which an extensive cover of chalk rocks was laid down. The Chalk now appears on the surface in the Paris Basin, and it is seen also in the neighbourhood of Mons, further east in the Hesbaye and Herve regions near Liège, and in South Limburg. Elsewhere it has either been removed by subsequent denudation before any Tertiary rocks were deposited, as over much of the plateau of Brabant, or it is deeply masked by newer deposits. Thus the anticlinal chalk ridge of Artois dips beneath the Tertiary rocks of the Flanders Plain in Belgium, and in the Kempenland and South Limburg colliery shafts pass through

---

[1] For a full account, see A. J. Pannekoek (editor), *Geological History of the Netherlands* (1956).

[2] Much detailed information has also been obtained from borings put down by the *Nederlandse Aardolie Maatschappij*, an oil company in which the Royal Dutch Shell and Esso groups have equal participation.

Chalk and other Cretaceous rocks at considerable depths on their
way down to workable Coal Measures.

In early Tertiary times a further widespread marine transgression
covered the Netherlands, most of Belgium and the Paris Basin. The
resultant deposits are to be found over much of the surface of central
Belgium. Those of Eocene age include the Flanders Clay on the
Flemish plain and the sands of Brabant and Hesbaye. Oligocene
sands and clays form a narrow interrupted belt along the southern
border of the Kempenland, and occur more extensively to the east in
Limburg. These older Tertiary rocks in the Netherlands are deeply
buried beneath younger deposits.

In late Tertiary times (Miocene and Pliocene) occurred the last of

Fig. 5.—Diagrammatic Representation of the Structural
Boundaries of the North Sea Basin.
Based on J. H. F. Umbgrove, *Symphony of the Earth* (1950), p. 45.

the major transgressions, and the sea again extended southwards
over much of what is now Belgium and even into northern France.
Vast amounts of coarse sandy sediment were laid down in the North
Sea basin. The extent and depth of this late Tertiary transgression
seem to have fluctuated, for occasional beds of brown coal among
the sands and clays indicate temporary conditions of lowland swamp
in which vegetation flourished.

Towards the end of Pliocene times began the steady shift north-wards of the coastline, as the seas receded. This was mainly the result of a widespread tilting movement; it seems that areas to the south of a line indicated approximately by the present Belgo-Dutch frontier were slowly uplifted, with the result that surviving patches of Lower Pliocene rocks now lie in southern Belgium and northern France at a height of approximately 500 feet. To the north of this line, conversely, the tilting movement was downward, so that the Lower Pliocene strata are found progressively deeper; at Utrecht borings have located them at 1,200 feet below sea-level.[1]

There was a marked difference between the subsequent development of the physical features of the North Sea lowlands to the south of this line of tilting and those to the north. The former areas comprise the Plain of Flanders and the 'low plateaus' of central Belgium, the latter include the composite Scheldt-Meuse-Rhine 'delta'. Furthermore, the former lay well to the south of the maximum extension of the continental Quaternary ice-sheets, while much of the northern area was either directly or marginally affected by these glaciations.

THE SOUTHERN LOWLANDS

This section of the North Sea lowlands for the most part consists of the basin of the Scheldt, together with the narrow valley of the Meuse from where it leaves the 'coal-furrow' of southern Belgium to where it opens out into its composite flood-plain with the Rhine.

The various rivers which comprise the Scheldt system flow more or less parallel across the Flanders Plain and central Belgium. The greater part of each of their courses trends from south-west to north-east, that is, approximately parallel to the North Sea coast. This river system developed, during the gradual emergence of the Pliocene sea-floor, as a series of initially independent consequents. Many of the basic features of the Flanders Plain and the low plateaus of central Belgium were formed as the result of active erosion by these rivers in Quaternary times; the valleys of today are far too extensive to have been eroded by rivers of their present size. This enhanced down-cutting was due partly to the increase in volume as a result of snow-melt on the uplands to the south, partly to various changes in base-level. The denudation almost completely removed the newer Tertiary deposits over the whole of Belgium, except for the Kempenland in the north-east and the isolated cappings on the hills in Flanders, Brabant and even as far south as Artois in France. These

---

[1] A map with contours showing the depth of the base of the Pleistocene (exceeding 600 metres in Noord-Holland) is given in A. J. Pannekoek, *op. cit.*, p. 8.

hills rise from the gently swelling interfluves between the wide shallow valley-troughs. This denudation therefore exposed the older Tertiary rocks such as the Flanders Clay and the sandstones of Brabant and Hesbaye. In central Belgium river erosion went even further and cut completely through the Tertiary deposits to expose ancient Cambrian and Silurian rocks in some of the valleys.

In immediate post-glacial times extensive sedimentation was effected by the heavily laden rivers, so that the floors of their valleys are thickly covered with alluvium, in places to a depth of over a hundred feet. Across these deposits the rivers meandered in flood-plains as much as four to five miles in width, towards the still fluctuating coastline. The rivers' courses, like the coastline, have now been artificially stabilised, but abandoned meanders can still be traced among the maze of drainage channels. These valleys, then, together with their gentle interfluves and occasional higher relics, comprise the main physical features of Flanders and the low plateaus of central Belgium.

Apart from some interesting changes due to river-capture, particularly in French Flanders (see p. 141), there is a further important element in the Scheldt drainage pattern. The middle Scheldt (that is, the section below the Lys confluence at Gent), the Durme and the Rupel together form a continuous west-east line, lying broadly at right-angles to the north-easterly direction of the Lys and the upper Scheldt. This line is continued by the lower courses of the Dyle and the Demer, but while the middle Scheldt and Durme flow towards the east, the Demer, Dyle and Rupel flow to the west, with the result that both trends focus on the lower Scheldt and its estuary. The westwards-flowing Demer has eroded a distinct 'furrow' between the southern edge of the Kempen plateau and the general northward slope of the low plateaus of central Belgium. This furrow, therefore, taps the consequents flowing northwards from the plateaus of Brabant and Hesbaye—the Senne, Dyle, Geete and upper Demer, and so leads their waters to the Rupel and hence to the Scheldt estuary.

The only other major Scheldt tributary is the Nethe, which, by means of its two main headstreams, the Groote- and Kleine-Nethe, drains the gentle western slope of the Kempen plateau of north-eastern Belgium. This plateau forms a broad and indeterminate watershed between these headstreams of the Nethe and a few right-bank confluents of the Demer, and those flowing north to the lower Meuse. The Nethe is wholly regularised in its lower course (it is actually siphoned under the Albert Canal), and finally joins the Rupel near the Senne-Dyle confluence.

Thus the drainage of virtually all Belgium to the north and west of the line of the Meuse makes its way to a single outlet. The only exceptions to this hydrographic unity are the Ijzer (*Yser*) and the

Aa, each of which breaks through to the North Sea after following the usual south-west to north-east trend in its upper course.

The present Meuse below Liège flows northwards in a quite deeply incised valley. Though it now receives few tributaries from the west, its past changes of course have profoundly affected the physical landscape of north-eastern Belgium and adjacent parts of the Netherlands. It is probable that the river once flowed eastwards beyond the position of Liège to the proto-Rhine; then it was diverted westwards over the Kempenland, and later still it developed its present northern course, succeeded lower down near Mook by a great bend westwards. These various changes of the Meuse have not been confined merely to the actual course of the river but have also involved alterations in base-level. At times, notably when the melting of the ice-sheets at the close of the Quaternary glaciation returned water to the seas and therefore produced a higher base-level, the response of the river to its resultant gentler gradient was extensive deposition because of the reduction of its load-carrying capacity. At other times, the result both of lower glacial sea-level and of the tilting which raised the land south of an axis more or less along the Belgo-Dutch frontier, the gradient of the river and therefore its erosive capacity were increased. The result has been the formation of a terraced valley, bordered by the Kempen plateau on the west and that of South Limburg on the east.

The results and inter-relations of the erosional and depositional processes of the Meuse have been analysed in considerable detail by Mlle M. A. Lefèvre,[1] who has distinguished between the 'aggradational' or 'depositional' flood-plains built up when the river was unable to carry its load because of a decrease of gradient, and the 'degradational' or 'erosional' flood-plains where the surface has been progressively lowered by the river as its channel migrated. Mlle Lefèvre applies these principles to the lower Meuse basin and distinguishes four *unités cycliques* or 'fluvial complexes'. Cycle IV, the oldest, is represented only by a series of flats at a height of about 600 feet above sea-level, traceable in the Condroz and Herve regions to the south, in South Limburg, and along a west-east line to the north of Aachen. Mlle Lefèvre suggests that this level represents the valley of a former course of the Meuse when it flowed eastwards to join the Rhine, incised in a still older erosion surface at about 725 feet. The Meuse was later diverted northwards, then westwards, and finally again northwards to its present position, producing three further 'fluvial complexes', each of which is represented by a

---

[1] M. A. Lefèvre: (i) 'Le Cône alluvial de la Meuse', in *Annales de la Société scientifique de Bruxelles, Série B, Sciences physiques et naturelles* (1928), vol. xlviii, pp. 121-38; (ii) 'La Basse-Meuse: étude de morphologie fluviale', in *B.S. Belge Et. G., Mémoire I* (1935).

degradational flood-plain (*e*) upstream and an aggradational flood-plain (*r*) further downstream (Fig. 32). The aggradational flood-plain of Cycle III is a *plateau du cône alluvial* (*IIIr*) laid down as the Meuse gradually changed its course in a series of slowly moving curves. It forms a horizontal 'fan' of coarse sand and gravel, with its apex just to the north-west of Maastricht at a height of about 340 feet. It is bounded quite steeply on the east by the later degradational terraces of the Meuse and on the south-west by the Demer valley, but it slopes very gently northward into the Netherlands and westward towards the Scheldt estuary. The deposits thin off from thirty to fifty feet near the apex, to about fifteen feet near the Dutch frontier. Cycle II was responsible for a degradational flood-plain which has been cut into the edge of the Kempen plateau, thus forming a distinct terrace between Maastricht and Maaseik at 130 to 150 feet above sea-level. Cycle I represents the modern flood-plain of the Meuse and its tributaries; the degradational plain is the present valley floor in the neighbourhood of Maastricht, and the aggradational plain is represented by the present joint flood-plain of the Meuse-Rhine and the alluvium-covered floors of the shallow valleys draining northwards across the frontier to the Meuse.

THE NORTHERN LOWLANDS

During the 600,000-year span of the Pleistocene, the glacial epoch produced considerable effects both on those parts of the North Sea lowlands actually covered by the ice-sheets and also on the periglacial fringes to the south.[1] These lowlands lay on the very margins of the maximum advance of the Scandinavian continental ice-sheets. This maximum occurred in the third glacial period (known as the *Riss* or in northern Europe as the *Saale*), about 150,000 years ago,[2] when the ice-sheet extended just to the south of the Zuider Zee. This limit is indicated by a discontinuous series of low sand-hills, extending south-eastward as the Utrecht-Gelderland ridge, then interrupted by the Rhine valley, and continued to the south-east of Nijmegen and into Germany almost to Krefeld (Fig. 6). It would hardly be correct, however, to regard these hills as terminal moraines in the accepted sense, although some Dutch geologists[3] go so far as to call them '*moraines frontales*'. They consist almost entirely of masses of sand and gravel, with little clay, and so these areas are

[1] A. Brouwer, 'De Glacigene Landschapstypen', in *T.K. Ned. A.G.* (1950), vol. lxvii, pp. 20-32, affords a most useful summary with several maps.

[2] Some Dutch geologists have given to the *Riss* (*Saale*) glaciation the local name of *Drenthian*, the only glacial phase in which a Scandinavian ice-sheet actually covered part of the Netherlands.

[3] Notably P. Tesch, 'L'Origine du sous-sol des Pays-Bas', in *T.K. Ned. A.G.* 1938), vol. lv, p. 548.

included in the category of 'sand country' in the regional divisions described below. The ridges may represent a series of *kames*, deposited along the edge of the ice by subglacial streams. On the other hand, they may have been caused by ice-pressure from the

FIG. 6.—THE '*MORAINES DE POUSSÉE*' OF THE SOUTHERN NETHERLANDS.

The abbreviations are as follows: **G**, Gooiland hills; **H**, the Hettenheuvel; **M**, the Montferland; **Ui**, the Uilenput; **Ut**, the Utrecht ridge; **V**, Veluwe.

Based on K. Oestreich, 'La Genèse du paysage naturel', in *T.K. Ned. A.G.* (1938), vol. lv, p. 562.

north, thus 'rucking-up' or 'bulldozing' the glacial drifts and possibly also the fluvial sands and gravels deposited in the preceding *Mindel-Riss* interglacial period. It can be clearly seen in several sand-quarries that layers of sand and gravel have been folded and even overthrust in a remarkable way, if on a miniature scale. If this supposition is correct, the name 'push-moraine' ('*moraines de poussée*', or in Dutch '*stuwwallen*') is justified. These same sandy ridges occur in the Veluwe, in eastern Gelderland and in Overijssel (Fig. 7). All this sandy area, to the south of the Vecht valley, is described by P. Tesch (*op. cit.*) as the '*région des moraines frontales*'.

To the north of the Vecht valley lies an extensive area in eastern Friesland and Groningen which Tesch calls the '*région de la moraine inférieure*' ; this represents, in fact, the ground-moraine of the *Riss* glaciation. Sand, with irregular gravel patches, is still dominant, but there are considerable tracts of boulder-clay. Sometimes two or three distinct layers of this boulder-clay occur, separated by sands and gravels which may well indicate slight fluctuations of this most advanced part of the continental ice-sheet. Further west, in Noord-Holland, the glacial clays occur at greater depths under newer deposits. The surface areas of clay are shown on Fig. 7. Some isolated upstanding masses form the nuclei of Wieringerlant and the island of Texel. Boulder-clay also underlies part of the Wadden Zee ; it was convenient that it occurred so near the line of the main dyke across the mouth of the Zuider Zee, since this material, dredged from the sea-floor and dumped into position, formed a compact basis for the dyke (see p. 49). In Friesland some mounds of sand and clay are of a drumlin-like character.

Occasional erratics are found, some of which are almost certainly of Scandinavian origin. In the province of Groningen and in the neighbouring parts of Drenthe some of these erratics have been assembled by man in the distant past to form dolmens, the famous '*Hunnebedden*' or burial-places, claimed to represent the oldest traces of human occupation in the Netherlands.

The Quaternary glaciation was but a temporary interruption to the development of the drainage system of the Rhine. By the beginning of the Pleistocene these northern lowlands were dominated by a great proto-Rhine, to which the Scheldt, Meuse and Thames were confluents. This system formed the outflow for the drainage of much of central and western Europe. This proto-Rhine and its confluents have built up a vast joint deltaic area, really comprising a complex series of contiguous and overlapping deltaic fans.

During the Pleistocene, sedimentation continued in the areas outside (i.e. south of) the immediate ice-sheet.[1] As the ice fluctuated, so did the base-level of the rivers, corresponding to the changing sea-level which resulted from a withdrawal of water when the ice advanced or a return of water when it regressed. Some periods of extensive deposition of gravel and coarse sand took place at various times when the rivers were heavily charged with detritus. Other periods

[1] G. C. Maarleveld, 'Fluvie-glaciale Afzettingen in Midden-Nederland', in *T.K. Ned. A.G.* (1955), vol. lxxii, pp. 48-58.

of renewed erosion occurred during stages of low sea-level, when the rivers entrenched their beds deeply into their own deposits to form terraces.

The chronology of these river terraces has been worked out in

FIG. 7.—GLACIAL AND FLUVIO-GLACIAL DEPOSITS IN THE NETHERLANDS.

The areas of the *moraines de poussée* differ slightly from those shown on Fig. 6, since they are drawn from different sources, and interpretations of the various deposits likewise differ.

Based on *Kleine Overzichtskaart van Nederland*, 1 : 600,000, produced by the Netherlands Geological Survey (1947).

considerable detail; a brief summary must suffice.[1] The highest Rhine terrace, found in Germany below Bonn, but not represented

[1] The Maas terraces are discussed by J. I. S. Zonneveld, 'De Kwartaire Rivierterrassen in Midden-Nederland', in *T.K. Ned. A.G.* (1955), vol. lxxii, pp. 329-43; he analyses, dates and names the various erosional terraces of the Maas, and provides a detailed map. See also A. J. Pannekoek, *op. cit.*, pp. 72-3, for a discussion of the Pleistocene, with a full bibliography and a chronological table showing the relationship of the terraces to the glacial phases.

in the Netherlands, indicates the position of the river in late Pliocene times. This is succeeded by the so-called High, Middle and Lower Terraces of Pleistocene age (Fig. 8). The High Terrace is found on

FIG. 8.—THE RIVER-TERRACES IN THE NETHERLANDS.

Based on *Kleine Overzichtskaart van Nederland*, 1 : 600,000, produced by the Netherlands Geological Survey (1947).

the surface only in the south of the Netherlands, extending across the German frontier between the valleys of the Meuse and its parallel northwards-flowing tributary the Niers, and further west along the present Belgian frontier. The Middle Terrace forms a much more extensive gravel sheet between the main distributaries of the Rhine, and covers a large area in Noord-Brabant and Limburg. The Lower Terrace occurs very extensively to the east of the IJssel Meer and along the Meuse valley, but it too is masked in the west and north of the Netherlands by recent superficial deposits. It is most hazardous to attempt to correlate these terraces with the whole glacial cycle, but some authorities tentatively ascribe the Middle Terrace to the *Riss* glacial period and the Lower Terrace to the date of the *Würm* (*Weichsel*) glaciation, the ice-sheets of which did not advance further south than the Elbe valley.

In addition to this river deposition, the higher sea-level during some inter-glacial phases resulted in the deposition of marine sediments. The most notable inter-glacial transgression is ascribed to the period following the *Riss* glaciation. The resultant marine deposits were first studied in the embayment to the south of the IJssel Meer, known as the Geldersche Vallei, drained by the small river Eem; as a result, the name *Eemian* has been given to them. These deposits, mostly consisting of marine clays and sands, are also found in Noord-Holland, along the coast of Friesland, in the islands of Terschelling and Ameland, and in parts of Groningen. It is suggested that the position of most of these Eemian deposits, lying more or less over the former extent of the Zuider Zee, represents the course of the pre-glacial Rhine; the broad lower valley of this proto-Rhine later formed the Zuider Zee depression.

One further important contribution to the superficial deposits of the North Sea lowlands was the deposition of a widespread cover of a fine-textured material, from which have developed brownish loam-soils. To this is given the names *loess* in Germany and *limon* in Belgium and France (Fig. 9). It seems that this is an aeolian deposit, laid down during dry steppe-like inter-glacial or perhaps immediately post-glacial periods. Wind, blowing outwards from high-pressure centres established over the ice-sheets to the north, exerted its sorting and transporting power on the finer elements among the vast supplies of unconsolidated materials deposited by fluvio-glacial action beyond the margins of the continental ice-sheets.

Limon occurs at all heights in central Belgium and the Paris Basin, both on the highest interfluves and plateaus and, though usually reworked and redeposited by subsequent river action, on the river terraces. Thicknesses of seventy feet have been recorded. As a result, the underlying solid geology, whether it be Chalk as in Hesbaye, Artois and Picardy, or Tertiary sands and clays as in Brabant and Hainaut, or Tertiary limestones in the central Paris Basin, is in places wholly masked. The stamp of the *limon* on landscape and agricultural economy is so marked that a distinctive zone

FIG. 9.—THE DISTRIBUTION OF *LIMON* AND ASSOCIATED DEPOSITS.

The French frontier is shown, since the distribution of *limon* deposits within and without this is taken from different sources.

Based on (i) *Atlas de France*, sheet 10, 'Dépôts et Formations Récents'; and (ii) *Internationale Bodenkarte von Europa*, 1 : 2,500,000, sheet VI.

of *limon*-covered country can be traced right across Europe from the Paris Basin, through central Belgium, and on across Germany (where the *loess*-covered region is known as the *Börde*) from the Rhine to Silesia.

POST-GLACIAL DEVELOPMENTS

The greater part of the western half of the Netherlands, as well as the valley-floors of the great rivers and the narrow strip immediately behind the Belgian coastline, is now covered with recent deposits, laid down since about 20,000 B.C., sometimes to considerable depths. The chronology of the post-glacial period has been worked out in detail in Scandinavia, and it is possible to attempt a correlation with the sequence of events in the Low Countries.

At the end of the Pleistocene, sea-level seems to have lain at about 200 feet below its present position, the result of the considerable amount of water still contained in the *Würm* ice-sheets. The floor of the present North Sea then formed continuous land between Britain and the continental lowlands of today. A gradual marine advance took place in the post-*Würm* period, the so-called 'Flandrian Transgression', which finally formed the English Channel, the Straits of Dover and the southern basin of the North Sea. From archaeological and other evidence, the final breaching of the Straits of Dover is ascribed to approximately 5000 B.C., the acknowledged end of the Lower Holocene. At this time the level of the sea lay sixteen to twenty feet below the present, and the coastline ran more or less parallel to, but a few miles seaward of, its present position. During the last few millennia the story in detail is complex. On the one hand there has been the accumulation of sand-dunes and marine muds, the deposition of river-silt, and the growth of fen-peat (Fig. 10). On the other hand, there has been a slight but continuous

FIG. 10.—THE SURFACE DEPOSITS OF THE NETHERLANDS
AND NORTHERN BELGIUM.

The areas of the various deposits are much simplified, especially of the river sands and clays, which form long 'ribbons' along all the streams. The term 'veen' is as used by the Geological Survey, and includes both the *laagveen* and *hoogveen*, whether reclaimed or not (see also Fig. 17). The greater part of the *hoogveen* in the east has now been removed. The dunes include both the 'old' and the 'new' dunes.

Based on *Kleine Overzichtskaart van Nederland*, 1 : 600,000, produced by the Netherlands Geological Survey (1947).

relative rise of sea-level, which is still in progress at the rate of some four to six inches per century, probably owing to the continued sinking of the floor of the North Sea Basin.

On to the results of these natural processes has been superimposed the contribution of reclamation and coastal defence, a fascinating story, though repeatedly interrupted by temporary setbacks due to storms and river floods; the last of these disasters flooded 400,000 acres in 1953. Today some two-fifths of Dutch territory and a considerable area of the maritime plain of Flanders would be inundated without the protecting coastal defences.

Regional Divisions.—It is clear from this brief introduction that several regional subdivisions manifest themselves (Fig. 11). There

FIG. 11.—THE REGIONAL DIVISIONS OF THE NORTH SEA LOWLANDS.

The numbers are as follows: **1**, the coastal lands of the Netherlands; **2**, Maritime Flanders; **3**, the Dutch river valleys; **4**, the heathlands of Belgium and the Netherlands; **5**, Interior Flanders; and **6**, the central low plateaus of Belgium and the Netherlands. These are described in Chapters 3 to 8 respectively. The letters refer to regional subdivisions described in the text.

is such a distinctive contrast between the embayed coastline of islands and estuaries from the Ems to the Wester Schelde (Chapter 3), and the long straight coast of Maritime Flanders from the Wester Schelde to the neighbourhood of Calais (Chapter 4), that these must be considered separately, with their hinterlands.   The alluvium-floored tracts of the Rhine-Meuse flood-plain form a broad belt across the centre of the lowlands (Chapter 5), and extensive areas of sand comprise the most westerly part of the heathlands of the North European Plain (Chapter 6).   The plain of Interior Flanders (Chapter 7) is succeeded inland by the low plateaus of central Belgium and of the extreme south-east of the Netherlands (Chapter 8).

CHAPTER 3

THE COASTAL LANDS OF THE NETHERLANDS

THE DEVELOPMENT OF THE COAST

The past sequence of events affecting the coastline of the North Sea has been described above in outline. At the end of the Lower Holocene, the coastline of what is now the Netherlands lay more or less parallel to but a few miles offshore from its present position, and the Straits of Dover had been recently breached. A great offshore bar then developed as a result of sand accretion, sweeping in a curve from the coast of western Flanders to the Scheldt-Meuse-Rhine delta, where the distributaries interrupted its continuity, and continuing again along the coast of what is now Zuid- and Noord-Holland. The bar was probably initiated during the change from the 'Boreal' to the 'Atlantic' climatic phase. Its nucleus consisted of sand mixed with masses of shelly fragments, forming a basal layer (Fig. 13) on which wind-blown sand accumulated to form dunes, usually referred to as 'the old dune-line'. These shelly sands now afford a valuable source of lime for agriculture.

As the dune-lines developed into an appreciable barrier, the sea was finally excluded and mud steadily accumulated in the shallow fresh-water lagoons. The surface level gradually rose as a result both of this accretion of mud and of the growth of fen-peat. The resultant layer, known as the Lower Peat-bed, is interrupted here and there by irregular patches of mud, sand and gravel indicating the courses of former streams which wandered vaguely over the marshland. A change to a slightly cooler climate seems to have interrupted this peat accumulation, but a return to moister, milder conditions just before the beginning of the historic period caused renewed plant growth and the formation of the Upper Peat-bed.[1] These peat accumulations are known collectively as 'low fen-peat' or *laagveen*, indicated on Figs. 10, 17. They occur extensively in Zuid- and Noord-Holland, in Friesland and in Groningen, and in places the thickness is as much as sixteen feet.

During the first millennium A.D. the position of this offshore bar gradually changed, the result of erosion in the south and of increased

---

[1] For a table of the sub-divisions of the Upper Holocene, with the sequence of the vegetation, its dating, and its archaeological associations, see A. J. Pannekoek, *op. cit.*, p. 108.

accretion in the north. The southern part of the old bar and dune-line, extending from near The Hague (Fig. 12) to the French coast at Sangatte, was completely destroyed, so that the present coastline (described in the next chapter) now lies three to five miles further inland. In the north accretion caused the position of the bar to move seawards until it reached a solid mass of boulder-clay which

FIG. 12.—THE COASTAL LOWLANDS IN THE NEIGHBOURHOOD OF THE HAGUE.

The initials refer to the following towns: **D**, Delft; **D.L.**, De Lier; **G**, The Hague ('s-Gravenhage); **H**, Hook of Holland (Hoek van Holland); **L**, Loosduinen; **Ma**, Maasland; **Mo**, Monster; **N**, Naaldwijk; **P**, Poeldijk; **S**, Scheveningen; **T.H.**, Ter Heide; **W**, Wateringen.

Based on the 1 : 50,000 series, *Geologische Kaart van Nederlanden*, sheets 30, 37.

now forms the 'core' of the island of Texel, and then curved eastward through the line of what is now the Frisian Islands. On this bar a second series of dunes was built up, which have been closely dated by means of archaeological evidence as originating from the beginning of the fourth century A.D.

The two dune-lines can still be traced along the coasts of Zuid-

and Noord-Holland, the older ones lying four or five miles inland of the newer dunes bordering the present beach. This zone forms such a valuable coastal defensive barrier, particularly when strengthened in various ways, that only a few short lengths of sea-dyke are required between The Hague and Den Helder, although the land to the east is well below N.A.P.[1]; this is almost the only section of the Dutch coast without sea-dykes. The inner dunes now form gently undulating terrain known as *Geestgronden* between the new dune-line and the polders (Fig. 13).

Behind this dune-wall, then, lay in Roman times a broad desolate plain covered with peat-fens and shallow meres, above mean sea-level but liable to inundation by spring tides; these marshes were known as the *Wapelinge*, after an old Frisian word for water. An extensive shallow lake, the *Lacus Flevo*, formed the progenitor of the Zuider Zee. Some of the Rhine waters flowed into this lake, which drained northwards through a broad channel known as the Vlie, to reach the North Sea through a gap in the dune-wall. This gap is now represented by the Terschelling Zeegat between the islands of Vlieland and Terschelling, and the main shipping channel leading between these islands to the port of Harlingen is still known as the Vliestroom.

During historic times the sea-level has risen continuously, and it is

FIG. 13.—DIAGRAMMATIC SECTION ACROSS THE DUNE- AND POLDER-LANDS IN NOORD-HOLLAND.

Based on P. Tesch, 'The Physiographic Regions of the Netherlands', in *Geographical Review* (1923), vol. 13, p. 511. Length of section is 10 miles.

evident that but for more than a thousand years of hard and sustained human effort the sea would today cover all Zeeland, the western part of Noord-Brabant and most of Zuid-Holland. The

[1] The datum used by the Netherlands *Topografische Dienst* is the mean tidal-level at Amsterdam. This was first calculated in 1875, and was known as *A.P.* (*Amsterdamsch Peil*). When the new precise levelling of the Netherlands was carried out in the years 1922–36, a revised datum, *N.A.P.* (*Nieuw Amsterdamsch Peil*), was used.

peninsula which projects northward between the North Sea and the Zuider Zee to form the province of Noord-Holland would consist merely of a narrow strip of dune-islands (Fig. 14).

Until approximately the beginning of the fourteenth century the sea had a net gain on the land. There are, it is true, records as early as the seventh century of reclamation around the shores of the *Lacus Flevo*, and some large dykes were constructed in Friesland and Groningen. A shallow channel across what is now Friesland, the *Friesche Middelzee* [1], which drained northwards between the dunes of what are now the islands of Terschelling and Ameland, was reclaimed by 1300. Men had even reclaimed most of the broad estuary of the Dollard, into which flows the Ems (*Eems*), but here enthusiasm outran technical ability, for in 1413 the sluices gave way and the waters flowed back, covering thirty villages. By 1300, therefore, notwithstanding some local and often temporary gains, the sea had advanced considerably. The new dune-rampart north of Den Helder was breached in several places (so forming the Frisian Islands), and the mud-flats within the dunes were inundated to form the Wadden Zee. This extended southward into the *Lacus Flevo*, flooding the low-lying peat-lands around its margins and so forming the Zuider Zee, under which numerous towns and villages vanished. The dune-wall south of Petten remained intact, but westerly projecting gulfs of the Zuider Zee (the Beemster and the Schermer in the north and the IJ in the south) covered all land below sea-level to within two or three miles of the North Sea (Fig. 14).

Further to the south, what is now the province of Zeeland and much of southern Zuid-Holland became an archipelago of more than sixty islands separated by tidal channels, into which the Rhine-Meuse-Scheldt distributaries poured their waters. The main islands had more or less attained their present outlines by 1300, but many subsequent changes in detail have taken place, partly through the southward shift of the major distributaries (see p. 89), and partly by the gradual regularisation of shipping channels.

Other changes occurred in the coastline as a result of storms which at intervals breached the dykes and caused vast inundations. Many floods of great magnitude have been recorded, the result of storm-surges set up when exceptionally high tides coincided with onshore gales; the fourteenth and fifteenth centuries seem to have been particularly prone. In 1413 the Dollard was flooded, as mentioned above. One of the most disastrous events was the '*St. Elisabeths-vloed*' of 1421, which drowned 10,000 people and inundated a vast area between Dordrecht and Geertruidenberg, so forming a new arm

---

[1] The origin and silting-up of the Middelzee is described by H. Halbertsma, 'Enkele oudheidkundige aantekeningen over het Middelzee', in *T.K. Ned. A.G.* (1955), vol. lxxii, pp. 93-105.

of the sea, the Hollandsch Diep, and leaving the desolate reed-covered Biesbosch (which still exists). As the techniques of coastal

FIG. 14.—NOORD-HOLLAND AT THE BEGINNING OF THE FOURTEENTH CENTURY.

The abbreviations are as follows: **Al**, Alkmaar; **Am**, Amsterdam; **Ed**, Edam; **En**, Enkhuizen; **Ha**, Haarlem; **Ho**, Hoorn; **Me**, Medemblik; **Mo**, Monnikendam; **P**, Petten; **S**, Schagen; **W**, the Wogmeer; and **Z**, Zaandam.

Based on a folding-map in *La Néerlande: études générales sur la géographie des Pays-Bas* (1938), facing p. 68, entitled 'Holland's Noorderkwartier in 1300', illustrating a contribution by J. B. L. Hol and H. van Velthoven, 'La Lutte contre les eaux'.

defence improved, really disastrous floods became rarer, but they still occasionally happened; in 1825 much of Friesland was inundated, and other serious floods occurred in 1825, 1877, 1881, 1883,

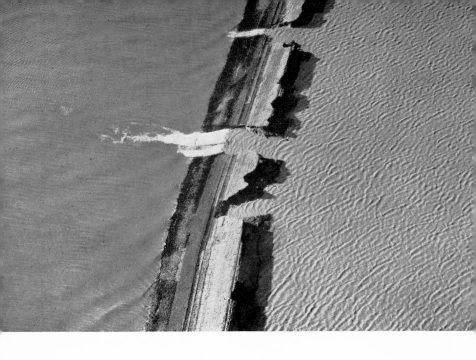

I, II The struggle against the sea: (*above*) a dyke-burst in Zeeland (1953); (*below*) the Veersche Gat dyke, between the islands of Walcheren and Noord-Beveland

III The Oosterschelde bridge, between the islands of Duiveland (background) and Noord-Beveland

IV The town of Emmeloord, North-east Polder of the IJssel Meer (1966)

1889, 1894, 1906, 1911 and 1916.[1] Inundations were sometimes caused by deliberate breaching for strategic or malicious reasons, as in 1944 by the Germans in the island of Walcheren. But the floods of February 1953 were the worst for at least a century (pp. 36–7).

Defence against flooding whether by the sea or the rivers, with the complementary function of land reclamation and improvement, involve the building of sea-dykes and river-dykes behind which basic unit-areas, known as *polders*,[2] can be reclaimed and maintained. The problems of the rivers, their regularisation and dyking, and their polder-lands, are described in Chapter 5. It is necessary now to consider problems of coastal defence and the creation of the sea- and lake-polders, with special attention to the greatest polder-scheme of all—the partial reclamation of the Zuider Zee.

THE SEA-DYKES

Dykes are built to safeguard areas of land which would otherwise be either permanently inundated or temporarily flooded by exceptionally high tides. These, together with the lands liable to river-floods, comprise 40 per cent of the total area of the Netherlands (Fig. 15), and include the very heart of the country, its chief cities and ports, and its most productive agricultural land.[3] The sea-dykes extend continuously from the Dollard along the coasts of Groningen and Friesland to the Zuider Zee. In some places there is a double dyke, occasionally even a treble series (Fig. 18), consisting of a high outer rampart with a crest fifteen feet above N.A.P., made of clay faced with concrete or basalt blocks, and one or more overgrown older dykes a mile or so inland. The several lines indicate progressive stages of reclamation. The Frisian Islands are faced with sections of dyke to amplify the dune-lines; the whole of the eastern shore of Texel, for example, is dyked. From the coast of Friesland the main Zuider Zee dam (Fig. 19) cuts for eighteen miles across what was once the open sea to the shores of Noord-Holland, so protecting the reclaimed polders and the low-lying lands around the former shores of the Zuider Zee.

[1] J. van Veen, 'Overstromingen Tijdens de negen Stormvloeden sinds 1877', in *T.K. Ned. A.G.* (1956), vol. lxxiii, pp. 1-6; this describes, with detailed maps, each of the last nine floods since 1877.

[2] P. Wagret, *Les Polders* (Paris, 1959), gives an authoritative and beautifully illustrated account.

[3] A delightfully written and authoritative account of all the varied aspects of Dutch reclamation is provided by Joh. van Veen (chief engineer of the *Rijkswaterstaat*), *Dredge, Drain, Reclaim: The Art of a Nation* (2nd edition, 1949). This includes a large number of photographs, diagrams and maps. A concise summary of the endless Dutch struggles against the sea is afforded by A. G. Maris, *De Dijken. Een Nationale Uitgave* (1954), a well-illustrated volume of 188 pp.

R.G.W.E.—C

From Den Helder to the Hook of Holland runs a sweeping curve of coast, sixty-two miles long, bordered by the new dune-belt with a maximum width near Zandvoort of about three miles. Dykes are

FIG. 15.—AREAS OF THE NETHERLANDS LIABLE TO INUNDATION.

The areas liable to inundation by the sea are shown in black, those by the rivers with a stipple. The two Zuider Zee polders yet to be reclaimed are outlined by a pecked line. The barrages under construction or completed as part of the 'Delta Plan' are indicated; they will be completed by 1978.

Based on W. C. Leeuw, *The Netherlands as an Environment for Plant Life* (1935), Fig. 2, with revisions.

only necessary in this section round the northern tip of the peninsula of Noord-Holland, where they link up with the Zuider Zee dykes, and in minor dune-breaks, as near Petten where there is a three-mile wall, the Hondsbossche Zeewering. This section of coast is nevertheless open to attack from the sea, and constant measures are necessary to check erosion of the dunes. Large numbers of groynes cross the beaches to well below low-water mark, usually further fortified by sunken mattresses of interwoven willow-boughs (known as *kraagstuk* or *zinkstuk*) to afford some protection against tidal scour and to enhance protective accretion. On some of the sand-flats fronting the dunes, osier-fences are constructed to form 'drift-dykes'which help to stabilise moving sand. Extensive planting of marram grass further restricts sand movement. Some of the narrower dune-belts are faced with stone, and sea-walls and promenades front the many holiday resorts. On the whole, this section of the Dutch coast, while needing constant care and maintenance, does not normally cause any major concern.

It is the 'delta region', with its islands, 3000 polders and deep-water channels, which affords such critical problems. Approximately 700 miles of dykes surround the Zeeland islands and border the main-land coast on either side of the estuaries. Some of the dykes are merely low earthen banks. Others are massive structures, such as the Westkapelle sea-wall, which protects the south-western corner of Walcheren island and is exposed to powerful attack by storm-waves. Its overall width, including fronting groynes and fascine work, is about a hundred yards.

Difficulties arise from the fact that the land in the centre of these islands and behind the mainland dykes is frequently appreciably lower than the beach, the result of drainage and compaction of the terrain. Another problem in the delta region is tidal scour, which removes material from the foreshore and so undercuts the dykes, causing them to slump forward. This is particularly liable where the banks are built on clay resting upon sand, though groynes and fascine work help to combat this danger. While the upkeep of much of the defensive work is the responsibility of each commune, the problem became so acute that the administrators of certain polders in Zeeland were empowered in 1870 to receive assistance from the State and the province; these are officially known as *calamiteus* polders.

A further problem in the delta region is the progressive salinisation of water in the river estuaries and creeks. As the shipping channels are deepened, the influx of salt water increases, especially when the river discharges are low, so that salt water goes far inland, thus harming the pastures, and making water in the ditches undrinkable for cattle.

It has long been clear that there were two possible methods of coping with the ever-present threat in the delta region. One was to strengthen and raise every dyke by about six feet, a tremendous undertaking. The other was to build massive dykes across the estuary entrances, except for certain shipping channels, and so exclude the tidal seas. This would form fresh-water basins, incidentally of great help to agriculture, both for the pastures and the market-gardens. One contribution towards this end was completed in July 1950, when the Briellsche (Brielle) Maas was closed-off from the sea.[1] One dam was built at the mouth near Oostvoorne, a second where the estuary divides from the Nieuwe Maas.

But three years later the floods of February 1953 made it clear that an overall 'Delta Plan' was a matter of urgent priority. The cause of the disaster of February 1st was a storm-surge which raised the water-level of the southern North Sea far above predicted heights; this increase was as much as ten feet at Hook of Holland. The storm-surge was associated with gale-force winds and storm-waves of exceptional power during a period of spring tides. Many of the dykes were overtopped, and the inrushing water eroded the inner slopes and weakened them so that breaches were readily formed (Plate I). Others were undermined by frontal wave-attack and so slumped bodily forward. There were sixty-seven major breaches, some of 300 yards' width, and many miles of dyke were otherwise damaged. The area flooded was officially stated to total 375,000 acres, while about 47,000 houses were destroyed or damaged and 1,800 people lost their lives.[2] The estimated cost of the ' Delta Plan', some £200 millions, was seen in its true perspective against a loss of over £100 millions as a result of this one event. Serious though the disaster was, it might have been much worse, for Dutch experts have calculated that even more adverse combinations of weather, tides and river-floods are quite possible, which might result in flood-levels exceeding the 1953 records by three feet.

The Dutch mobilised their resources and skill; within a month of the disaster only eight breaches remained, and by July only four

[1] K. F. Valken, 'De Afdamming van de Briellsche Maas en haar Consequenties', in *T.E.S.G.* (1951), vol. 42, pp. 113-18.
[2] Details of the disaster are given by *The Battle of the Floods* (1953), published for the benefit of the Netherlands Flood Relief Fund in Amsterdam. See also W. E. Boerman, 'The Storm Floods in the Netherlands', in *Geography* (1953), vol. xxxviii, pp. 178-82, and K. C. Edwards, *ibid.*, pp. 182-7, 'The Netherlands Floods: Some further Aspects and Consequences'. G. W. Hoffman, 'The 1953 Flood in the Netherlands', in *G.R.* (1954), vol. xliv, pp. 423-5, gives considerable bibliographical detail of the causes and consequences of the floods. J. H. G. Schepers, 'Een Stormvloed teisterde Zuidwest-Nederland', in *T.K. Ned. A.G.* (1953), vol. lxx, pp. 126-55, describes the effects of the floods, with tables, maps and aerial photographs. The problems of reconstruction are discussed by M. W. Heslings, 'Het Herstel en de Sanering van het Rampgebied in Zuidwest Nederland', *ibid.* (1953), vol. lxx, pp. 273-308, and by S. Herweijer, 'Het agrarisch Herstel en de Herverkavelingen in het Rampgebied', *ibid.* (1955), vol. lxxii, pp. 297-306.

were not yet closed, three on Schouwen-Duiveland and one on Zuid-Beveland. The last gap, at Ouwerkerk, was sealed before the end of the year, when concrete caissons were towed into the breaches and sunk in position.

The flooding and consequent salinisation of so much land was a grievous blow, and moreover 25,000 head of cattle in this prosperous dairying region were lost. The experience derived from the reclamation of Walcheren, which was under salt water for sixteen

FIG. 16.—THE DELTA PLAN.

All dykes are shown, completed, in progress or projected, though the whole scheme will not be finished until 1978.

Based on various official Dutch maps.

months after the war of 1940–5,[1] was of immense help and the recovery programme was carried out with remarkable rapidity. The work of desalinisation and the removal of the vast quantities of sand which covered so much of the farmland were executed by companies under Government supervision; the cost was borne by the State, except for certain improvements to which the proprietors contributed. The Government took the opportunity to carry out some redistribution of land, on a compulsory basis; a number of small sub-marginal farms were enlarged or amalgamated, the dispossessed farmers being settled on the new lands in the IJssel Meer polders.

[1] An account of the recovery of Walcheren is provided by Joh. van Veen, *Dredge, Drain, Reclaim: The Art of a Nation* (2nd edition, 1949), pp. 122-7.

Considerable drainage improvements were also effected.

The 'Delta Plan' involves the construction of four major outer dykes interlinking the islands (Fig. 16), with sluices for the discharge of river water and floating ice, and lochs for shipping.[1] These are across the Haringvliet between Voorne and Goeree (to be completed 1968); across the Brouwershavensche Gat leading to the Grevelingen between Goeree and Schouwen (1969); across the Ooster Schelde between Schouwen and Noord-Beveland (1978); and across the Veersche Gat between Noord-Beveland and Walcheren (completed 1961) (Plate II). These dykes, totalling in length 20 miles, will keep the sea out of the delta, converting the estuaries into a large non-tidal sheet of fresh water, to be known as the Zeeuwse Meer. The mouths of the Wester Schelde and the Nieuwe Waterweg (New Waterway) will not be sealed, since these are the shipping approaches to Antwerp and Rotterdam respectively, and traffic is too heavy to pass through locks without immense inconvenience. If tidal waters should build up in the Waterweg, they will be diverted through sluices on the Oude Maas into the Zeeuwse Meer, which will act as a vast temporary reservoir. A controlling dam was built (1955–8) across the Hollandsche IJssel to the east of Rotterdam, with large sluices and navigation locks, to protect the vital low-lying polders of Zuid-Holland and Utrecht from flooding.

Other subsidiary dykes are necessary partly to prevent dangerous currents from concentrating in the channels during the building of the major dykes. The small Zandkreek dyke between Zuid-Beveland and the eastern end of Noord-Beveland was completed in 1960. Inner dykes across the eastern end of the Grevelingen and between Over-flakkee and Beijerland will be constructed; the latter will separate the Volkerak from the Haringvliet. In 1965 a fine pre-stressed con-crete bridge, 3 miles long, was opened across the Ooster Schelde (Plate III); this forms part of a new trunk-road ('de Centrale Weg'),[2] from Rotterdam southward over the islands. Another outer road will run from Rotterdam over the Veersche Gat dyke to Middelburg. Yet another highway farther east ('the Benelux road') will run directly south from Rotterdam, utilising the Volkerak dyke, hence via Bergen-op-Zoom to Antwerp.

The whole scheme will be completed, it is hoped, by 1978. There

[1] J. Koopman, 'Het Deltaplan en zijn Waterstaatskundige, Economische en Sociale Aspecten', in *T.K. Ned. A.G.* (1956), vol. lxxiii, pp. 113-33; this contains numerous plans and photographs. The Delta Plan is also discussed by M. C. Verburg, *Het Deltaplan. Verleden, Heden en Toekomst van het Deltaplan* (1955); S. E. Steigenga-Kouwe, 'The Delta Plan', in *T.E.S.G.* (1960), vol. 51, pp. 167-75; and J. Lingsma, *Holland and the Delta Plan* (1964).

[2] J. M. Roof, 'De Centrale Weg als Zeeuwse Verkeersspil', in *T.E.S.G.* (1956), vol. 47, pp. 48-53.

have, it is true, been some doubts and objections,[1] mainly from the Zeeland fishermen.

Some Dutch engineers look still further ahead and envisage a similar series of excluding dykes to link the Frisian Islands, and so enable the Wadden Zee to be reclaimed.[2] This will provide the Netherlands with a smooth coastline, unbroken but for the carefully protected shipping channels. But this lies far in the future.[3]

These problems concerning the indeterminate margin of land and sea are emphasised by the very considerable area that lies between the mean high- and low-water marks, not including the reclaimed lands. The official land area of the Netherlands is 12,528 square miles, but the total area to the mean low-tide mark is 15,789 square miles.[4]

THE POLDERS

The sea-dykes and the river-dykes provide for the exclusion of extraneous water from the areas they protect. The unit of organised reclamation behind these main dykes is the *polder*, which may vary in size from a tiny irregular-shaped patch of land reclaimed from a small tidal inlet or a piece of fen, to major units such as the Oost Polder of the Zuider Zee scheme, of about 133,000 acres. Some polders lie well below sea-level, occupying former areas of open sea or deep lakes. Pumping is constantly required to remove excess water through rainfall and seepage, and so to maintain the water-table at a predetermined level. Other polders lie just above N.A.P. and are surrounded by lower dykes or *kaden*; from these water can usually be removed through sluices by gravity flow at low tide. Still others are well above sea-level, but may be subject to temporary winter waterlogging; a system of ditches and channels will usually provide adequate natural drainage.

The low-lying polders reclaimed from the sea or from lakes are known generally as *droogmakerijen*, literally 'dry-making'. Each unit is enclosed by a ring-dyke, for the centres of lake-polders in particular are considerable lower than their margins, a tendency emphasised by compaction resulting upon drainage. Outside the

[1] A summary of the many socio-economic changes involved in the implementation of the Delta Plan is given by M. C. Verburg, 'De Functie en de Resultaten van het economisch-geografische Onderzoek met Betrekking tot de structurele Wijzigingen als Gevolg van het Deltaplan', in *T.E.S.G.* (1956), vol. 47, pp. 311-22 ; this has a bibliography of eighty-three references.

[2] A map of the Netherlands of the future, after both the Delta Plan and the closing of the Frisian '*zeegaten*' are completed, according to J. Th. Thijsse, is given by J. H. G. Schepers, *op. cit.*, p. 150.

[3] In December 1960 an official Dutch commission published a 1200 pp. report on coastal defences, urging a strengthening and enlarging of the entire dyke-system.

[4] As computed by the *Stichting voor Bodemonderzoek* (the Soil Survey Institute) at Wageningen in 1950.

ring-dyke is a peripheral canal, known as a *ringvaart*, into which is pumped water from a close rectilinear pattern of drainage channels (*sloten*) intersecting the polder-floor. Formerly these lake-polders were characterised by a ring of windmills which worked the pumps, standing on the dykes. In the nineteenth century these were largely superseded by steam-pumps, and in this century by diesel engines or electric pumps. Most windmills are now inoperative, but many remain as a characteristic feature of the polder landscape.

Several interesting major polder-schemes have been successfully accomplished. One of the earliest large-scale enterprises was the drainage of the Beemster, a lake to the south-east of Alkmaar, which was reclaimed between 1609 and 1612, using a ring-canal and twenty-six windmills. Many other deep lakes were drained in Zuid-Holland, forming the Zuidplas Polder in Schieland to the north-west of Rotterdam, reclaimed between the years 1828 and 1839, and the Prins Alexander Polder, which was covered by a lake twenty-one feet deep and became finally dry by 1874. The largest scheme, before the Zuider Zee plan was started, was the reclamation of the Haarlemmermeer [1] which lay in the triangle between Haarlem, Amsterdam and Leiden (Fig. 20); it covered 40,000 acres and was nearly twelve feet deep. After the extensive floods of 1836 which inundated much of Leiden and Amsterdam, citizens of these towns were stimulated to action. A ring-dyke was built and then steam-pumps began to remove the water, a process completed by 1852.

Reclamation from the sea has also produced several major gains, apart from the recovery of the small tidal creeks and marshes (*slikken*) around the Zeeland islands. In the north of Noord-Holland several polders were created from the Zuider Zee long before the present scheme. The Zijpe Polder was reclaimed in 1597, and in 1847 an extensive gain was made when the Anna Paulowna Polder (Fig. 19) was created out of a shallow gulf to the south-east of Den Helder. Another accomplishment was the reclamation of the Binnen IJ (Fig. 14), which as late as 1865 formed a wide arm of salt water extending westward from the southern Zuider Zee almost to the North Sea coast near Velsen. This had long been dyked, but it virtually cut Holland in two, and perpetually menaced with flooding Amsterdam on its southern shores. It was finally reclaimed by a major effort between 1865 and 1876. The North Sea (*Noord-Zee*)

---

[1] A detailed study of the Haarlemmermeer is given in a monograph by Chr. van Paassen, P. J. Kouwe and G. A. Wissink, *De Haarlemmermeer* (1955), *Publicatie No. 11A uit het Geografisch Instituut der Rijks Universiteit te Utrecht*; this deals fully with the problems of a polder-community in highly urbanised surroundings. An account of the century of progress since the Haarlemmermeer was drained is provided by G. A. Wissink, 'Bij het Eeuwfeest van de Haarlemmermeer', in *T.K. Ned. A.G.* (1955), vol. lxxii, pp. 200-18.

Canal was constructed from Amsterdam to IJmuiden (Fig. 22), and the IJ itself was converted into a series of polders ranging from eight to seventeen feet below N.A.P. The peat-cover was stripped off and today the underlying marine clays form fertile farm-land.

FIG. 17—'*HOOGVEEN*' AND '*LAAGVEEN*' IN THE NETHERLANDS.

G, Groningen. Much of the *hoogveen* has now been removed, especially in the north-east. Areas in Germany are not shown.

Based on W. C. Leeuw, *The Netherlands as an Environment for Plant Life* (1935), Fig. 8.

Although each polder is reclaimed as a unit, its maintenance must be integrated with that of its neighbours, as well as with the navigable waterways. This requires detailed organisation and vigilant

c 2

administration. The local administrative body is the *Waterschap*. These organisations consist of representatives elected by land-owners within the polder or group of polders concerned. Formerly powerful autonomous bodies, their powers have necessarily been reduced as the growing complexity of drainage schemes, together with the often conflicting needs of navigation, have necessitated increasingly centralised administration, with financial assistance from the *Department van Waterstaat* and the provincial *Waterstaats*.

The method used in complex drainage areas, notably in Noord- and Zuid-Holland, is to create a group of polders within which a common water-level is maintained and from which the disposal of excess water can be organised. Unless a polder borders the sea or a major river, it is necessary to utilise temporary storage areas until the water can be passed away. These storage areas are known as *boezem* and may be lakes, portions of canals, or rivers; the unit served by a single *boezem* or inter-connected group of them is a *boezemgebied*. The water-level in the *boezem* is maintained to avoid fluctuations which may on the one hand endanger the dykes and on the other affect navigation. Noord- and Zuid-Holland are covered by seventeen *boezemgebied*; several are very large, notably the Schermerboezem (Fig. 19) which serves most of Noord-Holland to the north of the North Sea Canal, the Rijnlandsboezem which occupies a quarter of a million acres, including the former Haarlemmermeer, and the Delflandsboezem in the south-west.

The net result of a millennium of effort is that there are today about 2,500 polders, of which a million acres are drained by gravity flow, and about two and a half million acres by pumping. A variety of soils overlies these reclaimed areas (Fig. 10). Along the coasts of Groningen and Friesland, and again in the islands of Zuid-Holland and Zeeland, are the heavy soils derived from recent marine clays (what the Dutch call '*jonge zeeklei*'), forming the chief arable lands. In many parts of Noord- and Zuid-Holland are the peat-soils of the *laagveen* (Fig. 17). These are mostly under permanent grassland, forming rich dairying lands, and the water-table is usually kept at a higher level than in the arable districts. The recent river-clays, derived from alluvium deposited along the flood-plains of the Rhine-Maas distributaries, are not as good as the marine clays for agriculture, and much is under permanent pasture.

Reclamation is still going on; the tidal mud-flats are being reclaimed along the coast of Groningen and Friesland, there are three polders to complete in the Zuider Zee, and while the Delta Plan is not primarily intended as a scheme of actual reclamation, it will add between 25,000 and 40,000 acres of new land.

Some lakes in Noord- and Zuid-Holland (such as the Alkmaarder Meer and the Aalsmeer) still remain reserved as *boezem*. The numerous lakes of Friesland have hardly been touched, as most of them lie in uneven hollows on fluvio-glacial sands and gravels, and the resulting poor soils would not be worth the cost of reclamation. But with these exceptions the polder-lands, covering much of the Netherlands below roughly the one-metre contour (above N.A.P.), form as a result of man's unending efforts the main agricultural districts of the country.

Regional Divisions.—The main regional divisions may be described under five heads : (*a*) the coastal lands of Groningen and Friesland ; (*b*) the Dutch Frisian Islands ; (*c*) the IJssel Meer reclamation area ; (*d*) Noord- and Zuid-Holland, with the western part of Utrecht province ; and (*e*) the south-western islands and estuaries (Fig. 11).

THE COASTAL LANDS OF GRONINGEN [1] AND FRIESLAND

The coastal lands of the two northern provinces extend from the Dollard round to the Noord-Oost Polder of the Zuider Zee. This section of coast is remarkably smooth, the only prominent indentation being the rectangular Lauwers Zee. Considerable reclamation has been effected along the coast, in essence a natural process although artificially assisted and accelerated. The tidal mud-flats (*slikken*) are colonised by a succession of plants, in the initial stages with eel-grass (*Zostera*, or in Dutch *Zeegras*) which assists the accretion of mud. When the level has been raised dense communities of marsh-samphire (*Salicornia*) establish themselves, causing mud to accumulate still more rapidly. Then comes the familiar rice-grass (*Spartina*), introduced along the Dutch coast only in 1924 but which has spread rapidly, and so the marsh gradually develops above the ordinary high-tide level. Finally the turf-forming grasses appear, thus producing the 'saltings' which are useful for grazing. This accretion of mud is assisted by the construction of wickerwork fences, nailed to rows of piles driven into the mud flats. These form what have been descriptively called [2] '*parcs de sédimentation*'. The mud which collects in them is colonised by marsh-plants to form what have been termed '*jardins de vase*'. In due course a low dyke is built on the seaward side of the salting to prevent inundation by exceptionally high tides, and as the salt is leached out by rain-water the pastures on the heavy clays become increasingly 'sweet'. In a number of places can be seen two or even three parallel dykes a mile or two apart and enclosing small polders, evidence of this progressive reclamation, with small villages strung out along the inner

[1] N. Oostinga, 'Water- en Afvalwaterproblemen in de Provincie Groningen', in *T.E.S.G.* (1964), vol. 55, pp. 2–7.

[2] F. Verger, 'Les Conquêtes sur la mer de la Zélande au Jutland', in *A. de G.* (1956), vol. lxv, pp. 270-87. This article includes some excellent photographs of reclamation sequences.

dyke. This process is illustrated most strikingly along the shores of the Dollard, where the main dyke is now nearly 200 yards inland of the high-tide mark, in Groningen near Uithuizen (Fig. 18) where in the last century three new polders were formed, and in Friesland between Holwerd and Nieuwebildtzijl.

The marine-clay lands extend inland for ten to twenty miles, most of the land being in polders, although the surface is a few feet above N.A.P. and normally drains by gravity flow.[1] The peat-lands further inland, however, are largely below N.A.P., and extensive lakes lie in the peat-hollows and in depressions in the sand-country further

FIG. 18.—DYKES AND '*TERPEN*' ON THE COAST OF GRONINGEN.

The letters indicate polders reclaimed since 1853 through the fixation of tidal mud-flats by natural accretion of mud, the growth of plants, and artificial assistance by means of osier fences, as follows: E, Ems polder; L, Lauwer polder; N, Noord polder; O, Oost polder; U, Uithuizer polder; and X, Xegenboeren polder.

Based on a folding-map in *La Néerlande: études générales sur la géographie des Pays-Bas* (1938), facing p. 76, illustrating a contribution by J. B. L. Hol and H. van Velthoven, 'La Lutte contre les eaux'.

south (see p. 139). The peat to the south-east of Groningen has been mostly removed (see p. 138), and little outward sign can be detected in the agricultural landscape of the transition from the coastal clay-lands to the improved sands.

No month near the coast has mean temperatures below freezing (Groningen, 34° F., January mean), although prolonged spells of frost may occur, especially further inland where the lakes may freeze at any time in winter. The mean annual rainfall at Groningen for

[1] An account of the marine clay-lands, their improvement and utilisation, and the associated problems of coastal defence in western Friesland, is given by P. du Burck, P. J. Ente and L. J. Pons, 'Het Zeekleigebied van Westfriesland', in *T.K. Ned. A.G.* (1956), vol. lxxiii, pp. 140-51; this includes a number of detailed maps and soil-profiles.

the period 1921–50 was about 29·3 inches, although the figure for 1953 was 26·9 inches and that for 1954 was 35·4 inches.

The coastal lands form rich farming country,[1] and nearly four-fifths of the area is under rotation grass, clover, potatoes (for which Friesland is the chief growing area in the country), cereals (particularly wheat and barley in Groningen), chicory and mustard. Although the emphasis is on arable crops on the clay-lands, large numbers of the familiar Friesian cattle are grazed on the coastal pastures and on temporary leys. There are few large towns, compared with Zuid-Holland, and the emphasis is therefore less on liquid milk than on the production of factory-made butter and cheese, frequently on a co-operative basis.

These northern provinces are fascinating, with the spacious landscape interrupted only by the prosperous-looking farm-houses with their glazed-tile, sometimes part-thatched, roofs, straight tree-lined roads, and quiet villages. Many of these settlements are situated on or near artificial refuge-mounds. More than 500 of these can be traced (Fig. 18), although many others have vanished; frequently the soil of which they were built has been spread on the near-by fields. In Friesland these mounds are known as *terpen*; they are usually small, with only a few houses and sometimes a church. In Groningen, where they are called *wierden*, they are much larger. The mounds stand usually eight to ten feet above the surrounding lands, an adequate margin for most floods, but the largest known, at Hoogebeintum, is thirty-eight feet high and covers an area of about twenty-two acres. Most of these mounds were built in late Roman times when sea-level was lower than at present, and when they were required as refuges only at rare intervals. After the thirteenth century it became necessary to build complete dykes along the coast, since sea-level had risen and major inundations had become more frequent. The refuge-mounds, therefore, became unnecessary. Those with churches survived as centres for their respective villages. Others were abandoned, for as reclamation developed the people left the refuge-nucleations, and in these coastal lands the population is now quite widely dispersed either in large farm-houses or in small scattered hamlets.

There is little urban development except for the provincial capitals, Groningen and Leeuwarden. This is partly because the two provinces have depended almost wholly on an agricultural economy for many centuries, partly because this was always a remote corner of the Netherlands and an oddly isolated part of western Europe. No great routes crossed here, either from the sea with the difficult approaches through the tidal-flats and the lack of natural harbours, or from the land with the interrupting gulf of the Zuider Zee to the

[1] Chr. van Welsenes, 'The development of the agricultural area of northern Groningen', in *T.E.G.S.* (1960), vol. 51, pp. 175-80.

west and the desolate moorlands to the east. Only the provinces of Zeeland and Drenthe have a lower proportion of urban population than have Groningen and Friesland.

The city of Groningen is situated where the areas of clays, sands and peat-bogs meet; it is described on p. 138 in connection with the reclamation of the bogs and heath. It is linked by the Eems Canal to the Dollard at Delfzijl. This little port has developed in some measure as an outport for Groningen (which can itself be reached by coasters), and it forms a servicing port for the prosperous agricultural region of the north-east. It imports coal, fertilisers, timber and animal feeding-stuffs, and exports large quantities of strawboard, paper, potato-flour and dextrine from the factories of Groningen. Delfzijl handled a million tons of freight in 1964. It now has a large aluminium refinery, using bauxite from Surinam and gas from the nearby field at Slochteren, and a new chemical plant. In Friesland, Leeuwarden (86,246) has the same dominating position as Groningen. It was once a port on the Friesche Middelzee, but by the end of the thirteenth century this long arm of the sea had been reclaimed. The old town is still surrounded by a moat, and several minor canals, used by small barges carrying agricultural produce, fertilisers, coal, bricks and timber, focus on it from the port of Harlingen, from Groningen by the Hoendiep, and most circuitously from Zwolle and Meppel in the south. Today Leeuwarden is the administrative centre for a rich agricultural district and it has famed markets for cattle, butter and cereals; only the market at Rotterdam handles more cattle annually in the Netherlands. Once the city was renowned for gold and silver work; the Friesch Museum in the town contains a silversmith's forge, an attractive collection of Frisian silverware, glass, pottery and numerous other products of former thriving local handicrafts. These have been replaced by a variety of modern industries, carried on in small efficient factories—the manufacture of shoes, vinegar, paint, soap, electro-plate, and (as an agricultural centre) of butter, cheese and, oddly enough, margarine.

Harlingen is a small artificial port, built during the years 1870–77 to serve Friesland. The approach through the Wadden Zee by the Vliestroom channel is so narrow and winding that it is used only by small coasters, although there are regular services to London and Hull. It handled only about 225,000 tons of freight in 1964, mostly exports of dairy products and strawboard, and imports of coal, timber and miscellaneous raw materials for the industries of Leeuwarden. The town stands in an area which has been devastated by floods several times in history; the village of Almenum, which disappeared in the flood of 1134, was on the same site, and in 1566 another serious flood devastated the whole district, since when enlarged dykes have prevented any further incursions. Several small industries have developed, notably the building of coasting vessels and barges, the canning and salting of fish, and leather-tanning.

A number of people in Friesland still speak Frisian, or more strictly West Frisian. The pure language, which has quite a considerable literature, is spoken in the countryside, the so-called *Landfries*, but a Frisian-Dutch dialect (*Stadsfries*) has gained ground in the towns.

THE DUTCH FRISIAN ISLANDS

Between the dyked coast of Groningen and Friesland and the line of the Frisian Islands lies the Wadden Zee, a considerable extent of tidal waters. The *Wadden* consist of sheets of mud and sand, mostly exposed at low tide, and crossed by a dendritic maze of creeks. The shoals have been notorious since the earliest times for the wrecking of ships; in 1799 the bullion-transporting *Lutine* (whose bell still summons the members of Lloyd's when some serious event has occurred) foundered on the banks off the island of Vlieland.

The Frisian Islands are strung out in a smooth curve, with Texel following the trend of the Noord-Holland coast just east of north, while the others are aligned progressively further and further in an easterly direction. Each island, with the exception of Texel which has a 'core' of glacial drift, consists of sand-flats with a line of dunes fronting the open sea, and all except Vlieland, which is wholly sandy, have small areas of marine clay on their inner sides. They represent fragments of the northern parts of the offshore bar already described, breached in many places between the eighth and twelfth centuries.

The larger islands are separated by straits (known as *zeegaten* or *gaten*), mostly with deep-water channels, although the gap between Texel and Vlieland is much shallower than the others. Navigation is made difficult by 'submarine deltas', which fan out as sand-banks on the seaward side of the *gaten*; the powerful ebb-tides sweep sand from the Wadden Zee through the *gaten* out into the deeper waters of the North Sea, where the strength of the tidal currents is checked.

The largest island is *Texel*, about 13½ by 6½ miles at its maximum extent, separated from the mainland to the south by a deep channel, the Marsdiep, which is kept clear of sand by a powerful tidal-race. The south-east of the island consists of a mass of glacial clay, rising to a height of 49 feet in a low hump known as Het Bergje. The west coast is fronted by a continuous dune-rampart and by a broad beach of fine sand, while the east coast is dyked along almost its whole length. In the north-east extensive mud- and sand-flats form the breeding grounds of gulls, terns and avocet; this part is locally known as *Eierland* and formerly there was a considerable export of eggs to Amsterdam. The small population mainly lives in the little town and ferry-port of Oudeschild, the inland villages of Hoorn,

Boorg and Waal, and in the seaside resort of De Koog. A once valuable fishing industry is now of negligible importance. Considerable flocks of sheep provide milk from which the famous 'Texel green cheese' is made, and a few thousand cattle and some pigs are kept.

Most of south-western *Vlieland* is an expanse of bare sand, a large part of which is covered by the highest tides. Further north there are lines of groyne-protected dunes, with a sea-wall on the south-east. Some small flocks of sheep and goats and a few cattle are kept. The small village of Oostvlieland is a popular summer bathing resort, linked by ferry-services to Harlingen.

Terschelling, sixteen miles long but only two in breadth, has a wide area of dunes in the centre, with extensive sand-flats both to east and west, and a broad sandy beach on the north. Along the south coast a low stone dyke encloses some small polders, with a string of tiny settlements—Oosterend, Hoorn, Midsland and Westterschelling. The last has a harbour, with services to Harlingen. Most of the land is under permanent grassland or is used for fodder crops; some cattle are kept, their milk being processed at a dairy-factory near Hoorn. An interesting if minor local occupation is the collection of whortleberries from the scrubby heathland for export to the mainland.

Ameland, about twelve by two miles in size, lies only five miles from the coast of Friesland, separated from it by the tidal-banks of the Friesche Wadden. In 1875 a causeway was built across, exposed at high water, but it is not now used and has been deliberately breached in places to allow the passage of fishing boats. The island has the usual pattern of beach, dunes, small polders, and a stone dyke along the south coast. The few villages include Hollum in the west, Nes and Buren in the centre, and a ferry is run at high water across to Holwerd on the mainland.[1]

The only other island of any size is *Schiermonnikoog*, consisting mostly of dunes and sand-flats, but with one large dyke-protected polder. A ferry from Oostmahorn on the shores of the Lauwers Zee brings visitors across to Oosterburen, which possesses several hotels. There are more Frisian islands—Simonszand, Boschplaat, Rottumeroog and others, but they are merely rather higher sand-flats, uninhabited save for the lighthouse keepers on Rottumeroog.

THE IJSSEL MEER RECLAMATION AREA

The gulf of the Zuider Zee has long offered an obvious challenge to the enterprising Dutch, for it penetrates far south into the heart of the country, and some 200 miles of dykes were required to safeguard the low-lying lands around its margins. The expense of main-

[1] L. H. Bouwman, 'Agrarische Hervorming op Ameland', in *T.E.S.G.* (1955), vol. 46, pp. 282-6.

tenance of these dykes was one of the arguments put forward when the legislation for the reclamation scheme was being discussed in the Dutch parliament in 1918. To a densely populated country, the additional area of agricultural land offered an immense opportunity, for the area of the Zuider Zee was about 1,430 square miles. It was estimated that 860 square miles, or about 60 per cent of the whole, could be reclaimed, thus adding approximately 10 per cent to the cultivated area of the country.

The Zuider Zee proper, with a maximum width of about forty miles, lies to the south of a narrower section between Noord-Holland and Friesland (Fig. 19). The floor of the southern part lay about eight to fifteen feet below mean low water, and before enclosure there was a small tidal range of about a foot. Discharge channels from neighbouring polders, several small rivers, and one major Rhine distributary, the IJssel, flowed into the Zee. The IJssel not only has a mean discharge of about 8,000 cubic feet per second, but it carries vast loads of sediment.

Many schemes were discussed over the years before a final plan was adopted in 1918. This involved the construction of a major dam or *Afsluitdijk* across the narrow mouth where the Zuider Zee opened into the Wadden Zee. Within this enclosed area a series of polders was to be reclaimed, leaving a much reduced body of water, the IJssel Meer, into which the rivers could discharge. This would in effect serve as a large-scale *boezem*, the level of which could be controlled by sluices in the main dyke. In times of obstructed discharge, as when exceptionally high storm-tides are experienced in the Wadden Zee outside, the sluices could be kept closed and the level of the IJssel Meer would then rise, acting as a reservoir.

Work started in 1920 with the construction of a short dyke connecting Noord-Holland at Van Ewijcksluis with Wieringen island, which was completed in five years. The boulder-clay for this section was dredged from the Balgzand, a shallow bay to the south-east of Den Helder. Work on the main dyke began in 1927. Vast quantities of sand were dumped on to some shallow banks to form the artificial island of Breezand; here were constructed two harbours for dredgers and hoppers. The dyke was then extended in each direction from this island.[1]

The *Afsluitdijk* had to be of immense strength since it is exposed to storms from the open sea. It not only crossed open water with

---

[1] J. W. Thierry, 'The Enclosure and Partial Reclamation of the Zuider Zee', in *G.J.* (1931), vol. lxxvii, pp. 223-37, provides much information, with illustrations, about the early stages of the project. See also Ch. A. P. Takes and A. J. Venstra, 'Zuyder Zee reclamation scheme', in *T.E.G.S.* (1960), vol. 51, pp. 162-7; and Ch. A. P. Takes, 'The settlement pattern in the Dutch Zuiderzee reclamation scheme', in *T.K.Ned.A.G.* (1960), vol. lxxvii, pp. 347-53.

a mean depth of ten feet, but it had to negotiate deeper channels of up to forty feet. The core of the dam was made of boulder-clay, which is tough and tenacious when wet, conveniently dredged from the nearby floor of the sea between Wieringen and Friesland, and tipped directly from hoppers on to the site. This clay core was backed on the inner side by a massive sand-bank deposited in the early stages from hoppers, then by suction dredgers through pipes. This sand-bank was covered with more clay, and then flanked on both sides by enormous brushwood mattresses, sunk as a protection against tidal scour. Both sides of the dam were faced with stone-work laid on rubble. By 1932 there remained only the sealing of the final gaps; this operation presented serious problems, since as the gaps narrowed so the force of the tidal flow was increasingly concentrated within them. The two gaps, in the Middelgronden and Vlieter channels, were finally closed on May 28th, 1932.

The result was a dyke eighteen miles in length between Den Oever, on what was Wieringen island, and the coast of Friesland near Zurich. Its overall width exceeds 400 feet, including a platform 112 feet wide along the inner side for the roadway and for a future double-track railway. The height of the crest is between 23 and 24½ feet above N.A.P., which gave a margin of about ten feet above the highest storm-tides recorded to that time. Two groups of sluices were built through which excess water from the IJssel Meer is discharged at low tide, one at the western end of the dyke near Den Oever, the other near the opposite end at Kornwerderzand. Each sluice is forty feet wide, and the gates close automatically when the rising tide reaches a certain level. Each set of sluices is accompanied by a navigation lock; the one at Den Oever can accommodate vessels up to the 2,000-ton *chalands*, the other takes vessels up to 600 tons.

By 1937 the water in the Meer was quite fresh. This now provides, incidentally, a valuable source of water; its summer level is maintained at ten inches above that of winter, so that water can be obtained for agricultural purposes—for market-gardens, water-meadows and the dairy industry. The salt-water fish have been replaced by pike, perch and eels; the last come from the Sargasso Sea and pass through the sluices in millions, to return there years later (if not smoked and eaten!) to spawn and die. In actual fact, about 5,600 tons of fish, of which two-thirds consisted of eels, were caught in 1964 by the IJssel Meer fishermen.

The Wieringer Polder.—In 1927, when the work on the *Afsluitdijk* was well advanced, the construction began of the first of the polders, which was to occupy the site of the Wieringermeer, a right-angled re-entrant of the sea in the north-east of Noord-Holland. Great preliminary care was taken, even to making a small trial polder at

Andijk on the margin of the Drechterland peninsula near the south-eastern corner of the new polder. This was intended for experiments

FIG. 19.—THE RECLAMATION OF THE ZUIDER ZEE.

The state of the project is shown as at mid-1966. Only the dykes and canals concerning the Zuider Zee polders are shown.

The new polder-towns and -villages are indicated by initials as follows: *Wieringer Polder:* **M**, Middenmeer; **S**, Slootdorp; **W**, Wieringerwerf; *Noord-Oost Polder:* **B**, Bant; **C**, Creil; **Em**, Emmeloord; **K**, Kraggenburg; **L**, Luttelgeest; **M**, Marknesse; **N**, Nagele; **R**, Rutten; **U**, Urk.

Based on (i) various official sources; (ii) P. Pinchemel, 'Le Polder du Nord-Est (Pays-Bays)', in *A. de G.* (1953), vol. lxii, pp. 348, 350; and (iii) J. W. Thierry, 'The Enclosure and Partial Reclamation of the Zuider Zee', in *G.J.* (1931), vol. lxxvii, p. 226.

with methods of desalinisation and then with possible crop successions on similar soils to those which would be found in the new polder.

The first task was the construction of the outer bounding dyke, eleven miles in length, from Medemblik to Den Oever, completed early in 1930. While this was being built, the main internal drainage canals were dredged out and two pumping stations were constructed, the *Lely* near Medemblik in the south and the *Leemans* near Den Oever in the north. The problem of the disposal of water from the Anna Paulowna and other adjoining polders to the west, which had previously drained to the Wieringermeer, was overcome by the construction of a canal along the western shore of the Wieringermeer, connected both with the old polder drainage system to the west and with the canals in the new polder. This runs into a small lake, the Amstel, left as a storage reservoir to the south of the dyke between the mainland and the former Wieringen island, and discharging into the open sea near Van Ewijcksluis. Another main canal runs along the south of the new polder between Winkel and Medemblik.

The enclosing dyke was completed in February 1930, and pumping at once began; by the end of August the polder (which had been ten feet deep) was dry. This was the largest area in the Netherlands ever to have been reclaimed from the sea, and amounted to nearly 50,000 acres, or 9 per cent of the land to be won by the whole IJssel Meer scheme. Internal canals divide this polder into four self-contained sections, each with its own water-table. Within these sections, the main drainage channels, navigable by small barges, further separate the land into rectangular strips, and these are sub-divided by feeder drains into units of approximately fifty acres, each bounded at one end by a metalled road.

A major problem was to get rid of the salt in the clays, which can only be removed by long-continued leaching. Throughout the winter of 1930–1 all rain water was pumped away, so gradually removing the dissolved salt. This was accelerated by spreading gypsum (calcium sulphate) over the land, to form a highly soluble compound with the sodium chloride in the soil. By the end of the winter of 1930–1 the higher parts of the polder were free from salt, but in the lower lands the process was to take three further years. The whole area was deep-ploughed several times in order to mix the light superficial sands with the underlying clay, and to expose as much material as possible to the beneficial effects of weathering.

So far all the work had been done by State-employed contractors, but in September 1931 the first farmers arrived as State tenants. They were leased holdings of one or more of the fifty-acre units; intended dairy farms were usually of one or two units, arable farms of two or three. The considerable demand for holdings was typical of Dutch initiative, and it was possible to select rigorously applicants with the necessary enthusiasm, aptitude and technical knowledge. By the end of 1934 forty-five holdings totalling 2,500 acres, or about 5 per cent of the total, were being farmed, and by 1940 the entire polder was under cultivation. The early crops of rye were gradually replaced by more profitable wheat, potatoes and other roots. Three villages were created, complete with schools, churches and amenities generally, including electricity supplies from the Grid: Wieringerwerf (the administrative centre), Middenmeer and Slootdorp.

The years of occupation, 1940–4, were difficult for the polder farmers, especially with shortages of fertilizers. But worse was to follow, for in 1944, when the end of the war was imminent, the German forces carried out an extensive programme of flooding, presumably for defensive purposes. Two breaches were blown in the outer dykes in the north-east by the retreating enemy, and the polder was inundated, fortunately only by fresh water from the IJssel Meer. Nevertheless, the floor of the polder inside the breaches was deeply scoured by inrushing water, and buildings and roads were swept away. The inhabitants immediately started work to seal the gaps. Fortunately the pumping-houses were undamaged, and after the liberation auxiliary pumps were brought in. By December 1945 the land was dry and in the following summer it was again under cultivation. But almost all the farms and villages had to be rebuilt, and this work was not concluded until 1953. Today it is once again a prosperous agricultural area.

The Noord-Oost Polder.[1]—The second polder to be tackled was the North-east, with an area of 119,000 acres, lying in the angle between the lowland of southern Friesland and northern Overijssel. Work on the enclosing dyke did not begin until 1936, and progress was slow. This dyke extends south to the former island of Urk, and then curves south-eastward to the south of the island of Schokland; the dyke was completed in 1940 during the German occupation. The deep-water channel of the Zwarte Water and the IJssel outfall (the Ketelmeer) was left to the south of the polder. Three pumping stations were built, at Urk, Lemmer and De Voorst at each of the three apices of the polder, and the ground had dried out by 1942. The land immediately inside the western dyke lies at about thirteen feet below N.A.P., rising gradually eastward. In the eastern half the water-table is maintained at 18·7 feet below N.A.P., i.e. nearly six feet below the surface.

Three main canals were dredged out before the polder was dry, with another along the western perimeter on the inner side of the dyke, to which drains a close network of minor canals and ditches. Some 96 per cent of the surface consists of young marine clays, sometimes with an admixture of sand. Considerable areas of fine sand

[1] W. M. Otten, 'De Noordoostpolder 1942–52', in *T.K. Ned. A.G.* (1952), vol. lxix, pp. 300-14, contains numerous maps and photographs; and Ph. Pinchemel, 'Le Polder du Nord-Est (Pays-Bas)', in *A. de G.* (1953), vol. lxii, pp. 347-63; this contains numerous large-scale maps and photographs.

are found, especially on and around the former islands of Urk and Schokland, and in the north-east occur peat deposits. The land was divided into 2160 units, mostly of the usual fifty-acre size, though some smaller lots of about twenty-five acres are used for intensive horticulture. About 5,000 acres, mainly in the north-east and on the sandy patches of Urk and Schokland, were planted with conifers. Eleven villages have been built (Fig. 19), and 295 miles of roads were constructed. Emmeloord, with about 15,000 people, supplies the administrative, social and shopping services for the population (Plate IV). Houses are built in terraces, with broad tree-lined grass verges and service roads. Schools, churches and public buildings have been carefully designed and sited, and the main shopping street has covered arcades. The town stands to the north of a small harbour where the three main canals meet, and light industries (at present mainly the servicing of agricultural machinery) are expected to develop around the port area.

Progress was, however, much slower than in the case of the Wieringer Polder, at first because of the difficulties of the war years, then because so much of the national effort after 1945 had to be devoted to reconstruction; notably the flooded areas of Zeeland and of the Wieringer Polder had first to be recovered. By 1949 the population had reached 3,000, then there was a rapid increase to 13,000, and by the end of 1964 it had reached 30,000. The whole polder was handed over from initial State development to its permanent cultivators, to form about 1,200 individual farms, by the beginning of 1958. Approximately 33 per cent of the agricultural land already in production is under cereals, 8 per cent under leguminous plants, 50 per cent under industrial crops, and 9 per cent under permanent pasture.

The Remaining Polders.—In the original plan there remained the large south-east and south-west polders. It was decided that the former was too big to handle as a unit, and accordingly it was divided into two, the Oost Polder [1] (known as Oost-Flevoland) and the Zuid Polder (Zuid-Flevoland). The former comprises 133,000 acres, the latter 99,000 acres. The West Polder (to be called the Markerwaard) will total 149,000 acres, and will be completed, it is hoped, by 1975, thus realising a scheme spread over sixty years which will have cost the equivalent of £200 millions.

Work on the Oost Polder was delayed by the destruction wrought by the storm of February 1953, which necessitated the employment of much Dutch drainage equipment, dredgers and hoppers. How-

---

[1] J. F. R. Van de Wall, 'De Groei van het Ontwerp voor de Oosterpolder', in *T.K. Ned. A.G.* (1953), vol. lxx, pp. 315-28, discusses the early stages of the reclamation of the Oost Polder.

ever, work slowly progressed and a dyke was built out north-westward from the coast near Harderwijk. On a dump of material in
the very centre of the southern part of the Zuider Zee, Lelystad was
created, to serve first as a base for workmen and equipment, later
to be developed as a town. Dr. Lely, incidentally, produced before
the end of the nineteenth century the plan which is the basis of
the whole scheme, and was Minister in charge of its early development; it is fitting that his name should be thus commemorated as the
future 'capital' of the new polder. A ship-canal, known as the
Oostvaardersdiep, 1,300 feet in width, runs south-westward to the IJ
Meer and to Amsterdam; this was dredged out during the winter of
1956–7 before the polder had been pumped dry.

At the rate of about a hundred yards a day the dyke was pushed
forward during 1955–6, until on September 13th, 1956 the last gap
to the north-east of Lelystad was filled, and Oost-Flevoland was
thus enclosed by a dyke fifty-six miles in length. Three pumping
stations were built, a diesel station near Lelystad and two electric
pumping stations near Harderwijk and in the north-east near the
IJssel estuary. Locks have been constructed to take shipping of up to
600 tons near Lelystad, and up to 300 tons near the IJssel estuary,
to enable vessels to pass into the IJssel Meer from the neighbouring
canals. An additional dam was built around the south-eastern
perimeter of the polder, completed also in 1956, leaving the narrow
Veluwe Meer as a ring-channel between it and the mainland. In
addition, a road-bridge, 1,200 yards in length, crosses the channel
between Oost-Flevoland and the Noord-Oost Polder near Urk, and
45 miles of main roads, together with 310 miles of minor roads, have
been built. The sites and lay-out of other towns were carefully chosen.

The Oost Polder, which slopes gently northward from six feet
below N.A.P. in the south to thirteen feet below in the centre, is
divided into two sections, with water-tables of seventeen feet and
of twenty feet below N.A.P. respectively. It represents a major contribution to the agricultural land of the country, since 96 per cent
of its surface is estimated to be of the category of 'very good soils',
compared with 70 and 80 per cent for the Wieringer Polder and
the Noord-Oost Polder respectively. Pumping proceeded steadily
during the winter of 1956–7 and the surface of the polder was dry
by the spring of 1957. By 1964 60,000 acres were scheduled as
agricultural land, almost all under arable crops. Work has followed
rapidly on the Zuid Polder, and by the end of 1966 about 7,500
people were living in the southern polders.

NOORD- AND ZUID-HOLLAND

From the northern tip of the Den Helder peninsula to the Haringvliet and the Hollandsch Diep lies the largest continuous area of

Dutch territory below N.A.P., yet it is one of the most densely populated parts of the world. At the end of 1964, Zuid- and Noord-Holland had densities of population of 2,608 and 2,077 per square mile respectively, compared with the average of 932 for the Netherlands as a whole. The density in western Utrecht is also very high, but as this province includes the sand-hills of Gooiland (see pp. 133-4), the average is reduced to 1,430 per square mile, which is nevertheless the third highest in the country. This density is due on the one hand to a remarkable urban development with its attendant flourishing commercial and industrial activities, on the other to an intensity of agriculture which is rarely equalled.

The western part of the region consists of lines of sand-dunes. In the south are the lowest portions of the Rhine interfluves, separated by distributaries flowing between massive dykes. Here are the low-lying polders to the north of Rotterdam, in Delfland, Schieland and the Krimpenerwaard. Further north are several large groups of polders which are the floors of reclaimed lakes, notably the Beemster and the Haarlemmermeer (Fig. 20). A number of lakes still remains, many lying in hollows left by peat-cutting and some retained as *boezem*. There is everywhere a maze of drainage and navigation canals, minor channels and ditches.

Soils are remarkably varied (Fig. 10), for they have developed from sands in the west, tracts of new marine clays in the south-west, some old marine clays on the floors of the drained lakes or where the peat has been removed, fen-peats, and river clays and sands in the south.[1] The following table summarises the areas of each of the main soil-types of Noord-Holland and Zuid-Holland:

Soil Types
(Percentages)

	Old Sea Clay	Young Sea Clay	River Clay	Peat	Dune Sands	Inland Sands
Noord-Holland	21	44	—	18	10	6
Zuid-Holland .	14	59	5	14	6	—

Source: *Jaarcijfers voor Nederland, 1957–8* (1960).

Agriculture.—A large part of the region is devoted to dairy-farming. The peat-land polders and many of the older lake polders are for the most part under permanent pasture, where a high water-table is maintained. The proportion of permanent pasture amounts to 56 per cent of the total farm land of both Noord- and Zuid-Holland.

[1] C. H. Edelman, *Soils of the Netherlands* (1950), affords a most detailed account, illustrated by a folding-map on the scale of 1:400,000.

The climate on the whole is mild and moist, and grass grows for much of the year. The mean temperatures at Den Helder range from 37° F. in January (appreciably warmer than in the east of the country) to about 62° F. in August. The 1921–50 mean of rainfall was about 26·8 inches, spread out through the year, for even the driest months (April and May) still had 1·4 inches each. As a result,

FIG. 20.—THE POLDERS SOUTH-WEST OF AMSTERDAM.

The reclaimed Haarlemmermeer lies within the Ring Canal to the south of Haarlem.

Based on *Chromo-Topographische Kaart van het Koninkrijk der Nederlanden*, 1:50,000, sheets 24 (E), 25 (W), and 25 (E).

dairying is based on grazing on permanent pastures, and cattle are kept out of doors for most of the year; little short-ley pasture and few fodder-crops are grown, although meadow-hay is cut for winter feed.

In 1964 there were about 509,000 cattle (of which 284,000 were dairy animals) in the two provinces, or more than a quarter of the total in the country. In Zuid-Holland a vast urban market exists for liquid milk. In Noord-Holland, by contrast, much milk is sent to large factories for processing into butter and cheese. The farms still produce a considerable output of cheese, notably the Gouda variety made in western Utrecht and eastern Zuid-Holland, and the red-crusted Edam cheese produced further north on the polder-farms bordering the IJssel Meer. Much of the cheese business is now centralised and highly organised; for example, a large proportion of Edam cheese is sold in the famous market at Alkmaar in Noord-Holland. Bullocks are reared in some areas; in the neighbourhood of Schiedam they are fattened on the residues from the distilleries.

Some arable farming is practised, but this does not compare in extent or importance with the Zeeland islands or with the Friesland-Groningen coastal clay-lands. The main districts under crops are the newer polders to the north-west of Rotterdam in Schieland, in the fertile IJ district, and on the old marine-clay floors of the reclaimed lakes. Here cereals, potatoes, sugar-beet and vegetables are grown.

Horticulture and fruit cultivation are carried on to supply both the towns and also a well-organised export market, especially in Great Britain. Market-gardens are important to the east of The Hague on the sandy soils (the *Geestgronden*), which being light and warm are extremely productive when heavily fertilised. Other significant areas are to the north of Alkmaar and in the triangle enclosed by Medem-blik, Enkhuizen and Hoorn, that is, the former peninsula of Drechter-land to the south of the Wieringer Polder. The district to the south of The Hague, known as the Westland, and the neighbouring Delf-land and Schieland, have an immense area under glass-houses. Zuid-Holland had 8,661 acres under glass in 1964, out of a total of 11,083 acres in the whole country. More than half of this glass was devoted to tomatoes, and about a fifth each to grapes and cucumbers, the rest being under melons, peaches and strawberries, all mostly for export.

One of the most profitable sides of horticulture is bulb-growing, for which the Netherlands is justly renowned; the output is almost entirely for export. There is a string of centres along the sandy strip to the east of the dunes extending between Leiden and Haarlem, notably concentrated at Sassenheim, Lisse and Hillegom. The heavily fertilised sandy soils are admirable for bulb-raising (Plate V), and some 30,000 acres were devoted to it in 1964. In spite of the competitive development of Lincolnshire, millions of bulbs are exported annually from the Haarlem district to Great Britain and elsewhere. There is an elaborate cut-flower trade, both for home and export, centred near Leiden, around Utrecht and notably at Aalsmeer near Schiphol. Nursery-gardens are widespread, the most extensive being at Boskoop, ten miles north of Gouda; its azaleas, rhododen-drons, clematis and roses are world-renowned. 2,244 acres were devoted to the cultivation of flowers (other than bulbs) in the two provinces in 1964, out of a total area in the whole country of about 3,000 acres.

All this diverse agricultural activity, carried on with an intensity and an enthusiasm rivalled perhaps only in Denmark, produces a valuable contribution to the Dutch economy. The horticultural districts have the densest rural population in the world, although the large dairy-farms of the permanent grass-polders and the arable farms of the lake-polders do not require as much labour. There are numbers of prosperous villages, some (as in the inter-riverine areas of Zuid-Holland) grouped around former refuge-mounds (here known as *woerden*), others (as in the polders further north) strung out along roads following the dykes. In the sand areas behind the dunes there is a chaos of villages interspersed with glass-houses, dwelling-houses and market-gardens. This then is one contribution to the high overall density of population in these provinces.

Towns and Industries.—Commercial and industrial development, which though long-established has nevertheless kept pace with modern progress, accounts for a complementary development of urban life. Most of the towns grew up in the Middle Ages as commercial centres on the banks of navigable waterways. In Noord-Holland several such towns bordering the Zuider Zee, once important as centres of commerce, have suffered because of their position on the coast of a shallow near-inland sea. Today these towns—Enkhuizen, Edam, Hoorn and Medemblik—are little if any bigger than they were in the seventeenth century, some indeed much smaller, and they now function as quiet pleasant market-centres for agricultural products.

The only Zuider Zee town to flourish in modern times is Amsterdam itself, by reason of its development of administrative functions, an enormous commercial life and a great range of industrial activities. Its main asset as a port is the magnificent North Sea (Noord-Zee) Canal, a waterway fifteen miles in length (Fig. 22), completed in the year 1876, by which the city firmly turned its back on the Zuider Zee and looked, as it necessarily was obliged to do in order to maintain its position, towards the North Sea. The city grew up in what must have been in many ways an unpromising position among tidal-flats and sand-banks. Near the point where the little river Amstel entered the southern shore of the IJ, a dam was built early in the thirteenth century to provide a sheltered harbour. Here sea-going craft could transfer their cargoes to smaller vessels which penetrated the inland waterways, hence the growth of the city's entrepôt trade. The 'Dam' today is a broad open place, the heart of the city's life. The urban area gradually extended southward in a semicircle, with the houses built on piles driven into the marsh. Its outward growth can be traced from the concentric semicircular canals or *grachten* crossed by radial channels (Fig. 21); it is said that the city in effect stands on three hundred islands. Each stage of growth had to be carefully planned, involving extensive drainage as the built-up area expanded southward. Occasionally drastic flooding forced its citizens to undertake ambitious large-scale reclamation schemes, and the city then spread a stage further on to the newly available land.

Since the war of 1914–18 the city has developed rapidly. In 1921 the area of the municipality was quadrupled, and considerable building programmes were put into operation. To the north of the IJ, for example, garden-cities were built, Oostzaan in 1920–1 and

FIG. 21.—CENTRAL AMSTERDAM.

Water areas are in black. This brings out (i) the ramifications of dock-basins along the North Sea Canal and the Afgesloten IJ, and (ii) the pattern of concentric semi-circular 'grachten', indicating the outward expansion of the city to the south as drainage and reclamation progressed. The word 'Dam' indicates the position of the main square, on the site of the original dam separating the river Amstel from the IJ. A group of six new 'tuinsteden' (garden-suburbs) is being developed to the west of the area shown on this map, with a planned total of 45,000 houses. Compare Plate VI.

The site of the projected road-tunnel is shown by a pecked line.

Based on *Falk-Plan Amsterdam* (n.d.).

Nieuwendam in 1925–6. In 1926 a plan was published for the overall development of 'Greater Amsterdam', but this was superseded by the famous 'Master Plan', published in 1934 after several years of intensive research, and which finally received Royal Assent in 1939.[1] This bold plan envisaged a population of almost a million in the year 2000; already (1966) the agglomeration of Greater Amsterdam totals 953,000. It involves the building of a number of garden-cities to the west of the present city, industrial development in the port area, and carefully integrated systems of communications, including a 'belt railway' raised on a twenty-foot embankment and a series of major radial highways. Although of course seriously delayed by the war of 1939–45, the plan is now making considerable progress; several garden-cities are being developed at Oostzaan Oost, Frankendaal and Slotermeer (built around an artificial lake).

Amsterdam is now (1966) a magnificent city of 866,342 people (Plate VI), with wide functions. Although the political seat of the Netherlands government is at The Hague, Amsterdam is in fact the capital. It is an important commercial, financial and cultural centre; for long it has had close relations with the now sadly reduced Dutch overseas possessions; and it is still a great entrepôt centre. Its port lies mainly along the eastern waterfront, the Afgesloten IJ, which is separated by the Oranje locks from the IJssel Meer, and there are some new basins for special purposes (such as the *Petroleum-Haven*) to the west. While it falls considerably behind Rotterdam in tonnage of shipping and freight accommodated, in 1964 it handled 14·7 million tons of sea-borne freight (though only 10 per cent of the Dutch total [2]). It is well connected with inland waterways, and in 1952 these connections were immensely improved with the opening of the new Amsterdam-Rhine Canal (see pp. 92-3 and Fig. 29).

Amsterdam, with its suburbs, is second in the Netherlands only to the Rotterdam conurbation as an industrial district. This extends along the North Sea Canal to IJmuiden (Fig. 22), and along the north bank of the IJ. Varied branches of the metallurgical and engineering industries are carried on, many of a precise nature and requiring a high degree of fabrication. Dutch engineering firms have a reputation for specialised machinery, including plants designed to process colonial products (machinery for sugar-refineries, margarine factories, oilfields and tin-mines), refrigeration machinery and electrical equipment. Although not as important as at Rotterdam,

[1] Aspects of the planning of Amsterdam are discussed by W. Dougill, 'Amsterdam: Its Town Planning Development', in *T.P.R.* (1931), vol. xiv, pp. 194-200; and 'Amsterdam: The General Extension Plan', *ibid.* (1934), vol. xvii, pp. 1-10. See also G. L. Burke, *The Making of Dutch Towns* (1956), pp. 141-53.

[2] In 1964, the Dutch ports handled 146·7 million tons of sea-borne freight, of which 69·8 were imports, 24·0 exports, the balance (52·9) in transit.

there is considerable shipbuilding activity; the *Oranje* (20,166 tons gross), for example, was built there for the Netherlands Royal Mail Line. Marine engineering is also highly developed; one firm, *Nederlandsche Werkspoor*, accounts for a fifth of the total Dutch output of marine engines, and several foreign firms build *Werkspoor* engines under licence. Plants which assemble cars, lorries and aircraft from parts made elsewhere include the *Citroën* and *Ford* works at Hembrug (a few miles west of the city on the shores of the North Sea Canal) and the *Fokker* works on the northern side of the port. A wide range of consumer goods, as one would expect in a capital city, includes clothing, pharmaceutical chemicals, footwear, paper, printing and bookbinding. Food-processing industries, as again one would expect in a port, comprise chocolate- and cocoa-making, sugar-refining, tobacco-processing, flour-milling, brewing (notably the delightful Amstel lager) and distilling. Others are specifically associated with the 'colonial trade'—oil-seed crushing, rubber and timber manufactures. A new oil-refinery was constructed in 1964–5 on the banks of the North Sea Canal at Zaandam. The long-established diamond-cutting industry still exists but on a much reduced scale, partly because of the growth of Antwerp as a rival centre, partly because of developments in the Republic of South Africa itself. In all, about 110,000 people are employed in factories within the Amsterdam district.

Few other large towns are found in Noord-Holland, partly because of its predominantly agricultural character, partly because it lies between the Zuider Zee (hence the decay of its former ports already mentioned) and the long sand-dune coast, with an almost complete lack of harbours.

The one North Sea port of any importance is IJmuiden, which only came into existence with the cutting of the North Sea Canal. It handled 4·05 million tons of freight in 1964, and is also important as the main Dutch fishing-port; about 114,000 tons, more than half of the total tonnage of fish landed in the Netherlands, were handled there.[1] In the Middle Ages the Dutch took considerable part in the herring fisheries of Europe; this was referred to as the '*principale goudmijne*' and was one cause which led to the growth of the Netherlands as a mercantile country. Fishing then was carried on from the Zuider Zee ports; indeed, the IJmuiden harbour was only built in the 1890's.

Adjacent to the northern side of the IJmuiden port-basins are the blast-furnaces and steel-works of the *Koninklijke Nederlandsche Hoogovens en Staalfabrieken N.V.*, the only fully integrated steel-plant in the country (Fig. 22). This was originally constructed as a

[1] This figure refers only to sea-fisheries; in addition there were further landings from inshore fisheries (unspecified, but about 40,000 tons).

result of the serious shortage of steel during the war of 1914–18, in order to mitigate this vulnerable position. It was decided that the industry could be more advantageously supplied with high-grade ores imported by sea than with poorer ores from adjacent countries such as France. A site of some 7,000 acres was chosen to the north of the seaward end of the North Sea Canal. It was intended to develop from the first a fully integrated steel-plant, but heavy post-war rises in costs made this impossible with the limited capital available. Three blast-furnaces were erected between 1923 and 1929, and by 1939 the output of pig-iron had reached about 280,000 tons. In point of fact this was then considerably more than the Netherlands itself could consume, so rather curiously the country became one of the world's largest pig-iron exporters. *K.N. Hoogovens* did later decide to develop the making of steel, and in 1938 a small oil-fired open-hearth furnace was put into operation, using about 40 per cent locally produced pig and the rest scrap. A rolling-mill was also erected in 1939 close to the steel-works, but even before production started it was dismantled by the Germans and transported to the *Hermann Goering* works at Watenstedt. This plant was recovered after the war and began operations again in 1947, producing principally steel plates for the shipbuilding industry.

After the war the Netherlands was faced with a vastly increased consumption of steel for the reconstruction of her damaged cities,

FIG. 22.—THE IJMUIDEN IRON- AND STEEL-WORKS, THE NORTH SEA (NOORD-ZEE) CANAL AND AMSTERDAM.

The built-up areas are shown in generalised form by means of a stipple.

Based on *Chromo-Topographische Kaart van het Koninkrijk der Nederlanden*, 1 : 50,000, sheets 24 (E) and 25 (W).

communications and industries, for her new specialised manufactures, and for her contribution to European defence. In 1950 Dutch industry was using 1·5 million tons of steel, but by 1955 this had risen to 2·4 million tons, a figure rather surprisingly only half a million tons less than the Belgian consumption, even with their long-established tradition of heavy industry. The Netherlands thus has become a very considerable importer of crude steel. The Government, in conjunction with the industrialists, planned to expand the IJmuiden plant as part of the country's post-war economic development. Whereas Dutch crude steel production had amounted to a mere 52,000 tons in 1938, it was planned to expand this to half a million tons in 1950 and then to about 800,000 tons by 1953. The open-hearth steel-furnaces were increased to five and their capacity has been considerably stepped-up. Several rolling-mills and a tin-plate plant were built at IJmuiden, operated by a newly formed company, *N.V. Breedband*, in which the chief shareholders are the State and the city of Amsterdam, while *K.N. Hoogovens* have a small holding. As a result of these various developments, Dutch production of steel rose rapidly, as the following table shows:

Output and Consumption of Steel

(*Thousand Tons*)

	1938	1952	1954	1958	1965
Crude steel	52	685	929	1,437	3,144
Finished steel . . .	—	444	707	1,197	—
Total finished steel consumption . . .	—	1,760	1,988	2,324	—

Source: *Mémento de statistiques*, published by the E.C.S.C., Luxembourg, annually.

Thus by 1955 the IJmuiden steel-works were producing about 37 per cent of all the steel used in the Netherlands, and this integrated concern is now one of the biggest units in Europe.[1]

With customary Dutch thoroughness, various by-product plants were erected on adjacent sites. Coke-oven gas is utilised in a nitrogen fixation plant, jointly owned by *K.N. Hoogovens* and *Royal Dutch Shell*, to produce ammonium sulphate, benzol, toluol and tar, while the remaining gas is piped through a grid to Amsterdam, Zaandam and Haarlem. Another company was formed, in conjunction with

[1] Summaries of the Dutch steel industry are provided by (i) L. A. Pennock, 'De Koninklijke Nederlandsche Hoogovens en Staalfabrieken N.V.', in *T.K. Ned. A.G.* (1948), vol. lxv, pp. 544-7; and (ii) 'The Dutch Iron and Steel Industry', reprinted from the *Monthly Statistical Bulletin* (1951), vol. 26, no. 11, of the British Iron and Steel Federation.

V The bulb-fields near Hillegom

VI Amsterdam

VII, VIII Rotterdam: (*above*) the rebuilding of Rotterdam;
(*below*) the docks at Schiedam

a Maastricht concern, to manufacture Portland cement from furnace slag, with an annual output of 200,000 tons, and another slag-processing plant produces road-making materials. A large power-station was built to the east of the iron-works, utilising part of the blast-furnace gas for electricity production, and supplying much of the province of Noord-Holland. There are also a jam factory, a tobacco factory and a paper factory.

Some of these concerns are situated in the municipality of Bever-wijk on the north side of the canal, where lives much of the labour used at the port of IJmuiden. Beverwijk has grown rapidly, from 5,329 people in 1899 to 22,109 in 1940 (when the communal bound-aries were increased) and to 40,899 in 1964. It is designed to expand still further as one of the 'new towns'; the plans being developed anticipate a population of 150,000 by 1980. The built-up area will expand to the north-east, absorbing some small existing villages, and a completely new town-centre will replace the present one. Con-siderable areas to the west and south-east of the town have been reserved as industrial sites.[1]

Haarlem, with a population of 172,010, is the fifth largest urban centre in the Netherlands, lying four miles to the east of the North Sea. The little river Spaarne winds through the town. Haarlem grew up as the home of the Counts of Holland, and developed pros-perous industries at an early date, although like so many others it suffered vicissitudes during the wars of the sixteenth century. Today, besides being the centre of the bulb industry, it has a variety of industries—engineering, railway rolling-stock and chemicals. Alk-maar (46,056) is the market-centre for much of Noord-Holland. It was once a small fishing village, surrounded by water (hence its name 'all sea') until the surrounding polders were reclaimed, when it became the centre of a rich pastoral district; its cheese-market is well known.

While Amsterdam clearly dominates the urban life of Noord-Holland, in Zuid-Holland and western Utrecht by contrast there are several large conurbations, known as the '*Randstad Holland*'. These include notably The Hague and Rotterdam (whose outskirts are only eight miles apart), which together contained in 1964 over 14 per cent of the total population of the Netherlands, and also Utrecht.

The city of Rotterdam is second to Amsterdam in size; in 1960 its official communal population (including within the city bound-aries Delfshaven and Kralingen on the north side of the river, Charlois, Katendrecht and Feijenoord on the south, and even Hook of Holland eighteen miles away) was 731,525. No official figure is given for the 'agglomeration', but it includes Schiedam (81,368) and Vlaardingen (71,941) to the west.

[1] J. M. Richards, 'New Towns in the Netherlands', in *Progress* (1956), vol. 45, pp. 147-57.

R.G.W.E.—D

Much of central Rotterdam has been rebuilt following extensive war damage (Plate VII).[1] One of the most interesting new features is the *Lijnbaan*, a shopping-centre built to the west of the town hall. While most of the streets were planned on usual lines—broad avenues, shops and flats above—the *Lijnbaan* consists of an attractive shopping district from which vehicular traffic is excluded. This project was started in July 1952 and completed in October 1953. A *métro* system is under construction.

Rotterdam (Fig. 23) is very much greater than Amsterdam as a port. It stands about eighteen miles from the sea, mainly on the northern bank of the Nieuwe Maas formed by the junction of the Lek and the Noord (see p. 91 and Fig. 29). It was near the confluence of the small river Rotte, which wanders in from the north, that the old town grew up in the fourteenth century. At first its trade was subordinate to that of Dordrecht, for long the leading Dutch port, but in the seventeenth century it began to forge ahead. The size of shipping grew in the late eighteenth and nineteenth centuries, while the problem of silting in the estuaries became increasingly acute, the result of the tendency of the Rhine distributaries to move south (see p. 89). Until the mid-eighteenth century shipping used the direct Briellsche Maas (Fig. 23), for long the main outlet of Lek water, but silting formed in this channel a large bank (which is now the island of Rozenburg), and this route was finally abandoned for another more than twice as long. This went southward through what is now the Noord and the Dordsche Kil, and so out to the sea through the Haringvliet between Voorne and Goeree-Overflakkee. In 1830 a channel (the Voornsche Canal) was cut across Voorne and used for thirty or forty years, but difficulties of navigation steadily increased as silting encumbered the Goeree channel with sand- and mud-banks. Many ships preferred to enter either through the Grevelingen channel between Goeree and Schouwen, then proceed round the eastern end of Overflakkee and down the Haringvliet to the Voornsche Canal, or even (particularly if they were coming from the south) through the Ooster Schelde and the Mastgat. All these routes were regrettably circuitous.

The final solution was a direct cut westward to the North Sea, the New Waterway (*Nieuwe Waterweg*), following mainly the line of the Scheur, the northern channel formed when the island of Rozenburg split the Maas into two. This involved cutting through the sandspit of the Hoek van Holland, and it took six years to construct, from 1866 to 1872. At first, however, this New Waterway (still known above Maassluis as the Scheur) was only ten feet deep, and

[1] A detailed summary (of 287 pp.) of the first ten years in the post-war reconstruction of Rotterdam is provided by C. van Traa, *Rotterdam; de Geschiedenis van tien Jaren Wederopbouw* (1955).

until 1885 larger vessels were still obliged to approach by the longer alternative circuits. It has been subsequently enlarged several times, and can now be negotiated by vessels drawing up to thirty-three feet. Ships enter between moles, nearly half a mile apart, at Hook of Holland (*Hoek van Holland*), which handles the considerable ferry traffic with England. Dredging is constantly necessary in the New Waterway, but with a mean tidal rise of about 5½ feet there is a useful natural scour, carefully directed and utilised by training walls.[1]

The port of Rotterdam consists of quays along both banks of the Nieuwe Maas (Plate VIII), together with numerous basins (*havens*),

FIG. 23.—ROTTERDAM AND THE NEIGHBOURING WATERWAYS.

The main built-up areas (generalised) are shown by stipple, individual village centres by a cross. Outside the conurbations are extensive areas of low-lying polders, with villages usually strung out along the dyked roads.

Based on *Chromo-Topographische Kaart van het Koninkrijk der Nederlanden*, 1 : 50,000, sheets 37 (W and E).

all with unlocked connection with the river. It is used regularly by *Holland-Amerika* and *Rotterdam-Lloyd* liners, and by many cargo vessels. In 1964 Rotterdam itself handled 114 million tons of sea-borne freight (80 per cent of the Dutch total), while if all the sub-sidiary ports along the New Waterway are included, the total was 121 million tons (84 per cent). Approximately 28,000 ships use the port and its subsidiaries each year. Rotterdam is the leading European port in terms of tonnage of freight handled. It is well ahead of London, it is normally equal to Antwerp and Hamburg

[1] J. W. de Vries, 'Uit de Geschiedenis van de Rotterdamse Waterweg', in *T.K. Ned. A.G.* (1953), vol. lxx, pp. 4-19, with the aid of detailed maps, describes the construction, maintenance, problems, etc., of the waterway, including the influence of radar on navigation.

combined, and, a still more impressive fact, it handles appreciably more freight than the port of New York. Much of this freight consists of bulk imports of mineral ores, cereals, timber, crude oil, coal, and such 'colonial' foods and raw materials as groundnuts, soya-beans, sugar and bananas. In 1964 forty-six million tons of freight were unloaded at the port, and seventeen million tons were loaded; the large balance of the total handled was in transit.

One major contribution to its importance is its situation relative to the Rhine distributaries (Fig. 29). The Noord and Waal form a highway leading south-eastward into Germany. The line of the Waal, the Maas-Waal Canal, the Maas and the Juliana Canal provides a route to Limburg and beyond to southern Belgium. A through-route can be followed to Antwerp via the Noord, the Hollandsch Diep, the Zuid-Beveland Canal and the Scheldt estuary, and several alternative minor waterways lead northward to Amsterdam. As a result, the port handled 52·0 million tons of freight by way of the inland waterways, or over 50 per cent of the Dutch traffic; 34·2 million tons constituted international traffic.

Since 1950 great developments, still in progress, have taken place in the port of Rotterdam. At the eastern end of the island of Rozenburg has been constructed the port of Botlek, to handle bulk imports of mineral- and vegetable-oil, and of chemicals. Several industrial undertakings have been built, including a huge *Esso* refinery, a shipyard for super-tankers, and a chemical factory. The port-works were completed in 1959. On an even bigger scale is the development of *Europoort*, at the North Sea end of the island of Rozenburg opposite Hook of Holland,[1] the first stage of which was completed in 1960. On the site *Shell*, *Caltex* and *Esso* have built huge terminals, the *Gulf* refinery was opened in 1965, and a 180-mile oil pipeline has been laid to Wesseling in West Germany. The port also handles bulk cargoes of coal and ore, both for a vast new steelworks on the site, and for western Europe generally. A ship-canal has been cut parallel to the New Waterway. Excavation of the dock-basins is well advanced, and *Europoort* will function as a major gateway for western Europe.

The Rotterdam conurbation forms the largest single industrial region in the Netherlands. From Vlaardingen through Schiedam and up-river to Dordrecht is a veritable Clydeside, with some fifty shipyards and other establishments engaged in ancillary industries. The output of ships is varied, for the industry both supplies the

<hr/>

[1] K. P. van der Mandel, 'Europort: the gateway to Europe', in *Progress* (1958), vol. 46, pp. 199-208. See also W. Evers, 'Europoort', in *Geographische Rundschau* (1959), vol. xi, pp. 298-304; and H. Kuipers, 'The changing landscape of the island of Rozenburg (Rotterdam Port Area)', in *G.R.* (1962), vol. 52, pp. 362-78.

Dutch mercantile marine and executes many foreign orders. These include tankers, merchant ships, motor coasting-steamers (a speciality of the Dutch yards), tugs, dredgers, hoppers and floating cranes. Warships are built both for the Royal Netherlands Navy and for foreign customers ; the famous Polish submarine *Orzel* was a product of a Dutch yard. Major vessels built include the *Rotterdam* (1959, 38,650 gross tons, flagship of the Holland-America Line), the *Nieuw Amsterdam* (1938, 36,667 tons gross), the *Statendam* (1956–7, 24,300 tons), the *Ryndam* (1951, 15,015 tons) and the *Maasdam* (1952, 15,024 tons). There has been a considerable post-war expansion in Dutch shipbuilding activity, particularly in the construction of tankers. A 78,000-ton tanker was launched in September, 1961, and a 100,000-ton vessel is on the stocks. Marine engineering is also well developed, while the manufacture of lock-gates, caissons, pontoons, pumps and bridges is an obvious reflection of the country's own requirements. Dutch firms carry out contracts for port-works, drainage and regularisation schemes in many parts of the world. There is a vast range of other metallurgical industries and the usual port industries : mineral-oil refining, distilling, vegetable-oil refining, the manufacture of paper, timber products, car assembly (*Chrysler, Simca*) and many more ; it would require an industrial directory to list the multifarious activities. Special mention may be made of *Unilever's* two huge factories, one making soap at Vlaardingen, the other margarine at Feijenoord. Two oil-refineries (*Royal Dutch Shell* and *Caltex*) are in the south bank suburb of Pernis adjoining the Petroleum-Haven to the west of the main port. Mention must be made of the distilleries at Schiedam, world famous for gin.

Vlaardingen, on the Nieuwe Maas between Rotterdam and Hook of Holland, has grown enormously in recent years, partly because of the development of its port and partly because of the introduction of new industries, while it also has some importance as the third fishing-port in the Netherlands. It is being developed as a 'new town' ;[2] the first stage, to house 25,000 more people, was completed by 1961, and further developments envisage a total population of 140,000. The method used is to build large rectangular blocks of flats of varying height, with community buildings and small parks. The first phase is being carried on in the western suburbs, and the new district is called Westwijk.

The Hague (known in Dutch both as 's-Gravenhage and Den Haag) is an attractively laid-out town, with broad tree-lined avenues

[1] This refinery has been greatly developed, and is the largest individual refinery in western Europe. A new dock, capable of accommodating 65,000-ton tankers, has been completed.

[2] J. M. Richards, 'New Towns in the Netherlands', in *Progress* (1956), vol. 45, pp. 147-57.

and imposing squares, substantial houses and Government buildings, new well-designed residential suburbs, pleasant gardens and wooded parks, in all 'an animated and cheerful city'. Originally situated two or three miles from the coast, it has expanded into the dune-lands, and Scheveningen (one of the most popular seaside resorts on the North Sea) and Loosduinen are now officially within the commune. Its population has grown rapidly from 56,000 in 1830 to 206,000 in 1899 and to 598,709 in 1965. The functions are primarily political and administrative, for it is the seat of government where the States-General meets (although Amsterdam is the actual capital), and it has been the seat of the Permanent Court of Inter-national Justice since 1922. Formerly the city had little commercial or industrial importance, but in the last few decades the number of banks and offices has increased, and some industries have been established. These include printing (notably the government station-ery office), paper-making, clothing, minor metal manufactures, furniture and food-processing. Scheveningen is the second Dutch fishing port; in 1964, 61,886 tons of fish were landed there, about 30 per cent of the Dutch sea-fisheries' catch, mostly consisting of herring, which are salted at several large plants beside the harbour.

Five miles to the south-east of The Hague is the quiet attractive town of Delft, with a population in 1965 of 76,020. It stands on the Schie, and the old town is enclosed by a rectangular moat, the Singel-Gracht. It was long famous for its pottery, although the industry nearly died out in the eighteenth century; a certain revival has taken place since the end of the nineteenth century. Delft has a variety of light industries—the making of cigars, dyes, alcohol, gelatine, margarine, yeast and electric cables—and it is a pleasant residential town with a certain attraction for tourists. Other impor-tant features include the *Topografische Dienst*, which produces the official Dutch topographical maps, and the large Hydraulic Labora-tory which carries out research investigations.

Leiden, a town of 98,806 inhabitants, lies about twenty-two miles north-east of The Hague, five miles from the coast of the North Sea. It stands among the branches of the Oude Rijn, which flow slug-gishly through and around the town. A former flourishing cloth trade now survives only in the manufacture of blankets and special livery-cloth, and at the height of its prosperity in the early seven-teenth century it had a population considerably greater than it has today. Leiden is in effect a cultural centre, and with its traditions of the past it also has some importance for the tourist trade. The few industries include printing and publishing, distilling and cigar-making, but these are of no great value.

Dordrecht (86,356) stands mainly on the south bank of the Oude Maas, near the meeting of the Noord, the Wantij and the Dordsche

Kil. Until the seventeenth century Dordrecht was the leading port of the Netherlands, but silting and the increasing size of ships caused Rotterdam, fifteen miles nearer the sea, to forge ahead in the nineteenth century. Nevertheless the deepening of the Oude Maas has helped Dordrecht, and it has extensive inland waterway connections. With Zwijndrecht on the opposite bank of the river it handled 1·76 million tons of freight in 1964, although this in point of fact amounted to less than one per cent of the total freight handled by Dutch ports. Its industrial activities are of much the same character as those of Rotterdam although on a smaller scale: shipbuilding, marine engineering, various metallurgical industries, chemicals, a *Unilever* oil-seed crushing-plant, and high quality glass-ware.

Utrecht (267,001), the fourth city of the Netherlands, is situated on the Kromme Rijn where it splits into the Vecht (which wanders off northwards to the IJssel Meer) and the Oude Rijn. The rivers are here markedly entrenched, and the city grew up on the high firm banks; the canals that intersect the town, the Nieuwe- and Oude-Grachten, lie far below the level of the bordering houses. It has long been an important centre of communications, for it stands in the centre of the 'isthmus' between the IJssel Meer and the Lek, at the junction of the peat-polderlands to the west and north-west, the river clay-lands to the south, and the morainic hill-country to the east. The Merwede and the Utrecht-Rhine Canals, several times enlarged, have linked Utrecht with Amsterdam and with the Lek. The completion of the Amsterdam-Rhine Canal (see pp. 92-3) has further improved the position of the town, as will the new state highways.

As a result of this central position Utrecht has many metropolitan functions; it is the seat of the Roman Catholic archbishopric, the headquarters of the *Nederlandsche Spoorwegen* (the State Railways), and it has a celebrated university. It is an important industrial town, with numerous engineering activities, the manufacture of railway rolling-stock and chemicals, tobacco processing, and an immense output of factory-made dairy produce. To the north-west, along the Merwede Canal, have developed the new industrial suburbs of Zuilen and Maarssen.

In this section on the Dutch coastal lands, considerable space has been devoted to these towns, the inevitable result of a remarkable development of city life within a small area of western Europe. The southern part of Zuid-Holland, with the great cities of Rotterdam, The Hague and Utrecht, are commonly referred to as ' *Randstad Holland*' (*Randstad* =conurbation).[1] Nevertheless, it must not be

---

[1] J. Winsemius, 'Urbanisation in the western part of the Netherlands ('*Randstad Holland*'), in *T.E.G.S.* (1960), vol. 51, pp. 188-99; and W. Steigenga, 'The Urbanization of the Netherlands', in *T.E.S.G.* (1963), vol. 54, pp. 46-52.

forgotten that a mere five miles from Amsterdam lie the fertile arable lands of the IJ Polders, that only a mile or two north of Rotterdam is the deep Prins Alexander Polder, and that many of the workers of Utrecht live on the wooded Gooiland Hills not far to the east. In this part of the Netherlands intensely developed urban and rural ways of life are in close juxtaposition.

THE SOUTH-WESTERN ISLANDS AND ESTUARIES

This sub-region comprises the whole of the province of Zeeland, (except for Zeeuwsch-Vlaanderen which is part of Maritime Flanders) (see pp. 83-5), together with the extreme south of Zuid-Holland. This is the delta-region, including the four major estuaries—the Wester Schelde, the Ooster Schelde, the Grevelingen Maas and Volkerak, and the Haringvliet. Between the first two are the islands of Walcheren, Zuid-Beveland and Noord-Beveland,[1] although the first and second of these were actually converted into a peninsula when causeways were built to carry the Flushing to Bergen-op-Zoom railway. The island of Schouwen-Duiveland and the peninsula of Tholen separate the Ooster Schelde from the Grevelingen Maas, and Goeree-Overflakkee divides the latter from the Haringvliet. This, as has been shown (p. 35), is the main area of exposure to flooding, comprising some 700 square miles of dyked islands and peninsulas consisting mainly of reclaimed heavy marine clays; the floors of the polders are well below the perimeter dykes and the mean level of the sea. It is the area that will be transformed by the 'Delta Plan' already described (see p. 38). In May, 1960, a phase of the Plan was finished when the dyke linking Noord- and Zuid-Beveland across the Zandkreek was completed, and in April 1961 the Veersche Gat dyke between Walcheren and Noord-Beveland was finished (Plate II).

This is one of the main arable districts of the Netherlands. No less than 59 per cent of the total area of Zeeland is officially classified as arable land, only 14 per cent under permanent pasture. About a quarter of this farmland grows wheat, and barley is also important. Approximately a quarter of the Dutch sugar-beet and flax output is grown, together with a considerable acreage of potatoes, onions, leguminous crops and other vegetables. Cultivation is intensive and yields are generally high; the wheat yield in Zeeland reaches thirty-one cwt. per acre, compared with the quite high figure of twenty-eight cwt. for the Netherlands as a whole. In Zuid-Beveland there is a large acreage of orchards and bush-fruit, especially red currants. Although this region as a whole is predominantly arable, in 1962 of the 96,000 cattle in Zeeland about a

---

[1] C. Hage, 'Noord-Beveland', in *T.E.S.G.* (1951), vol. 42, pp. 86-98.

fifth were dairy animals. This figure is, however, by far the lowest for any Dutch province, the next being Limburg with 187,000.

A certain amount of inshore fishing is practised among the islands; for many years the oyster and mussel beds of the Ooster Schelde have been carefully managed. The loss of these is one disadvantage of the Delta scheme which has in fact caused some opposition.[1]

In spite of the intensive and prosperous agriculture, only the provinces of Friesland and Drenthe have a density of population lower than that of Zeeland; its density of 430 people per square mile in 1964 was rather less than half that of the country as a whole and only about a sixth that of Zuid-Holland. This is due to the absence of large towns; a mere 18 per cent of the population lived in towns of 20,000 or over in 1964, compared with 62 per cent for the Netherlands as a whole, and only Drenthe had a smaller urban population. The only town of any size is Flushing (*Vlissingen, Flessingue*), with a population of 28,856, on the southern tip of Walcheren. It is the third port of the Netherlands, though its former packet-services with Harwich have not been resumed since the war of 1940–5. It has extensive oil- and coal-bunkering facilities, and also the large shipbuilding yard of the *Koninklijke Maatschappij De Schelde*. The capital of the province is Middelburg, once a seaport, now linked by canal to Flushing and to the Veergat on the north of the island. It is a pleasant quiet administrative and market centre, with the old town still surrounded by a moat. Veere, at the northern end of this canal, is another former port, which with Zierikzee on Schouwen and several other tiny places, have ceased to be of any importance as a result of the silting-up of their harbours and the increased size of shipping.

The population then is dispersed among the arable lands of the islands. Some villages are grouped around refuge-mounds, similar to the *terpen* and *wierden* of the north, though known in Zeeland as *vliedbergen* or simply as *hillen*. Other villages are strung out along the lines of ancient dykes or on sandy ridges that indicate the positions of former silted channels.

---

[1] The results of the closing of the estuaries under the Delta Plan on the cultivation of oysters and mussels, together with the lobster and shrimp fisheries (especially in the Ooster Schelde, centred on Yerseke), is described by A. G. U. Hildebrandt, 'De Gevolgen van de Afsluiting van de Zeegaten voor de Visserij', in *T.E.S.G.* (1956), vol. 47, pp. 189–98.

CHAPTER 4

MARITIME FLANDERS

The coastal plain from the estuary of the Wester Schelde in the north-east to where the chalk hills of Artois reach the Channel coast at Sangatte, a few miles west of Calais, forms a distinct regional unit, referred to as 'Maritime Flanders'. About thirty-five miles of this North Sea coast are in France, forty-two in Belgium, and eight miles in the Netherlands, while a further forty miles form the southern shore of the Wester Schelde. The whole length provides a remarkably straight and unembayed coastline, characterised by a broad extent of sandy beach uncovered at low tide, and backed by a continuous barrier of sand-dunes strengthened in places by artificial defences. Behind this again lies a flat plain, seamed with drainage channels and extending landwards for some six to ten miles to approximately the five-metre contour.

THE EVOLUTION OF THE COAST

The evolution of this coastal plain has already been described down to the end of the Lower Holocene, at about 5000 B.C. On the offshore bar, which extended far to the north-east beyond the Scheldt, Meuse and Rhine breaches (see p. 28), accumulated a line of sand-dunes behind which lay a marshy lowland. Here sediment-ation was considerable, and with the onset of the mild damp con-ditions of the Atlantic phase, the growth and decay of vegetation led to the formation of peat-beds. This continued into the Sub-Boreal phase, although under those cooler and drier conditions much less peat accumulated, but with the return of a milder damper climate peat accumulation was again accelerated. Neolithic finds in Flanders testify to the presence of man in the region at this time.

The development of the coastlands of Flanders in historic times has been studied in detail by Belgian geologists and botanists.[1] There have been several phases of marine transgression. The *Dunkirk I* phase, from the second century B.C. to the first A.D., was responsible for considerable sedimentation near Veurne and Ostend. The second phase, *Dunkirk II*, occupied the period from the fourth to the eighth centuries; at its maximum in the fifth century this transgres-sion covered the coastal plain as far inland as the five-metre contour,

[1] R. Tavernier, 'L'Evolution de la plaine maritime belge', in *Bulletin de la Société belge de Géologie* (1947), vol. 56, p. 332.

and much silt and fine sand was deposited. Only a few sandy islands, the remnants of the former dune-line, remained above the water-level. Conversely, tidal channels were cut down into the peat-beds; their courses can still be traced by deposits of coarse sand, for when the level of the surrounding peat-lands was later lowered through drainage and resultant shrinkage and compaction, the winding sand-filled channels were left outstanding. The areas covered by the silts and sands are referred to generally as the *Oudland*.

From the eighth century onwards the sea slowly receded, and the progressive drying-out of the shallow lagoons was assisted both by natural sedimentation and by some reclamation by man; documents as early as the tenth century relate to the building of dykes. Considerable protection was afforded by the accumulation of another line of dunes (see p. 29), which like its predecessor originated as an offshore bar built up by the waves.

There was a further but less extensive transgression in the tenth century, referred to as *Dunkirk III A*. It caused several breaks through the new dune-line, but the artificially strengthened defences helped to limit the extent of this inundation. The estuary of the Ijzer (in French *Yser*) became a broad sheet of water, and the enlarging of a breach near Knokke was responsible for the Zwin. An extensive marshy depression (probably caused by peat-cutting), known as the Groot-Moeren or Grand-Moëres, which extended across the position of the present French frontier, was also flooded.

Towards the end of the eleventh century a renewed transgression (*Dunkirk III B*) particularly affected the Zwin estuary, resulting in a rapid growth in the importance of the port of Bruges. The deposits associated with the *III A* and *III B* transgressions cover the now reclaimed areas referred to as the *Middelland*, found along and to the east of the Ijzer estuary and between Blankenberge and Bruges.

Reclamation went steadily on, furthered especially by grants of land to the Cistercian religious houses. But as in Groningen and Friesland many set-backs were experienced, for sometimes too extensive an area was reclaimed with inadequate protection, so that some storms did grievous damage. In the succeeding centuries catastrophes occurred at intervals, notably in 1277, 1288 and 1357. In 1377, when the Wester Schelde was enlarged into its present estuary form, twenty-two villages were inundated with great loss of life. A very disastrous flood occurred in 1404, and as a result the *Graaf Jansdijk* (*digue du Comte Jean*) was built by the Counts of Flanders to buttress the dune-wall; this can still be traced in places, well inland of the present coastal defences. Other inundations were sometimes a result of neglect during the wars to which Flanders was grievously and frequently subject, sometimes deliberately caused as part of military strategy; the so-called '*Polders historiques d'Ostende*' to the south of that town were flooded by the beleaguered Dutch between 1601 and 1604. These polders incidentally were maintained as water-areas until 1800 to serve an unusual purpose; at low tide the sluices were opened and water from the polders flowed strongly seawards, helping to scour the shipping channel and maintain an adequate depth of water in Ostend harbour.

Unlike the Netherlands, since the seventeenth century little serious flooding has taken place in Belgium. No major rivers bring massive contributions of flood-water to the coastal lowlands, the strengthened dune-line is straight and continuous, and no area actually lies below the Ostend datum, although some land is below high-tide level. The only area flooded since the seventeenth century in Belgium has been the IJzer estuary, twice deliberately for defensive purposes in 1783 and in 1914–18, once in 1928 by the collapse of a temporary dyke during a storm. A very small area to the east of De Zoute was inundated by the floods of 1953. There have been inundations, however, both in Dutch and French Flanders, along the estuaries of the Scheldt and the Aa.

Marine erosion has pushed the coastline a little landwards in historic times. Between Dunkirk and Nieuwpoort and again near Ostend the present coastline lies a few hundred yards inland of its position in the tenth century. Testereph and Scarphout were formerly ports which had silted up by the twelfth century, but today their sites lie some distance offshore. There are other such records, but for the most part the coastal defences which protect against inundation have also served against erosion.

The features of the Flanders coastal plain are described under first the beach and dune-rampart, and second the polder-lands (Fig. 24).

THE BEACH AND DUNES

The broad beach, uncovered in places for a width of nearly a quarter of a mile at low tide, consists of sand, strikingly free from pebbles, which is fortunate for the Belgian resorts. The set of the currents and a longshore drift move some sand and mud, although this is largely checked by groynes (Plate IX).

Behind the beach rises a long rampart of dunes, cut through only at Dunkirk and by the Aa estuary at Gravelines in France, and at four places in Belgium—at the mouth of the Ijzer below Nieuwpoort, at Ostend, near Zeebrugge where the ship-canal from Bruges reaches the sea between the moles, and at the shallow mud-covered inlet which marks the former mouth of the Zwin estuary. Between the Ijzer mouth and Dunkirk the dune-belt is over a mile wide, and

Fig. 24.—The Flanders Coast south-west of Ostend.
The complicated pattern of the drainage canals is much simplified.
Based on *Carte de Belgique au 1:100,000°*, sheets I, II, VII, VIII.

between Ostend and Wenduine and again near Knokke it is nearly as wide. On the other hand, to the west of Ostend it becomes a narrow single dune-line. The highest dune is the 'Blekker', which rises to 167 feet near Oostduinkerke, and many more exceed a hundred feet. The dune-line is chaotic in appearance, a tossing sea of sand, with clusters of crests separating broad depressions (known as *pannes*), but with a steep uniform slope falling to the beach. An irregular cover of vegetation consists of marram grass planted to help stabilise the sand, patches of scrubby bushes—osiers, willows, gorse and aromatic shrubs, and here and there plantations of conifers.

This coastline within Belgium is an almost continuous holiday resort, for apart from the major centres, Ostend and Blankenberge, there are many *-baden* and *-plages* fronted by promenades and concrete sea-walls.[1] Among the dunes are individual villas, hotels, holiday-camps and huge caravan-parks. The remains of Hitler's 'Atlantic wall' are visible—massive gun-turrets that have slumped down the dunes, and pill-boxes that have been converted into public conveniences or refreshment kiosks.

Apart from the tourist industry and the presence of packet-ports, the coast has little economic importance. The old town and citadel of Calais stand on what was a dune-island, surrounded by several basins and canals, and approached from the sea between long converging jetties. The port-works stand on piles which go down through the sands into the Flanders Clay. The new town, with the industrial suburbs of St. Pierre, has developed to the south ; factories make lace, rayon, clothing and embroidery, and there are several food-processing establishments and timber-yards. Calais is important as a ferry-port at the terminal of the shortest sea-route between Britain and the Continent, and imports of timber, ores, chemicals, cellulose and other bulky raw materials are unloaded for the northern industrial area of France. About 2,600 ships used the port in 1963, with a total net tonnage of 2·9 millions, and 808,000 passengers entered.

Dunkirk (*Dunkerque*), its tremendous scars from the summer of 1940 now largely healed, is an important entry for the north-eastern industrial region of France and the western Flanders Plain. The turning-basin and large maritime locks, under construction before 1939, have been finished since the war, and the harbour handles a large car-ferry traffic with England. Its freight handled, which totalled 12·2 million tons in 1963, has grown enormously in recent years, as it has become one of the main ports of the northern industrial region ; the main items are oil, iron-ore and manufactured steel. The town has a few processing industries, mostly in the suburb of

---

[1] O. Vanneste and G. Declercq, *Le Littoral et son hinterland: essai d'une étude d'économie touristique* (1955).

St. Pol-sur-Mer, where a large oil-refinery, owned by the *Société française des Pétroles B.P.*, had a through-put of 3·25 million tons in 1962. A new large integrated steel-works began operation in 1962, owned by *Usinor*, and a thermal power-station was opened in the same year.

Ostend (*Oostende* in Flemish, *Ostende* in French) is an important ferry-port at the terminus of an international railway-route. It is also the chief Belgian fishing-port, for in 1964 it handled about 35,000 tons of fish out of a Belgian total of 48,000 tons, and there are associated fish-curing and canning plants, refrigeration plants, and fertiliser factories. A large shipyard builds trawlers and such specialised craft as dredgers. The chief importance of the town, which in 1964 had a population of 56,850, is as a seaside resort.

Nieuwpoort (in French *Nieuport*), situated about two miles from the sea up the Ijzer estuary, has a harbour for small tramp-steamers and fishing-boats, and its local industries include a chemical works to the south of the town. Zeebrugge is a wholly artificial port, protected by a mole nearly five miles in length, and linked to Bruges by a ship-canal. The port handles a varied commercial traffic, mostly imports of coal and oil and exports of coke, chemicals and cement. To the south of the inner harbour the large *Solvay* chemical-works and a coke-oven plant both depend on imported coal and raw materials. The largest glass-furnace in the world is located here. In 1965 began the construction of an oil-refinery, with a throughput of 2 million tons.

THE POLDERS

Inland of the dune-belt lies a long narrow strip of what is referred to as the Flemish polderland. This widens in two places, along the valleys of the Aa and the Ijzer.

The Aa polders, in French Flanders, occupy more or less a triangle with its apex at St. Omer (where the river leaves the low clay-covered plateau) and its base on the dune coast. The Aa, rising to the south-west of St. Omer on the eastern slopes of the chalk hills of Artois, enters the polderland below that town, and flows to the sea beyond Gravelines between high dykes built well above the surrounding countryside.

The Ijzer follows in its upper course the general south-west to north-east direction of the Flanders rivers (see p. 15), but then makes an abrupt right-angled bend northwards and breaks through to the North Sea coast near Nieuwpoort. It probably owes this change of course to the *Dunkirk II* marine transgression, which produced several shallow embayments into one of which the upper Ijzer was diverted. This estuary seems to have extended as a broad sheet of water as far inland as Loo until the tenth century, but gradual reclamation has since reduced it to the narrow tidal creek of today. Several sluices at Nieuwpoort are used to regulate the levels of the coastal canals and to dispose of flood-water brought down by the river. These sluices were operated to flood the Ijzer valley as part of the defence of Nieuwpoort in the war of 1914–18.

The surface of the polder-land is interrupted only by depressions, usually the result of peat-cutting or of digging clay-loam for brick-making, and by sandy hillocks rising twenty feet or so above the general level. Some of these hillocks near the coast are the remnants of older dunes, those further inland are 'islands' of Pleistocene sand; they sometimes form useful village sites, as in the case of Gistel to the south of Ostend. The soils are variable; patches of yellow sand, black silt and grey or blue marine clays can be seen within a few yards of each other, although the clays usually predominate.

The polders are covered with a maze of drainage ditches (Fig. 24), many in orderly geometrical patterns, others in irregular chaos; some of the latter were formerly tidal creeks. They lead into larger channels known as *leeden, vaarten, waterganden* and *grachten*, and then into a few major outfalls, such as the Lys Derivation and Leopold Canals, which take most of the water to the north-east of Bruges, and the Noord Eede. The rivers Ijzer and Aa also help. The small navigable waterways (Fig. 25), along which it is possible for a barge to move from Calais to Bruges more or less parallel to the sea, play little or no part in the drainage since they are usually enclosed within dykes some feet above the surrounding countryside; frequently a drainage canal at a lower level runs parallel to a water-way, and may even pass under it in a concrete siphon.

The polders are divided for drainage purposes into units, under the control of elected syndicates or *wateringues*, many dating from developments in the twelfth century. In each polder the water-table is maintained at a specific level; excess water is removed by gravity when the sluices into the main outfalls are opened at low tide, or occasionally by pumping. One additional problem, the result of much of the polders lying below normal high-tide level, is the infiltration of salt water into the subsoil should too much fresh water be pumped away.

These Flemish polder-lands may be divided into several units (Fig. 11). In the west the French polders lie within the Aa basin, succeeded eastward by the more extensive Belgian polders, and along the southern shores of the Wester Schelde are the polders of Dutch or Zealand Flanders (*Zeeuwsch Vlaanderen*). In addition, the lands bordering the Scheldt estuary and the Antwerp region itself must each be considered separately. These are lettered 2a to 2d respectively on Fig. 11.

FIG. 25.—THE WATERWAYS OF BELGIUM AND NORTH-EASTERN FRANCE.

The abbreviations are as follows : **A.C.**, Aire Canal ; **A.P.C.**, Antoing-Pommerœul Canal ; **B.A.C.**, Blaton-Ath Canal ; **B.N.C.**, Blaton-Nimy Canal ; **B.C.C.**, Brussels-Charleroi Canal ; **Bo. C.**, Bourbourg Canal ; **B.R.C.**, Brussels-Rupel Canal ; **B.Z.C.**, Bruges-Zeebrugge Canal ; **C.C.**, Centre Canal ; **Co. C.**, Colme Canal ; **D.C.**, Deûle Canal ; **G.O.C.**, Gent-Ostend Canal ; **G.T.C.**, Gent-Terneuzen Canal ; **R.C.**, Roubaix Canal (continued to the Scheldt as the Espierres Canal) ; **S.C.**, Sensée Canal ; **S.O.C.**, Sambre-Oise Canal ; **St. Q.C.**, St. Quentin Canal ; **V.C.**, Veurne Canal.

Based on W. Seghers, *Kaart der Binnenscheepvaartwegen van N.-W. Europa* (n.d.).

The French Polders.—The polders of French Flanders, though nowhere below mean sea-level, remained as marshland much later than did those of Belgium. Little in the way of reclamation was accomplished until the eighteenth century, and even in the nineteenth winter flooding was still widespread. These polders are wet because of the proximity of the chalk-edge to the west, from which copious spring-water is discharged.

The reclaimed polders are now the scene of a prosperous arable farming. Some cattle are reared, both for dairying and for meat, to supply the industrial towns in the Lille area and on the northern French coalfield, but livestock are not so important as in Belgian Flanders. As the marshes were reclaimed, they were put under cereals, beans and clover, and some districts concentrated upon flax-growing. These crops are still grown, although the area under flax has notably declined, and the largest acreage is now devoted to sugar-beet, for which the north-east is the most important producing region in France; several large refineries have been built since the 1914–18 war. There are many prosperous market-gardens, and chicory is a local speciality in sandy areas.

Several factories processing agricultural commodities are situated at points along the banks of the canals, equipped with wharves to handle imported coal and raw materials. These include distilleries, breweries, chicory-mills, vegetable canneries and saw-mills, and they help to provide full employment in this agricultural countryside.

The population lives either in villages straggling in linear pattern along the embanked roads and on slight eminences, or in large prosperous-looking though isolated farmsteads, for there are few towns. St. Omer stands at the junction of the polder-land with Interior Flanders, where the Neuffossé Canal is linked with the canalised river Aa. It is a small market-town, with a few factories manufacturing clothing and underwear. Other towns are Bourbourg, also with some small factories, and Bergues at the junction of three waterways surrounding the town, which give it a Bruges-like appearance.

The Belgian Polders.—In Belgium about 50 per cent of the polders are under permanent grassland, while much of the remainder is under rotation grassland, with oats and green crops for fodder. Large dairy herds produce liquid milk for the towns of central Belgium. Sheep, the basis of the mediaeval Flemish woollen industry, were grazed on the salt-marshes and grass-covered mud-flats (*schorres*). Some sheep are still to be seen, mostly in Oost-Vlaanderen near the Dutch frontier, but are few in number in comparison with past centuries. Pig-rearing is usually associated with dairy farming. Further south, on the slightly higher lands towards

Interior Flanders, sugar-beet, flax and malting-barley are grown. The demands of neighbouring urban markets have resulted in market-gardening on the sandy soils where the dune-belt meets the polders ; these produce early vegetables, notably potatoes and carrots.

Farms usually stand on sandy ridges or hillocks away from the damp pastures, and with an occasional line of pollarded willows or poplars they form the only interruptions to the sweeping open countryside. The many dispersed villages each consist of little more than a nucleus of a church, an inn and a few shops, situated at a road-confluence or where a road crosses a canal. A few small market-towns include Veurne (in French *Furnes*), the focus of four waterways, six roads and a railway, the market-centre of the frontier district ; it has a few small processing industries. Its population in 1964 was only 7,000.

Bruges (its official Flemish form is *Brugge*) is the largest town, with a population of about 52,500, situated on the edge of the polder-land eight miles from the sea, to which it is linked directly at Zee-brugge by a ship-canal and also by a much longer waterway (the Gent-Ostend Canal) which wanders leisurely across the plain to Ostend. The old town, encircled and intersected by canals, exists mainly on its dual function as an attractive tourist centre and as a market-town for the northern districts of the province of West-Vlaanderen. On the north side of the town considerable industrial developments have taken place alongside the canal basins, including small shipbuilding yards, engineering works which construct bridges and rolling-stock, breweries, flour-mills, a yeast factory and several timber-yards. A number of craft industries still cater profitably both for tourists and for export—lace-making (largely a domestic industry), embroidery, wood-carving, fine printing and glass-painting.

Dutch Flanders.—In the north the strip of polder-land widens and trends almost at right angles along the southern shore of the Wester Schelde. Most of these polders are in Dutch territory, forming what is called *Zeeuwsch-* (or *Zeeuws-*) *Vlaanderen* (Zealand Flanders).[1] They are bordered by tidal marshes and mud-flats seamed with creeks. As late as the fourteenth century, the northern corner of Zealand Flanders consisted of an archipelago of islands—Kadzand, Wulpen, Oostburg and others—intersected by branches of the Zwin estuary. Silting took place, stimulated by dyking along the Wester Schelde, to the great detriment of Bruges at the head of the Zwin. The coastline is now protected by a thick earth dyke, reinforced with stone-facing along virtually its whole length. Substantial flooding

[1] S. E. Steigenga-Kouwe, *Zeeuws-Vlaanderen* (1950), *Publicatie no. 2 uit het Geografisch Instituut der Rijks Universiteit te Utrecht* ; this is a very full account, with detailed maps.

has nevertheless occurred at times, the last in February 1953 (see p. 36), when the dykes were breached near Terneuzen and on either side of the northward-projecting Hoek van Ossenisse. One piece of reclamation has been completed since the war of 1939–45; the broad creek known as the Savojaards Plaat, which dried out at low tide leaving only the Braakman channel, has been dyked-off from the open sea. The Braakman was the outlet of a canal from Gent via Ertvelde to the Wester Schelde as early as the tenth century, and also the outlet of the Sasvaart in the sixteenth century from Gent via Sas-van-Gent. This canal had silted up by the end of the eighteenth century, and finally the Gent-Terneuzen ship-canal was cut across the polder-lands in 1827.

This canal, two-thirds of which is in Belgium, has been enlarged several times, so that it can now take sea-going vessels up to 10,000 tons gross, as determined by the dimensions of the triple sea-locks at Terneuzen where the canal enters the Wester Schelde. One internal lock at Sas-van-Gent in the Netherlands near the frontier, larger than the sea-locks, was constructed to cope both with flood-water, since extensive flooding on the upper Scheldt and the Lys is relieved by way of this canal, and also with exceptionally high tides in the Wester Schelde; the sea-locks are opened for several hours before and after high tide. It is twenty miles long, with a width of 164 feet at the surface, and has a minimum depth of seventeen feet. It is at present (1966) being enlarged to take vessels of 35,000 tons. In 1963 the canal transported over ten million tons of freight; 653,000 tons of coal and 571,000 tons of building material and quarried products were unloaded at ports along its banks.

These Zealand Flanders polders are low-lying, some well below mean sea-level, notably the Pauluspolder to the south of the Ossenisse peninsula. The reclaimed heavy marine clays are almost entirely under arable cultivation, although dairying, pig-rearing and (on the salt-marsh pastures) sheep-grazing are practised. The main crops are cereals and roots grown in rotation, together with market-gardening and fruit-cultivation. Large prosperous-looking farms are dispersed over the open countryside, and villages are few and scattered, occasionally curiously forlorn in appearance, sometimes rather attractive. Some, such as Sluis, are decayed ports; this formerly stood on the shores of the now silted Zwin, although it is still connected to Bruges by a small canal constructed during the régime of the United Netherlands. Biervliet was a fishing village, where it is said the method of curing herrings was invented; a herring-vane surmounts the spire of the town hall. Other small towns—Zuidzands, Oostburg and Ijzendijke in the west, and Axel, Hulst and Zuiddorp in the east—are market-centres.

Terneuzen (sometimes known simply as Neuzen) stands at the

seaward end of the ship-canal to Gent.[1] The port tranships coal and raw materials into barges, some transit traffic passes through to Gent, and it has a small fishing industry. The canal does not handle cargo originating locally (this, mainly fruit and agricultural produce, is despatched by rail). It has benefited Sluiskil to the south, where coke-ovens (using imported coal) and an ammonia plant have been built, and coke and fertilisers are exported.

THE SCHELDT ESTUARY

The estuary of the lower Scheldt is dyked on both sides, for most of the bordering polder-lands lie well below high-tide level.[2] The lowest official point in Belgium is actually at Austruweel (half a mile downstream from Antwerp on the river bank), just one metre below the Ostend datum. In the east the alluvial soils change gradually to the sands of the western Kempenland, while to the west is the fertile *Waasland* or *pays de Waes*.

The distance between Antwerp, where the Scheldt is nearly six hundred yards wide, and the mouth of the estuary (indicated by a line between Flushing and Breskens), is fifty-eight miles, of which thirty-four lie in Dutch territory. This outlet is known as the Wester Schelde, between the islands of Walcheren and Zuid-Beveland to the north and the low-lying dyked coast of Zealand Flanders to the south. This estuary, a vitally important outlet for Antwerp, seems to have become established only in historic times, and it was not until the fifteenth century that it became the major outlet of the Scheldt system with a continuous navigable channel. The altitudes involved are so slight that without regularisation a mere accident of tidal-scouring can convert a minor creek into a main outlet, and artificial alteration is easy. Until 1866, for example, some of the water of the river Scheldt escaped through the Ooster Schelde, the estuary to the north of the Walcheren-Zuid Beveland islands, but in that year a dam was built to carry the Flushing railway between Zuid-Beveland and the mainland, and the gap was sealed.

The long story of 'the Scheldt question' is a direct result of the fact that the greater part of the estuary is under Dutch sovereignty, which for many years sought to cripple the trade of Antwerp by denying maritime access to it, hence the closure of the Scheldt from 1648 to 1792. It was not until 1863 that the Dutch right to levy tolls on Scheldt navigation was finally bought out by Belgium and other interested maritime countries. Today the Wester Schelde (the

[1] M. C. Verburg, 'The Gent-Terneuzen development axis in the perspective of the European Economic Community', in *T.E.S.G.* (1964), vol. 55, pp. 143-50.

[2] R. Havermans, 'Het Waterstaatkundig Landschap in de Antwerpse Noorderpolders', in *B.S. Belge Et. G.* (1954), vol. xxiii, pp. 59-84.

western part of which is known as the Honte) has a dredged and
buoyed fairway, at its narrowest over 150 yards, and with a least
depth of twenty-four feet right up to Antwerp. In effect vessels
drawing up to thirty-three feet can reach the port at high water.

THE ANTWERP REGION

The influence of Antwerp (in Flemish *Antwerpen* and in French
Anvers) is sufficiently marked to justify the appellation of the '*région
Anversoise*' to an area on either side of the lower Scheldt from the
Rupel confluence to the frontier, where the waterway bends almost
at right angles. The city lies almost entirely on the right bank of the
river, beyond its easterly 'elbow', with an extensive dock system
downstream of the built-up area (Fig. 26). Apart from two small
basins constructed during the Napoleonic period, most of these docks
were built in the latter part of the nineteenth century; they are
connected with the river by means of three locks. The large Hansa
Dock, completed in 1932, is linked directly to the river further downstream as well as to the other docks. The total water area of these
docks is about half as much again as those at London or Liverpool,
and there are about thirty miles of quays, of which three miles
stretch along the river frontage of the city. The barge-docks are
the focus of inland waterway traffic down the Scheldt system from
Flanders, along the Albert Canal from Liège (see pp. 126-9), and
up the estuary from the Netherlands and the Rhine via the Zuid-
Beveland Canal. Considerable extensions of the dock-system are
in progress, and in 1956 details were published of a scheme to
extend the port still further within the next twelve years at a cost of
£30 million; considerable progress has been made.

Antwerp is one of the world's great ports, and through its docks
passes about four-fifths of the foreign trade of the Belgo-Luxembourg
Union. In 1964 unloadings at the docks totalled 45·1 million tons
(36·4 by sea, 7·3 by inland waterways), and loadings amounted to
23·8 million tons (16·9 and 6·2 respectively);[1] these figures include
transit and entrepôt traffic. A wide range of commodities is included
—imports of mineral oil, ores, coal, timber, foodstuffs, 'colonial
goods' and raw materials generally, and exports of manufactured
goods, especially steel, chemicals, glass and textiles.[2]

Mainly as a result of these port-functions and of its long commercial and industrial traditions, Antwerp was a city of 249,000 people
in 1964; with its half-circle of densely inhabited contiguous communes to the east and south, the total population of the conurbation

[1] The balance in each case was handled by rail within the docks-area, and is
included in the returns '*enregistré par l'administration des douanes*'.
[2] M. de Roeck, 'Le Port d'Anvers: situation et problèmes', in *Report of the
International Geographical Week, Brussels* (1958), pp. 54-9.

FIG. 26.—THE ANTWERP REGION.

Water areas are in black. The area surrounded by pecked lines indicates dock extensions in progress. The two oil-refineries marked in the new dock area are *Esso-Standard* and *S.I.B.P.* **F**, indicates each of the perimeter forts. **V.T.**, vehicular tunnel under the Scheldt; **F.T.**, foot-tunnel. **Cath.**, Cathedral.

Based on (i) *Kleine Falk von Antwerpen* (*Falkplan*) (n.d.); (ii) W. Seghers, *Kaart der bevaarbare Waterwegen van Belgie en Noord-Frankrijk*, inset plan, 'Antwerpen'; and (iii) official information.

was about 700,000. A variety of industry has developed in the suburbs and the surrounding countryside, especially concentrated along the right bank of the Scheldt in Hoboken and beyond in Hemiksem and Schelle, and in the north-eastern suburb of Merksem. The usual port-industries include vegetable oil- and sugar-refineries, flour-mills and tobacco factories, and chemicals, soap, margarine, chocolate and rubber goods are manufactured. Almost all Belgium's mineral-oil refineries are situated within the Antwerp area; they include *S.I.B.P.*, *Esso-Standard* (*Antwerp*), *Albatross* and *R.B.P.* (*Antwerp*); *Atlas* and *Radian* each owns a smaller refinery. The varied metallurgical and engineering industries include shipbuilding, marine engineering, the construction of cranes, bridges and heavy machinery, and car assembly (*Ford*, *Chrysler* and *G.M.C.*). An immense range of 'consumer-goods' is manufactured. Along the estuary are large glass, pottery, brick and cement works. At Hoboken are tin, lead and copper refineries. The famous diamond industry, established for a little over a century, is now considerably more important than that of Amsterdam.

Much of the polder-land of the '*région Anversoise*' is intensively cultivated, largely to supply the demands of the city's population. In the Waasland, reclaimed since the beginning of the fourteenth century, market-gardens specialise in cauliflowers and tomatoes, and there are orchards of bush-fruits, dairy farms and poultry farms. This must be one of the most highly cultivated and productive agricultural districts in Europe. Numerous prosperous looking villages —Beveren, St. Gillis, Verrebroek and Kieldrecht—are the homes of Antwerp commuters who travel daily into the city by train to the Tête de Flandre station on the left bank. (No bridges, incidentally, span the Scheldt at Antwerp; people cross either by ferry or through the two tunnels, for vehicles and foot-passengers respectively.) The 'capital' of the Waasland is Sint-Niklaas, which stands on the northern edge of a low range of hills overlooking the polders. It really belongs to the hierarchy of industrial towns of Interior Flanders, manufacturing textile goods (cottons, linen, lace, carpets, hosiery), and pottery, tiles and bricks, while it is the chief clog-manufacturing centre in Belgium.

The polder-lands along the right bank of the Scheldt below Antwerp are much less developed, and the emphasis is on stock-rearing both for milk and veal. As the sandy soils of the Kempen-land are approached, market-gardening becomes more important; a speciality is the cultivation of asparagus. A few small villages are situated mainly on sandy 'islands' above the polders—Hoevenen, Stabroek and Sandvliet. Only one settlement of any size, Lillo, near one of the main defensive forts around the perimeter of Antwerp, stands near the lonely and rather desolate banks of the Scheldt.

CHAPTER 5

THE DUTCH RIVER VALLEYS

The broad clay-floored valley of the Rhine distributaries and the closely parallel Maas forms a distinctive region across the southern part of the Netherlands, extending westward from the German frontier near Nijmegen. Deposition of alluvium in this delta-region has been facilitated because the rivers enter the sea in the neighbourhood of a tidal node, an area of limited tidal range.

THE RHINE AND ITS DISTRIBUTARIES

The proto-Rhine in immediately pre-glacial times entered the sea further to the north than at present, by way of the valley of what is now the Eem and through the proto-Zuider Zee (see p. 23). Since then the main Rhine outlets have been gradually displaced further to the south. This tendency was probably initiated by the blocking of the northern outlets by the ice-sheets of the third glacial advance (see p. 18), but in post-glacial times this has been largely a result of the fact that the tidal range increases southward towards the Straits of Dover. This amounts to only five feet at Texel Gat, increasing to more than twelve feet in the Scheldt estuary. The southerly distributaries therefore experience a more rapid fall of water level at low tide than those to the north, which causes an increased scouring action by the ebb-tide in collaboration with the river current. Thus the southern outlets have been progressively deepened and widened, and the northern ones (except for the IJssel) have become correspondingly silted-up, and reduced to little more than back-waters. In Roman times the main stream flowed westwards along the line of the Kromme Rijn and the Oude Rijn, so reaching the sea to the west of Leiden (Fig. 27); this was for long the northern frontier of the Roman Empire, for the main Rhine outflow formed a prominent defensible obstacle. Today the main discharge is by the Waal, the most southerly distributary, which carries three times the volume of the Neder Rijn and six times that of the IJssel.

The Rhine enters the Netherlands from Germany near Lobith, approximately a hundred miles from the sea. Its régime is variable as a result of the different contributions of its numerous tributaries; the flow can vary at Lobith from 50,000 cubic feet per second to nearly 400,000. Two periods of high water are experienced, during late autumn and winter, and again in early summer following snow-

melt in the Alpine head-streams. Between these maxima, low water
occurs in January and February during the winter freeze (which may
be very pronounced in central Europe, as in 1947 and 1956), and
again in late August–October before the effects of the autumn rains
are felt so far downstream.

The Rhine divides initially a few miles within the Netherlands;
the main stream continues westwards as the Waal, while a right-
bank distributary forms the Neder Rijn. The latter utilises for ten
miles an artificial channel cut in 1710 to stabilise the river for navigation, for the Waal at that time was drawing off so much of the
flow that the Neder Rijn and IJssel were rapidly silting-up. This

FIG. 27.—THE RHINE-MAAS DISTRIBUTARIES.

P.C., Pannerdensch Canal (see also Fig. 28). The major outer dams, projected or completed, for the ' Delta Plan ' are marked (see p. 38)

Based on P. R. Bos and J. F. Niermeyer, *Schoolatlas der Gehele Aaarde* (1936),
plates 13-16.

Pannerdensch Canal was therefore cut to make a more direct connection between the Waal and the Neder Rijn (Fig. 28), so avoiding
serious flooding.

The Neder Rijn itself sends off from just above Arnhem the circuitous distributary of the IJssel (Plate X), which wanders casually
north-eastwards then northwards in a series of meanders, finally
entering the IJssel Meer. The Neder Rijn, 300 feet wide at Arnhem,
flows westwards to Wijk-bij-Duurstede, at which point its former
course via Utrecht and Leiden is indicated by the much reduced
Kromme Rijn and Oude Rijn. The Neder Rijn below Wijk is

known as the Lek, which continues westwards, joined and greatly enlarged by the Noord, a distributary of the Waal, to form the Nieuwe Maas, and so flows past Rotterdam through the New Waterway to the sea. This last channel was deliberately created (see p. 66), so leaving the Lek's former outlet, the Briellsche or Brielle Maas to the south of Rozenburg, as an insignificant stream, now dammed off from the sea.

The Waal, carrying some two-thirds of the Rhine's water, continues westwards past Nijmegen (Plate XI) and approaches the Maas closely near St. Andries; here the river is almost 300 yards wide. Below this point the pattern of waterways is confusing, and the complexity of the various interlinked distributaries can best be appreciated by examining Fig. 27.

There have been several recent changes in the course of the Waal, both natural and artificial, the latter designed to check flooding and to improve navigation. The bulk of Waal water now passes through the Nieuwe Merwede, cut in the latter part of the nineteenth century, and so via the Hollandsch Diep and the Haringvliet to the North Sea. Part of the Waal water, however, flows as the Noord to join the Lek and so to form the Nieuwe Maas already mentioned.

Navigation on the Rhine Distributaries.—The main artery of navigation through this maze of waterways is the line of the Waal – Merwede – Noord – Nieuwe Maas (Fig. 29), focusing on Rotterdam and its outlet to the sea through the New Waterway. No locks are required on this through-route, eighty miles in length, other than where branch canals enter, and large Rhine barges, drawing ten feet or more and with a freight capacity of up to 4,000 tons, can navigate with ease, while small sea-going steamers can pass up the waterway into Germany.

The Waal is linked at several points with the Maas, since it flows in close proximity to it soon after entering the Netherlands, and the inter-riverine area was for centuries the scene of extensive flooding. The rivers are now separated by massive dykes, and connections have been established where they approach, as at St. Andries, where the locks can take 2,000-ton barges. In 1928 the Maas-Waal Canal, just eight miles long, was built to link the Maas at Mook with the Waal below Nijmegen, involving locks at either end which can accommodate 2,000-ton barges. This now forms the most important and direct link between the Maas navigation and Rotterdam.

The Neder Rijn – Lek waterway is far less important than the Waal, although 2,000-ton barges can use it under normal conditions. It joins the Noord a few miles above Rotterdam, and so affords direct contact between that port and Arnhem.

A number of minor canals provide links, although somewhat

inadequate, between Rotterdam and Amsterdam. For many years
the latter has been concerned about a direct connection with the
Rhine. For long the only route was by way of the Zuider Zee and
the river IJssel, but later connections were developed via Utrecht
to the Lek at Vreeswijk, and also via Gouda. The Merwede Canal
to Utrecht was enlarged in 1893 and was continued south to the Lek
at Vreeswijk as the Utrecht-Rhine Canal, and thence to Gorinchem
on the Waal. This waterway had an overall length of forty-four
miles and was enlarged several times before 1939, so that it could

Fig. 28.—The Regularisation of the Rhine near the German-Dutch
Frontier.

Based on R. Schuiling, *Nederland* (1934), vol. i, facing p. 243.

accommodate barges of up to 2,000 tons capacity. During the
1930's the project was sanctioned of a new canal to run south-
eastward from Utrecht to join the Waal much further upstream
towards Nijmegen, so as to cut off the right-angled bend which the
Utrecht-Rhine Canal involved for barges moving to or from Amsterdam by way of Nijmegen and the Waal. This scheme involved the
further widening and deepening of the Merwede Canal, together
with a new south-easterly section on which work started before the
war. This passes Utrecht to the west, crosses the Utrecht-Rhine
Canal at Jutphaas and the Lek at Wijk-bij-Duurstede, and joins
the Waal above Tiel through the Prince Bernhard lock, 1,100 feet

in length. This waterway, the new Amsterdam-Rhine Canal,[1] was inaugurated by Queen Juliana in May 1952 (Fig. 29). It is almost exactly the same length as the Amsterdam-Gorinchem connection, but it shortens the distance between Lobith and Amsterdam by twenty-five miles, or by about twenty hours for a barge journey.

The Rhine and its connections occupy such an important place in Dutch inland navigation that it is useful at this point to summarise

FIG. 29.—THE WATERWAYS OF THE RHINE-MAAS ESTUARIES.

The links between the Hollandsch Diep and Antwerp which have been contemplated at various times are indicated by dotted lines.[2]

The abbreviations are as follows : A.C., Albert Canal ; A.R., Amsterdam-Rhine Canal ; G.-T.C., Gent-Terneuzen Canal ; H. Diep., Hollandsch Diep ; J., Jutphaas ; M.W.C., Maas-Waal Canal ; N.-B., Noord-Beveland ; N.H.C., Noord-Hollandsch Canal ; N.-M., Nieuwe-Maas ; N.-W., Nieuwe-Waterweg ; N.Z.C., Noord-Zee Canal ; O., Overflakkee ; P.C., Pannerdensch Canal ; S., Schouwen ; T., Tholen ; U.R.C., Utrecht-Rhine Canal ; W., Walcheren ; W.C., Wilhelmina Canal ; Z.-B., Zuid-Beveland ; Z.-B.C., Zuid-Beveland Canal ; Z.-W.C., Zuid-Willems Canal.

Based on (i) R. Schuiling, *Nederland* (1936), vol. 2, p. 420 ; and (ii) W. Seghers, *Kaart der Binnenscheepvaartwegen van Noord-West Europa* (n.d.).

the overall picture for the country as a whole. In 1964 the Netherlands' waterways transported 181 million tons of freight. Of this, 72 million tons represent internal movement within the country, or a third of all freight carried by road, rail and water. The Dutch inland

[1] W. H. Brinkhorst, 'Het Amsterdam-Rijnkanaal', in *T.K. Ned. A.G.* (1952), vol. lxix, pp. 285-99.

[2] R. Tausma, 'The projected Antwerpen-Rhine Canal', in *T.E.S.G.* (1964), vol. 55, pp. 150-64.

fleet consists of over 20,000 barges, of which 10,500 were of over a thousand tons capacity, together with more than 2000 tugs.

The situation of the Netherlands relative to the Rhine valley implies that the waterways must play an important part in international traffic. In 1964 about 104 million tons of foreign freight negotiated the Dutch waterways, both imports for Dutch consumption and exports of Dutch produce, together with transit freight which passed along the waterways from one foreign country to another, while the balance involved trans-shipment at Dutch ports.

The importance of the Rhine navigation is shown by the freight figures recorded at Lobith, the German-Dutch customs post. About 73 million tons of freight passed this point in 1964, of which 46 moved upstream. A large proportion of this upstream traffic consisted of grain, oil, timber and various bulk raw materials transshipped at Rotterdam and other Dutch ports for despatch to West Germany, France and Switzerland. Most of the remaining upstream freight originated in Belgian ports, and moved direct to the same three countries. Downstream traffic was mainly from West Germany, particularly coal (some in transit to Belgium and France), steel and manufactured goods for export from Rotterdam, and also potash from Alsace for the Dutch chemical industry.

THE RIVER MAAS

The river Meuse, having pursued a lengthy course through the scarplands of Lorraine and across the Ardennes, follows the 'coalfield furrow' between Namur and Liège. It flows northwards for about a hundred miles, forming the frontier between Belgium and the Netherlands from Lanaye to Maasbracht (except in the Maastricht district), and then becomes a wholly Dutch river, the Maas. To the east of the international section lies the Cretaceous plateau of South Limburg, while in the west is the continuous line of the Hesbaye-Kempenland-Peel plateaus. Past changes in the course of the Maas, discussed on pp. 17-18, have resulted in the formation between Liège and Maasbracht of a quite steep-sided valley, some two miles broad and with three distinct terraces on each side (Fig. 32). Particularly in the west, this valley-edge is pronounced; near Daalgrimbie, for example, the plateau descends prominently from about 300 feet to the river-terrace at 150 feet. Further north the plateau-edge becomes progressively less marked and recedes further from the river, although the flood-plain is still bordered by low bluffs rising fifty feet or so, until the river begins to swing westwards and approach the Rhine. The last feature of any prominence to separate the two valleys is the sandy ridge of the Uilenput (see p. 134), to the south of Nijmegen. At Heumen, near the German frontier, the

FIG. 30.—THE JULIANA CANAL.

B.N.C., Briegden-Neerharen Branch Canal.

Note: The Selfkant was returned to West Germany in 1963 by the treaty of 8 April, 1960.

Based on W. Seghers, *Kaart der Binnenscheepvaartwegen van Noord-West Europa* (n.d.).

Maas, now two hundred yards in width, is at only thirty feet above sea-level, and as a result, it meanders across its flood-plain towards the sea. The seasonal variation in volume in its lower course is very marked. The river finally reaches the Hollandsch Diep through the Bergsche Maas, cut in the latter part of the nineteenth century to form a direct outlet distinct from that of the Waal just to the north.

Navigation on the Maas.—While the Rhine is of course the premier waterway artery of the Netherlands, the Maas is of importance, particularly for the south of the country.[1] The improvement of navigation downstream from Maastricht obviously assists the economic development of South Limburg, which is rather remote from the rest of the country, and is particularly valuable for the exploitation of the coalfield there (Fig. 48).

The regularisation of the Maas, both to improve navigation and to assist in flood control, is a long story. The river is now contained between massive embankments, and several large meanders have been cut through. Five locked barrages have been built to stabilise depths for navigation at Grave (the lowest), Sambeek, Belfeld, Roermond and Linne (Plate XII). The Rhine and the Maas below Mook were separated by dykes, with links via the Maas-Waal Canal and the St. Andries lock already mentioned. The outcome of these schemes, completed just before the war of 1939–45, was to make the Maas navigable for vessels of at least 1,500 tons, and as a result of post-war dredging and further improvement the river can now be negotiated by 2,000-ton barges.

It will be appreciated, however, that these measures were concerned with the Maas below Maasbracht, where it becomes wholly a Dutch river. From Lanaye to Maasbracht, with the exception of the short stretch through the city of Maastricht (Fig. 48), the frontier runs along the centre of the river, which meanders through its valley, its course impeded by gravel- and sand-banks, islets and backwaters. With Belgian unwillingness to undertake any joint scheme of regularisation, unilateral action by the Netherlands to improve the river was impossible. The solution from the Dutch point of view was the construction of the lateral Juliana Canal along the right bank, wholly in Dutch territory, between Maastricht and Maasbracht (Fig. 30), while the Belgian solution was the construction of the Albert Canal (see pp. 126-9). The portion of international river between Maastricht and Maasbracht has therefore remained virtually unnavigable.

[1] C. F. Egelie, 'De Problemen van de Scheepvaartwegen in het Gebied de Maas', in *T.K. Ned. A.G.* (1954), vol. lxxi, pp. 321-38; this deals with the navigation of the Maas and the Rhine connections, and provides a detailed map.

IX The Belgian coast near Heist

X The Rhine–IJssel divergence near Arnhem

XI The River Waal at Nijmegen

XII The regularised Maas near Bergharen

The Juliana Canal leaves the Maas at Limmel in the northern suburbs of Maastricht (Fig. 39). The river is canalised within the city and lined with quays, but it ceases to be navigable below the Boss-cherveld barrage at the point where the canal takes off, a barrage designed to keep the depth uniform within Maastricht. The Juliana Canal is twenty-one miles in length, and the fall in level of forty-five feet is accommodated by four locks—at Limmel, Born, Roosteren and Maasbracht. The canal has an overall width at water-level of 152 feet, with a bottom width of just over fifty feet and a depth of 16·5 feet; it can accommodate 2,000-ton barges. Apart from the river-port of Maastricht and two basins opening off the canal at Maasbracht, two canal-ports were constructed specifically to serve the South Limburg coalfield (see pp. 171-5). The canal was completed and opened in 1936.[1] It carries annually about 15 million tons of freight, of which a fifth consists of coal, and nearly half of building materials (cement, bricks, stone).

THE RIVER-POLDERS

Most of the Rhine-Maas distributary pattern is now constrained within regularised channels, since this rectification is intimately bound up with the inter-related problems of navigation, already discussed, and of flood-control. The gradients of the rivers are slight, and they therefore tend if uncontrolled to wander across the alluvial plain, depositing vast quantities of clay and fine sand. Gradually their beds have been raised above the surrounding country, a dangerous state of affairs made worse by the slight sinking of this adjacent land as a result of drainage and compaction. It has long been necessary therefore to create defences along the river banks against flooding, and there seem to have been small dykes as early as the eighth century, which were progressively enlarged and strengthened. Slowly other improvements were effected; meanders were cut off, groynes and training-walls were built, and major rectifications of the actual course included the Pannerdensch Canal (Fig. 28) and the Nieuwe Merwede already mentioned. But floods continued to be a menace because technical skill was inadequate to build unbreachable dykes against the tremendous volume of flood-waters which both rivers can bring down. Selected sections of dyke (each known as an *overlaat*) were therefore kept deliberately weaker or lower than the rest, through which flood-waters could escape into reserved areas which acted as temporary reservoirs, and so relieve the pressure on the dykes protecting lands further downstream. Sometimes an exceptional river-flood would far exceed the bounds

[1] F. J. Monkhouse, 'Albert and Juliana: two great Waterways', in *Scottish Geographical Magazine* (1956), vol. 72, pp. 163-76.

of these storage areas, causing widespread destruction and loss of life. The most serious floods resulted from the proximity of the Waal and the Maas, especially in the neighbourhood of Heere-waarden, where the two rivers are only 300 yards apart. As the Waal with its larger volume and greater powers of sedimentation has a higher bed, in times of flood its water flowed through the *overlaten* into the inter-riverine area and then into the Maas. But usually that river was also in flood, and thus not only were the inter-riverine lands inundated but the flow of the Maas was obstructed, and floods backed far up the valley. This happened so frequently that large areas of formerly fertile river-clays degenerated into sour swampland, useful only as temporary pasture.

From 1880 a long programme of river works was put into effect. The Maas and the Waal were separated by an enormous dyke. When the Bergsche Maas was cut as a direct outlet for the Maas, the former course of the river lower down (the Afgedamde Maas, which had joined the Waal at Gorinchem) was sealed off except for locks at either end. After the floods of 1926–7, when the Maas dykes burst in several places and the inter-riverine area (*Land van Maas en Waal*) was widely flooded, a further programme of works was undertaken, already described. The scheme was completed by 1939, and the menace of Maas floods has been virtually removed.

The Rhine distributaries are dyked along almost their whole length westward from the Dutch frontier, except near Arnhem where the sandy uplands of the southern Veluwe come close to the north bank of the Neder Rijn (see pp. 134–5). The Maas is also dyked along both banks below Grave, and along the right bank upstream for a further ten miles to Mook.

Much of the land between or adjacent to these rivers would be liable to inundation without this protection. Indeed, west of a line from Utrecht to Gorinchem the rivers flow through country below N.A.P., which would be inundated anyway without the sea-dykes. East of this line to about the Amsterdam-Rhine Canal, the surrounding land is well below even the mean summer-level of the rivers, and further east again the land, though higher, is still below the level of winter floods. Between the main river-dykes themselves lies a considerable extent of land, for they are necessarily built well back from the summer-channels; these lateral strips (known as *uiterwaarden*) are usually inundated in winter, but afford useful summer pastures. Outside the main dykes are the river-polders, enclosed units wherein pumping may be either occasionally or continuously necessary to remove excess water.

Land-Use.—These polders are covered with river-clays and occasional patches of gravel and coarse sands. The soils derived from these

4659

riverine materials are not generally as good as from the marine clays, since the alluvium tends to be damp and often rather sour, the result of constant infiltration of water. Between 50 and 80 per cent of these valley-lands are therefore under permanent pasture, and an even higher proportion is found in the districts of Neder-Betuwe, Tielerwaard and Bommelerwaard to the south of Utrecht. This is therefore a predominantly dairying area, though further east, where the land is rather higher and a low water-table can be maintained, mixed farming becomes more important (Plate XIII).

Since the war of 1939–45 increasing attention has been paid to these low-lying areas of damp river-clays; they are known generally as *Komgrondengebieden* ('basin soil districts'). Because of the damp, rather sour soils and also because of isolation due to the absence of roads and railways and the stretches of unbridged rivers, they have long constituted areas of agricultural under-development. Since 1945 the State has carried out schemes of drainage, installed pumping stations, provided financial help and advice for colonists, and fostered programmes of research. The work was furthered in 1953 by the creation of the *Stichting tot Ontwikkeling van Komgrondengebieden* ('Foundation for Basin Soil Districts') as a co-ordinating and stimulating organisation. It supervises the work of local committees, encourages cultural and social activities, assists in the building of farms, and maintains to the south-west of Heerewaarden a 'groundwater-level research establishment'. Between 1945 and 1960 about 50,000 acres were opened up and divided into holdings, and work is in progress on a further 54,000 acres.[1]

The most prosperous of the inter-riverine alluvial areas lies between Arnhem and Nijmegen, the *Over-Betuwe*, usually known simply as the *Betuwe* or 'the good land'. This is the chief orchard district in the Netherlands, with many trees growing in grassy meadows, and extensive market-gardens.

The alluvial valleys include the long narrow flood-plain of the IJssel, enclosed by the sandy heathlands of Overijssel on the east and by the prominent edge of the sand-country of the Veluwe on the west. The IJssel wanders through its flood-plain between dykes along much of its course. The Vecht, flowing from Germany, approaches within nine miles of the lower IJssel, then swings away northwards to make a separate entry into the IJssel Meer by way of a narrow stretch of water deliberately left between the North-east and East Polders (Fig. 19). Several small river-polders in the lower

[1] J. A. C. van Burg, 'Komgrondengebied in Ontwikkeling', in *T.K. Ned. A.G.* (1956), vol. lxxiii, pp. 49-65; this provides numerous detailed maps and a number of plates. See also A. M. Lambert, 'Farm consolidation and improvement in the Netherlands: an example from the Land van Maas en Waal', in *E.G.* (1961), vol. 37, pp. 115-23.

IJssel valley are below N.A.P., notably the Mastenbroek Polder in the angle between the Zwarte Water and the IJssel. The IJssel valley is mainly under pasture, with dairying and pig-rearing, and some orchards.

Settlement and Towns.—The interfluvial lands are not densely populated in comparison with many parts of the Netherlands, for the liability to flooding has precluded much settlement except for a few towns on locally favoured sites. Such places as Heusden and 's Hertogenbosch are placed several miles away from the river, on the edge of the flood-plain. Even in the Betuwe there are few settlements of any size; Elst is a pleasant little town right in the centre, with a market and various fruit-preserving industries, and a few more villages are set among the orchards—Valburg, Heteren, Elden and others. Tiel, an old town on the north bank of the Waal, had some commercial importance in the Middle Ages, and today has several jam-making and fruit-preserving factories.[1] Lower downstream is Gorinchem, another old town with a varied history; it was one of the first places to be captured by the 'Water Beggars' in 1572. Its old patterned brick and stone houses and fortified gateways, and its long-established cattle-market, contrast strikingly with modern factories which make glucose and mustard, refine sugar, and preserve fruit.

The two main towns of this central alluvial valley are Arnhem on the northern banks of the Neder Rijn, and Nijmegen on the southern side of the Waal. They stand opposite to each other, ten miles apart, on the outer edges of the flood-plain, where the Veluwe hills and the Uilenput ridge respectively (Fig. 6) afford firm sites. Both towns have grown outwards and upwards on to the slopes of these hills. Arnhem, the capital of Gelderland, and an important route-centre, had a population of 130,399 in 1965. Its position has always made it of strategic importance, right down to the closing stages of the war of 1939–45, when desperate attempts were made by Allied airborne troops to secure the river-crossing, in conjunction with similar attempts at Nijmegen. Arnhem has become a prosperous commercial town with large markets, and is an important industrial centre with a variety of manufactures—rayon, rubber, pharmaceutical chemicals, clothing, light metallurgical work, barges and river-craft. It has a tin-smelting plant, opened in 1929 to refine tin-ores from the then Netherlands East Indies, and which today smelts about a fifth of the world's tin output.

Nijmegen (139,781 people) is also an important route-centre, and its river-port on the Waal (Plate XI), served also by the Maas-Waal Canal from the south, handles over a million tons of freight each

[1] J. Visscher, 'Tiel als Streekcentrum', in *T.E.S.G.* (1951), vol. 42, pp. 136-42.

year. It too has a varied industrial life, including the manufacture of electrical apparatus, light engineering products, tungsten wire, rayon, river-craft, chemicals and food products. The town is also the centre of a considerable brick-making activity; no less than twelve brick-yards are situated along the banks of the Waal between the Neder Rijn divergence and Nijmegen, and many more are found downstream. The bricks are made from the alluvial clays; many of the clay-pits are worked only in summer, for they are inundated in winter. Coal for the kilns is brought by water from both the Ruhr and South Limburg. A large atomic power-station, of 50 mW capacity, is under construction, to be completed by 1968.

The IJssel valley stands out as a strip of denser population by comparison with the heathlands on either side. Some towns are actually on the river banks, and have been trading-ports for centuries, such as Zutphen, Deventer and Kampen. The biggest is Deventer, with 58,407 people in 1964. Its port was once easily accessible to sea-going ships, and the *Handelshaven* is still there, although but little used. Today it is a prosperous town with cotton- and flour-mills, a chemical works, and some light engineering factories. (It is also famous for its honey gingerbread, known as *Deventer Koek*.) Lower down the valley is Zwolle [1] (57,405 people), the capital of Overijssel, which stands on slightly higher ground between the IJssel and the Vecht, here only nine miles apart. Zwolle is an important railway-centre and market-town, and retains much of its old-world charm, with the old town surrounded by the broad tree-lined *Stadsgracht* or moat. The lowest town along the valley is Kampen (28,339), on the left bank of the IJssel some four miles above its entry into the short arm of the IJssel Meer between the two big polders. It was once a member of the Hanseatic League, and in the fifteenth century it was a thriving port before the harbour silted up. It too retains much of its old interest, with a moat and several fine gateways, and is now a quiet market-town.

A second important line of towns in the IJssel valley is strung out where the western edge of the flood-plain meets the eastern slope of the Veluwe. The largest is Apeldoorn (112,235 people), and others are Eerbeek, Loenen, Epe and Heerde. These towns have manufactured paper for centuries, and today Apeldoorn and Renkum have large modern paper-mills. Apeldoorn itself is a prosperous residential town; near by is the royal summer palace of Het Loo.

THE GELDERSCHE VALLEI

The Geldersche Vallei forms a low trough between the Utrecht-Gelderland ridge on the west and the hills of the Neder-Veluwe on

---

[1] K. Dekker, 'Zwolle: ritme en functie van een middelgrote Stad', in *T.E.S.G.* (1962), vol. 53, pp. 57-61.

the east. It is not, however, strictly an alluvial valley, although it contains numerous streams, and was probably occupied by a small tongue of ice when the continental ice-sheet was at its maximum (see p. 18). Except in the north, where there are clays, most of its soils are either sandy or peaty. The depression forms a link between the flood-plain of the Rhine and the southern shores of the IJssel Meer. It approaches the Rhine flood-plain near Wageningen on the Neder Rijn, although the river is carefully shut off from the Vallei by a large dyke. The northern part is drained by a series of streams coming from the Veluwe, and coalescing near Amersfoort to form the river Eem. The whole area is low-lying; although oddly enough the plain north of Amersfoort is known as the Hoogland, this is only in comparison with the lands bordering the IJssel Meer, which are well below N.A.P. and were formerly subject to flooding. A dyke now borders the IJssel Meer coast; when the South Polder is completed a ring-canal between the dykes will separate it from the Vallei.

About 60 per cent of the area of the Vallei is under permanent pasture, and it is a prosperous dairying and pig-rearing district. It is not very densely populated; there are scattered farms and a number of villages such as Veenendaal, Scherpenzeel and Hoevelaken. Baarn, in the west of the Vallei, is the centre of a large-scale poultry-farming activity. The only town of any size is Amersfoort (72,554), which is the market-centre for the district, a focus of railway routes rounding the southern end of the IJssel Meer, and an industrial town with small metallurgical manufactures and textile mills. Recently an assembly plant for the *British Motor Corporation* has been opened there.

CHAPTER 6

THE HEATHLANDS OF BELGIUM
AND THE NETHERLANDS

GENERAL FEATURES

Heathlands occupy much of the North European Plain, extending in a broad belt from the basin of the middle Oder to north-eastern Belgium. Though differing in detail, these heathlands have many features in common: poor leached soils developed on superficial sheets of sand and gravel; a considerable extent of bare sand, often blown into dunes; a vegetation cover of the characteristic heath associations, notably the dominant ling (*Calluna vulgaris*); and in the higher bleaker parts extensive tracts of moorland which have developed where waterlogging has been caused by an underlying impervious layer. Reclamation and improvement have progressed slowly; some parts now carry conifer plantations, while other areas provide either reasonably useful and carefully fostered pastures or rather poor arable land on which is grown rye, potatoes and sugar-beet. But the extent of unreclaimed heath is still considerable.

The sheets of sand and gravel on which the heathlands have developed are of two different types. Those which occur to the north and east of the Rhine-Maas valley across the south-central Netherlands are of glacial or fluvio-glacial origin. Sheets of sands and gravel, occasional erratics, patches of boulder-clay and much-dissected morainic ridges occur in eastern Friesland, southern Groningen, Drenthe, Overijssel and eastern Gelderland (Fig. 31). The German-Dutch frontier runs southward through their eastern parts, and on either side the name Bourtanger Moor (Moer) is applied. Between the IJssel valley and the IJssel Meer lies the sandy region of the Veluwe, with the narrow Gooiland ridge further to the south-west. The Hettenheuvel-Montferland hills form two small detached heathlands between the Rhine and the valley of the Lijmers, and a small patch, called the Uilenput after its highest point, straddles the frontier in the acute angle between the Waal and the Maas.

Lying across the Belgo-Dutch frontier and extending southward for seventy miles between the valleys of the lower Maas and the Demer, is another continuous area of heathland—Noord-Brabant and northern Limburg in the Netherlands, and the Kempen (in French *la Campine*) in Belgium.[1] The sands and gravels upon which

[1] N. P. J. de Vries, 'The Benelux central region: some results of a survey of two frontier regions', in *T.E.S.G.* (1964), vol. 55, pp. 164-71.

these have developed are, however, of fluvial origin, laid down by the immediately post-glacial Meuse, vastly swollen in volume and bearing an immense load of coarse sand and gravel (see pp. 17-18 and Fig. 32).

The Character of the Heathlands.—The surface features of the heathlands are dominated by sheets of sand, diversified by intercalated layers and occasional superficial patches of gravel, a thin veneer of alluvium in the valley floors, and some peat in the higher depressions. Because of the extremely permeable nature of these sands, surface streams are usually absent, and the water-table occurs at some depth except where an impervious pan causes waterlogging. The podsol-type soils developed on the sands are dry, partly because of their low water-holding capacity and partly because they are subject to rapid evaporation from their friable surface. They suffer constant leaching from the swiftly percolating rain-water, and this results in the removal of the soluble bases, particularly calcium; the soils are thus deficient in nutrients and lack fertility. Only a small amount of humus forms, derived from the matted fibrous remains of mosses, lichens and woody heath plants, and as this is not neutralised it remains highly acid in character.

The typical soil-profile of the heathland reveals first a surface layer of dry, compact and rather acid peat,[1] varying in thickness from one to eight inches; in depressions, however, this peat may be much thicker, forming a dark layer of two or three feet consisting of raw acid humus mixed with some silt. Below the peat is a layer of sand, often stained a chocolate colour by humus compounds carried down by the acidified rain-water, and this passes into yellow or white sand, interrupted occasionally by layers of pebbles. Below this leached layer, at depths varying from eighteen inches to a yard, is a hard impermeable stratum or pan, sometimes consisting of humus compounds and sometimes of sand-grains or gravel stained reddish-brown and solidly cemented by the ferric salts deposited from percolating solutions. Under this are the unaltered sands and gravels.

The surface sand layer is to be found at all levels, occurring both in the form of extensive sheets and as undulating hills and dunes. Expanses of yellow, dazzling white or greyish sand present an almost desert-like aspect, level but for wind-ripples and tiny hillocks of sand which has drifted and accumulated around occasional tufts of spiky grass. In many parts the sand has accumulated into low swelling mounds separated by hollows, arranged in a confused and chaotic manner. In other parts, especially on the exposed higher areas, there is a distinct tendency for the dunes to be orientated from south-west

[1] For details of these peat-soils, see C. H. Edelman, *Soils of the Netherlands* (1950), pp. 78-86.

to north-east. For the most part these dunes are fixed with coarse grass and heath flora, and in places they are planted with conifers, so

FIG. 31.—THE HEATHLANDS OF WESTERN EUROPE.
The areas of heathland are derived from various geological and land-use maps, and from plotting in the field.

H, Hettenheuvel; M, Montferland. The southern limit of the Quaternary glaciation is marked only in the Netherlands.

that surface sand appears only where footpaths wind between the dunes. Occasionally, however, even the dunes fixed by vegetation have one side of bare sand, sometimes with an overhanging 'cornice'

of matted ling and grass roots. These fixed dunes vary in height
from ten to forty feet and exceptionally even to fifty or seventy feet
above the intervening hollows.

In places the sand accumulates in forms approaching those of the
migratory dunes of the Landes in south-western France (see p. 361).
They display a grouping in long inter-connected trails, with the axis
of each dune more or less at right angles to the prevailing winds, and
with curving, almost crescentic, 'wings'. The horizontal movement
is not great, because the unvegetated and therefore 'unfixed' areas
are small in extent. The movement of the sand is within the dune
area itself: the wind piles up, destroys, levels and hollows-out, producing a chaotic and ever-changing relief. On the open wind-swept
plateaus the sand is in constant motion where there is no fixation by
vegetation. Many of these dune areas owe their existence to the
direct or indirect influence of man in the past: to the clearance of
woodland, to the overgrazing of heath, to the lowering of the water-
table as a result of the draining of intervening hollows and valleys,
and to the excavation of sand and gravel.

On these sands occur heathlands, given the name of *heide* in both
Belgium and the Netherlands, although in the former the terms *heyde*,
bruyères and *landes* are also used. The rainfall totals in these areas
range from about twenty-four to thirty inches. It is true that the
sandy permeable soils and the frequent strong winds on the exposed
plateaus considerably reduce the 'effective total' of the rainfall, with
the result that the heathlands are colonised in the unreclaimed and
unimproved parts mainly by plants with xerophytic characters, capable of withstanding these conditions.

These rainfall totals are, however, sufficient to support tree-growth,
and it seems that the present heathland has resulted from the destruction or degeneration of former woodland; the dominant trees probably comprised oak, birch and hornbeam. Mediaeval texts, old
maps and place-names containing woodland elements[1] bear evidence
to the former extensive woodlands in the present heath areas of both
Belgium and the Netherlands, and botanists by pollen-analysis of
peats and by the examination of surviving patches of woodland
plants support this evidence. But large clearance schemes by religious houses, the slow but gradual widening of the perimeter of
arable land and of pasture around the villages in the valleys, and the
wholesale cutting for fuel by the armies which repeatedly fought over
the Low Countries, all took their toll. Once the woodland had been
cleared, natural regeneration became increasingly difficult, for clearance allowed the rapid destruction of the mild humus which forms
under deciduous woodland and its replacement by a thin acid layer

[1] See F. J. Monkhouse, *The Belgian Kempenland* (1949), p. 38, for a map of
Kempen place-names containing woodland elements.

in which heathland associations flourish. Further, regeneration was often prevented by the grazing of sheep, goats and rodents which destroyed the young seedlings. Another adverse factor was the development of the 'hard-pan' layer, which forms readily when the soil has been deprived of its protective deciduous cover and cannot easily be penetrated by the roots of young trees. Perhaps the highest and bleakest parts, over 250 or 300 feet, where the soils are exceptionally poor and the surface is much exposed to strong winds, have never been wooded ; it is possible therefore that the high heathland is primitive and is the natural type of plant community developed on these soils under the particular climatic conditions. But in most areas the heathlands are the result of the destruction of a former woodland cover.

It is not easy to describe the heathlands in general terms, since their aspect varies considerably from place to place as the plant associations change. The most characteristic feature is the dominance of ling. The growth is usually close, but even with old woody and 'leggy' plants the height of the layer is rarely over eighteen inches or two feet. In spring there are tints of pale green with the new growth, in autumn tones of deep purple or sepia, but after a widespread fire (a common occurrence, both deliberate and accidental) whole tracts are of unrelieved black or grey. One can walk for miles across these heathlands, their dreariness and monotony relieved only by pine plantations, occasional meres, and the apparently rather aimless paths and tracks. While ling is overwhelmingly dominant, several other layers can be distinguished—bilberry, dwarf gorse, mosses and lichens.

A more varied type of vegetation, known as 'mixed heath', is found locally among the ling. *Erica cinerea*, or purple bell-heather, sometimes occurs, and on sunny slopes it forms considerable stretches of colourful landscape which contrasts with the sombre ling. In the damper areas, as in shallow depressions, the cross-leaved heath (*Erica tetralix*) is common. A group of species characterised by their tolerance of high soil acidity, by some degree of adaptation to summer drought, and by a very low demand on plant nutrients in the soil, includes broom, dwarf whin, juniper and gorse. The bracken fern is not a true heath-plant but it does occur in some places, and there are extensive thickets of brambles.

Over many parts a more open heath is found, especially where constant burning or grazing has kept the ling from full development. These grass-heaths occur beyond the arable lands and improved pastures around the villages, where the ling, frequently fired, sometimes grazed, sometimes cut for litter, has retreated. True heath-plants are much less numerous, and are replaced by heath-grasses, notably *Agrostis* sp., *Festuca* sp. and wavy hair grass (*Deschampsia*

FIG. 32.—THE TERRACES OF THE LOWER MEUSE VALLEY.

The abbreviations *Ie* to *IIIr* are explained on pp. 17-18. Commune centres are indicated as follows: **Bi,** Bilzen; **Bo,** Bocholt; **Ei,** Eigenbilzen; **G,** Genk; **He,** Herderen; **L,** Lanaken; **Mak,** Maaseik; **Ne,** Neeroeteren; **Nh,** Neerharen; **Op,** Opitter; **St,** Stamproy; **To,** Tongeren; **Vr,** Vronhoven.

The international frontier is indicated by a heavy pecked line, except where it follows the river Meuse (Maas). Only the left-bank terraces are shown.

Based on M. A. Lefèvre, 'La Basse-Meuse: étude de morphologie fluviale', in *Société Belge d'Etudes Géographiques, Mémoire I* (1935).

flexuosa), growing in low clumps or tufts separated by bare sand, or sometimes forming a more or less continuous turf carpet.

Scattered silver birch grow sporadically among the grass-heaths and even occasionally in the *Calluna* heath; sometimes they are so numerous and continuous as to be called birch-woods. In the lower heathlands, particularly on the valley-margins, the birch grows in association with dwarf oak and other deciduous trees, and sometimes such tracts justify the name 'oak-birch heath'. Scrubby woodlands of dwarf oak, willow, hazel, alder and ash may form a dense layer six feet or so in height, often interlaced with brambles, while the slender trunks of the silver birch rise fifteen to twenty feet above the thicket. Here and there are isolated conifers, subspontaneously spreading from neighbouring plantations. Occasionally, too, dwarf oaks form continuous thickets, with an associated shrub layer which includes broom, buckthorn, bilberry and bracken.

A characteristic feature of the heathlands is the large number of small lakes and meres, some on the alluvial floors of shallow valleys, others in depressions on the higher parts of the plateaus. In Belgium they are known as *Waters*, *Gooren* and *Vennen*, in the Netherlands as *Meren*. They consist of irregular sheets of shallow water which vary in extent with the rainfall, except where they have been artificially restrained by embankments. In the damp depressions around these lakes, aquatic and heath communities come into close juxtaposition. In addition, the broad, gently sloping valleys contain swampy areas; the lines of the streams and the ditches leading into them are indicated by reeds, alders and willows.

In many parts appear extensive areas of what can be called generally 'wet heath'; these are known as *Moeren* or *Gooren* in Belgium, and as *Hoogveen* or *Moeren* in the Netherlands.[1] The vegetation associated with them suggests a transition between heathland and aquatic communities. In the waterlogged hollows are found *Carex* spp., *Phragmites* spp. and sometimes alders, then comes the wet heath dominated by the blue moor grass (*Molinia cærulea*), with the cross-leaved heath (*Erica tetralix*), and higher still the drier grass-heath with patches of ling.

[1] There is apt to be some confusion in the various terms applied in different countries because of the temptation to translate in terms of cognates. The word *Hoogveen* is applied in the Netherlands to the acid wet heaths and sometimes to the true bogs, while *Laagveen* indicates the basic fen-peats of the lowlands (see p. 28 and Fig. 17). The Belgian terms *Moeren* and *Gooren* are used for the wet heaths. On the higher areas, where true peat-bogs have developed, similar to the upland Mosses of Britain, the Belgians use *Moeren* or *Hochmoeren*, the Dutch *Hoogveen* or *Moor*. In Germany, *Flachmoor* indicates the lowland fen-peat, *Moorgeest* the wet heath and *Hochmoor* the high peat-bog.

On the higher parts, at altitudes exceeding 250 feet, are to be found small areas of true peat-bog, akin to the *Hochmooren* of Germany and the Pennine 'Mosses'. They occur in the higher parts of the north-east Kempenland, in the Peel district of Dutch Limburg, in the Bourtanger Moer, and in other parts of the eastern Dutch heathlands. Even though the soil is sandy and highly permeable, the upland hollows become waterlogged because the hard-pan is well developed and the drainage on the indeterminate water-sheds is so poor that much surface water remains stagnant. The bog is closely related to the heath which surrounds it, for it has the same poverty of mineral nutrients and the same high acidity; the difference is that its surface is permanently damp while the true heath is mostly dry. The characteristic plant association comprises blue moor grass, which often occurs in great tussocks, *Sphagnum* and other bog-mosses, cotton grass and heath-rushes. Considerable thicknesses of highly acid and nutrient-poor peats develop in these hollows. These form the bleaker parts of the upland heaths, and can properly be termed 'moors'.

It is probable, however, that the bog-peat covering in the higher sandy areas of both Belgium and the Netherlands was formed under conditions of higher rainfall after the end of the last phase of the Quaternary glaciation. There is now, it seems, enough rainfall for them to maintain themselves if undisturbed, but the present summers are too dry for the *sphagnum* mosses to develop to any extent. The more accessible areas have been drained, the peat cut and used for fuel, and the underlying sands reclaimed for agriculture, and so the bogs have been reduced to mere fragments of their former extent.

RECLAMATION OF THE HEATHLANDS

The reclamation of the heathlands in both Belgium and the Netherlands has proceeded for many centuries; records date back to the twelfth century describing attempts mainly by the religious houses. Throughout the centuries the perimeter of cultivated land around each isolated heathland village was pushed outwards. Occasionally official stimulus was applied, notably in Belgium in the sixteenth century, when grants of land were made to individuals on condition that these areas were cleared of heath and made productive, and again in the eighteenth century during the reign of the Empress Maria-Theresa.

In both countries the farmers in the small scattered communities pursued a way of life which enabled them to win a meagre subsistence from their limited environment. They owned strips of improved arable land on which were grown crops of rye, potatoes and buckwheat, and patches of enclosed valley pasture. In addition they exploited in various ways the neighbouring common heath-lands, known as *marken* in the north-east of the Netherlands and *gemeynten* or *gemeinten* in Noord-Brabant, Limburg and the Kemp-enland. These heathland common-rights included the grazing of sheep and the cutting of turves and ling. The last was of consider-able value, for when dried it provided litter for the stock ; the young shoots were browsed by large flocks of sheep ; the woody stems and roots served as fuel, valuable in a largely treeless region for they were burnt with dried peaty clods dug from the wet heaths or bogs ; and the stalks were chopped and mixed with mud for the lath-and-daub method of cottage construction.

Efforts were made to improve the sandy soils for cultivation by the use of compost and dung provided by the animals, the development of various crop rotations, and occasionally the development of simple irrigation systems to improve the meadows where the village lay near a river. But these schemes of improvement were of a small-scale nature, compared with the area of heathland which remained virtually untouched except in the immediate neighbourhood of the villages. In fact, in both countries the opposition to government edicts which aimed at furthering any large-scale schemes by external interests was considerable, for the communes jealously guarded the common-rights on the heathlands.

In the latter half of the nineteenth century, however, both Belgium and the Netherlands included in their programmes of economic development a great increase in the extent of agriculturally produc-tive land in order to help meet the demands of their growing populations. A law was passed in Belgium in 1847, for example, by which the State was authorised to order the compulsory sale of unimproved communal heathlands. The new occupant was granted a reduction or even complete remission of taxes and tithes, in return for which he was obliged to convert the waste into arable land or pasture. This edict applied to 107 communes in Belgium and was strictly enforced. As a result, many of the communes themselves embarked on policies of improvement in order to avoid losing their lands, and there was considerable State encouragement and financial help by way of technical assistance and interest-free loans. In the Netherlands particularly, co-operative organisations developed. In 1888 the *Nederlandsche Heidemaatschappij* (the Dutch Heath Society) was founded. Helped by the Government, it serves as a distributor of financial assistance, carries out reclamation schemes and leases the land to approved tenants, furthers research projects and disseminates information about their results. The Belgian Ministry of Agricul-ture, at its *Station de l'Etat pour l'Amélioration des Plantes* at Melle, sponsors research into the problem of mixtures of grass-seed suitable for dry sandy soils—quick-growing, drought-resistant and with tenacious binding roots.[1]

In the Netherlands much reclamation has taken place in the high peat-moors, the stimulus coming sometimes from cities such as Groningen, from individual communes and from private companies. Groningen started reclamation as long ago as the sixteenth century, when its citizens began to remove peat from the surrounding moor-lands for fuel, using canals to transport it to the city. When the peat had been stripped off, agricultural settlements, known as *veenkolo-niën*, were established. Manure from the flocks and herds and garbage from the cities were dug in, and in the nineteenth century cheap chemical fertilisers, mainly from Germany, were used. In the north-eastern moorlands these reclaimed lands are now growing potatoes, rye and oats, mainly for industrial purposes; factories making starch, glucose and strawboard have been established.

Irrigation schemes have been tried in both countries to improve the dry soils for both horticulture and pasture, and at the present time irrigation is still used in a limited way. In some of the market-gardening areas along the southern margins of the Kempenland water is taken from navigation canals; near Herentals, for example, smallholdings and market-gardens are supplied with water from a short cul-de-sac off the Herentals-Bocholt Canal. Many of the meadow-lands in the shallow valleys within the heathlands are inter-sected with ditches which serve as drains in winter and as irrigation channels in summer. In dry summers the efficacy of these systems is particularly noticeable by the contrast between the brown heath-land beyond the irrigated area and the green meadows. These areas are supplied with water by gravity from streams and canals. But the higher heathlands, where improvement is most needed, cannot be irrigated because of the absence of streams on the plateau surfaces, and the area improved is only a small proportion of the total extent.

Some of the sandy heath, then, has been improved for arable farming, particularly in the Netherlands. In Belgium, however, during the last century there has been little overall increase in the arable area; most communes in fact show a decrease. This is not because heathland has not been improved, but because the nature of the farming system in the Kempenland as a whole has changed. Under the influence of the nearby markets offered by Antwerp, Mechelen, Brussels and other towns in central Belgium, the emphasis is now on cattle-keeping for milk and veal, and the area of permanent pasture has been greatly increased at the expense of cereals. What arable land remains either consists of intensively cultivated market-

---

[1] A detailed bibliography of works relating to the improvement of the Kempen heathlands is given by F. J. Monkhouse, *The Belgian Kempenland* (1949), pp. 234-5.

gardens along the heathland margins or is under fodder crops.

The establishment of plantations of soft-woods often affords the most profitable, sometimes the only possible, utilisation of tracts of sandy soil, and also helps to meet the increasing demand for constructional timber, pit-props and pulp-wood. Extensive planting has been carried out in the higher eastern parts of the Kempenland and in the Veluwe by the respective States, the communes, various public bodies and private individuals. In the Belgian province of Limburg, for example, the proportion of communally-owned woodland forms about one-third of the total. This is the most profitable way in which the communes have been able to make the heathlands contribute to their revenues, especially as the State assists them in the costs of clearing and of planting. As a result, one of the most characteristic, if alien, features of the heathland landscape is the frequent occurrence in plantations of stands of Scots pine and occasionally of Corsican pine. These trees have the advantage of attaining maturity within thirty or forty years. They are usually planted in long straight lines forming square or rectangular blocks intersected by rides. Only occasionally do these conifers occur less formally; a few scattered pines have colonised adjacent oak-birch heath, and here and there clumps of trees have been planted in the dune areas to assist their stability, or for shelter and decorative purposes in the vicinity of collieries, factories and housing-estates. About one-seventh of the Belgian heathlands have been planted with conifers, about twice as much as the proportion in the Netherlands.

Finally, it must not be forgotten that other changes have taken place in the heathland landscape. Villages and towns have grown up, factories have been built, and roads and railways now link formerly isolated settlements. Most significant of all, the Kempenland is underlain by exploitable deposits of coal, and it has become a considerable industrial area. Industrial developments have not been as prominent in the Dutch heathlands. Coal has been located under the Peel at depths exceeding 3,000 feet, and also further north in Gelderland, but there has been no exploitation as yet. Some factories have been built in the Dutch heathlands, mainly for processing agricultural produce; occasional interesting introductions include the cotton-textile industry of a group of towns in the Twente area of central Overijssel.

The individual heathlands are numbered on Fig. 11 from 4a to 4f.

THE KEMPENLAND

This area of heathland extends westward for about sixty miles from the steep slope overlooking the Meuse valley to the reclaimed polders around the Scheldt estuary. The southern boundary is indicated by the line of the rivers Rupel, lower Dyle and Demer, while the heath-lands continue northward to the Dutch frontier. The main features of the Kempenland relief may be described under three headings: the plateau, the plateau edge and the plain.

The Kempen plateau is demarcated more or less by the 160-foot contour, although much of the eastern part exceeds 250 feet, and in the extreme south, where the Kempen is linked to the plateau of Hesbaye, the height just exceeds 330 feet. Some Belgian geologists consider that the Kempen plateau is partly of tectonic origin, and that it is the result of a gentle anticline trending approximately from west to east along a line to the north of Liège. But the consensus of opinion is that the plateau represents a depositional surface surviving between the Meuse on the east and the Demer on the south-west, both of which have been entrenched not only into the Quaternary sands and gravels but also into the underlying Tertiary rocks. The surface consists of gentle swelling eminences known as *bergen*, alternating with shallow marshy depressions. The plateau forms a broad somewhat indeterminate watershed between rather vague streams which drain northwards to the Meuse and southwards to the Demer. There are areas of marsh and much artificial drainage.

To the west and north the plateau descends inconspicuously towards the plain. To the south-west and east, however, it is more sharply defined by the valleys of the Demer and Meuse respectively, forming a marked change of slope, the *rebords d'érosion* (literally 'erosion edge') of the Belgian geologists, where the rivers have cut their terraces into the deposits during a degradational phase in their cycles. This is quite a steep slope (Fig. 33), embayed by the valleys of numerous streams between low spurs and isolated knolls. In the neighbourhood of Diest, the Demer's right-bank tributaries have cut back deeply into the plateau, leaving interfluves orientated from north-east to south-west, frequently separated by transverse valleys now left streamless because of the lowering of the water-table in the more deeply eroded Demer valley. The superficial deposits have been removed, and these interfluves now form rounded hillocks of heavily iron-stained compacted sandstone; these are in fact exposed Lower Pliocene (*Diestian*) sandstones. The hillocks are known as the Diestian Hills; their summits rise from 30 to 130 feet above the Demer valley floor, the highest being the Lazarijeberg which attains a height of 217 feet above sea-level.

The Kempen plain slopes away gently northward into the Nether-lands and westward to the Scheldt. It is almost impossible to say where the plateau ends or the plain begins, although the 160-foot con-tour might be taken as a somewhat arbitrary line of demarcation. The plain is rarely absolutely level, for it is interrupted on the one hand by sand-dunes, on the other by the gentle slopes of the

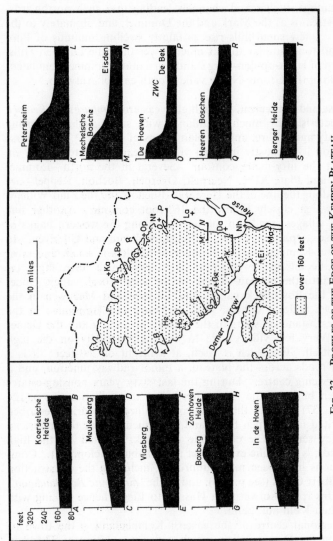

FIG. 33.—PROFILES OF THE EDGE OF THE KEMPEN PLATEAU.

Various sheets of the *Carte topographique et militaire de Belgique* were used to determine precise heights along the lines of profile. The vertical exaggeration is ten times.

The commune centres are indicated as follows: **Bo**, Bocholt; **Da**, Daalgrimbie; **Ei**, Eigenbilzen; **Ge**, Genk; **He**, Helchteren; **Ho**, Houthalen; **Ka**, Kaulille; **La**, Lanklaar; **Ma**, Maastricht; **Nh**, Neerharen; **Nt**, Neeroeteren; **Op**, Opitter; ZWC, Zuid-Willems Canal.

river valleys and by marshy depressions containing meres and small lakes, the typical *vennen* and *gooren* mentioned above. Drainage is so vague and indeterminate that considerable areas are patterned with drainage ditches and channels leading into such northwards-flowing streams as the Mark and the Dommel, and ultimately to the Meuse. A few small hills rise as faintly swelling mounds of Pliocene sandstone, similar to but much lower than the Diestian Hills. The town of Heist-op-den-Berg stands on a quite prominent eminence overlooking the Groote-Nethe valley south-east of Antwerp.

Land-Use and Settlement.—The higher eastern *Limburgsche Kempen* is characterised by much heathland, with sandy soils supporting but scanty agriculture, and by plantations of conifers.[1] The sparse population lives mostly in small villages near the plateau edge on or about the fifty-metre contour. Several in the north—Lommel (Fig. 34 and Plate XIV), Neerpelt, Overpelt, Bocholt, Reppel—are located along the line of the Herentals-Bocholt and the Zuid-Willems Canals which closely follow the 160-foot contour. Another line of small villages stands on the terraces along the western banks of the Meuse—Ophoven, Maaseik, Eelen, Stokkem and Uikhiven. In the central Kempenland the number of hamlets is small, and most of them lie on the lower slopes of valleys which form slight re-entrants into the plateau—Genk in the Stiemerbeek valley, Opoeteren in the Boschbeek valley, and Ellikom and Meeuwen in the Molenbeek valley. Others, such as Voort and Houthalen in the south-west, stand on spurs of the plateau projecting into the Demer valley. Very few villages are to be found actually on the high plateau itself. One such is Asch, at a height of 260 feet; it is a focus of roads across the plateau, a minor railway junction, and a small servicing centre. During the last sixty years housing-estates have been built for the labour needed in the collieries (see p. 124 and Fig. 37) and at the chemico-metallurgical works described below, sited in the open heathland conveniently near the industrial units they serve. The commune of Genk, situated on the high heathlands, is a specific example of remarkable development. Communications have been much improved, including the construction of the Albert Canal (see p. 126), and of the '*autoroute Roi Baudouin*', which runs from Antwerp via Hasselt to Liège, hence linking with the Aachen-Köln autobahn.

The regional centre of the eastern Kempenland is the town of Hasselt in the Demer valley, which had a population of 37,848 in 1964. As the administrative centre of the province of Limburg, a market- and shopping-centre, with main-line and light-railway con-

---

[1] A. Bodeaux, 'Les Landes à callune de Campine et les conditions de leur reforestation', in *Revue de l'Agriculture* (1957), pp. 1509-37.

nections running north-eastward to Genk and the higher plateau, with a busy port on the Albert Canal and a variety of industrial activities, Hasselt well fulfils its function. It has a number of food-processing industries—flour-mills, distilleries producing a remarkable range of spirits, tobacco factories, breweries and a gelatine-works.

FIG. 34.—LAND-USE IN THE KEMPEN HEATHLANDS NEAR LOMMEL.

The numbers in the key are as follows : **1**, arable land ; **2**, coniferous plantations ; **3**, heathland ; **4**, marsh ; **5**, bare sand and dunes ; **6**, permanent pasture. Waterways are shown by a thick black line, roads by a double line, and railways by a single barbed line. Houses and industrial buildings are shown in solid black. The two factories in the west are metallurgical refineries.

The abbreviations are as follows : **B.B.C.**, Beverloo Branch Canal ; **H.B.C.**, Herentals-Bocholt Canal.

Other industries include a brick- and tile-works, timber-yards, several tanneries, a glue-works, a soap-works and fertiliser factories.

The character and aspect of the lower *Antwerpsche Kempen* change gradually westward towards the city of Antwerp. There is progressively less heathland, more deciduous trees, more fenced fields, more market-gardening and dairy-farming, and more villages and small towns indicating a greater density of population. Several large villages are situated near road junctions, such as Oostmalle at the convergence of six roads and light railways, Hoogstraaten, Brecht and Herentals. The settlements avoid valleys that are liable to flood; thus Heist-op-den-Berg clusters around the slopes of a hillock rising to nearly 150 feet, while only a mile away the floor of the Groote-Nethe valley is less than twenty-five feet above sea-level. In the northern part of the western Kempenland, villages such as Wuustwezel, Loenhout and Kalmthout avoid the marshes and meres along the valleys of the rivers which flow northwards into the Netherlands.

The regional centre of this part of the Kempen is Turnhout,[1] with a population of 36,909 in 1964; it is a prosperous market, industrial and administrative town, on the railway line between Antwerp and Tilburg, and with a busy port on the Desschel-Turnhout-Schoten Canal. One group of factories, many of them owned by old-established companies, is situated within the city itself, in blocks among the houses and shops, with frontages along the streets. Several of these factories carry on various aspects of Turnhout's leading industry—the manufacture of drawing-paper, stationery and fine papers; it has important printing and bookbinding trades, and is the world's largest centre for the manufacture of playing-cards. Other old established industries include the manufacture of coarse linen, twill, sacking and canvas, and lace is still made as a piecework domestic industry, mainly for export. Then there is the manufacture of cigars, pottery, leather and various foodstuffs, and a small diamond-cutting industry carried on by a branch of a big Antwerp firm. A second and newer group of factories, producing bulky commodities, is built to the north-west of the town near a basin on the Turnhout-Desschel-Schoten Canal—timber-yards and saw-mills, a cement-works, a flour-mill, and a small steel-works making agricultural implements. Turnhout is the centre of one of the main Belgian brick-making districts and twenty-nine brick-yards, making about a quarter of the Belgian output, are sited along the banks of the Desschei-Turnhout-Schoten Canal on either side of the town. The kilns stand on the canal banks, behind which lie large clay-pits, some abandoned and water-filled, others still in operation, from which is excavated the fine clay (*terre glaise*). The pits are connected with the brick-yards by narrow-gauge lines, sometimes by aerial ropeways. Cement is also made near Turnhout and Beerse. The *Ravels* works to the east of Turnhout has its own fleet of barges, to bring lime from the kilns near Visé in the Meuse valley. Barges return with clay from

---

[1] *De Turnhoutse Kempen: Haar economische en sociale betekenis* (1953), published by the *Vlaams Economisch Verbond* (Antwerpen).

the Ravels pits to another cement-works owned by the same company at Visé-Loën, a nice example of industrial development at each source of the two main raw materials linked by cheap water transport.

Mol is another small industrial and market town on the main-line railway between Antwerp and Neerpelt. Within the town several old-established factories make cigars, leather goods, pottery, small articles of metal and wood, textiles and clothing. Three mills specialise in the production of patterned blankets; the frontages of the buildings lie along the main street. Belgium's main atomic energy plant is situated near Mol. Herentals has similar small-scale industries, including also the manufacture of copper and bronze articles and of glassware. Many establishments are little more than artisan workshops, and such units as tanneries, brick-yards, distilleries and flour-mills are dispersed at each market town.

Modern Industrial Development.—Apart from these small industries, localised in the towns and villages, the Kempenland now contains a number of major industrial units deliberately sited in the heathlands. These, with the seven large collieries, make the Kempenland one of Belgium's important industrial regions.

The material losses to Belgium through the German occupation of 1914–18 were enormous but, as in the case of north-east France, certain positive advantages and opportunities resulted from enforced reconstruction. Not only could factories be built on efficient lines and installed with modern plant, but industry need no longer be tied to old-established districts on the southern coalfield by reason of the capital values of site and plant. The Kempenland offered considerable advantages ; the cheapness of land for spacious factory sites, the unpopulated areas available for the lay-out and segregation of noxious or dangerous industries, the gradual development of the new coalfield, and the proximity of the port of Antwerp were all encouraging factors. The region was reasonably well served by railways and waterways, and the building of the Albert Canal in the 'thirties was a major contribution. Of the seventeen large industrial establishments shown on Fig. 35, all but two lie on the banks of a waterway, and most are at a rail–water intersection.

In the period of reconstruction, then, a number of new factories was built, and the firms which already had small establishments before 1914 took advantage of the capital available through reparations and government loans to rebuild or enlarge their works. These include four large zinc refineries, mostly owned by Liège groups, where refining had developed in the nineteenth century. Several establishments produce a variety of other non-ferrous refined metals—lead, silver, copper and cadmium, and a factory at Oolen refines uranium and radium from Congo pitchblende. These concerns also manufacture a variety of chemical derivatives such as sulphuric acid. A chemical works near Beerse refines copper and makes copper nitrate and copper sulphate, the latter mainly for export to France and Italy to spray in solution on the vines. The Reppel works specialise in arsenic derivatives (including an insecticide for use against the cotton boll-weevil), exported in large quantities to America. At Tessenderloo a chemical factory, destroyed during the war of 1939–45, was rebuilt

FIG. 35.—THE LOCATION OF THE MAJOR INDUSTRIAL ESTABLISHMENTS
IN THE KEMPEN HEATHLANDS.

The factories were located from large-scale maps and from information supplied by the various companies, and plotted on a small-scale map. They are named on a map in F. J. Monkhouse, *The Belgian Kempenland* (1949) (p. 146).

The seven collieries are indicated by initial letters (for their names, see Fig. 36). The canals are shown by heavy lines (for their names see Fig. 38), the main-line railways by barbed lines. A new Ford motor-assembly plant was opened in 1963 at Genk on the banks of the Albert Canal, and in April 1963 the new Allegheny–Longdoz steel-plant, the result of an American–Belgian merger, began production of stainless steel in the same district.

in 1947 and produces chemicals such as caustic potash, bleaching powder, potassium sulphate, muriatic acid and liquid chlorine. There are four large explosives works, segregated in uninhabited open land behind lines of protective sand-dunes. Belgium is one of the leading producers of glass, manufactured before the war of 1914–18 almost entirely in the Liège area. A large establishment, employing over fifteen hundred workers, was built in 1921–3 at Mol-Gompel by the huge *Glaver* firm; this is now one of the world's largest producers of sheet-glass. A smaller factory, making laboratory ware, bottles and glass insulators, is situated north of Mol. The glass-sands are worked in the communes of Mol and Gompel, some of a quality approaching the famous deposits near Fontainebleau; other supplies are imported from Heerlerheide in South Limburg in the Netherlands. An atomic-energy plant is situated near Mol.

The Kempen Coalfield.[1]—Before the war of 1914–18 the whole of the Belgian coal output was obtained from the Sambre-Meuse field (*Bassin Sud*), and production rose steadily during the nineteenth century as Belgium developed as one of the most highly industrialised countries in the world (see pp. 502–6). The output of coal increased from 2·6 million tons in 1835 to 16·8 million tons in 1880, and then to 23·5 million tons in 1900, at which total it remained more or less stationary until 1914. But the actual consumption of coal increased much more rapidly than did this production, and it became progressively more obvious that the southern field alone would soon be unable to supply Belgium's needs. This was indicated by the increase in imports of coal and coke, which in 1835 had amounted to less than ten thousand tons but by 1900 had attained three million tons. Increasing attention was therefore paid to the possibility of the existence of exploitable coal deposits in other parts of Belgium.

During the latter part of the nineteenth century considerable developments had taken place in the South Limburg coalfield on the eastern side of the Meuse valley (see p. 171). Belgian geologists and mining experts were increasingly interested in the possibility that these coal deposits might well extend into the Kempenland. The coal-bearing strata are effectively hidden under a considerable depth of newer deposits, and much geological speculation therefore took place. The first mention of the possibility of a coal basin in northern Belgium was in fact as early as 1806, and as time went on many distinguished geologists, notably Guillaume Lambert and André Dumont (whose names are perpetuated in the titles of two of the present colliery companies), contributed to the body of published material. It was evident that only trial borings could verify the various suppositions; the first was put down in 1877 to the north of Liège. Success was finally attained when a company (*La Nouvelle Société de Recherche*) sank a boring at Zuiden near Asch, and on August 2nd, 1901 this reached a coal seam at a depth of 1,775 feet, from which a sample was triumphantly brought to the surface. Fifty years later a *fête commémorative* was held at Genk to celebrate

[1] General monographs concerning the Kempen coalfield include the following: H. Basselman, *Das Kempenbekken und seine Bedeutung im belgischen Kohlenbergbau* (1935); C. Demeure, *L'Industrie belge du charbon et du coke* (1930); P. Gruselin, *Le Bassin minier de la Campine* (1925); G. de Leener, *Le Charbon dans le Nord de la Belgique* (1904); and K. Pinxten, *Het Kempisch Steenkolenbekken* (1937).

this momentous event.[1] Geological prospecting has gone on steadily, and more than a hundred borings have now been put down, the deepest of which, at Wijvenheid, attained a depth of 6,273 feet.

The existence was proved of a coal basin extending westward for fifty miles from the Dutch frontier towards Antwerp, and 500 square miles in area. The coal does, however, lie at a considerable distance below the surface, and half of the exploitable reserves are estimated to occur at depths exceeding 3,000 feet. In the east, between Eisden and Genk, the first usable coal is at 1,565 feet, but at Vlimmeren, near Turnhout in the west of the Kempenland, coal was only reached at 2,940 feet. The borehole evidence was sufficiently conclusive to encourage the granting of concessions. At first the Belgian government, stimulated by the example of the Netherlands (see p. 171), considered the question of exclusive State ownership and operation of the coalfield. Possibly because of the enormous cost obviously involved in initial exploitation and the necessity of attracting both Belgian and foreign capital, the government contented itself with demarcating three State reserves, occupying about a sixth of the proven area, strategically placed in the west, centre and east of the field. At the present time ten concessions are held by seven individual companies, together with the three still unexploited State reserves; their positions and extent are shown on Fig. 36, with the seven active collieries. Three of these are in the commune of Genk, on the heath-covered plateau which forms the watershed between the Demer and the Meuse systems at a height of about 250 feet above sea-level. Another is in the east of the coalfield overlooking the Meuse valley, and the others lie to the north-west of Genk, the most westerly being the Beringen-Koersel colliery.

In 1906, when the first concessions were granted, the companies started the immense task of developing the field. The overlying deposits of sands and gravels, unconsolidated and often water-logged, meant that technical problems of shaft-sinking were considerable, and in fact the shaft-freezing process (*congélation*) had to be used. This process was slow and immensely expensive. The deepest shaft is at Zwartberg, which reaches a depth of 3,314 feet and took four years and three months to complete. The development of the underground workings was also long and costly, and

[1] A detailed account of the long preliminaries and the final success of these explorations is given by André Grosjean, *Prologue aux fêtes commémoratives de la découverte du charbon en Campine (août 1901-août 1951)* (*Extrait du Bulletin de l'U.I.Lv.*) (Bruxelles, 1952): '*Dans un document de 1903, ceux-ci avaient dépeint leurs propres sentiments en disant: "Nous nous étions lancés comme dans une mer inconnue à la recherche d'un nouveau monde", et l'on a pu, à juste titre, comparer leur aventure à celle de Christophe Colomb*' (p. 13).

Fig. 36.—The Kempen Coalfield.

The collieries are indicated by their initial letters, as follows: **BK,** Beringen-Koersel; E, Eisden; **Ho,** Houthalen; **HZ,** Helchteren-Zolder; **Wa,** Waterschei; **Wi,** Winterslag; **Z,** Zwartberg. Helchteren-Zolder and Houthalen were amalgamated in 1965, and the Zwartberg colliery was closed in 1966, the result of an E.C.S.C. decision.

The individual concessions are numbered from I to X.

Waterways are indicated by abbreviations as follows: **B.B.C.,** Beverloo Branch Canal; **K.D.C.,** Kwaadmechelen-Desschel Canal; **Z.W.C.,** Zuid-Willems Canal.

Based on maps in various volumes of the *Annales des Mines* (Bruxelles).

was further retarded by the war of 1914–18. As a result, the first coal was not raised until 1917 from Winterslag (Plate XV), followed by two more collieries in 1922 and by the others at later intervals; Houthalen did not start production until 1938. The first colliery to produce a million tons in a year was Waterschei (1·08 million tons in 1930). Helchteren-Zolder and Houthalen amalgamated in 1965.

The Kempenland was not at first sight a promising area for industrial development. The surface consisted of heathland, with few settlements and with almost no local sources of labour. In the decade following 1920 there was a marked shortage of labour in most branches of Belgian industry, especially in the less attractive of these. This shortage was met, particularly in the collieries, by the importation of labour from other countries, and from 1922 onwards train-loads of foreign workers arrived in Belgium. The result is shown by the fact that while the seven Kempen collieries employed only 2,951 men in 1920 during the stage of initial exploitation, this figure had risen to 18,657 in 1935 and to 30,000 in 1964. Today foreign workers comprise three-tenths of this total mining force, and a higher proportion, three-sevenths, of the underground workers. The effects can be appreciated in the commune of Genk [1] in the heart of the heathlands, the fourth largest commune in Belgium, and containing the three collieries of Winterslag, Zwartberg and Waterschei which actually produce one-seventh of all Belgian coal. The population of Genk was 1,776 in 1846 and still only 3,422 in 1910. But by 1964 it was no less than 51,778, of whom about 16,000 were foreign, half of them Italians. The result of this population increase, not only in Genk but in other communes on the coalfield, was that provision had to be made within the former virtually empty heathlands of settlements where the workers and their families could live. This is the reason for the housing estates, built near the collieries on the lines of 'garden-cities', known in the Kempenland as *tuinwijks* or *zwijnwijks* (Fig. 37).[2]

Thus a great building programme was necessary, both for the colliery installations and for housing the labour. In one respect the situation of the collieries in the open heathlands was a positive advantage, for the installations and the housing estates could be laid out on spacious and often attractive lines. Each colliery purchased its land on leasehold terms from the commune; in Genk the three collieries bought about one-ninth of the total area.

Over parts of the Kempenland, therefore, the dark sombre stretches of heathland are now replaced by large modern collieries and new

[1] The industrial development of Genk is fully discussed by J. Thomas, *Genk, Centrum voor Nijverheid* (1954), with numerous detailed maps and photographs.

[2] F. J. Monkhouse, 'Housing Estates in the Belgian Heathlands' in *T.P.R.* 1954, vol. xxv, pp. 195-206.

towns. As one travels across the open country, in the distance can be seen the tall chimneys, cooling towers, concrete pit-head installations and vast pyramidal spoil-dumps. But much is still heathland; more than a quarter of Genk commune is of untouched heath and another quarter has been planted with conifers. The ceaseless activity at the collieries and the dense agglomerations of population

FIG. 37.—HOUSING-ESTATES IN GENK COMMUNE IN THE KEMPENLAND.
T, *Tuinwijk*. The colliery spoil-heaps are indicated by hachuring.
Based on a manuscript map made available by the *S.A. des Charbonnages Winterslag*.

in the housing estates actually emphasize the emptiness and loneliness of the heathlands within which they stand as relatively isolated 'industrial oases'.

Progress has been steady during the fifty years of development. Output in 1965 was 9·7 million tons, or about 45 per cent of Belgium's total production. The individual output of the collieries in 1965 was as follows:

(*Thousand Tons*)		(*Thousand Tons*)	
Beringen-Koersel . . .	1,684	Waterschei	1,343
Eisden	1,575	Zwartberg	1,354
Helchteren-Zolder–Houthalen *	2,302	Winterslag	1,448

Total output 9,706

* *Note:* Output of two amalgamated collieries.

Source: *Associate der Kempische Steenkolenmijnen*, Hasselt, by correspondence.

The type of Kempen coal varies considerably, from semi-anthracite to highly volatile long-flame coals. Especially valuable to Belgium, which is short of coking-coal, is the *demi-gras* variety used for the production of hard metallurgical coke, and the *gras* and *Flénu* coals used for gas, by-products and soft-coke manufacture. About 7 per cent of the output is used in the local industrial region—at the brick-works along the canals, in the metallurgical refineries, and at the great Mol-Gompel glass-works. A further 11 per cent is consumed by the collieries themselves or distributed free to their miners. The remaining four-fifths moves out of the region to contribute to the industrial life of Belgium.[1]

Despite the success of the Kempen collieries, the Belgian government, in response to the Coal and Steel Community's programme of reduction of output, was obliged to close the Zwartberg colliery in 1966. This caused considerable unrest, culminating in riots.

The Albert Canal.—The greater part of the Albert Canal, today one of Europe's busiest inland waterways, crosses the southern margins of the Kempen heathlands. The concept of a canal linking the Scheldt and the Meuse goes back at least to Napoleon I, who realised the advantages of the position of Antwerp ('It is a loaded pistol that I hold against England's throat', he is reputed to have said), and so he planned a '*Canal du Nord*' from Grimlinghausen on the Rhine above Düsseldorf to the Meuse at Venlo, thence via Bocholt and Herentals to Antwerp. Work did in fact start in 1808, but was soon abandoned. Under the régime of the United Nether-lands several waterways were built, notably the Zuid-Willems or Maastricht-'s Hertogenbosch Canal (Fig. 38), completed in 1826. This leaves the Meuse just below Maastricht, skirts the eastern edge of the Kempen plateau to Bocholt, and then runs to 's Hertogenbosch and ultimately rejoins the river near Engeln. The final recognition of Belgian independence in 1839 divided this canal into three parts: a short Dutch portion within the Maastricht area, a Belgian section from Smeermaas to the frontier near Bocholt, and a northerly Dutch portion. Thus of its total length of eighty miles, forty-seven are in the Netherlands. It will take barges up to 450 tons, and although there are twenty-two locks to negotiate, in 1961 the Belgian portion transported 9·9 million tons of freight. The canal performs a very useful function in serving the towns and the agricultural areas of both the eastern Kempenland and the Dutch province of Noord-Brabant.

In 1844 the newly independent Belgium took advantage of the

---

[1] This distribution and use of Kempen coal is described by F. J. Monkhouse, 'The Movement of Coal in Belgium, with special reference to the Kempen Field', in *Transactions of the Institute of British Geographers* (1951), publication no. 17, pp. 97-110.

existing eastern section of the Zuid-Willems Canal, and began to construct from this waterway at Bocholt a new canal, known as the Meuse-Scheldt Junction or Kempen Canal. Until the ultimate completion of the Albert Canal, this was the only water-route from Liège to Antwerp. But the most rapid voyages between the two cities by this canal took forty-three hours for a motor-barge and seventy-seven hours for a tow of four dumb-barges. Several other serious disabilities included ten locks and numerous swing- and lift-bridges which had to be negotiated; the depth was only about seven feet and the barge capacity was limited to six hundred tons; and barges were obliged to pass through Dutch territory in the Maastricht area on their way to Liège. When the Albert Canal was built it incorporated the western section of this Junction Canal, and the remaining portion was renamed the Herentals-Bocholt Canal (Fig. 38).

Even before the war of 1914–18, a growing sense of the inadequacy of these canals had developed a preoccupation with the problem of creating a new major waterway across north-east Belgium. This would not only form a direct all-Belgian route between Antwerp and Liège, but would provide necessary cheap transport for the output of the newly developed Kempen field. Various companies interested in the coalfield considered that the construction of a *Canal charbonnier* would prove to be a most important factor in its development. It was argued that it would have a strategic value as a defence across the north-east of the country, duplicating the obstacle of the Meuse.

Various projects were put forward in the years following the war of 1914–18. One canal was actually started in 1923, following a direct line between Hasselt and Visé, and involving fifteen locks and a tunnel, but this was soon abandoned owing to the immense engineering difficulties and obvious great cost. After lengthy deliberations by the *Commission Bouckaert*, set up by the Government, a route from Hasselt via Eigenbilzen to the Meuse valley at Vise was adopted.[1]

The Albert Canal, eighty miles in length (Fig. 38), proved to be an immense undertaking which took ten years to complete; ironically and bitterly it was officially opened during the German occupation on Christmas Day 1940, for the intended opening during the International Water Exhibition at Liège in July 1939 was postponed owing to a disastrous breach in the embankments near Hasselt. The canal takes off from the Meuse below Monsin Island (Fig. 116), utilising the old Liège-Maastricht Canal, which runs parallel to and on the west side of the Meuse, as far as the Ternayen lock near Lanaye.

[1] F. J. Monkhouse, 'Albert and Juliana: two great Waterways', in *Scottish Geographical Magazine* (1956), vol. 72, pp. 163-76; V. Neesen, 'The Albert Canal as shipping artery and site for the location of industry', in *T.E.S.G.* (1964), vol. 55, pp. 172-8; and R. Lievens, 'Le Canal Albert, axe des transports du Limburg belge', in *Revue Navig. Intér. Rhén.* (1958), vol. xxx, pp. 8-14.

This canal, built in 1850, was enlarged to the overall dimensions of the new waterway between new embankments. The major physical obstacle was the upland 'neck' linking the Kempen and Hesbaye plateaus, which the canal had to pierce in order to circumvent the western boundary of the Maastricht area. A series of vast cuttings was made (Fig. 39); the 'Tranchée de Caster' was excavated through

FIG. 38.—THE ALBERT CANAL.

The abbreviations are as follows: **D.T.C.**, Desschel-Turnhout Canal; **H.B.C.**, Herentals-Bocholt Canal; **T.S.C.**, Turnhout-Schoten Canal; **Z.W.C.**, Zuid-Willems Canal. A connection between the Juliana and Albert Canals, by way of the huge Lanaye locks, now enables 2,000-ton barges to pass through (see Fig. 39).

Based on A. Delmer, *Le Canal Albert* (1939), of which vol. II consists of maps, including four sheets covering the canal on a scale of 1 : 100,000.

the St. Pietersberg ridge, and then followed the immense Vroenhoven-Veldwezelt cuttings, nearly six miles long, some 200 yards wide and in places over 200 feet below the surface of the plateau. The huge quantities of excavated earth were removed to other sections further west to build the embankments. From Briegden to Genk the Eigenbilzen cutting was made through a series of low hills, and then the canal was continued westward along the Demer valley into the Scheldt lowlands. For some thirty miles it incorporated enlarged sections of the old Meuse-Scheldt Junction Canal and its Hasselt

XIII Dinxperlo, near the edge of the heathlands and the Rhine plain

XIV Lommel, a heathland village in the northern Kempenland

XV The Winterslag colliery, Genk, Kempenland

XVI The Philips electrical works at Eindhoven

Branch. Along most of this 'lowland course' it is contained within embankments 200 yards in width at their base. The canal enters the port of Antwerp by way of the Strasbourg and Lefebvre Docks.[1]

The fall of 184 feet between Liège and Antwerp is negotiated by six groups of locks, the locations of which are shown on Fig. 38. A seventh lock at Monsin is intended to ensure that the level of the Meuse at Liège remains stable at about 200 feet above sea-level, and is normally kept open. Each group of locks is triple ; the two largest can accommodate 2,000-ton Rhine barges, the third 600-ton barges. Sixty-five bridges were constructed, which (with one exception) were destroyed during the war of 1939–45, but have been subsequently rebuilt. Canal ports were developed, apart from the important terminals at Liège and Antwerp, notably three coal-ports specifically constructed to handle Kempen coal. The port of Genk, managed by the *Société du Port Charbonnier de Genck S.A.*, was constructed jointly by the Winterslag, Zwartberg and Waterschei companies with whose collieries it is linked by rail, and is used also by Houthalen. This basin has unlocked connection with the canal, and is extremely well equipped for handling coal, with extensive sidings and mobile overhead loading bridges. Kempen coal can be shipped from the Genk coal-port to Liège in about seven hours, and to Antwerp in nine or ten hours. The port handled 2·81 million tons in 1965. The Zolder and Beringen ports, situated further west along the canal to serve the Helchteren-Zolder and Beringen-Koersel collieries respectively, handled between them a further 1·51 million tons in 1965. Two large ports on the Meuse valley section of the canal, at Lixhe and Haccourt, handle large quantities of cement from neighbouring works. About 30 million tons of freight are transported annually.

The construction of the Albert Canal made possible another valuable contribution to the pattern of Belgian waterways. A link-canal, the Briegden-Neerharen Branch, three miles in length and involving two locks, was constructed in 1935 around the north-western perimeter of the Maastricht district (Fig. 39). It connects the Zuid-Willems Canal near Smeermaas, before it enters the Nether-lands from the north, with the Briegden Basin on the Albert Canal, so providing a continuous all-Belgian water-route along the eastern edge of the country.

THE HEATHLANDS OF THE SOUTHERN NETHERLANDS

These southern heathlands are merely the continuation of the Maas 'fan' across the frontier, described on pp. 17-18. The heathland dips gently northward to the alluvium-covered flood-plain of the Maas,

[1] A full account of the construction of the Albert Canal, including a volume of maps, is given by A. Delmer, *Le Canal Albert* (1939).

R.G.W.E.—F

FIG. 39.—THE ALBERT AND JULIANA CANALS IN THE MAASTRICHT DISTRICT.

The proposed new connection between the port of Maastricht and the Albert Canal, and possible developments in the neighbourhood of the Lanaye lock, are shown by pecked lines. The proposed new channel of the Meuse in the south will rejoin the river a few miles upstream, so avoiding the bends and islets of the section by-passed.

Based on various large-scale Belgian and Dutch maps and plans.

though in the west bluffs rising to fifty or seventy-five feet overlook the drained polders bordering the Ooster Schelde. The Mark, Donge, Leij and Dommel flow vaguely northwards to the Maas from a watershed which lies mainly in Belgium. Their shallow valleys form narrow 'tongues' of alluvium across the heathlands, and the streams are regularised in their lower courses.

In the east the plateau projects prominently north-westward, forming a flattish ridge 170 feet in height known as the Peel, lying across the provincial boundary between Noord-Brabant and Limburg. It forms a low secondary divide between streams flowing north-east to the middle Maas and those going north-west to the Aa and the lower Maas. Under the surface of the Peel lies a considerable thickness of Chalk (2,150 feet have been measured near Oploo), and below that again the Netherlands Geological Survey has proved the existence of a deep coalfield, for coal was reached near Helenaveen at a depth of 3,238 feet in August 1906. These coal deposits are separated from the South Limburg field by a down-faulted trough where the Upper Carboniferous strata have been carried down to 8,000 feet below the surface. This Peel field clearly has seams accessible by modern techniques, although the immense development costs which will be entailed have so far precluded any initial exploitation.[1] Other hidden fields have been proved further north in Overijssel and Gelderland. Borings at Winterswijk in eastern Gelderland have proved the existence of reserves of about 80 million tons.

The heathland is similar in character to that of the Kempen to the south, although it is generally lower. Numerous depressions in western Noord-Brabant indicate former channels of the Scheldt, others in eastern Noord-Brabant those of the Maas, now filled with peat-mosses. The Peel (Fig. 40) still contains one of the largest areas of peat-bog in the Netherlands.

This is one of the most scantily populated areas in the Netherlands, served by few roads and with only a few scattered villages. It is, however, crossed by the main-line railway between Eindhoven and Venlo, near which occasional *veen-koloniën* have been created, such as Greendtsveen, Sevenum and Helenaveen (Fig. 40).[2] At the last of these in 1853 the brothers Jan and Nicolaas van de Griendt, pioneers of reclamation in the Peel, founded a company to develop a colony. The first stage was the cutting and removal of peat for

[1] One colliery is now under construction at Vlodrop near the German frontier, situated in the south-eastern extension of the Peel field across the Maas beyond Roermond. It is estimated that 75 million tons of coal lie here within 4,000 feet of the surface.

[2] R. Kok, 'Een Eeuw Helenaveen', in *T.E.S.G.* (1955), vol. 46, pp. 243-52; this affords a detailed account of the founding of the colony and the development of a settlement based on horticulture.

FIG. 40.—AN AREA IN THE PEEL.

This area lies to the north-east of the Belgian frontier, between the Zuid-Willems Canal (the waterway in the west of the map) and the Maas valley. The highest point (the sand-dunes of the Stippelberg) is about 100 feet above N.A.P., but the general altitude of this rather desolate area is about 75 feet. The areas of *veen* and woodland are necessarily generalised. Near Helenaveen, deep borings have reached coal at a depth of 3,238 feet.

Based on *Topografische Kaart van het Koninkrijk der Nederlanden*, 1 : 200,000 sheet 18.

sale (which is still in progress in some districts); then the company gradually introduced agricultural enterprises (horticulture, cattle- and poultry-rearing), and individual tenants rented plots of land. In 1940 631 people lived there, but unfortunately the district was badly damaged during the final stages of the war of 1939–45; this has been made good. Further north the Peel is even more sparsely populated, with only a few scattered villages such as Milheeze and Deurne. To the south-east of the Peel proper the bleak moors of Weert and Venraij continue towards the edge of the Maas valley. A few villages are located near the Belgian frontier at a height of about 150 feet—Reusel, Luijksgestel, Budel and Stramprooij. Further north settlements increase in frequency on the sides of the long re-entrant valleys, and farms are scattered among surviving patches of heath.

A string of towns lies along the northern edge of the sand country bordering the clay-lands, from Bergen-op-Zoom in the west in an arc through Roosendaal, Breda and 's Hertogenbosch to Grave on the Maas. A second line of larger towns lies further south—Tilburg in the Leij valley, Eindhoven in a shallow embayment where a fan of tributaries converges to form the Dommel, and Helmond on the Zuid-Willems Canal. All these are long-established market-towns which have recently developed such industries as electrical, metallurgical and light engineering, the manufactures of textiles, chemicals, cigars, rubber and leather goods.[1] Eindhoven is the home of the vast Philips electrical company,[2] with a population in 1859 of under 5,000, but in 1965 this had risen to 178,336, and it is now the fifth city of the Netherlands. Also at Eindhoven is the factory of the *Van Doorne Automobielfabriek N.V.*, which since 1928 has manufactured motor-trucks and other commercial vehicles. In 1958 the company started production of *D.A.F.* saloon-cars, the only Dutch models.

THE MINOR HEATHLANDS OF THE CENTRAL NETHERLANDS

Several small patches of sand-country lie between the southern shores of the IJssel Meer and the Rhine-Maas distributaries. Little remains of true heath, although considerable areas are carefully maintained as parks. The Utrecht-Gelderland ridge runs dis- continuously south-eastward from the IJssel Meer to the Neder Rijn. This ridge is known in its northern section as the hills of Gooiland, further south as the Soesterberg, the Huister Heide and the Darthuizerberg, the last of which rises to 190 feet (Fig. 41).

[1] P. C. A. t'Hoen, 'Postwar industrial development in the south of the Nether- lands', in *T.E.S.G.* (1960), vol. 51, pp. 180-8.
[2] N. de Vries, 'De N.V. Philips' Gloeilampenfabrieken en Eindhoven', in *T.K. Ned. G.* (1948), vol. lxv, pp. 534-43.

These ridges are only four to six miles wide but stand quite boldly above the polder-lands of the Vecht valley to the west and of the Geldersche Vallei to the east.

The ridges are either planted with coniferous woodland or are built upon. The Gooiland Hills are only ten miles from Amsterdam and less than that from Utrecht, and so small villages have developed during the last few decades into residential towns from which 'commuters' travel in daily to work—notably Hilversum (which in 1965 had a population of 102,992) and Bussum. The former, with numerous specialised light industries and the main Dutch radio station, is attractively laid out; it has been described as 'the Chisle-hurst of Holland—a discreet and wealthy suburb'. Further south, a line of small towns—Zeist, Driebergen, Doorn (the home for so long of the exiled ex-Kaiser Wilhelm II), Amerongen and Rhenen—is situated along the southern edge of the hills among market-gardens (which flourish on the heavily fertilised light warm sands), orchards and woodlands.

Another distinct line of these sandy hills trends south-eastward from the Waal at Nijmegen across into Germany near Kleve, con-tinuing south-eastward towards Krefeld; this forms a somewhat indeterminate watershed between the Maas and the Rhine. The highest point in the Dutch section of these hills is the Uilenput (315 feet). Nijmegen rises steeply from the southern bank of the Waal on to the north-facing abutment of this ridge (Plate XI), where its new suburbs have grown (see pp. 100-1). On the wooded hills to the south of the town are such pleasant residential villages as Berg-en-Dal and Beek, situated among rounded hills.

A third outlying patch of sandy hills, known simply as the Bergh, lies between the Rhine where it enters the Netherlands and the drained marshlands of the Lijmers valley. The south-western part of these low hills was formerly in German territory, but the Elten frontier rectification in 1949 put this area wholly within the Nether-lands. The hills culminate in the Hettenheuvel (345 feet) and the Montferland (272 feet), and are wooded with conifers.

THE VELUWE

This extensive area of sandy country, the name of which means literally 'barren land', occupies a broad triangle between the IJssel Meer, the IJssel and the Lek. The land is highest in the east, the *Over-Veluwe*, and a string of hummocky *bergen* can be traced from the Woldberg southward in a gentle arc (Fig. 41); the highest are the Torenberg a few miles to the west of Apeldoorn, and the Galgenberg further south, both exactly 351 feet above N.A.P. The *Neder-Veluwe* slopes gently westward from about 150 to 50 feet. The margins of the Veluwe are much dissected by streams flowing east to the IJssel, south to the Neder Rijn and west to the Geldersche Vallei; their valleys are characterised by a curious asymmetry.[1]

The sands are remarkably continuous and as a result the Veluwe is the largest area of sparse population in the Netherlands, bearing extensive tracts of coniferous plantations (Plate XVII).   Wide

FIG. 41.—THE VELUWE AND ITS NEIGHBOURHOOD.

expanses of ling still exist, some now in nature reserves, and the several large estates include the royal summer residence.   About two miles north of Arnhem is the well-known open-air 'Folk Museum', which displays houses, bridges, windmills, etc., typical of each of the Dutch provinces.   A few hamlets and resorts are located in the Neder-Veluwe—Staverden, Garderen, Milligen, Harskamp, Otterloo and Schaarsbergen, and further west still some larger towns lie in

[1] The problem of these valleys is examined in detail by (i) C. H. Edelman and G. C. Maarleveld, 'De Asymmetrische Dalen van de Veluwe', in *T.K. Ned. A.G.* (1949), vol. lxvi, pp. 143-6; and (ii) G. C. Maarleveld, 'Over de Erosiedalen van de Veluwe', *ibid.*, pp. 133-42, which deals with various types of valley formed during the periglacial climate of the Würm glacial period.   See also H. Lehmann, 'Periglaziale Züge im Formenschatz der Veluwe', in *Erdkunde* (1948), vol. ii, pp. 69-79.

the valleys of the streams draining to the Geldersche Vallei—Voorthuizen, Barneveld and the largest town Ede; industrial developments have made the last of these a commune of 65,308 people.

THE EAST GELDERLAND-OVERIJSSEL HEATHLANDS

These heathlands extend between the valleys of the Lijmers and the Vecht, a stream which flows westwards from Germany to the IJssel Meer. In the centre of the district is a line of distinct morainic hills; these sandy humps, each with a distinctive -*berg* name, are known generally as the Lemelerberg-Holterberg ridge, and rise to a highest point of 262 feet. In the east much of the heathland is above 200 feet, the highest point, the Gelgenberg (229 feet), actually lying just over the frontier in Germany. These higher areas are almost entirely of sand, interrupted by the broad Twente depression, where the convergence of numerous streams has produced an extensive though thin veneer of alluvium. Some areas of heath still survive, interrupted by strips of alluvium; there are large blocks of coniferous plantations; and reclamation has provided considerable although scattered areas of pasture (especially on the shallow valleyfloors) and some arable land. The peat-bogs along the frontier region have been almost entirely removed. In the north-east of Overijssel, for example, to the east of the river Vecht, the bogs have been worked for peat since the twelfth century.[1] So much peat has been removed that extensive irregular lakes have been formed, and the mediaeval arable landscape has been replaced by meadows, swamps and shallow meres. Some 15 per cent of Overijssel is still uncultivated.

The high heathland in the east is thinly populated; there are, however, a few *veenkoloniën* in the north-east of Overijssel, such as Langeveen near the frontier, Daarlescheveen and Vriezenveen. Further west a much closer pattern of settlement has developed, particularly in the Twente,[2] where several large towns are engaged in the cotton industry, notably Enschede, Hengelo and Almelo. Other industries (clothing, engineering, electrotechnical activities and the production of chemicals) are related to the dominant textiles. It is perhaps surprising that Overijssel has a larger proportion of its gainfully employed population engaged in industry than any other Dutch province.

THE NORTH-EASTERN HEATHLANDS

North of the Vecht valley the sandy areas continue through Drenthe into Groningen and eastern Friesland, and eastward across

[1] M. K. E. Gottschalk, 'De Ontginning der Stichtse Venen ten Oosten van de Vecht', in *T.K. Ned. A.G.* (1956). vol. lxxiii, pp. 207-22.

[2] J. Buursink, 'De Twentse Industrieformatie', in *T.E.S.G.* (1964) vol. 55, pp. 233-41.

the German frontier.   The name 'veld' is applied to these spacious heathlands—the Zuidenveld in the south-east, the Ellertsveld south-east of Assen, and many more.   The most striking relief feature is the low undulating sand-ridge of the Hondsrug,[1] which extends south-eastward from near Groningen to the corner of Drenthe.

It was on the sands in the centre and east of Groningen and Drenthe that the high peat-bogs (hoogveenen) were formerly so wide-spread.   Here are the moeren, such as the Oostermoer to the east of the Hondsrug and the desolate Bourtanger Moer extending into Germany.   Some high bog still remains, especially along the frontier, but much has been cleared, especially in the province of Groningen where the veenkoloniën are most numerous.   Many of these were systematically established in the seventeenth century on the moors adjacent to the city.   In the early nineteenth century the Stads-kanaal was cut across the Oostermoer south-eastward to the German frontier, and a series of straggling villages with surrounding rectangu-lar drainage patterns was established.   Veendam and Hoogezand are seventeenth-century colonies within ten miles of Groningen; Gielerveen, Stadskanaal, Vledderveen and many others followed in the nineteenth.   Fields of potatoes, rye, oats and occasionally sugar-beet have replaced the desolate peat-moors.[2]   Root-crops are grown for fodder and cattle are kept, both stall-fed and grazed on permanent pastures, providing manure for the sandy soils.   Pigs are fed on skimmed milk, and poultry and bees are other items in a remark-ably prosperous economy.   Reclamation still goes on in Drenthe (Plate XVIII), where nearly 30 per cent of the province is still classified as waste land, compared with a mere 2 per cent in Groningen.

The sandy heathlands as well as the moors have been greatly reduced in extent, particularly in the lower western parts, and in places they carry market-gardens and orchards, notably of bush-fruits.   Much land in Friesland and Groningen has been converted into permanent pasture.   These reclaimed lands have now a re-markably dense population for a rural area, and are virtually indis-tinguishable from the coastal districts on the fertile clays.   A close pattern of villages amid a prosperous agricultural landscape is the reward of nearly four centuries' effort.

An interesting development in the last fifteen years has been the discovery and working of mineral oil near Schoonebeek in south-eastern Drenthe by the Nederlandse Aardolie Maatschappij.   The first oil was produced in 1944, the first gas in 1947.   In 1964 the out-put of oil totalled 2,270,000 tons, a not inconsiderable contribution

---

[1] G. H. Ligterink, 'De Hondsrug en het Dal van de Oer-Eems', in T.K. Ned. A.G. (1954), vol. lxxi, pp. 105-21.

[2] C. van Welsenes, 'The development of the agricultural area of northern Groningen', in T.E.S.G. (1960), vol. 51, pp. 175-80.

to the Dutch requirements,[1] but it is believed that the Dutch wells have passed their peak.

Groningen,[2] the 'regional capital' of the north and, with a population of 152,315 in 1965, the seventh city of the Netherlands, is situated at the northern extremity of the Hondsrug where this sandy ridge meets the coastal clay-lands and the former peat-bogs in the south-east. It is a minor port, for the Eems Canal links it to the Dollard estuary, and it is the focus of the minor inland waterways of the north-east of the country. The city is a market-centre for the densely populated agricultural neighbourhood, and has a variety of industries connected with the processing of agricultural commodities—flour-milling, brewing and distilling, and the making of industrial alcohol and strawboard, as well as such newly introduced industries as chemicals, rayon, and electrical apparatus.

Vast deposits of natural gas, said to be one of the largest in Europe, have recently been discovered at Slochteren; the gas consists of 90 per cent methane. A consortium has been created, including the State, the State Mining Company and the *Shell* and *Esso* companies, to develop this source of energy.

The municipality of Emmen in the extreme east of Drenthe, only a few miles from the frontier, is the scene of some interesting developments, for it is one of the Netherlands' scheduled 'new towns'.[3] Emmen is a municipality about ten by twelve miles in extent, comprising a number of individual hamlets and fen-colonies. The population, as returned in the censuses, therefore, is deceptively high; it totalled 19,425 in 1899 and had reached 66,771 by 1960. Only about 16,000 actually live in the town of Emmen itself, for it is a servicing focus for the agricultural area around. It has been the centre of peat-digging for centuries and the peat has now almost disappeared. New industries are being deliberately introduced into a scheduled industrial zone in the south-east of the municipality, where chemical factories, strawboard-mills and a nylon-spinning factory have been built, and others will follow. The aim is to check the drift of population from these eastern heathlands to the overcrowded districts of the western Netherlands. A new town is growing to the east of the old urban centre, separated from it by woodland to be retained as a park; when completed the population of the town of Emmen will be increased to 23,000. Further schemes may result in

---

[1] Details are given in an article under the auspices of the *Nederlandse Aardolie Maatschappij*, 'Olie en Welvaart in Z.O. Drenthe' in *T.E.S.G.* (1955), vol. 46, pp. 217-21, including a map of concessions.

[2] C. van Welsenes, 'De stad Groningen', in *T.E.S.G.* (1963), vol. 54, pp. 145-53.

[3] J. M. Richards, 'New Towns in the Netherlands', in *Progress* (1956), vol. 45, pp. 147-157.

a total population of fifty to sixty thousand in the centre and about a hundred thousand in the municipality.

The Laagveen of Friesland.—Further west in Friesland extensive areas of 'low fen' still lie in waterlogged hollows among the sand country, and peat-cutting has added to this extent of stagnant water. To the south-east and south of Leeuwarden, the provincial capital situated on the clay-lands, there is an extensive area of irregularly shaped lakes with interconnecting channels. Few of the meres have been drained, unlike the clay-floored lakes of Noord- and Zuid-Holland, because their sandy floors would provide such poor soil that it would not be worth the cost of reclamation. (In years of hard frosts, incidentally, the famous 'Eleven Towns' skating race is held, over a distance of 125 miles, linking the chief towns of the province). But such is the reputation of Frisian dairy-farming that even on these sandy areas stock-rearing has developed, using fertilisers to grow fodder-crops and importing cattle-food for stall-feeding.

Few large settlements exist in the *veen*-area of Friesland, although many small, often quite isolated, hamlets, most of them fen-colonies, do occur. Heerenveen, for example, has a tiny nucleated centre and a population spread out in individual farms and hamlets over much of the considerable area of the commune. Some colonies, curiously, such as Frederiksoord, Wilhelminaoord and Willemsoord (between Heerenveen and Meppel), were founded by a charitable society during the famine of 1816–17 ; each family settled was supplied with some land and a few animals. The settlement at Veenhuizen, just over the Groningen border, was originally established for 'orphans, paupers and beggars', and that at Ommerschans near Meppel for 'the idle and the disorderly'. These are today thriving little settlements. Many of the fen-villages stand solitarily among the meres and their interconnecting creeks; Giethoorn, for example, to the north-west of Meppel, consists of houses scattered among devious channels, accessible only on foot by way of narrow bridges or more usually by punt. Sneek is a busy little town on the transition zone between the fen and the coastal claylands, with an important butter- and cheese-market. It has also a holiday function similar to that of some of the centres in the Norfolk Broads. Shallow reedy meres provide interconnected waterways to the IJssel Meer both southward to Lemmer and south-westward to Stavoren, and so Sneek is a renowned sailing centre with several regattas each year.

CHAPTER 7

INTERIOR FLANDERS

Between the polder-lands of the maritime plain and the low plateaus of central Belgium lies an area known as Interior Flanders (in Flemish *Binnen-Vlaanderen*). It forms a triangle with its base along the south-eastern edge of the chalk hills of Artois and Cambrésis and its apex at the junction of the rivers Scheldt and Rupel above Antwerp. The region may be broadly defined as lying between the five- and fifty-metre contours; the latter generally coincides with a steeper and quite prominent slope on the eastern side of the Dendre valley, rising to the low plateaus of central Belgium. Interior Flanders consists of three geological elements: the recent alluvium deposited over the valley-floors, the Eocene rocks (Flanders Clay in the south-west and sands to the north) on the interfluves between these valleys, and a few higher relict patches of newer Tertiary rocks (mostly Pliocene sands) in the south.[1]

THE PHYSICAL FEATURES

As described above (p. 15), the upper Scheldt and its tributaries the Lys (*Leie*) and Dendre (*Dender*) developed courses almost parallel to the North Sea coastline. Their valleys are two or three miles wide, filled in with alluvium often to depths of a hundred feet or more, across which the rivers meander in great loops, many of which have been cut off either naturally or as a result of the regularisation they have undergone. Gradients are gentle; the Lys, for example, falls only twenty-eight feet from the French frontier to its confluence with the Scheldt at Gent in a distance of sixty-seven miles.

The tributaries of the three main streams within the Belgian portion of the plain are numerous but short, rising on the indeterminate watersheds between each. The only tributary of any size is the Mandel, which flows parallel to the Lys in its upper course before it turns almost at right angles to join the main river near Grammene. The upper courses of the Lys and Scheldt, however, display a considerable complexity, and it is clear that river-capture has modified their pattern. The Lys rises on the Artois hills and flows in a northerly curve in a trench through the chalk country, leaving it for the clay-lands near Aire on the edge of the plain. These clay-lands are naturally wet and swampy, since copious springs emerge from

[1] R. Nistri and C. Prêcheur, *La Région du Nord et du Nord-Est* (1959); and the *Atlas du Nord de la France* (1961).

the Chalk, and in spite of an extensive grid of drainage channels similar to that of the polder-lands, flooding is still liable following periods of heavy rain. This part of the upper Lys valley, sometimes given the name of the *Pays de Weppe*, is almost a basin, as is shown by Fig. 42, since to the north the low plateau of Ieper (*Ypres*) and to the south the Gohelle chalk platform project eastward, rising to over a hundred feet. The basin then distinctly narrows below Armentières, since the Flanders Clay plateau of Ploegsteert and Messines and the hills of Ferrain approach the banks of the river from north and south respectively. Sixteen miles below Aire the Lys is joined by the Lawe, also flowing from the hills of Artois, and at Deulémont on the Belgian side of the frontier it receives the Deûle. It seems that the Deûle once continued north-eastwards beyond Lille as the then upper part of the proto-Scheldt. It was captured by a tributary of the Lys, and so the river now makes, below Lille, a sharp right-angled bend to the north. Its deserted lower valley is followed by the Roubaix Canal and its Belgian continuation, the Espierres Canal (Fig. 25), which joins the Scheldt at Espierres and thus resurrects the former river course.

Further to the south-east river-capture has been even more active. The upper Scarpe once flowed north-eastwards to join the Dendre, but this section was captured by a northwards-flowing subsequent stream, leaving only the small truncated West Dendre. This subsequent developed still more actively and captured the upper waters of yet another consequent, the lower part of which is now the eastern Dendre, and then successively two more, the former head-waters of the Senne and the Sennette. This subsequent is known as the Haine, which joins the Scheldt at Condé; its valley is followed by the Mons-Condé Canal and by the western part of the Centre Canal, so forming a useful west-east link across the Franco-Belgian coalfield. The Haine rises only two miles from a left-bank Sambre tributary.

The most striking diversification of Flanders is the result of isolated patches of Pliocene sands resting on the Flanders Clay, forming the higher interfluves in the south and south-west. In Belgium, between the Dendre and the Scheldt, appears the gently undulating ridge of the Ronse hills; they form several rounded summits, notably the Pottelberg (515 feet) to the east of Ronse, Mont St. Aubert (489 feet) to the north of Tournai, and the Kluisberg rising prominently from the edge of the Scheldt valley to 463 feet. Other outlying hillocks extend for thirty miles across south-western Belgium into France. The prominence of these summits was to elevate them to a strategic eminence in the war of 1914–18 far beyond their actual altitude, and their names have achieved a notorious place in military history (Fig. 42). The ridge first becomes evident near Passchendale and trends south-westward to the south of Ieper, culminating in Belgium

FIG. 42.—THE PLAIN OF WESTERN FLANDERS.

The simplified geological outcrops illustrate the main pattern of relief: the edge of the chalk hills of Artois to the south-west, the Eocene sands and clays forming a low plateau mostly over 150 feet, and the alluvium, seamed with drainage channels, of the Aa valley, Maritime Flanders in the extreme north-west, and the almost enclosed upper Lys Basin. Small patches of Pliocene sands form higher points on the west-east ridge which forms a divide between the rivers of Maritime Flanders and the Lys.

The individual hills are indicated by abbreviations as follows: **Cs.**, Mont Cassel; **Ct.**, Mont des Cats; **K.**, Kemmelberg; **N.**, Mont Noir; and **R.**, Mont des Récollets. The canals are named on Fig. 25. Heights are given in feet.

in the Kemmelberg (512 feet). It then extends westward into France, capping the Ieper clay-plateau (which forms a watershed between the polders of the upper IJzer to the north and the Lys basin to the south), and culminating in the summits of Wytschate, Mont Kemmel (512 feet), then Mont Noir (515 feet) across the frontier, and the Mont des Cats (518 feet). After a distinct break in this ridge, caused by the cutting-back of the upper valley of the Becque, it rises again to the summits of the Mont des Récollets and Mont Cassel, each attaining 515 feet. The ridge ends quite markedly in the west, overlooking the Aa valley near Watten ; it drops in a short distance from 236 feet to less than six feet above sea-level. The line of hills is dissected by the numerous north-flowing tributaries of the Ijzer.

Another element contributes to the diversification of the relief of French Flanders. Several areas of the Chalk form projecting spurs and even isolated masses, separated by faulting or by river erosion from the Artois hills to the west. Such is Vimy ridge, another name famous in the annals of war, and Notre-Dame-de-Lorette.

The southern part of French Flanders, between the Lys valley and the Chalk of Cambrésis to the south-east of Valenciennes, is one of

FIG. 43.—REGIONAL UNITS OF WESTERN FLANDERS.

This map is intended to provide a key to the general position of the regional units referred to in the text. The boundaries are frequently necessarily arbitrary, although various criteria (geological outcrops, significant contours, etc.) are used where possible.

considerable diversity, resulting in a number of *pays* (Fig. 43). The low hills in the angle of the Deûle and the Lys are known as the *Ferrain*, and the chalk uplands which project as a low promontory east of Lille towards Tournai form the *Mélantois*. The Eocene plateau between Lille and La Bassée is the *Carembault*. The *Pévèle* extends southward from the edge of the chalk hills of Mélantois to the valley of the Scarpe, forming a basin of Eocene clays overlying the sands which outcrop on the margins, particularly in the south-west, to form low hills; the highest are the Mons-en-Pévèle (371 feet), where the sands are sufficiently compacted to be used as building-stone, the Mont de Moncheaux (328 feet) and the Mont de Bachy (236 feet). The clay plain itself lies at about 130 to 160 feet, and is covered with streams and drainage ditches. The *Ostrevant* is a *pays* situated between the Scarpe and Sensée-Scheldt valleys, an area of sands and clays overlying the Chalk, and consequently rather dry. It is low in the east, but rises towards Douai as undulating wooded hills. Underlying the Ostrevant is the concealed basin of the Nord coal-field. The *Gohelle* lies between the Pévèle and the Artois chalk-hills, and forms a gently undulating plain crossed by the upper Deûle; like the Ostrevant, it is underlain by a concealed coalfield, the Pas-de-Calais basin. Other *pays* can be distinguished; the *Tournaisis* lies between the Pévèle and the Scheldt valley near Tournai, the name *Escrebieu* is often applied to the Douai district, and the *Bareul* is the area between Lille and Tourcoing.

AGRICULTURE

Interior Flanders has been for centuries one of the most closely settled and densely populated areas in Europe. It has long possessed a flourishing agricultural, industrial and commercial economy, and many of the towns have been prosperous centres of urban life since mediaeval times, as their architectural glories testify.

Agriculture is carried on intensively, much of it virtually on a horticultural scale, for holdings are small, particularly in the northern parts of the province of Oost-Vlaanderen. Long before the Agrarian Revolution in England, the hard-working Flemings had discovered the value of heavy manuring of the sandy soils, and had thereby obviated the necessity of a period of fallow. The proximity of the large towns has encouraged market-gardening, and hops, potatoes, sugar-beet, chicory, flax and even wheat are grown in small patches, often by spade-cultivation. On many holdings more than one main crop is produced each season; turnips, for example, sometimes follow a cereal. High yields are general, the result of heavy manuring both with artificials and dung. Clover and fodder-crops are included in the rotations to feed dairy cattle; each holding usually has a small herd of two or three animals, sometimes stall-fed, to produce milk, butter, cheese and veal. The number of co-operative dairies has grown in recent years, but these are still inadequate to stimulate a really flourishing dairying industry; it is merely one contributory item in a mixed farming economy.

Towards the south in West-Vlaanderen, Hainaut and French Flanders, the size of the farms increases, mechanisation replaces the patient laborious spade-cultivation of northern Flanders, and larger fields of wheat and sugar-beet become dominant. Some specialisation has developed in industrial crops—flax in the valley of the Lys near Kortrijk and Tielt and in the Scarpe valley, tobacco in the Ieperle valley, and chicory between Kortrijk and Roeselare and near Aire, while potatoes are extensively grown in the sandy soils. Dairy farming also increases in scale southward; many farms in French Flanders have herds of twenty to a hundred animals to supply the densely populated industrial districts. Some permanent pastures occur in the water-meadows in the upper Lys basin and on the flat floors of other river valleys, and much clover and fodder-beet are grown as supplementary feeding.

INDUSTRY

Industry is carried on in close association with agriculture throughout Flanders. Many factory workers live in the country, often owning a small-holding which they cultivate on a family basis, and travelling daily some distance to their work. Domestic industry has declined, it is true, but it is still practised quite widely. The three main groups of activities are the mining, metallurgical and textile industries.

The Coalfield of Northern France.—Underlying the sands and clays of French Flanders is a synclinal depression where the rim of the Artois ridge dips steeply to the north-east. Below the Chalk lies the concealed coalfield of the Nord and the Pas-de-Calais; the Coal Measures, exposed on the surface further to the east in Belgium, are found progressively deeper to the west, and cease to be exploitable just south-west of Aire. French geographers have coined a graphic name, '*Le Pays Noir*', to denote this area.[1]

As in southern Belgium, the field is situated rather unfortunately from a structural point of view, since it was subject not only to the

---

[1] R. Gendarme, *La Région du Nord: essai d'analyse économique* (1954). For detailed reviews of recent developments, see I. B. Thompson, 'A geographical appraisal of recent trends in the coal basin of northern France', in *Geography* (1965), vol. 50, pp. 252-60; and 'A review of problems of economic and urban development in the Northern Coalfield of France', in *Southampton Research Series in Geography* (1965), no. 1, pp. 31-60.

FIG. 44.—THE COALFIELD OF NORTHERN FRANCE.

There is a slight discrepancy between the areas of the concessions shown on this map and on Fig. 114, the result of different interpretations as shown on the two source-maps.

Based on the *Atlas de France*, plate 44, with revisions from various sources.

Hercynian orogeny, but also to the complex fracturing associated with the stages of uplift of the Ardennes during early and mid-Tertiary times (see pp. 486-7). In places overthrusting has forced older sedimentary rocks above the Coal Measures, especially in the south-west of the field, and moreover the workable coal is separated by faults which divide the field into several individual productive areas. The two main basins are those of Douai-Valenciennes in the east and Béthune-Lens in the west, separated by barren ground (Fig. 44). The coal is worked at considerable depths, the mines averaging well over 1,300 feet and at times attaining 3,000 feet below the surface. Moreover, the earth-movements have affected the Coal Measures in detail; many of the individual seams are interrupted and displaced by faults and sometimes they dip at high angles. The large number of thin seams makes for difficult and expensive exploitation; the average thickness worked is only about a yard and some seams are as little as a foot.

Despite these many physical disadvantages, the field is of vital importance to France, since in 1963 its forty-seven active collieries produced 24·7 million tons, rather more than half of the total national output of 49·2 millions. About two-thirds came from the Pas-de-Calais section, the most important producing areas being around Lens, Nœux, Béthune and Bruay (Fig. 45). In the *département* of Nord, the main districts are near Douai (Plate XIX) in the west Aniche, and as far east as Anzin and Condé, the regional centre being Valenciennes. Largely because the coalfield was entirely restored and re-equipped in the decade following the war of 1914–18, a high proportion of mechanical operation takes place. In the post-1945 period too, much modernisation has been effected; this has been systematised in two stages, the first 1947–56, the second still in progress. The number of collieries has been more than halved since 1947 as a result of the policy of concentration.

The quality of coal is extremely variable, not only in various parts of the basin, but with depth; the upper seams consist mainly of high volatile gas-coals, the lower ones of semi-anthracite. Thus in 1963 about 7·6 million tons of anthracite and semi-anthracite (*maigre*), 4·5 million tons of semi-bituminous coals used for metallurgical coke production (*demi-gras*), 9·5 million tons of bituminous coals (*gras*), and about 3·1 million tons of long-flame coals (*flambant gras*) made up the output of this northern field.

Rather more than half of the coal produced is consumed on the coalfield itself at the coke-ovens, patent-fuel plant and thermal-electric power-stations. About one-third of the French coke output (which totalled 13·9 million tons in 1963) was made at pit-head cokeries, most of them large units built since 1918. Two-thirds of these cokeries are situated in the Pas-de-Calais section of the field near Fléchinelle (the most westerly unit), Ferfay, Bruay, Grenay, Lens and Hénin-Liétard. The three Nord cokeries are mainly in the Douai district to the west of Valenciennes. Considerably more than half of the gas manufactured in France is produced at these cokeries, mainly for use in industry; it is distributed over the northern industrial area by a gas-grid which links Béthune, Douai and Valenciennes, together with the Lille industrial district to the

FIG. 45.—THE BÉTHUNE-LENS INDUSTRIAL REGION.

Names of towns and villages are lettered in their correct positions, without symbols (other than the *cités-ouvrières*).

Based on *Carte de France au 50,000e*, sheet XXIV/5.

north of the coalfield. Eight large power-stations are owned either by *Electricité de France* or the *Houillères nationales*; the largest is at Hornaing in Nord.

A large amount of coal-dust and small coal is unavoidably obtained from the shattered seams, and modern methods of recovery from the screening and washing plant enable much former waste material to be utilised. As a result, over five million tons of *briquettes* (large blocks used for locomotive and bunker fuel) and *boulets* (small 'ovoids' burnt in domestic stoves) are manufactured each year by mixing the dust with pitch obtained from the tar-distillation plant, mainly at Aniche, by far the most important centre, and also at Anzin, Bruay, Courrières, Nœux and Oignies.

About two-thirds of the coal produced in the northern field is consumed elsewhere, and Lens and Douai are the main handling centres. It is significant that both are on inland waterways; coal moves by canal towards Paris and to many parts of northern and central France. Some is used in other industrial areas of north-eastern France, notably in the textile factories of the Lille-Roubaix-Tourcoing area, and further east in Lorraine.

A very considerable chemical industry has developed on the coal-field, associated with the by-products of the cokeries. Thus in 1963 about 350,000 tons of coal-tar, 83,000 tons of sulphate of ammonia and 99,000 tons of benzine were ôbtained, the raw materials for a wide range of chemical and pharmaceutical products, ferti-lisers, aniline dyes, detergents, plastics, acids, motor fuels and industrial alcohol. The main plants are in the neighbourhood of Béthune, Liévin and Courrières.

The Metallurgical Industry.—Many of the towns in Belgian Flanders, particularly Gent, Tournai, Kortrijk and Ronse have a variety of metallurgical manufactures, including textile machinery, electric motors and diesel engines.

The two French *départements* of Nord and Pas-de-Calais form the most important part of the *Région Nord* of the *Chambre Syndicale de la Sidérurgie Française* (Fig. 72). No iron-ore is mined in this region, and ore and pig-iron come both by rail from Lorraine and Luxembourg and by sea through the port of Dunkirk from Nor-mandy, Sweden and Spain. As a result of this dependence on imported raw materials, the smelting of iron-ore is here less impor-tant than steel manufacture; in 1963 about 2·71 million tons of pig-iron were produced, and about 4 million tons of steel. About 2·3 million tons of the latter consisted of 'Martin steel' made in basic open-hearth plant. As might be expected, a considerable variety of steel-using industries, both light and heavy, provide quantities of scrap for the steel hearths.

The metallurgical industry has developed both on the coalfield and away from it. The major concentration on the coalfield is around Valenciennes, both along the canalised Scheldt and to the west of it. The largest company in the northern industrial region is *Usinor* (*Union Sidérurgique du Nord de la France*), incorporated in 1950. It owns large integrated plants to the south of Valenciennes at Trith and further west at Denain; extensive developments have taken place at these establishments under the post-war modernisa-tion plans. *Usinor* has recently amalgamated with the *Lorraine-Escaut* company, with a combined capacity of 8 million tons of steel.

While much semi-finished steel is sent away to the Paris industrial district, to Lille and to southern Belgium, a varied range of metal-using industries is active within the coalfield area—rails, locomotives, boilers, chains (a speciality at Anzin), steel wire at Trith, textile machinery and agricultural implements. Douai is the centre of various engineering industries.

Although Lille's chief industrial importance depends on textiles, numerous metallurgical and engineering establishments make, as might be expected, a range of textile machinery and also agricultural implements for the Flanders Plain and the Paris Basin. In the industrial suburbs such as Fives and Hellemmes, which have grown up to the east of the city particularly in the post-1918 period of construction, heavy engineering is carried on. This includes the construction of locomotives and rolling-stock for the *Région Nord* of the *S.N.C.F.*, electric motors and boilers. Roubaix-Tourcoing, five miles away to the north-east, also has textile machinery works. Further west, at Isbergues in Pas-de-Calais, the *Cie. des Forges de Châtillon, Commentry et Neuves-Maisons* operates a large modern integrated steel-plant, largely rebuilt in the post-1945 years and again modernised since 1960.

The Textile Industry.—The Flanders Plain has been one of the world's leading textile-manufacturing areas since the Middle Ages. In early times there was a concentration on woollens, first using local wool from sheep on the neighbouring hills and then importing Cotswold wool. This branch of the industry, now consuming wool from South Africa and Australia, is still important in French Flanders, especially in the Roubaix-Tourcoing conurbation and near Cambrai, but the main centre in Belgium moved as early as the fifteenth century from Flanders into the Verviers district to the east of Liège. Some interesting specialisations in woollen manufacture survive in Belgian Flanders at such towns as Gent, Kortrijk and Eekloo.

Linen has also flourished for centuries along the Lys valley at Armentières, Wevelgem, Kortrijk, Gent and a multiplicity of smaller places, and also at Roeselare, Lokeren, Aalst, Ronse, Roubaix, Lille and Valenciennes. The industry had such advantages as locally grown flax, the pure water of the Lys for retting, and a dense, hard-working population. As late as the nineteenth century most of the flax used was still grown locally in the Belgian province of West-Vlaanderen and in French Flanders, cultivated mainly on small-holdings and harvested on contract by large firms who retted the flax and sold the fibre to the mills. Today, however, home-produced flax supplies only a fifth of the requirements and the rest is imported. Fine linens still constitute a major product and are a valuable export item. Cotton is now the pre-eminent textile in Belgian Flanders, despite competition from Japan and India in recent decades. More than half of the spindles are located in and around Gent; factories are situated within the city itself and at such growing suburbs as Gentbrugge, Wetteren and Ledeberg. The industry has also spread along the valleys of the Scheldt (at Oudenaarde and Ronse) and of the Dendre (at Aalst, Ninove, Geeraardsbergen and Ath). A number of individual small firms specialise in different branches of the industry, though a few large combines have been created through mergers, such as the *Union cotonnière* at Gent. Even the small independent companies have for the most part grouped themselves into marketing organisations, such as the *Association belge de Tissage*. An immense variety of both thread and fabrics is made. A special line at Gent, Aalst and Dendermonde is the manufacture of cotton blankets for use in the tropics.

The mills of Belgian Flanders dominate the cotton industry in that country, but those of French Flanders have important rivals in the lower Seine valley near Rouen, in Alsace and in the Central Massif. Nevertheless Lille, Roubaix-Tourcoing, Armentières and La Bassée have many large factories, and specialisations include the manufacture of muslins and voiles at Lille itself.

These long-established branches of the textile industry have helped to create both a tradition and a labour force. As a result, other textiles (jute, rayon and nylon) are now produced, in more or less the same centres, Gent and Kortrijk being dominant in Belgium, and Lille and Roubaix-Tourcoing in France. A vast range of associated industries in both countries uses yarns and cloths; in fact almost every town in Flanders, and in central Belgium too, possesses some branch of the textile industry. Some of these towns, such as Brussels, Vilvoorde and Lier, lie further east on the central plateaus and will be mentioned later. Others are in Flanders itself; Tournai, for example, has long been famous for carpets, Lille has an immense output of ready-made clothing, and the Roubaix-Tourcoing agglomeration makes clothing, hosiery, knitting-wool, carpets, tapestries and furnishing fabrics.

THE WATERWAYS

The waterway system of Flanders comprises the regularised Scheldt and its almost parallel tributaries Lys and Dendre, interlinked by several transverse canals (Fig. 25), and also connected with the waterways of the Paris Basin across the Artois watershed and with the Sambre-Meuse system to the south-east. The river Lys, the most northerly of the Scheldt family, has been embanked for most of its length, and cuts have been made across several loops. Six locks are required to maintain a minimum navigational depth of about seven feet. Although the river is usually very sluggish, there is a considerable difference in régime between the low-water flow of late summer and the high-water of winter. The river is navigable for barges as far upstream as Aire.

The Scarpe, which is wholly a French river, joins the Scheldt a mile from the Belgian frontier. It is canalised from Arras for a distance of nearly forty miles, and as it crosses the northern coalfield by way of Douai it forms a very useful waterway, particularly as it is linked northward to Lille by the Deûle Canal and southward to the Scheldt by the Sensée Canal. Douai, at the junction of these several canals, has extensive basins and wharves, for it is an important coal dépôt. The river itself is, however, closed to navigation within the city between the Pont des Dominicains and the Pont d'Alsace, traffic using an artificial loop.

The Scheldt is an important waterway both to France and to Belgium. Above Cambrai in France the river is unnavigable, but navigation is continued southward across the watershed to the Seine system by the St. Quentin Canal. Below Cambrai the river has been canalised, and a navigational depth of seven to eight feet is maintained by sixteen locks in France and a further six in Belgium. Thus the Scheldt affords thirty-nine miles of waterway in France and a further 125 miles in Belgium. It crosses the eastern part of the Nord coalfield, flowing through such important towns as Cambrai and Valenciennes, and its banks are lined almost continuously with wharves and warehouses. It serves too the rich agricultural area in the neighbourhood of Cambrésis, with the considerable production of sugar-beet and cereals; several sugar-refineries are located on its banks. Then in Belgium the river flows across the densely populated plain of Flanders through such textile towns as Tournai and Oudenaarde before its junction with the Lys at Gent.

The Scheldt and its tributaries are interlinked in France by a continuous chain of transverse canals, so that it is possible for barges to move south-eastwards from Calais and Dunkirk as far as the Scheldt, following a line broadly parallel to the Belgian frontier at a distance of about twenty miles. This traffic first utilises the Calais Canal and the canalised river Aa to St. Omer, and continues along the short Neuffossé Canal to Aire. The Aire Canal then runs south-eastward through Béthune, and at Bauvin joins the Deûle Canal. The last is a very important waterway, forty miles in length, since it links the Lys and the Scarpe across the western part of the coalfield, it serves the industrial centre of Lille, and a branch-canal bordered by almost continuous coal-wharves serves the Lens section of the Pas-de-Calais field. The Roubaix (or Espierres) Canal continues the line of the Deûle to the north-east of Lille, crosses the frontier, and joins the Scheldt at Espierres. Finally, the Sensée Canal leaves the Scarpe near Douai and completes the chain by linking it to the Scheldt near Etrun. The Sensée is especially useful, since it forms the main connection between the various coalfield waterways and Paris by way of the St. Quentin Canal. The chief items carried on these waterways are, as might be expected, coal and coke; pit props, pyrites, salt and soda (the last two from Lorraine) were other important items.

It is a reflection both of the economic orientation of the Flanders Plain towards the lower Scheldt and Antwerp and also of the pattern of natural drainage that few waterways connect the Lys-Scheldt system with the North Sea coast. The river Ijzer has been canalised, but is of very fluctuating depth and is sometimes unnavigable for several months in summer. It is linked by the Ieper-Ijzer Canal with the town of Ieper; formerly this continued south over the watershed to the Lys as the Ieper-Lys Canal, which was destroyed during the war of 1914–18, and it was decided that its rebuilding was not worth while. Further east is the Gent-Ostend Canal, begun as long ago as 1614, and completed to the coast at Ostend by 1753; it is a useful waterway, forty-two miles in length, serving the agricultural plain of Flanders.

The chalk ridge of Artois extends south-eastward from the Boulonnais, forming a range of low hills which presents an appreciable barrier between the waterways of the Flanders Plain and those of the Seine system. It is, in fact, crossed only by the St. Quentin Canal, a waterway fifty-seven miles long, which leaves the canalised Scheldt at Cambrai and negotiates the watershed by means of 42 double locks and two tunnels near the divide, descending to the Oise Lateral Canal at Chauny, and so to Paris. The importance of this link is such that it has been enlarged several times; in 1928, for example, the summit divide tunnels were widened and deepened. Electric tractors are used for haulage to increase the working capacity of the canal. Much freight carried by the St. Quentin consists of coal from the northern coalfield en route to the Paris region.

The Scheldt system is connected with the Sambre-Meuse by two link-canals. The Mons-Condé Canal is a straight west-east waterway sixteen miles long, running from the French Scheldt at Condé across the frontier to Mons, and so serving both the French and Belgian portions of the coalfield. A second link, wholly within Belgium, joins the Scheldt near Antoing with the Mons-Condé Canal at Pommerœul. Several other interconnections have been developed in this area. The Blaton-Ath Canal uses twenty-one locks to cross southward from Ath in the Dendre valley to the Antoing-Pommerœul Canal. The Centre Canal continues the Mons-Condé Canal eastward through the coalfield area to join the Brussels-Charleroi Canal at Houdeng-Goegnies. The Centre has the steepest gradient of any Belgian waterway, with an average rise of about one in

230, although it needs only six locks. Modern electrically-operated barge-lifts are used.

The waterways within the western part of the Scheldt system and their links with neighbouring rivers therefore serve much of the coalfield of northern France, the important French industrial complex of Lille-Roubaix-Tourcoing, and the Belgian textile area of the Lys-Scheldt valleys, as well as the cities and ports of Gent and Antwerp and a dense agricultural population in the Flanders Plain.

POPULATION AND SETTLEMENT [1]

It is not surprising that Interior Flanders has such a dense population. Most of the rural population is dispersed widely over the countryside, with individual houses situated within small-holdings, and perhaps only a church to indicate the commune centre ; Flanders is in fact a type-area for 'dispersed' rural settlement.

The industrial towns, comprising as a rule an old centre, often walled and water-ringed, with a girdle of new suburbs, are strung out along the main and subsidiary valleys ; these have been mentioned already in connection with their long-established textile industries. In the *département* of Pas-de-Calais, Lens, Béthune, Bruay, Nœux and many more towns form a densely populated industrial district ; the old towns, the new housing estates (*cités-ouvrières*), the collieries, coke-ovens, by-product plants and spoil-dumps are spread over the countryside (Fig. 45). In the east is the Valenciennes basin, where Douai,[2] Denain and Anzin have developed similarly.

Gent [3] (*Gand* in French, *Ghent* in English), surpassed in size in Belgium only by Brussels and Antwerp, has long been an important city in the Flanders Plain. The Lys and the upper Scheldt meet in the south-east of the city, and the lower Scheldt, tidal up to the Gentbrugge weir, then flows gently eastwards towards Antwerp and its estuary. Several minor rivers (such as the Lième and Moere) and drainage-canals intersect the city, the ship-canal from Terneuzen on the Wester Schelde enters the docks in the north-east (see p. 84), and a smaller canal comes eastward across the plain from Bruges and Ostend. Wherever one goes in Gent, in fact, one has to cross water ; there are said to be over two hundred bridges within the city, and the built-up area actually lies on twenty-three islands.

[1] J. Beaujeu-Garnier, 'Géographie de la population de la région du Nord de la France et problèmes d'aménagement régional', in *B.S. Belge Et.G.* (1961), vol. xxx, pp. 67-92.

[2] J. R. Leborgne, 'Le Site et l'évolution urbaine de Douai', in *A. de G.* (1950), vol. lix, pp. 109-21.

[3] M. E. Dumont, *Gent : Een Stedenaardrijkskundige Studie* (1951), provides much detail, including an atlas volume.

Gent has had a long and prosperous history; as early as 1500 it had a population of over 100,000, the result of its rich industrial and commercial activity. In 1963 the population of the commune was 155,951 but several adjacent suburbs bring the population of the agglomeration to over 220,000. It is a useful port, second to Antwerp in Belgium; in 1964, 2,705 sea-going ships were accommodated, and it handled about 6·3 million tons of freight. Vessels of up to ten thousand tons can dock there.

As has already been made evident, Gent is the dominating centre of all branches of the Belgian textile industry except the woollen, and it has an immense variety of related manufactures, such as carpets and clothing. Textiles today, however, account for only half of its industrial importance. Chemicals (especially dyestuffs), fertilisers, metallurgical products and glassware are made, and around the docks (Plate XX) and in the eastern and northern suburbs are flour-mills, saw-mills, tanneries, paper-mills (one of these produces half of Belgium's consumption of newsprint), a low-temperature carbonisation plant, and a huge electro-chemical works. The *Belgian-Shell* company owns a bitumen-refining plant with an annual capacity of 130,000 tons. Other factories are situated along the banks of the ship-canal to the north. A modern integrated steel-plant (*Sidemar*) at Zelzaete, between Gent and Terneuzen, has a capacity of 1·5 million tons. These modern industrial developments and the new suburban housing estates contrast remarkably with the old inner town, where stand some of the architectural glories of Belgium—the *Hôtel de Ville*, the *Halle aux Draps* (Cloth Hall), the cathedral and other attractive buildings. Many towns of Belgian Flanders share, on a smaller scale, the general character of Gent.

Lille lies on the right bank of the canalised Deûle; the old town was contained within massive triangular fortifications, which with the imposing pentagonal citadel were largely the work of Vauban. During its long history the town has generally prospered, but it has suffered periodically from the wars which so often beset Flanders, for as a great strong-point it was frequently involved, often besieged and sometimes taken; even in the war of 1914–18 it was heavily shelled although it was declared an open town at the outbreak of hostilities. Lille's outstanding growth has been during the last century and a half, when it has become the leading agricultural and industrial city of north-eastern France, although so near the Belgian frontier from which attack has come three times in the last ninety years. Outside the city a close ring of industrial suburbs spreads into the country-side and has absorbed the former individual villages. Lille had a population in 1962 of 199,033, though with the eleven other communes which comprise the official agglomeration the total was 439,524. It is a vital communications centre, for here a main-line railway from Calais and Dunkirk to Strasbourg crosses the main Paris-Brussels and Paris-Gent lines. There is a useful river-port, since the Deûle Canal links the Scarpe with the Lys. Lille's manufactures are many and varied; it is the largest single textile-making town in France, it has a range of metallurgical and chemical industries, and there are sugar-refineries, flour-mills, tobacco factories, distilleries, breweries, tanneries and chocolate factories.

The twin towns of Roubaix and Tourcoing, with their neighbouring communes, formed an agglomeration of 341,204 people in 1962. They lie only a mile from the Belgian frontier and seven miles from Lille,[1] to which they are virtually connected by continuously built-up areas. Each has a long industrial history; as early as the eleventh century Tourcoing was famed for its velveteens and serges. As at Lille, industrial expansion was rapid in the nineteenth century and the textile industry, particularly wool, flourished. The two towns produce four-fifths of all French woollen yarn, and other items such as carpets, tapestries, furnishing fabrics and clothing. Textiles are predominant, but other manufactures include leather, rubber, miscellaneous metallurgical products and chemicals. Many Belgian workers cross the frontier daily to factories in the two towns.

The Flanders landscape is thus a remarkable palimpsest on which a millennium of vicissitudes has left its impressions. Before its final nineteenth-century division between France and Belgium, it had belonged to the Counts of Flanders, then it was successively under Burgundian, Austrian, Spanish and French rule. During the war of 1914–18, French Flanders suffered the devastating results of the most concentrated and prolonged static warfare that the world has ever experienced; two rich *départements* were ruined, the most important industrial regions of France were devastated. Southern French Flanders was a shattered wilderness in 1918; towns such as Lens, Arras and Cambrai (the centre of which was mined when the Germans evacuated in 1918) suffered immense damage, and many of the collieries and mining villages were just wiped off the landscape. Some compensation did in fact result in the long run, for the coalfield was rebuilt on modern lines. But the vast war cemeteries, the occasional plaque stating that a village once stood here, and the memorials (as at Vimy) are tragic monuments to the sufferings of Flanders fifty years ago.

[1] P. Bruyelle, 'Les Grandes Villes françaises, Lille-Tourbaix-Tourcoing', *Notes et Etudes Documentaires* (1965), no. 3206, p. 111.

CHAPTER 8

THE CENTRAL LOW PLATEAUS OF BELGIUM AND THE NETHERLANDS

GENERAL FEATURES

The land rises gently towards the east and the south-east from the edge of the Flanders Plain, forming what can be called 'the central low plateaus'. This rise is of the order of 3½ feet per mile, from about 150 feet above sea-level to a height of 650 feet near the southern margin of the region, where the land then falls quite steeply to the long curve of the Sambre-Meuse valley; the highest point is actually 722 feet above sea-level, to the north-east of Namur. This profile is well illustrated by the main line from Brussels to Liège via Tienen. From Brussels there is an up-gradient of the order of from 1 in 200 to 250 as far as Ans on the plateau above Liège, where the line reaches its maximum altitude of 591 feet. It then descends to the valley-floor at about 225 feet in a distance of less than four miles, with an average gradient of 1 in 32. This difficult section of line, although opened as early as 1842, had to be operated by cable-haulage for goods traffic until 1871, and, until the recent electrification of the line, trains were assisted by banking locomotives.

It might reasonably be argued that this area ought not to be included in the broad regional unit of the North Sea Lowlands on grounds of relative altitude. But the countryside has the general character of a lowland, certainly in comparison with the much higher Ardennes to the south, and indeed the area is commonly known as 'the low plateau of Middle Belgium'.

Palaeozoic rocks such as slates and quartzites, together with some associated igneous intrusions, underlie the plateaus at no great depth in the centre and south. The Senne and Dyle have cut down their valleys through the newer overlying strata, thus exposing the basement rocks; these are quarried for road-metal and setts in a number of places. Porphyritic diorites are worked at Quenast (Plate XXV) and Lessines. Small outcrops of Devonian and Carboniferous rocks are also revealed in the valleys to the east of Mons. At Ecaussines in the Sennette valley and again at Soignies in the Senne valley are extensive limestone quarries; the bluish limestone, known in the district as '*petit granit*', has long been worked for building-stone, and when cut and polished it has an attractive marbled surface. Upper Carboniferous rocks appear on the surface in the south of the Hainaut plateau. This is part of the 'coal furrow' of southern Belgium (see pp. 502-6), which is exposed further east within the narrow trench of the Sambre-Meuse beyond Charleroi, but in the Mons-Centre districts the coal is concealed beneath newer deposits.

The Chalk adds another contribution to the solid geology of these plateaus. It outcrops near Mons, again between Tienen and Liège, and beyond the valley of the Meuse over the greater part of South Limburg and the Pays de Herve. Frequently, however, a superficial cover of recent deposits occurs. Chalk is not present even at depth in the northern part of the low plateaus near Brussels, since it was long ago removed by denudation.

These Palaeozoic and Mesozoic rocks furnish abundant evidence of the complexity of the structural history of the plateaus. Some Belgian geologists consider that the Palaeozoic rocks represent an anciently established 'horst' or massive block, the southern bounding edge of the 'North Sea basin' (Fig. 5). This was involved in the Hercynian folding at the end of Carboniferous times (see p. 483), and may even have formed part of the 'foreland' against which the folding took place. There is, however, evidence that the ancient rocks were themselves folded to form a very complex 'Brabant anticline' (Fig. 108), though much less intensely affected than the Ardennes further south. The northward limb of this fold dips gently under an increasingly thick cover of newer rocks, forming the Kempen syncline which contains Coal Measures.

Then followed the prolonged sequence of alternate denudation, marine transgression and deposition in Tertiary times already described (pp. 13-15). The net result was the formation of the present widespread cover of Older Tertiary rocks, consisting mostly of Eocene sands (although clays predominate in the south-west), together with occasional surviving patches of Oligocene and Pliocene sands.

Uplift and late Tertiary denudation combined to produce a broad surface dipping gently northward from the High Ardennes away to the North Sea basin. Belgian geomorphologists distinguish a 'surface plane' at 590 to 650 feet along the southern edge of the Brabant and Hesbaye plateaus, which has been correlated with similar surfaces to the south of the Meuse valley on the margins of the Ardennes. But the 'furrow' eroded by the Sambre and the Meuse, a relatively recent feature (see p. 489), lies transversely across this once continuous erosion plane, and thus separates the plateaus of 'High Belgium' from these central low plateaus.

This northward tilt of the low plateaus is naturally reflected in the courses of the main rivers in the eastern Scheldt basin (the Senne, Dyle, Gette and upper Demer), until each in turn is picked up by the east-west line of the Demer, Dyle and Rupel in yet another transverse 'furrow', south of the Kempenland plateau (see p. 16). Only in the extreme south, where, as has been described (see p. 141), the Haine flows to the west, and in the east, where the Méhaigne and Geer make their way eastwards to the Meuse, have streams developed athwart this northward tilt.

In the broad valleys of the rivers much alluvium has been deposited. In addition, forming a most important contribution to the agricultural economy, a widespread cover of *limon* (Fig. 9 and see p. 23) lies on the interfluves of the plateau surface. On this have developed brownish loams of excellent quality. Brabant and Hesbaye in fact have much in common with Beauce and with the *Börde* of Hanover and Magdeburg.

Large hedgeless fields grow wheat and sugar-beet (Plate XXI), producing high yields from the heavily fertilised loam-soils, with numerous prosperous-looking nucleated villages and occasional large isolated farms (Plate XXII). The low plateaus have an average density of population of the general order of four to five hundred per square mile. These figures, however, are swollen by the considerable urban population, for some of the towns have had a flourishing existence for a thousand years or more. If rural population alone is considered, the average is considerably less than in Interior Flanders, mainly because farms are much larger and there is less of the intensive small-holding system.

Differences are nevertheless evident between various parts of these low plateaus. Brabant and Hainaut may be considered as one region, for these names refer mainly to adjoining administrative provinces and they have geographically much in common. Further to the east, within the obtuse angle of the Meuse, is the plateau of Hesbaye. Across the north, from the Rupel to the Gette-Demer confluence, lies the 'furrow' between the Kempenland and the low plateaus; the transitional character of this district is indicated by the fact that some Belgian geographers name it the '*Région Mixte*',[1] but nevertheless it does belong mainly to the 'northward slope' of central Belgium. Finally, beyond the Meuse valley are the eastern low plateaus, comprising the Pays de Herve of eastern Belgium and its continuation northward across the frontier into South Limburg. These six units are numbered from 6a to 6e respectively on Fig. 11.

BRABANT AND HAINAUT

The western low plateaus include the greater part of the province of Brabant and the eastern part of the province of Hainaut, corresponding more or less to the valleys and interfluves of the Dendre, Senne and Dyle. Both plateaus have an extensive *limon* cover, in

[1] As, for example, J. Halkin, *Atlas classique* (1934), plate 18, and see Fig. 2.

Hainaut resting largely on clay, in Brabant mainly on sands. The floors of the valleys are broad and alluvium-covered. To the north the *limon*-derived soils gradually become sandier as the edge of the Meuse 'fan' is approached in the Demer-Dyle valley. The Palaeozoic rocks are never far below the surface, and are even exposed in places; as a result surface drainage is abundant even in the sandy country and very plentiful on the Hainaut clays. The plateau is much dissected, particularly in the south, by steep-sided valleys.

Both Brabant and Hainaut are agriculturally of great importance, and wheat and sugar-beet dominate in both in terms of acreage. The sandier soils of Brabant, however, carry a much higher proportion of arable, while in Hainaut there is more pasture, partly the result of the widespread damp clay-lands, partly due to the requirements of the mining towns for dairy produce. Hainaut is the chief horse-breeding region of Belgium; in spite of some mechanisation many farms in central Belgium use these heavy draught-horses.

In the neighbourhood of Brussels there is a tremendous concentration on market-gardening, dairying, pig and poultry farming, the production of flowers and nursery cultivation, in obvious response to the adjacent urban market. To the north-west of the city, particularly between Berchem and Assche, are immense areas of glass-houses, mainly producing early vegetables and flowers, while in the south-east beyond the Forêt de Soignes are more glass-houses devoted to grapes, especially in the communes of La Hulpe, Rosières, Hoeilaart (Plate XXIII) and Overijsche.[1]

The industrial importance of the Brabant-Hainaut region is considerable. The two outstanding areas are of course the Brussels conurbation, and the Mons (Borinage) and Centre basins of the southern coalfield of Belgium; it is, however, more convenient to describe the whole coalfield as a unit within the Sambre-Meuse valley (see pp. 502-11). Apart from these special cases, many towns have a great variety of industries. The Flanders textile industry extends eastward into Brabant—particularly at Brussels itself, Braine-l'Alleud and Anderlecht. In the Senne valley the towns of Halle, Braine-le-Comte and Soignies have miscellaneous metallurgical, textile and food-processing industries. At Clabecq[2] a large integrated iron- and steel-works is situated in the Sennette valley fifteen miles south of Brussels on the banks of the Brussels-Charleroi Canal; this affords an example of the location of a heavy industry away from both fuel and raw material, but with excellent communications with areas which can supply these needs and with

---

[1] S. W. E. Vince, 'Viticulture in Belgium', in *G.J.* (1946), vol. cvii, pp. 135-40, deals with the production of table-grapes under glass.

[2] An immensely detailed account is by R. Mangelinckx, 'Clabecq et sa sidérurgie', in *Revue belge de Géographie* (1963), vol. 87, pp. 260-344.

XVII The Veluwe

XVIII The reclamation of the moorland in Drenthe

XIX Collieries and *cités-ouvrières* near Douai

XX Industrial suburbs in Gent along the Gent–Terneuzen Canal a large accessible consuming market. Further east are Leuven, Nivelles and a host of smaller towns, many within the Brussels orbit, and all sharing the well-developed industrial life of Belgium. Leuven (in French *Louvain*), with a population of 34,481 in 1964, stands in a well-marked gap through the northern edge of the Brabant plateau. It is a town of long-established antecedents, since its nucleus was a ninth-century castle on a wooded hill above the marshes of the river Dyle (hence the derivation of its name from *loo*, a wooded height, and *veen*, a marshland). Until the late fourteenth century it was a prosperous textile town, but then the city fell on hard times, remedied only slowly after the fifteenth century. Today it is a market centre for the surrounding agricultural countryside, and it has extensive food-processing industries, particularly brewing, flour-milling, the manufacture of potato-starch and vegetable-canning. In addition, it has a number of metallurgical industries, including the manufacture of agricultural machinery, and chemical works, tanneries and saw-mills. The Leuven-Dyle Canal is a useful waterway linking the town with the Rupel and the lower Scheldt, since the river Dyle itself is little used; the canal carries a considerable tonnage of such bulky commodities as fertilisers, flour, bricks and timber.

Vilvoorde (population 32,822) is situated somewhat similarly to Leuven, where the Senne cuts through the northern edge of the plateau of Brabant in a well-defined gap, also followed by the Willebroek Canal. It too has had a long and prosperous history, and until it became involved in the fifteenth-century wars its cloth industry was thriving. Following a long period of decline, the town shared in the nineteenth-century expansion of Belgian industry and particularly in the prosperous period of 1896–1914. As a result, the manufacture of fertilisers, chemicals, electrical appliances, vegetable oils, glue, starch and leather is established on the banks of the Willebroek Canal in the suburbs, and many specialised factories (textiles and gloves) still operate within the town itself. There is also a coking-plant and a car-assembly plant.

Brussels.—The city of Brussels (in French *Bruxelles*, in Flemish *Brussel*), capital of Belgium, has for long been one of the main cities of Europe.[1] In 1964, while the population of the commune of Brussels itself was only about 170,000, the agglomeration (including eighteen contiguous communes) had a total of 1·6 million people. The city originated in the sixth century on the Ile-St. Géry, one of the many islands among the marshland of the braided river Senne, hence the probable derivation of its name from *broek* (a marsh) and

[1] P. Gourou, 'L'Agglomération bruxelloise', in *B.S.R. Belge G.* (1958), *fasc.* I-IV, pp. 1-83.

R.G.W.E.—G

sele (a dwelling). The river now flows through the western part of the city, vaulted over for much of its course and incorporated within the city's drainage system, although it emerges into the daylight in the north-western suburbs. The town developed rapidly from the eleventh century as its varied industrial and commercial activities increased. The built-up area grew on the drier terraces along the east bank, and it has now spread on to the sandstone plateau at 120 to 135 feet above sea-level, as compared with the valley floor at about fifty feet. There is a clear distinction between the 'lower town', with the commercial quarter, the spacious *Grand' Place* flanked by the magnificent fifteenth-century Gothic *Hôtel de Ville*, the docks and the canal-port, and the residential 'upper town', the centre of which is the attractive *Quartier Léopold*, with its parks, boulevards and *places*. As the capital, Brussels has a wide range of administrative functions, it is a great commercial centre and is the main industrial district of Belgium. Its industries are extremely varied, including a wide range of metallurgical products, textiles (carpets, blankets, clothing), chemicals, paper, furniture and consumer goods generally. Heavy industry has developed notably along the canals in the northern and southern suburbs.

Brussels is indeed a port in its own right, for there is a series of four large basins in the north-west of the city. The Brussels-Rupel Canal (Fig. 25), sometimes known as the Willebroek, enables vessels to reach the capital from the Scheldt estuary via the Rupel. The original waterway was built in the sixteenth century, but it was enlarged during the 1830's and again at the end of the century, and now has a depth of twenty-one feet right into the port of Brussels. Barges and small sea-going vessels of up to about 3,000 tons can reach the port, but three locks and numerous bridges somewhat delay progress. Nevertheless, 8·0 million tons of freight were conveyed in 1963, an indication of the importance of this link between the chief port and the capital. From the southern end of the port the Brussels-Charleroi Canal (Fig. 25) leaves to cross the plateau of Brabant to the Sambre industrial region. The canal was originally constructed in 1827-32 to take vessels of some seventy tons, but successive works of enlargement have been carried through, and by 1922 300-ton barges could be accommodated. The main difficulty is a rise of about 350 feet, negotiated by utilising the valleys of the Senne and Sennette and with the aid of twenty-six locks and two short summit-canals, followed by a further eleven locks down to Charleroi. In 1963, 4·6 million tons were conveyed along the canal including coal from the southern field, building materials and oil. This route is obviously so important that a project was put forward in the late 1930's for the creation of a 2,000-ton capacity canal, then unofficially referred to as the 'Léopold III Canal'. A modified scheme to enable 1,350-ton barges to use the canal was completed in 1965. It now provides a valuable waterway circuit around eastern Belgium, linking the southern and northern coalfields, the chief port and the capital.

Considerable developments have taken place in Brussels since the war of 1939–45, including a great extension of suburban housing estates and the building of vast blocks of flats and offices within the central area. Brussels is a most important railway focus, for seven main lines carrying international express traffic converge upon it, and the country's largest marshalling-yard is at Schaerbeek in the north-eastern suburbs. The two main stations are *Nord* and *Midi*, formerly linked only by circuitous belt-lines both to west and east of the city, although only two miles apart in a straight line. Their junction by an underground link was begun as long ago as 1903, but the interruptions of two wars and more urgent reconstruction delayed the completion until 1955. Since 1945 the *Nord* and *Midi* stations have been rebuilt and there is a new underground *Gare Centrale*.[1] Road communications too have developed since 1965, and the construction of several 'urban motorways' is still in progress. The three ring roads (at distances of a mile, three miles and five miles approximately from the city centre) have been reconstructed, providing separate lanes for through and local traffic. Eight road-tunnels have been built to carry ring traffic under the radial arteries and so prevent obstruction of flow at these busy intersections. The *autostrade* from Brussels to Ostend runs straight across country, bypassing to the south towns such as Aalst, Gent and Bruges, and all side roads are carried over it. This highway was begun in 1936, and by the outbreak of war the Aalter-Jabbeke section was finished ; the road was completed in 1956. The construction of the Brussels *métro* began in 1965. In all, Brussels is one of the most attractive and progressive capital cities in Europe.

THE PLATEAU OF HESBAYE

The northern part of Hesbaye has the prevailing northerly tilt of the central low plateaus, and several streams flow northwards to the Demer. In the south, however, two river systems have developed athwart the slope. The Méhaigne flows eastwards, having captured successively several north-flowing tributaries, former headstreams of the Gette, before it breaks southwards through the plateau-edge to join the Meuse just above Huy. The Geer also flows eastwards through Tongeren, to join the Meuse above Maastricht.

Like the plateaus of Hainaut and Brabant, Hesbaye is largely

[1] M. Pardé, 'Sur la jonction ferroviaire entre Bruxelles-Nord et Bruxelles-Midi', in *A. de G.* (1953), vol. lxii, pp. 296-8.

limon-covered, but while in the north this superficial deposit rests on sand, in the south and east it is underlain by the Upper Chalk. The combination of the friable porous *limon*, sometimes over fifty feet thick, and the permeable Chalk has resulted in a notable absence of surface drainage, except in the few shallow valleys of the Gette, upper Demer, Geer and Méhaigne. Compared with the dissected plateaus of southern Brabant and Hesbaye, therefore, the surface is much more uniform. Some broad shallow depressions are the product of subsidence following solution of the underlying Chalk. Particularly in the east shafts or 'pipes' occur in the Chalk, known as '*aardpijpen*' or '*orgelpijpen*', due to localised solution down fissures. Now filled with sands or clays, they vary in diameter from one to seven feet, and penetrate for a distance of from three to sixty or more feet. These features are particularly well developed in the extreme north-east, where the Hesbaye plateau projects into the Maastricht territory. Belgian geomorphologists have given the name of '*plateau subkarstique de sous-sol crayeux*' to this part.

The countryside consists of open fields; arable farming is predominant, and in southern Hesbaye the emphasis is almost exclusively on the cultivation of wheat and sugar-beet on large holdings. Further north agriculture becomes more mixed in character, and includes market-gardening and fruit-growing on the sandy loams, as in the neighbourhood of Tongeren, Borgloon and Sint-Truiden.

Southern Hesbaye has many small towns and villages nucleated into compact groups of houses and farms, and separated by stretches of open farmland. This nucleation was due originally to the clustering of houses within communal lands farmed on the openfield system. Most of these settlements have fewer than 5,000 inhabitants; they include Gembloux, Perwez, Hannut and Jodoigne, with local agricultural industries and occasional specialisations such as cutlery manufacture at Gembloux. Further north, however, a line of larger towns is strung out along the mediaeval trade-route from Antwerp and Bruges via Leuven to the Rhineland; these include Tienen in the valley of the Grande-Gette, Saint-Truiden and Tongeren, a line continued eastward through Maastricht and Aachen. As a result, these towns have a long commercial and industrial tradition. Tienen (*Tirlemont*), with its 22,556 inhabitants, lies on the northern margins of an extensive sugar-beet area, and in fact possesses the largest sugar-refinery in Belgium, as well as other agricultural-processing industries—flour-mills, tanneries, starch factories—and it is the world's largest producer of citric acid.

The plateau of Hesbaye to the north-east of Tongeren just enters the Netherlands where the frontier makes its westerly loop away from the centre of the river Meuse to form the district of Maastricht (see pp. 168-9). The river Geer (known as the Jeker in the Netherlands) flows parallel to the Meuse and about two miles to the west of it, thus demarcating the promontory of St. Pietersberg to the south-west of the town. The surface of this hill, which attains 403 feet in elevation, is partly covered with Oligocene sands which have given a heath-like appearance to the landscape, and much is planted with conifers or reserved as military training-grounds.

The Chalk in the Maastricht area is the youngest of the system; the name *Maastrichtian* is in fact sometimes applied to these formations. It consists of a soft but compact sandy limestone, yellowish in colour, described as chalky tufaceous marl (the Dutch term is *tufkrijt*), which is highly fossiliferous. It has been quarried for many centuries, possibly since Roman times, since the stone is easily cut into blocks yet the surface hardens on exposure to the air. A vast labyrinth of galleries supported by residual pillars has developed during the centuries in these quarries, which can be entered near Slavante about two miles south of Maastricht. The Chalk is still extensively quarried, mostly to provide raw material for the neighbouring cement-works, both in the Netherlands and at Lanaye and Visé in Belgium.

THE 'RÉGION MIXTE'

This intermediate strip between the low plateaus of central Belgium and the Kempenland consists of districts known in the west as *Petit Brabant*, in the centre as the *Campine brabançonne* and in the east as the *Hageland*.[1] It follows more or less the line of the broad Demer valley, and represents a transition (interrupted by the alluvial floor of the Demer valley) from the sandy loams of Brabant to the coarser Pliocene sands of the Kempenland. The Demer has been regularised and straightened (Fig. 46), and its floor is a maze of cut-offs, minor drainage channels and ditches.

The light warm sandy soils on either side of the river, when heavily fertilised, are suitable for the intensive cultivation of vegetables, particularly of early varieties. Such crops as peas, sown at the end of January and picked in early June, asparagus, early potatoes, carrots and chicory are grown along the valley between Mechelen and Diest, a 'golden belt' of horticulture. Glass-house produce, bush- and orchard-fruits, and flowers are also important. Numerous villages and towns form market-centres both for the southern Kempenland and the Demer valley, and have varied flourishing industries. Diest (population 9,891) is a centre of flour-milling and various other forms of food-processing, brewing and distilling. Aarschot (12,113) also carries on food-processing, Lier (28,627) manufactures textiles and chemicals, and Duffel (13,223) has textile and metallurgical works.

[1] G. Scheys, 'Hageland, Boden en Landschap', in *B.S. belge Et. G.* (1954), vol. 23, pp. 85-121.

The most important industrial town is Mechelen (*Malines*), with a population of 65,224 in 1964.   It is situated at only twenty-five feet above sea-level on the banks of the tidal Dyle, which flows through the town in several branches.   Like Leuven, it is an agricultural and market-gardening centre and has a wide range of industries.   Its lace, famous for centuries, is still a useful export item.   There are numerous furniture factories, varied textile and clothing factories, paper-mills and printing works, a *Mercedes* car-assembly plant, tanneries, and food-processing factories.   Boom (with 17,879 inhabitants), situated on the north bank of the Rupel, is one of the

FIG. 46.—THE DEMER VALLEY.

The maze of minor drainage channels and ditches is not shown.   The contour-lines are in metres.

Based on *Carte de Belgique au 100,000ᵉ*, sheets X, XI.

main centres of brick-making (Plate XXIV);   in fact about half of Belgium's output of bricks is made at yards which line the river banks between Boom and Rumst near the Senne-Dyle confluence.

THE PAYS DE HERVE

Lying between the Meuse valley and the German frontier, and bounded on the south by the valley of the Vesdre, is the plateau of the Pays de Herve.   Although this rather remote region is often grouped with the Condroz and the other southern plateaus because it lies 'beyond the Meuse', its surface rocks mostly consist not of Palaeozoic sandstones and shales but of Upper Chalk with a superficial cover of *limon* and Clay-with-Flints (Fig. 47).   It has in fact more of the character of Hesbaye than of the ridge and valley structure of Condroz (see p. 500).   In the east, however, the valleys are cut down through the Chalk into the underlying Palaeozoic rocks. Zinc-ores are associated with these rocks, and mines have been worked for centuries in the valleys at Welkenraedt, Lontzen, Moresnet, La Calamine and Bleiberg to the west of the German frontier. The zinc industry of Liège formerly depended on these and other small deposits in the Meuse valley, but the Belgian output of ore has now ceased, and the zinc concentrates used (for Belgium produced 223,000 tons of zinc metal in 1964) are imported from Australia, Mexico, Canada and Jugoslavia.

Almost all the plateau is over 600 feet in altitude, many parts exceeding a thousand feet; the highest point is 1,161 feet near Henri-Chapelle. Belgian geomorphologists have distinguished two clearly-defined erosion surfaces, the lower at 590 to 650 feet, the higher at 900 to 1,000 feet; these correspond to similar surfaces in the Ardennes to the south-west. A few rivers have cut prominent

FIG. 47.—THE MEUSE TERRACES BELOW LIÈGE.

The length of the section is about ten miles.

Based on a diagram in *Handboek der Geografie van Nederland* (1949), vol. i, p. 251, illustrating chapter III, 'Geomorfologie', by J. B. L. Hol.

valleys into the plateau surface, notably the Geule (in Dutch, the *Geul*) which flows across the north-east of the region into South Limburg, and the Berwinne flowing westwards to the Meuse. A few short streams drain the southern plateau and join the Vesdre, otherwise there is a marked shortage of surface drainage.

Mixed farming is carried on in the Pays de Herve on the clay soils; oats and fodder crops predominate on the higher plateau, wheat in the lower areas, with widespread pasture. The main emphasis is, however, on stock-breeding; it is a prosperous dairying district and numbers of animals are sold off to farmers further west.

Settlement is curiously dispersed, particularly in the west, a remarkable contrast to the plateau of Hesbaye where it is nucleated, although the same combination of *limon* on Chalk forms a broadly similar physical environment. This dispersion is largely the result of the widespread dairy-farming. A considerable number of people in the southern part of the Pays de Herve travel daily to work in Verviers.

Verviers, with a population of 35,545 in 1964, is situated at an altitude of about 575-600 feet in the steep-sided valley of the Vesdre, which joins the Ourthe to the south-east of Liège. The town has expanded on to the hill-slopes south of the river, and to a less extent along the valley of the Dison, a northern tributary. Since the fifteenth century, Verviers has been important for the manufacture of woollen textiles, and with some surrounding small towns (Ensival, Dison, Theux, Pepinster) and others even further away, such as Eupen, the district now dominates the Belgian woollen industry. The reasons for this are partly geographical (plentiful soft water and local wool from the Ardennes and the Eifel) and partly histori-cal (freedom from the restricting guild regulations of Flanders, the introduction of the first carding and spinning machines in Europe by William Cockerill in 1798, and the enterprise of the local merchants). After the construction in 1844 of the railway between Liège and Aachen, which passes through the town, it grew apace. A wide range of woollen fabrics is produced, and in addition leather-goods, brushes, chemicals, glue and chocolate are manufactured. Its situation between the Pays de Herve and the Ardennes has helped it to become a busy market- and servicing-centre.

SOUTH LIMBURG

The southern part of the Dutch province of Limburg consists of an ' appendix ' that projects southward between West Germany and Belgium for more than twenty-five miles, and widens from what before 1949 was a narrow corridor merely three miles across to more than twenty miles further south. All South Limburg lies on the east side of the Maas except for the district of Maastricht, where the town of that name stands mainly on the left bank of the river, while the frontier makes a loop some $2\frac{1}{2}$ miles further to the west on to the plateau of Hesbaye.

The historical reasons for this apparent geographical anomaly are complex. The long-drawn-out negotiations which followed the break-up of the united Kingdom of Holland and Belgium after the revolution of 1830 culminated in the treaties of London in 1839. The King of Holland, in return for the cession to Belgium of what is now the province of Luxembourg, received in a personal capacity part of the province of Limburg. Included in this territory was the former enclave surrounding the city of Maastricht, which had been, with intermissions, a detached portion of Dutch territory since its capture from the Spaniards during the Thirty Years War

(1618–48). The 1839 settlement made Maastricht contiguous with other Dutch territory, although both the city and the rest of Limburg remained in the category of personal possessions of the King of Holland until 1867, and in fact were individual members of the German Confederation. In that year, at the Conference of London, Limburg was fully incorporated into the kingdom of the Netherlands, and became a Dutch province.

At the end of the 1939–45 war, the Netherlands made strong claims for a number of frontier revisions at the expense of Germany.[1] One of these concerned the ' Selfkant ', immediately to the east of the narrow corridor near Sittard. On April 23rd, 1949, the Selfkant was transferred to the Netherlands and placed under a special commissioner, while on January 1st, 1952 it was incorporated into the province of Limburg (Fig. 48). In 1963, however, this territory was returned to West Germany by treaty.

South Limburg consists for the most part of a plateau of Cretaceous rocks, with some surviving patches in the north-east and west of Younger Tertiary sands and marls. The Cretaceous rocks consist mainly of Upper Chalk; in the west they are soft tufaceous limestones, in the east they comprise chalk rocks known as the *Gulpien* (*Gulpensch Krijt*) and the *Kunradien* (*Krijt van Kunrade*), so-called after the localities in which they are well developed.

Rarely, however, do the Chalk or the Tertiary rocks appear at the surface, except in the valley of the Geul. As far north as Sittard the surface is covered with loams, believed to be *loess* (*limon*) deposits of wind-borne origin. This may be so in part, but some Dutch geologists regard them as residual loams formed by the decomposition *in situ* of the Upper Chalk, reworked and redeposited by stream-action, and with possibly a mixture of true *loess* material, as the name given to them (*loessoïde*) would indicate; the resultant soils are referred to as *loessleem* and cover almost exactly a quarter of Limburg. Whatever their origin, these loam-soils are among the most fertile in the country.[2]

One further important element enters into the geological make-up of South Limburg. Across the centre of the region lies the westward continuation of the Upper Carboniferous rocks found along the northern edge of the uplands of central Europe; the Aachen and Eschweiler fields of western Germany can be traced over the German-Dutch frontier into Limburg, and then across the Meuse into the Kempenland. The Coal Measures of Limburg are

[1] L. M. Alexander, 'Recent Changes in the Benelux-German Boundary', in *G.R.* (1953), vol. xliii, pp. 69-76.

[2] See A. J. Pannekoek (editor), *Geological History of the Netherlands* (1956), pp. 102-3, for a full discussion, with bibliography, of the problem of these deposits.

concealed by younger rocks, except for minor outcrops in the extreme east in the valley of the Wurm, a left-bank tributary of the Roer. There are estimated to be 10,000 feet of Upper Carboniferous rocks, mostly shales and sandstones. Several faults, running approximately from south-east to north-west, divide the field into blocks in which the depth of exploitable coal varies considerably. The overall dip is towards the north-west, and so workable coals near the upper part of the series are found at about 200 feet depth in the east but at over 2,000 feet in the west. Major faults bound the field, beyond which coal lies at great depths, probably at as much as 8,000 feet in the north.

The present surface-features of South Limburg are mainly the result of river action. As in the Kempenland and Noord-Brabant, the Maas and its tributaries have exercised profound effects in late inter-glacial and post-glacial times, and they are now markedly entrenched. The erosional and depositional terraces discussed on pp. 17-18 are well represented. The plateau is bounded on the west by the clearly defined alluvium-floored trench of the Maas, and is cut into three individual blocks by the Geul and the Geleen, its two right-bank tributaries. In the north-east, extending across the frontier into Germany as far as the Roer valley, is the *IIIr* level (described on p. 18), the highest gravel-covered terrace. Between the Geleen and the Geul this *IIIr* level again appears, mostly at over 300 feet, rising to a well-marked erosion level at 590 feet, from which project residual summits such as the Ubachsberg and the Vrouwen-heide (each 712 feet). South of the Geul valley, the erosion terraces of both Cycles *II* and *III* are well developed, and the 590-foot level is also quite extensive. Along the Belgian frontier to the south, parts of the 900 to 1,000-foot erosion surface of the Pays de Herve extend into South Limburg, rising to the rounded summit of the Vaalserberg (1,056 feet), the highest point in the Netherlands, almost at the junction of the triple frontier. The rivers are here swift-flowing, and in places their valleys are steep-sided with occasional rocky slopes.

South Limburg is a pleasant, prosperous-looking agricultural region, and farming is predominantly mixed. The loam-soils are excellent for sugar-beet and potatoes, there are extensive market-gardens, and it is one of the chief fruit-growing districts in the country. Large orchards have been established under grass, with tree-crops of apples, plums and pears, and also others intercropped with bush-fruit. It is an important dairy-farming and pig-rearing area. Many of the valleys are wooded, and clumps of fine beech trees add to the attractive verdant character of the countryside.

Nevertheless, only one province in the Netherlands (Overijssel) has a higher proportion of its occupied population engaged in industry—

48 per cent, compared with 45 per cent in Limburg. This industrial importance is mainly due to the presence of the coalfield and associated industries.[1]

The Coalfield.—The importance of the Limburg field to the Netherlands is that as yet it is the only productive one.[2] It was possibly the first to be worked in Europe, for it is recorded that the monks of Kloosterrade Abbey mined coal by open-cast methods in the valley of the Wurm near the German frontier. Further sporadic operations were carried out during succeeding centuries but only on a small scale; in 1845, for example, some mining took place to supply fuel for the newly opened Maastricht-Aachen railway. It was not until 1895 that the first large-scale concession was granted to the *Domaniale* Company at Kerkrade, and during the next five years further leases were obtained by the *Laura en Vereniging* Company at Eygelshoven, by the *Willem-Sophia* Company at Spekholzerheide, and by the *Oranje-Nassau* Company with its headquarters at Heerlen ; these four were initially floated by French, German and Belgian interests. The extent of these private concessions and the location of the eight collieries they developed are shown on Fig. 48. The most recently opened of the private collieries were *Julia* in 1926 and *Oranje-Nassau* (number IV) in 1927.

Alarm, however, was increasingly felt in Dutch political and industrial circles towards the end of the nineteenth century that the country's mining enterprise had passed under the control of foreign interests, and it was considered desirable for the State to assume a considerable measure of future responsibility. It was not intended that existing foreign concessions should be expropriated, but that private and State mines should exist side by side. The State therefore reserved to itself most of the non-conceded proven area by an Act of June 24th, 1901, and in 1912 it formally extended its domain over the whole province, except for areas already conceded. A State company, the *Staatsmijnen in Limburg*, was established, and the first coal was produced in 1906 by the *Wilhelmina* colliery, developed in the southeast enclave. The palatial headquarters of the *Staatsmijnen* were established in Heerlen. Three other state collieries were built— *Emma* in 1911, *Hendrik* in 1915 and the great *Maurits* undertaking (Plate XXVI) in 1923. The output of coal in South Limburg since the initiation of the field in 1895 is summarised in Fig. 49, which differentiates between the State and private mines. It will be seen that the former, although later developed, increased their output

---

[1] L. Haas, 'Sociaal-economisch structuurbeeld van de Nederlandse provincie Limburg', in *T.E.G.S.* (1965), vol. 56, pp. 32-7.

[2] F. J. Monkhouse, 'The South Limburg Coalfield', in *E.G.* (1955), vol. 31, pp. 126-37.

steadily; by 1924 they produced exactly half the total, and since 1926 they have been responsible for about 60 per cent.

When South Limburg was liberated by allied troops in the autumn of 1944, the mines were standing idle as a result of military operations.

FIG. 48.—THE SOUTH LIMBURG COALFIELD.

The boundary of concessions in the neighbouring Kempen coalfield is shown by pecked lines. In 1963 the Selfkant was returned to West Germany.

Letters are used to indicate names of individual collieries as follows: **D**, Domaniale; **E**, Emma; **H**, Hendrik; **J**, Julia; **L**, Laura; **M**, Maurits; **O.N.**, Oranje-Nassau; **W**, Wilhelmina; **W.S.**, Willem-Sophia.

Based on P. R. Bos and J. P. Niermeyer, *Schoolatlas der Geheele Aarde* (1936), Plate 11 B.

Apart from some material damage the chief handicap to immediate development was a shortage of labour, partly because many miners had joined the allied armies, partly because of the aversion felt towards mining as a result of German forced labour decrees. There was also a shortage of materials and mining equipment, and maintenance had been neglected during the later years of the war. The overall recovery from the trough-year of 1945 represents a substantial achievement; output rose from little over five million tons in 1945 to a post-war peak of 12·6 millions in 1961, but has since declined to 11·2 millions in 1965. At the present time six of the private collieries each produce more or less half a million tons per annum, while *Oranje-Nassau No III* and *Julia* are responsible for about three-quarters of a million. The four State mines are much larger units, each exceeding a million tons; *Maurits*, with an annual output of about 2·4 million tons, is the biggest individual colliery in Europe, and *Emma* is not far behind.

The coal seams vary in thickness from about two to eight feet. They are, however, considerably disturbed by folding and faulting,

FIG. 49.—OUTPUT OF COAL IN SOUTH LIMBURG.
Based on statistics obtained from successive volumes of
the *Jaarcijfers voor Nederland*.

and moreover are interlaminated with dirt, so that careful washing is necessary. One great advantage is that the coal is found in wide variety; about half consists of high-grade coking-coal and 10 per cent of anthracite. In all, the province contains estimated reserves of 4,000 million tons, of which a quarter lies within existing concessions. Only about 500 million tons of the latter, however, are classified as 'economically workable'.

The importance of the Netherlands' coal output, even though it is small compared with that of its neighbours, is that it is able to supply a considerable portion of the country's fuel needs, since 1945 some 80 per cent; actually, for several years before the war a slight surplus was available for export. Increasing post-war industrialisation in the Netherlands, coupled with the export drive and the rearmament contribution which the country must sustain, at first reduced the proportion of home consumption which the Limburg field could contribute. In each of the years 1955 and 1956, home consumption exceeded seventeen million tons. Output has now been stabilised at 10–11 million tons annually, and indeed the industry is suffering from over-production of certain types of coal. This is partly the result of the development of gas resources (see p. 138). It is planned to close the Hendrik colliery in 1967, and to use its buildings for the new headquarters of the N.A.T.O. *Alfcent* command, transferred to Limburg from France. *Maurits* also will be closed during the next few years.

The Limburg field is situated in a remote corner of the Netherlands, and the transport of such bulky items as coal and coke demands special organisation, both by rail and water. The Limburg mines are served by a single-track standard-gauge line operated by the Mines Railway Department, with its headquarters at Heerlen. Each colliery has its own sidings, with the main marshalling-yard at Susteren in the north, and the system is linked to the State Railway at several points. Some three million tons of coal are carried along the Juliana Canal (see p. 97).

As in other countries, the building up of a labour-force results in housing needs. In the Netherlands the post-war building programme has been put in the hands of two corporations, *Ons Limburg* and *Thuis Best*, on which serve representatives of the Government, the mining companies, the workers and the municipalities. These corporations draw up building plans and supervise the construction by contractors; some 4,000 permanent houses and several blocks of flats have been built since 1945.

About a quarter of Limburg coal is coked on the field itself in plants situated at the Emma and Maurits mines. The former was built during the war of 1914–18, the latter in 1929, and subsequent additions of batteries of ovens have made the Maurits coking-plant the biggest unit in Europe. A new plant (Emma II) was completed at Beek in 1954. Over 4·6 million tons of coke were produced in 1964. The fine quality of some grades of Limburg coal, which produce coke of high crushing strength and low phosphorus and sulphur content, has given Dutch coke a considerable international reputation, and about half the output is exported. Half the gas produced is used to heat the coke-ovens, some is used in by-product plants, and the rest is put into a high-pressure gas-grid, 120 miles in length, which links the ovens with industrial and domestic consumers throughout the provinces of Limburg and Noord-Brabant. This grid is connected to the Ruhr by way of Alsdorf, and a further link with the Belgian grid in the Sambre-Meuse valley is projected.

Another important industrial unit in South Limburg is the Nitrogen Fixation Plant, built in 1930 at Geleen near the Maurits colliery, and owned by the State Mines Company; it was enlarged in 1949. Liquid ammonia, carbon dioxide and ethylene are produced, and a range of other products—ammonium sulphate, calcium nitrate, sodium nitrate and other nitrogenous fertilisers, nitric acid, alcohol, cleaning agents, detergents and solvents, phenol and many more commodities. In addition, a distillation plant produces tar-oils, naphthalene and pitch, the last of which is used as binding material in a neighbouring briquette and ovoid plant.

The power-stations at both State and private mines not only supply the collieries with their required power, but also the coking-plant and the Nitrogen Fixation plant. About a quarter of the generated energy, surplus to the collieries' requirements, is supplied to private consumers in Limburg and parts of neighbouring provinces through a grid.

Deposits of brown coal are found in the Miocene rocks of Limburg along the German frontier, notably in the south near Brunssum (to the south-east of the Hendrik colliery), and further north near Kerkrade. The deposits have been worked since 1917, but only one quarry, near Kerkrade, has remained active; in 1958 it produced about a quarter of a million tons, but it ceased production in 1961. Glass-sands, also of Miocene age, are worked near Heerlerheide; they are nearly pure quartz and are excellent for the making of high-quality glass. About 100,000 tons annually are worked, much of which is shipped to Liège and Mol-Gompel in Belgium.

Settlements.—Several mining towns therefore have grown from agricultural villages during this century. The centre is Heerlen, which had a population of only about 6,000 in 1890; soon after this date exploitation of the coalfield began, and communications were improved by the construction both of State Railway lines and the Mines Railway. The State mining company and the private

Oranje-Nassau company each has its headquarters in Heerlen, and eight collieries lie within or near the commune. As a result its population in 1964 was 75,285. Other towns on the coalfield are Kerkrade (50,766) near the German frontier, Brunssum and Hoensbroek. Many of the workers employed in the big *Maurits* State colliery live in or near Lutterade in the north-west, where several of the chemical by-product plants are situated. Market-towns include Sittard (32,165) and Geleen serving the northern area, Valkenburg in the Geul valley, Margraten on the plateau to the south, and Vaals on the German frontier.

The regional centre of South Limburg is *Maastricht* (94,216 people in 1964), which is mainly situated on the left bank of the Maas, with the suburb of Wijk on the opposite side. It has owed much to its being a crossing-point of the river since Roman times; the name is derived from the Latin *ad Mosam Trajectum*, where a ford was used on the important route to the Rhineland. The bridges have always been vital strategic points right down to 1939–1945, when a V.C. was won for an aerial attack on the *nieuwe Maasbrug*, constructed in 1932. A fine new bridge has been built since the war. During the latter part of the nineteenth century the town expanded, first as a result of improved waterways; the Maas is unnavigable below the town, but the Liège-Maastricht and Zuid-Willems Canals were useful. In the 1930's the lateral Juliana Canal was completed, thus linking Maastricht to the Maas below its international section (see p. 97). The development of railways also helped Maastricht, which is rather remote from the rest of the Netherlands, and the exploitation of the coalfield to the east afforded a great stimulus to industrial development. There are now various steel-using industries, brick-, tile- and cement-works, a tannery, a soap-works, a tobacco factory, a woollen mill, several rubber factories, a glass factory which has made the attractive '*Crystal Maastricht*' ware since 1834, and one of the largest paper-mills in the country. It is still an important market-town and shopping- and servicing-centre for this part of the Netherlands, spaciously and attractively laid out. With its remarkable collection of churches, ramparts and the oldest surviving town-gate in the country, the city still retains much of its ancient interest and charm, and has an appreciable tourist traffic.

CHAPTER 9

THE LOWLANDS OF NORTHERN FRANCE (1)

GENERAL FEATURES

The greater part of northern France consists of a structural depression lying between the Ardennes, the Central Massif and Armorica. This has been filled in with sedimentary rocks ranging in age from the Jurassic to the Miocene, while in places a thin cover of superficial Recent deposits is present (Fig. 50).

A series of Jurassic limestones and clays appears on the eastern margins, and is continued in the south along the flanks of the Central Massif. Again in the west they can be traced in a narrowing outcrop from the coast of Calvados along the eastern margins of the Armorican Peninsula. In succession outwards from the centre of the basin can be seen the Portland, Corallian and Oolitic Limestones, best represented in the cuestas of Lorraine (Chapter 11). Between the limestone outcrops, river erosion has developed valleys along the various Jurassic clays (a narrow outcrop of Kimmeridge and the much more widespread Oxford and Lias Clays).

The Cretaceous rocks comprise the most extensive element in the surface geology, for they completely encircle the region, attenuated only in the south. The Lower Cretaceous (*Albien*) Gault Clay appears as a crescentic exposure in the east. A soft clayey sandstone known as *gaize* (equivalent in age to the Upper Greensand in England) forms the ridge of the Argonne, and other greensands outcrop in Puisaye in the south. The most widespread surface rock in the Cretaceous is the Chalk, except in the south where it is buried under Tertiary deposits.

The central part of the region is occupied by Tertiary rocks, including limestones, sandstones, marls and clays, and varying in age from the Lower Eocene, exposed only in the deeper valleys, to the Miocene in the south-west. The limestones are the dominating surface rocks in the centre of the region, forming a series of low plateaus.

These Mesozoic and Tertiary rocks are in many parts masked with superficial deposits. Residual clays, such as the Clay-with-Flints, are common over the limestones and the Chalk, distinctive gravels occur on terraces in the valleys at different heights, and much alluvium has been deposited on the flood-plains of the rivers. The most important of the superficial deposits is *limon* (see pp. 23-4);

its widespread distribution in north-eastern France is shown on
Fig. 9.

These rocks then were laid down during long periods of geological
time in the structural depression (Fig. 5). In mid-Tertiary times the

FIG. 50.—GEOLOGICAL MAP OF THE PARIS BASIN.

Based on the *Carte géologique de la France*, 1 : 1,000,000, published by the *Service de la Carte géologique détaillée de la France*.

strata were affected by movements associated with the Alpine folding
to the south, though of a gentler character on these outskirts of the
orogenic zone. The resultant shallow basin-form causes the strata
to dip gently inward from the outer rim, and denudation therefore
affected the higher marginal areas more markedly. The more

resistant limestones and chalk alternate with the clays and marls, so that a succession of outward-facing cuestas and intervening clay-vales has been produced.[1]

The folding movements also caused flexures which have produced significant results upon the landscape (Fig. 51). Several distinct though low anticlines can be traced, trending in a more or less north-west to south-east direction, and these cause marked undulations in the surface features. In the north-east the anticline of

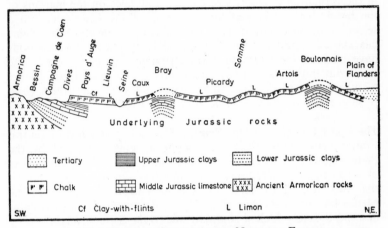

FIG. 51.—SIMPLIFIED SECTION ACROSS NORTHERN FRANCE.

The length of the section is about 280 miles.

The superficial covering of Clay-with-flints in the west and *limon* in the centre and east is indicated by letters; this covering is of course not continuous.

Based on A. Cholley, *La France* (n.d.), pp. 77, 161.

Artois forms a prominent line of hills bordering the Flanders Plain. The Boulonnais, the structural continuation of the Weald, is another anticline which has been extensively denuded, so that infacing chalk cuestas now form a 'horse-shoe' around a depression in which Jurassic rocks are revealed (Fig. 60). Bray is also a denuded anticline, with Upper Jurassic clays and limestone exposed in the centre (Fig. 61).

THE RIVER SYSTEMS

A whole pattern of rivers has developed, flowing transversely across this tilted basin-structure, and focused on the lower Seine. Most of the tributaries drain from the south and east, and only a few

---

[1] The standard work on the morphology of the Paris Basin is A. Cholley *et al.*, 'Carte morphologique du Bassin de Paris', in *Mémoires et Documents* (1956), vol. v, pp. 7-103. This detailed text accompanies a volume of four morphological maps on the scale of 1 : 400,000, published by the *Centre de Documentation cartographique et géographique* (Paris).

short confluents, such as the Essonne and the Eure, are received from the west. In addition, the right-angled bend of the middle Loire trenches across the sequence of sedimentary rocks in the south-west, while the northwards-flowing Meuse and Moselle are involved in the eastern scarpland margins. A few short streams—the Canche, Authie and Somme—cut across the chalk-lands of Picardy directly to the English Channel.

The development of this drainage pattern has not only resulted in the formation of a series of cuestas and vales on the margins of the basin, but has caused the dissection of the inner part into a series of distinct unit-areas. The centripetal effect of the Seine has caused repeated river-capture, while successive rejuvenations have enabled the rivers to form strikingly incised valleys. The numerous individual *pays* so characteristic of France generally are to a large extent demarcated by river valleys, while others comprise portions of the valleys themselves (Fig. 52).

The Upper Confluents of the Seine.—The main watershed of central France between the Seine and Saône systems is formed by the Plateau de Langres, a Jurassic upland which links the ancient masses of the Vosges and the Morvan. From it flow northwards the Marne, the Aube, the upper Seine and the Armançon, together with the Meuse further to the east (Fig. 53), while numerous short streams descend the steep faulted southern side to the Saône trough.

The upper Seine, the Ource, the Aube and the Aujon rise at a height of about 1,500 feet on the limestone plateau, known to the inhabitants as *La Montagne*. Their sources break out as springs in the deeply-cut valley-floors, and the rivers may disappear and reappear a number of times during the first few miles of their courses. It has been known during exceptionally dry periods for the bed of the Seine to be dry as far downstream as Châtillon. The neighbouring Marne and Meuse, however, have cut their sources further back through the Oolite into the Upper Lias clays that lie on the south-western margins of the Vosges. These impermeable rocks afford a better water-supply than does the limestone, and as a result the upper Marne has a larger and more regular volume than the Seine. Again, further to the west the Yonne rises on the crystalline rocks of the Morvan, while its tributary the Armançon flows from the Lias marls which flank that upland on the east. Thus the Yonne makes a considerably larger contribution to the volume of the middle and lower Seine than do the other head-streams ; indeed, rapid run-off following sustained rainfall or a period of snow-melt in central France may in fact cause serious flooding, which on several occasions has affected Paris.

This batch of head-rivers flows northwards across the succession of progressively younger Jurassic and Cretaceous rocks, forming a

series of alternate vales and cuestas—the narrow Oxford Clay vale at
the foot of the Oolitic Limestone plateau, then the Corallian scarp,
the Kimmeridge Clay vale and the Portland Limestone plateau (Fig.
53).   The rivers meander across each of these clay vales, then by
contrast cut through the next cuesta in steep-sided winding trenches.

FIG. 52.—THE PATTERN OF THE *PAYS* IN THE LOWLANDS OF NORTHERN FRANCE.

The abbreviations are as follows: **Cler.,** Clermontois; **Dr.,** Drouais; **Fo.,**
Fontainebleau; **Noy.,** Noyonnais; **Yv.,** Yvelines.

Based on a map, 'Régions géographiques de la France', 1 : 1,400,000, published by
the *Institut National de la Statistique et des Etudes Economiques* for the *Ministère de
l'Economie Nationale.*

They next enter the Gault Clay lands, to which is given the *pays*-name
of *Champagne humide*.   Some river-capture has developed here
between the Portland scarp and the Chalk; thus the Armançon
turns abruptly west along the strike at St. Florentin as a subsequent
stream to join the Yonne above Joigny, and similarly further to the

east the Ornain turns west near Bar-le-Duc to join the Marne at Vitry-le-François. The main rivers then cross the chalk country of *Champagne pouilleuse*, wandering sluggishly over the flat floors of their entrenched alluvium-lined valleys, fed by numerous springs issuing from the foot of the chalk slopes.

The Seine flows westwards for forty miles along the edge of the

FIG. 53.—THE SCARPLANDS OF THE SOUTH-EASTERN PARIS BASIN.

The escarpments are shown in generalised form by heavy lines, and are lettered as follows: **A,** Tertiary (Falaise de l'Ile de France); **B,** Upper Chalk; **C,** Middle Chalk; **D,** Upper Greensand (*Gaize*) of the Argonne; **E,** Portland Limestone; **F,** Corallian Limestone; **G,** Oolitic Limestone; **H,** Lias.

Some towns mentioned in the text are indicated by their initials as follows: **An,** Anglure; **D,** Dijon; **Ep,** Epernay; **L,** Langres; **M,** Montereau; **O,** Orléans; **P,** Paris; **R,** Reims; **T,** Troyes.

Based on (i) *Atlas de France*, sheet 9 (*Morphologie*); and (ii) F. Machatschek, *Das Relief der Erde* (1938), p. 54.

central Tertiary plateau, a direction initiated by the Aube further to the east. This is another example of river-capture. One can regard the proto-Yonne and the lower Seine as an original consequent stream, joined by a powerful right-bank subsequent which in due course captured the upper Seine and the Aube; the small beheaded trunks of these rivers now continue their original northward trends to join the lower Marne.

Below Montereau the Seine is joined by the Loing, one of its few left-bank tributaries, the probable evolution of which is discussed below in connection with the middle Loire. The Seine here flows at 160 feet above sea-level and is 150 miles in a direct line from the English Channel, although its official distance for navigation is no less than 306 miles, an indication of its meandering course. It crosses the limestone plateau through a broad trench cut into the Tertiary rocks, receiving its major right-bank tributaries, the Marne and the Oise, above and below Paris respectively. A number of terraces can be seen at different levels, the result of continued down-cutting in ancient alluvium while the meanders were swinging freely. E. Chaput [1] has distinguished at least four terraces at specific levels : at twelve to fifteen metres, at thirty to thirty-five metres, at fifty-five metres, and a few fragments of ancient surfaces at higher levels still. The flint-gravels on the upper terraces contain remains of animal life, including bones of mammoth and reindeer.

The Middle Loire.—It is necessary at this point to mention the incursion of the Loire into the lowlands of northern France ; indeed, some of the northward-flowing headstreams of the Loing rise only five miles from the Loire itself. It seems probable that the upper Loire once continued northwards to the proto-Seine system, cutting through the Portland Limestone cuesta, and so forming the most westerly member of the tributaries converging on the lower Seine. But this river, coming from the Central Massif, was captured by the back-cutting of a powerful stream flowing westwards to the Bay of Biscay, hence the right-angled bend. The much reduced Loing remained, now far too small for its broad valley (the *Plaine du Gâtinais*), and joining the Seine a few miles below Montereau (Fig. 59).

The Loire itself, greatly enlarged in volume by the accession of its near-parallel confluent, the Allier, flows through the Lias Clay plain of *Nivernais*, and breaks into the main basin through its southern Portland Limestone rim. The river swings westwards and northwards to its most northerly point near Orléans, and finally southwestwards towards the Bay of Biscay. [2]

The Right-Bank Seine Tributaries.—The course of the upper Marne has already been discussed, for it is one of the family of parallel upper tributaries which flow from the Jurassic rim on to the chalklands. It continues still further northwards as the chalk belt itself swings in this direction, until the river comes under the centripetal influence of

[1] E. Chaput, *Recherches sur les terrasses alluviales de la Seine entre la Manche et Montereau* (*Bulletin Service de la Carte Géologique de France*, 1924).

[2] The monumental work on the valley of the Loire is R. Dion, *Le Val de Loire* (1934), a volume of 752 pp., copiously illustrated and documented.

the inwardly-dipping strata of the basin and bends westwards to the Seine confluence. The Marne cuts through the edge of the Tertiary escarpment just below Epernay, forming a striking steep-sided valley in the limestone, and receiving numerous affluents from the clay-covered plateaus both to the north (*Tardenois*) and the south (*Brie humide*).

The Oise forms a complex drainage system, since not only do its headstreams rise in the Ardennes, but the Aisne and its tributary the Aire have their sources in the eastern scarplands not far from both the Marne and the Meuse (Figs. 63–4). The Oise itself actually rises just within Belgium near Bourlers on the south-western slopes of the Ardennes, flows westwards over the Gault Clay and Chalk, then through the rim of the Tertiary escarpment, and finally in a broad flat-floored valley with uniform plateau-surfaces on either side to its junction with the Seine.

The upper Aisne is a longitudinal stream draining northwards through the Gault Clay vale to the west of the sandstone ridge of the Argonne, from which it receives numerous affluents. The river wanders peacefully through its broad marshy valley across the clay-lands, to be joined near Challerange by the Aire, the most easterly of the Seine system (Fig. 64). The Aisne then escapes from the north-south trend of the scarplands, and flows in a clearly defined trench across the chalk-lands and the limestone plateau. It receives another large tributary, the left-bank Vesle, which crosses the chalk country and penetrates the escarpment in a gap, near the entrance of which stands Reims. The Aisne itself continues westwards, its deeply-cut valley separating the distinctive *pays* of *Soissonnais* and *Valois*, to join the Oise at Compiègne.

The Lower Seine and its Estuary.—The Seine below Paris forms a series of swinging meanders, incised 300 feet or more below the surface of the flanking chalk plateaus. Narrow at first, the valley widens below Rouen, though still within its prominent bounding walls. The river is bordered by reclaimed alluvial flats through which the channel is regularised and confined between massive dykes. A bore (the *mascaret*) is experienced for some distance upstream.

The broad estuary opens out towards the west; between Le Havre and Trouville it is nearly nine miles across. A shipping-channel is dredged from the deep-water Carosse roadstead off Le Havre upstream to Rouen through ever-changing sand-banks. By way of this estuary the waters of the Seine, the runoff from the surface of some two-fifths of France, find their ultimate way to the ocean.

The Somme and its Neighbours.—Part of the extreme north of these lowlands is drained by a few rivers which flow independently to the

English Channel—the Canche, Authie, Somme, Béthune, Arques and other smaller streams. The only river of any size is the Somme, which rises on the dip-slope of the chalk hills of Cambrésis near St. Quentin at a height of about 240 feet. Only seven miles to the north is the source of the Scheldt, with an intervening dry gap at about 460 feet above sea-level; this is one of the natural routeways between Flanders and the Seine basin. The Somme wanders westwards in a broad flat-bottomed valley, alluvium-lined and in places marshy, followed by a lateral canal. Below Amiens the river is trenched in the *limon*-covered chalk plateau; it enters the sea through the broad Baie de Somme.

The Waterways.—These natural waterways afford a valuable system of communications, linking Paris[1] with the northern and eastern industrial districts of France and with southern Belgium (Fig. 54). Much regularisation has, however, been necessary; the depth of water is controlled by weirs with locks, of which there are twenty-one along the Marne, seven on the Oise and seven on the Aisne. Each is now paralleled along its upper course by a lateral canal; this was easier and much cheaper than extensive regularisation of the rivers.

The Seine too has been improved for navigation. The river is not navigable above Marcilly, although a lateral canal prolongs naviga-tion as far as Troyes for small barges. Between Marcilly and Paris thirty-nine locks and barrages are required, and cuts have been made through tortuous braided sections. Below Paris the Seine provides a waterway in which a depth of ten feet is maintained by six weirs with large sluices, built during the inter-war period both to check flooding and to assist navigation.

The Seine carries the greatest volume of traffic of any French waterway, since not only is it joined by several tributaries, but the lower river forms an important line of communication between Paris and its ports of Rouen and Le Havre. The various sections of the Seine carry between seven and eleven million tons of freight, about a quarter consisting of coal. Then, too, link-canals connect the main rivers across the intervening plateaus between the Oise and the Aisne and between the Aisne and the Marne. Others link the Seine system with the Flanders waterways to the north (the St. Quentin Canal), with the Sambre-Meuse system in the east (the Sambre-Oise and Ardennes Canals), with the Rhine to the south-east (the Marne-Rhine Canal), with the Saône to the south (the Marne-Saône and Burgundy or *Bourgogne* Canals), and with the Loire to the south-west (the Nivernais, Loing and Orléans Canals) (Fig. 54). The links have not been easy to construct because of the complex relief features of

[1] M. Chartier, 'Problèmes de la navigation fluviale dans la région parisienne', in *Bulletin de l'Association de Géog. franç.* (1965), nos. 338/9, pp. 41-51.

the concentric cuestas; the Sambre-Oise Canal, for example, needs thirty-eight locks in its forty-one miles to cross the chalk divide in the district of Cambrésis, the Marne-Saône Canal has 114 locks and two tunnels, the Marne-Rhine Canal 178 locks and five tunnels, and the Burgundy Canal no less than 189 locks and a tunnel.

FIG. 54.—THE WATERWAYS OF THE PARIS BASIN.

Abbreviations are as follows: **A.L.C.**, Aisne Lateral Canal; **A.M.C.**, Aisne-Marne Canal; **C. du N.**, Canal du Nord; **M.L.C.**, Marne Lateral Canal; **O.L.C.**, Oise Lateral Canal; **T.C.**, Tancarville Canal. The line of the formerly projected Canal du Nord is indicated by a dotted line.

Based on W. Seghers, *Kaart der Binnenscheepvaartwegen van N.-W. Europa* (n.d.).

Regional Divisions.—Although the term 'lowlands' may be applied in a general sense, as a result of these diverse rocks, structures and drainage systems the relief is distinctly varied, including flat or gently undulating plateaus, deeply-cut alluvium-floored valleys, steep cuestas and open vales. Land-use is equally diverse. There are rolling expanses of arable lands with fertile loamy soils growing wheat and sugar-beet; extensive tracts of poor grazing on bare chalk and limestone; heavy well-watered clay-lands with prosperous dairy farms; dense plantations of conifers on sandstone ridges; market-gardens along the valley-floors; and serried rows of vines on south-facing slopes. Moreover, this part of France has been important for millennia, and has a well-developed urban life with a considerable number of towns, large and small. The greatest of these is Paris, the heart, the focus, of these lowlands, as indeed of France itself. It is for this last reason that the name Paris Basin is commonly applied to the region as a whole. Sometimes, however, the term is used in a wider sense to include the eastern scarplands, but as pointed out above (p. 9) it is more convenient to include those areas east of the Meuse in Lorraine. For purposes of detailed regional description, five main divisions have been distinguished (Fig. 55).

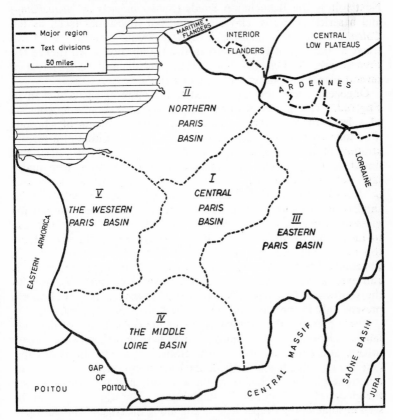

FIG. 55.—KEY-MAP TO THE MAJOR DIVISIONS OF THE LOWLANDS OF NORTHERN FRANCE.

The numbers **I** to **V** refer to the major areas described in each section of the text. A more detailed pattern, including a large number of *pays*, is given on Fig. 52.

I. THE CENTRAL PARIS BASIN[1]

The central Paris Basin consists of a gently undulating plateau of Tertiary strata dipping towards the centre. The oldest rocks, over-lying the Chalk, are beds of plastic clays (*argiles plastiques*), which are responsible for a distinctive spring-line along many valleys. Above these are Lower Eocene sands, notably the *Sables de Bracheux* (equivalent to the Thanet Sands in the London Basin, hence the French term *Thanétien*). Then succeeds the coarse *Calcaire grossier* which has long been quarried for building purposes ; this seems to be of marine origin in its lower strata, of estuarine origin in the upper. Next follow the Beauchamp Sands (*Sables moyens de Beauchamp*) and a series of marls, clays, gypsum and limestones (such as the *Calcaire* or *Travertin lacustre de St. Ouen*), equivalent to the Barton Clays at the top of the Eocene in the Hampshire Basin (hence the French term *Bartonien*). The gypsum, incidentally, is quarried in several places for plaster ('plaster of Paris').

Oligocene rocks are represented much more extensively than in England. The thin layer of the *Calcaire de Brie* commonly consists of a band of millstones or *meulières*, large fragments of siliceous limestone embedded within layers of the clayey residue of a former stratum of limestone, though in places, as in southern Brie, this limestone does appear as a more continuous stratum, with marly layers above and below. Next come the famous *Sables supérieures de Fontainebleau*, beds of sand in places compacted into a solid sandstone. In some districts the sands have long been worked for glass-making ; large quantities are still exported for this purpose to Liège and to Mol-Gompel in the Belgian Kempenland. At the top of the Oligocene is the *Calcaire lacustre de Beauce*, a tough siliceous limestone which makes an excellent building-stone and is still extensively quarried ; it outcrops over a considerable area to the south-west of Paris. Finally, the Miocene sands and clays are present only in the angle of the middle Loire near Orléans.

These then are the Tertiary rocks of the central part of the low-lands. Denudation has removed some here and there, so exposing others, and thus has given considerable variety to the landscape. One can pass in a few miles from the level monotonous surface of the limestone plateau of Beauce to the fantastic sandstone rocks among the glades of the Forêt de Fontainebleau. The whole range can be seen in some of the deeper valleys and along the edge of the outward-facing escarpment which bounds its eastern and south-eastern margins. The term '*Ile de France*' having been bestowed on the

[1] P. George and P. Randet, *La Région parisienne* (1959), in the series *France de Demain*.

central plateau (it is thought first by Froissart in the fifteenth century), the escarpment is known as the '*Falaise de l'Ile de France*'.

THE VALLEYS

The chief contrast in relief generally is between the higher surfaces of the intervening plateaus and the valley-floors. The latter are cut down into the clays and lined with alluvium over which rivers meander, formerly with considerable areas of marsh, now for the most part dyked and regularised. Their valleys have long afforded routeways, notably along the Oise from Flanders and the Ardennes and along the Marne from Lorraine, now followed by main roads and railway-lines, and lined with prosperous industrial towns— Chauny, Noyon, Compiègne, Creil and Pontoise in the Oise valley, Soissons and Attichy in the Aisne valley, and Epernay, Château-Thierry, La Ferté, Meaux and Lagny in the Marne valley. Indeed, in effect Greater Paris extends 'fingers of linear industrialisation' and of close settlement far along these valleys. Elsewhere the alluvial valley-floors contain meadowlands (utilised by a rich dairying industry producing milk for the metropolitan market), woodlands, and market-gardens[1] cultivated with typical French assiduity.

THE PLATEAU-LANDS OF THE ILE DE FRANCE

Although tongues of denser settlement project along the valleys, the limestone plateaus support an agricultural population of merely a rural order of density.[2] An indication of the land-use figures of the three *départements* which mainly comprise the Ile de France, that is, Seine-et-Oise, Seine-et-Marne and Oise, will be helpful, although it must be remembered that the western parts of the Aisne and Marne *départements* also form part of this region.

Land Use, 1963

(Percentages of Total Area)

	Arable (inc. Wheat)	Wheat	Permanent pasture	Woodland
Seine-et-Oise . . .	51	14	6	19
Seine-et-Marne . .	59	22	7	20
Oise	57	19	15	19

Source: *Ministère de l'Agriculture*, published in *Annuaire statistique de la France* (1964).

[1] M. Phlipponneau, *La Vie rurale de la banlieue parisienne* (1956), provides a detailed study of horticultural activity.

[2] P. Brunet, *Structure agraire et économie rurale des plateaux tertiares entre la Seine et l'Oise* (1960), a detailed text of 552 pp.

These figures reveal a striking overall uniformity. More than half the total area is under arable, a direct response to the gently undulating *limon*-covered tablelands, and about a fifth is devoted to wheat. The paucity of permanent pasture is a result of the generally rather dry and well-drained surfaces. What there is occurs as meadowland along the alluvium- and clay-covered floors of the valleys, and in a poor almost heath-like form on the patches of Clay-with-Flints or on the limestone where the *limon* covering is absent.

Woodland covers parts of the valley-floors and some of the outcrops of sand. Some forested areas have been deliberately maintained, notably the Forêt de Fontainebleau [1] on the sands between the limestones of Beauce and Brie, and the Forêts de Rambouillet, Chantilly, Sénart and St. Germain. Fontainebleau, with its varied trees, stretches of heath and fantastic groups of rocks, is a favourite outlet for Paris; it was, incidentally, the home of the famous '*Barbizon*' school of landscape painters—Millet, Corot, Diaz and others.

Beauce.—A journey from Paris in a south-westerly direction to Orléans crosses a wide expanse of Oligocene limestone of unusually level surface. This Beauce Limestone is several hundred feet in thickness, much fissured and extremely permeable, and surface drainage is markedly deficient. But except in the south where some areas of heathland occur on the bare limestone, Beauce is blessed with a *limon*-mantle sufficiently thick to hold moisture, providing an excellent loamy soil for arable-farming. Here are the extensive wheat-lands ('*les vastes horizons de culture*'), with some sugar-beet and barley; from the air one sees a chequer-board of cultivation, from the ground a monotonous vista of unfenced fields. Settlements are rare, and consist either of large prosperous farms or of nucleated villages built around a broad market-place. Wells have to be sunk so deeply through the limestone that they are necessarily expensive and therefore infrequent. A few towns—Etampes, Malesherbes, Pithiviers and Chartres with its cathedral—are market- and route-centres.

Brie.—The Plaine de Brie occupies the area between the middle Seine and the Marne. This has undergone considerably more denudation than has Beauce; the Beauce Limestone and the Fontainebleau Sands have been completely removed, exposing the *Calcaire de Brie* over considerable areas. This in its turn has been cut into by the numerous streams which flow north-westwards across the plateau—the Yères directly to the Seine and the Grand and Petit Morin to the Marne—so revealing the underlying marls. Much of this Brie Limestone has been weathered, producing a surface mantle

[1] An account of the ancient forest, its changes and developments, is given by A. Kh. Iablokoff, *Un Carrefour biogéographique: le massif de Fontainebleau* (1953).

of residual clay, particularly extensive in the north-east where it causes considerable waterlogging with numerous tiny lakes and areas of marsh (Fig. 58); their extent has been reduced by reclamation, although some of the surviving lakes are used for pisciculture. This part is known as *Brie humide* in contrast to *Brie pouilleuse* of the limestone, over much of which, however, *limon* is fortunately present.

The agriculture of Brie is therefore more varied than that of Beauce because of the greater range of soils. Wheat and sugar-beet are the chief crops grown on the *limon*-covered limestone. In addition, since 1940 such crops as colza, white mustard, cameline and flax (developed as a result of the need for vegetable oils during the German occupation) have been cultivated for industrial purposes. Some interesting specialisations include the production of rose-bushes on the heavy clay soils near Crisy-Suisnes. Fruit cultivation has been developed, with long rows of cordon trees.

The wetter clay soils in the north and in the valleys carry pasture, which, supplemented by fodder-crops (particularly lucerne), enables a considerable dairying industry to thrive. About 119,000 cattle were found in Seine-et-Marne in 1963, of which half were dairy animals, providing milk both for the Paris market and also for a lucrative cheese-making industry; Brie cheese is famed and large quantities are exported, particularly to Great Britain. Though sheep are no longer so numerous as in the past, the limestone pastures, used in conjunction with the practice of folding the animals on stubble and roots, enabled 160,000 animals to be kept in Seine-et-Marne in 1963.

The plentiful supply of surface water and the accessibility of well-water at no great depth have occasioned a pattern of agricultural settlement quite different from that of Beauce. Many dispersed farms and small villages are situated in valleys or depressions surrounded by orchards, and provide a pleasantly varied and prosperous looking landscape as compared with the rather open austerity of Beauce. Towns are market- and route-centres, such as Brie-Comte-Robert in the west on the plateau above the valley of the Yères, and Provins in the east. The regional name is a common element, as in Valence-en-Brie, Le Chatelet-en-Brie and Rozoy-en-Brie.

Tardenois, Valois and Soissonnais.—Between the Marne and the Oise-Aisne valleys, the Tertiary limestones form the low plateaus of *Tardenois*, *Soissonnais* and *Valois*.[1] Their surfaces vary in detail, for they have been much dissected by the tributaries of the Marne, Aisne and Oise; the Marne, for example, cuts right down into the Chalk. Denudation has in fact removed more and more of the overlying Tertiary rocks as one goes north-eastwards from Beauce. Tardenois has an interrupted covering of Brie Limestone, Soissonnais of

[1] M. Chamard, 'La Plaine du Valois', in *A. de G.* (1935), vol. xliv, pp. 496-508.

Upper Eocene limestone, Valois of the Lower Eocene *Calcaire grossier*. Most of the limestones are *limon*-covered. Other rocks introduce variety into the landscape; surviving outliers of the *Sables de Fontainebleau*, for example, form a distinct east-west ridge across the plateau rising to over 800 feet, deeply dissected by the head-streams of the Ourcq and heavily wooded. Some of the streams—the Vesle, Aisne and Ailette—have cut down through the limestones, forming broad flat-floored valleys; these were formerly marshy and although now drained they still have damp heavy soils. In Valois the tributaries of the Ourcq and the Oise have eroded less markedly to form somewhat narrower valleys, rarely penetrating the limestone to the underlying clays and sands.

These *pays* form areas of prosperous and varied agricultural activity. Wheat with sugar-beet in rotation predominates on the *limon* soils, the cultivation of fodder crops in conjunction with pasture on the clays allows dairy-farming, and there is much fruit-growing and market-gardening in the valleys.

The northern part of Valois on the plateau above the left bank of the Oise carries a succession of fine deciduous forests of oak, beech and lime—the Forêts de Compiègne (fifty-five square miles in area), d'Halatte, de Chantilly and several others. Further south between the Aisne and the Ourcq valleys is the Forêt de Villers-Cotterêts. Most of these woodlands grow on the *sables moyens de Beauchamp*, except for that of Compiègne on the Lower Eocene sands and clays. Some of the sandy areas have been planted with pines, notably the '*désert d'Ermenonville*' to the east of Chantilly, the so-called '*mer de sable*' with its white sand-dunes. Soissonnais too has its wood-lands—the Forêt de l'Aigle in the angle of the converging Aisne and the Oise, and the Forêt de St. Gobain further to the north-east.

Population is concentrated in pleasant villages along the spring-lines in the valleys. Several larger towns, such as Laon and Sois-sons, have grown up as market-centres and as points on the route-ways radiating from Paris. Laon stands on a prominent out-lier of limestone 600 feet above sea-level, isolated between two head-streams of the Ailette and overlooking the chalk plain to the east known as *Laonnais*. Many of the towns contain industries of a varied nature, usually long-established. Several large sugar-refineries are at such towns as Nogent-sous-Coucy and at Eppeville. Glass is made at Thourotte (to the north of Compiègne) and at Chauny, using glass-sands from the St. Gobain and Coucy districts. Along the valley of the Oise, notably at Creil, Montataire (with its new *cité-ouvrière*) and Nogent-sur-Oise, are various metallurgical industries; a new rolling-mill was opened by *Usinor* in 1950 at Montataire to provide sheet-metal for the Paris industrial area. Creil has large repair shops for locomotives and Nogent has waggon-

XXI The arable lands of the Dyle valley between Leuven and Mechelen

XXII A farm on the plateau of Brabant

XXIII Glass-houses at Hoeilaart, south-east of Brussels

XXIV Brick-works at Boom on the Rupel estuary

building and -repairing works. Chemicals and pottery are also made at these last two towns. At Creil and Porcheville are two large thermal power-stations, each with an annual output of over 2 million kWh.

THE SEINE AND PARIS

Paris has grown from a small Gaulish settlement to its position as the leading city of continental Europe.[1] Its gradual concentric expansion from a nucleus on the Ile de la Cité[2] (Plate XXVII) has resulted in its present official area (the *agglomération urbaine*) of 142 square miles, while its dormitory satellites spread out into neighbouring *départements* (Fig. 56).[3]

For a distance of some twenty miles from the Charenton sluice at the Marne confluence to the river-port of Gennevilliers, the Seine flows through Greater Paris (Fig. 57); eight miles of the river lie within the municipality. The banks are concreted and lined with wharves and quays, and a navigational depth of ten feet is maintained. The channel is intersected by several islands, and the chief impediment to navigation (particularly at high water) is the numerous bridges; twenty-seven cross the main stream within the city itself and another nineteen are downstream to Gennevilliers. Factories and wharves line the river through a continuous succession of industrial suburbs.

Traffic on the river is heavy, as can be expected from the large population and varied industrial activity of Paris. In 1963 the wharves within the city handled 3·5 million tons of freight, and the port ranked third in France to Strasbourg and Rouen, though if the whole of the '*agglomération parisienne*' is considered it was easily outstanding with no less than 19·4 million tons. Another four million tons passed along the river in transit. More than two-thirds of this traffic was incoming, consisting of coal (from the northern coalfield), wheat and sugar (from the eastern farm-lands of the Paris Basin), pig-iron and crude steel (from Lorraine), building-stone (from the Morvan and the Central Massif), sands and gravels by way

[1] See, for example, A. Demangeon, *Paris; la ville et sa banlieue* (1934); G. R. Crone, 'The Site and Growth of Paris', in *G.J.* (1941), vol. xcviii, pp. 35-47; P. George *et al.*, *Etudes sur la banlieue de Paris* (1950); P. H. Chombart de Lauwe *et al.*, *Paris et l'agglomération parisienne* (1952). R. E. Dickinson, *The West European City* (1951), devotes a chapter (pp. 223-35) to the site and function of Paris.

[2] M. Foncin, 'La Cité', in *A. de G.* (1931), vol. xl, pp. 479-503, affords a detailed exposition of the historical geography of the Ile de la Cité.

[3] See J. Bastié, 'La Population de l'agglomération parisienne', in *A. de G.* (1958), vol. lxvii, pp. 12-38. He defines the *agglomération* as comprising 55 communes in addition to the *ville*. The *zone suburbaine* occupies another 161 communes. See also J. Bastié, *La Croissance de la banlieu parisienne* (1964); and G. Pourcher, *Le Peuplement de Paris* (1964), published by the *Institut National d'Etudes Démographiques*.

R.G.W.E.—H

of the Seine tributaries, and a variety of raw materials (ores, chemicals, wool, cotton, petroleum, timber and wood-pulp) imported via Le Havre or Rouen. The tonnage of outgoing water-borne freight was less than a third that of imports, since so much of the exports consist of small-bulk high-value goods which can stand rail charges.

FIG. 56.—PARIS AND ITS SUBURBS.

The abbreviations of the railway stations are as follows: **A**, Austerlitz; **E**, Est; **L**, Lyon; **M**, Montparnasse; **N**, Nord; **St. L.**, St. Lazare.

The medium shading indicates the area of the municipality, the more open shading the area of the *département* of Seine.

Based on (i) *Environs de Paris, Carte au 100,000ᵉ (Michelin*, sheet 96); (ii) *Nouveau Plan de Paris (Carte Taride)*; and (iii) G. R. Crone, 'The Site and Growth of Paris', in *G.J.* (1941), vol. xcviii, p. 37.

Cement, coke from the Paris gas-ovens to be used in central heating, bricks, plaster of Paris, and refuse to be dumped in disused quarries outside the city were the main bulk items.

Three canals are within Paris itself. The St. Martin Canal, three miles in length, leaves the Seine just below the Pont d'Austerlitz, continues in a tunnel under the Place de la Bastille and emerges near the Faubourg du Temple to end in the Bassin de la Villette to the north-east of the Gare de l'Est. From this basin the St. Denis Canal continues to the Seine at La Briche. This is quite a busy little canal for it serves important industrial suburbs. The two canals therefore form a direct water-route across eastern Paris, short-circuiting the lengthy westward loop of the main river around the Bois de Boulogne. The Ourcq Canal joins the Bassin de la Villette fron the east; it serves the eastern industrial suburbs of Pantin, and also supplies water to the St. Martin and St. Denis Canals by way of the Bassin de la Villette on the divide between the two.

The functions of Paris are immensely varied. It is the seat of government of a highly centralised administration, a remarkable focus of communications (Fig. 56), a centre of trade, commerce and tourism, the largest industrial city in continental Europe, a vast residential and servicing centre, and in fact a world focus of life and thought. The chief industrial concentrations are in the north-eastern suburbs in St. Denis, St. Ouen and Aubervilliers; in the eastern parts along the Ourcq Canal and in the suburbs of Pantin, Montreuil and Vincennes; in the Seine valley between Ivry and Choisy-le-Roi; and most important of all at a string of towns extending downstream from Billancourt on either side of the bend of the river as far as Gennevilliers and Argenteuil. Several works make steel castings for specific purposes at Ivry, Courbevoie, St. Ouen and St. Denis, and in the last-named district are produced waggons and rolling-stock, boilers, barges and other river craft, armaments, turbines and diesel engines. Although some factories were deliberately removed before 1939 to ostensibly safer areas, aircraft are manufactured at Levallois-Perret, Puteaux, Nanterre and Gennevilliers. Machine tools are made at Asnières and St. Ouen. The two main French automobile producers, *Renault* and *Citroën*, are situated in the Paris district at Boulogne-Billancourt and Grenelle respectively. The former company was nationalised in 1945 when the *Régie Nationale des Usines Renault* was created, retaining the structure of a private concern but with ownership vested in the State. Its main factories extend along both banks of the Seine and on the intervening island of Seguin (Plate XXVIII), and since nationalisation a huge new plant has been built at Flins-sur-Seine, some twenty miles downstream. The necessarily vast public utilities include thermal power-stations, gas-works, sewage-works and abattoirs.

In the industrial suburbs an extensive range of consumer goods is manufactured, not merely the world-renowned '*haute couture*' and '*articles de luxe*', but chemical products, electrical apparatus, food products, tobacco and cigarettes, paper, books, soap, furniture, footwear, glassware, pottery, rubber products, linoleum, musical instruments, etc., etc.

It is as difficult to give a figure for the population of Paris as it is for London or New York. The *ville* in 1962 had a population of 2,811,171 ; the official *agglomération urbaine*, which includes Paris *ville* and twenty-three adjacent communes, had 7,439,110 ; the population of the *département* of Seine was 5,652,000. Finally, if one takes the *agglomération parisienne et de la zone suburbaine*, an

FIG. 57.—THE PORT OF PARIS.

The light pecked line indicates the boundary of the municipality of Paris. The heavy pecked line indicates the underground section of the St. Martin Canal. **N.D.**, the Cathedral of Notre-Dame on the Ile de la Cité. Each individually named 'port' is indicated by **P**, the more important being named in full.

Based on W. Seghers, *Kaart der Binnenscheepvaartwegen van N.-W. Europa* (n.d.).

overall total of nearly ten million people is attained. This *zone suburbaine* includes a number of towns with a dual rôle ; they have their own industrial activities and also house the 'commuters' who travel daily to their work in Paris.[1] The vast growth of Paris, which has

[1] A. Lucchi, 'Les Migrations alternantes dans la région parisienne', in *A. de G.* (1966), vol. 75, pp. 39-56.

absorbed 40 per cent of the total French population expansion during the last fifteen years, has caused much concern. Special efforts are being made in the various national and regional plans to curb this tendency. A new 'master-plan' for the whole Paris region has been published.[1]

THE FALAISE DE L'ILE DE FRANCE

The eastern rim of the Ile de France forms a distinct out-facing escarpment, sweeping in a curve around its eastern and southern margins. It rises to about 700 feet, reaching its maximum point (942 feet) in the Montagne de Reims (Fig. 58) near the town of that name. It then sinks gradually to the south until near Montereau it only attains about 480 feet (Fig. 59). A sequence of rocks, from Oligocene limestones to the *argiles plastiques* and the underlying Chalk at the base, is exposed on the face of the escarpment. Weathering and downwash have produced a thick cover of soil on the lower slopes.

The northern part of the escarpment, as a result of river erosion, is by no means continuous; in turn the Aisne, Vesle, Marne and Petit-Morin cut deeply through its edge. The last of these rises just beyond the escarpment in an area of marshland, the Marais de St. Gond, still quite extensive in spite of reclamation, but its valley through the escarpment is far too well developed for such a small stream. Probably its former head-waters lay further to the east, but were captured by the Somme, a left-bank tributary of the Marne ; the elbow of capture is near Ecury-les-Repos. The Marne to the west of Epernay forms a striking almost gorge-like valley between steep cliffs of *Calcaire grossier*.

The edge of the escarpment projects boldly eastward between each of the valleys, forming peninsula-like extensions of the plateau ; a notable example is the Montagne de Reims between the Vesle and the Marne valleys (Fig. 58). Many minor valleys also interrupt the continuity of the Falaise, leaving spurs and isolated knolls rising above the plain to the east, such as Mont Aimé, a knoll separated from the Côte des Blancs to the south of Epernay. A little further to the west a similar hill, crowned by the well-named village of Toulon-la-Montagne, is but a few feet lower. Some of these knolls were fortified to protect the towns in the valley route-ways. Thus Reims was defended by Fort de Brimont on a prominent hill to the north of the city, and by the Forts de Witry-les-Reims and de Nogent-l'Abbesse on an elongated knoll five miles to the east.

[1] *Schéma Directeur d'Aménagement et d'Urbanisme de la Région de Paris* (1966).

To the south of the valley of the Petit-Morin the escarpment (known as the *Côte Champenoise* or as the *Falaise de Champagne*) swings more continuously westward, with the Seine flowing along

FIG. 58.—THE CHAMPAGNE AREA.

The area of vineyards (stippled) is very generalised. The edge of the *Falaise* is shown by hachuring; spot-heights are in feet. Some of the main vine-growing centres are named. The small *étangs* in the south-west are shown in black.

Based on: (i) *Carte de France et des frontières au 200,000ᵉ*, sheet 17; (ii) *Carte de la France vinicole* (1949).

its foot, until below Montereau the river cuts abruptly northward towards Paris (Fig. 59).

Several towns stand in the gaps through the cuesta or near its foot—Neufchâtel on the Aisne, Reims on the Vesle, Epernay on the Marne, and then the line of Romilly, Nogent and Bray along the middle Seine. Reims is grouped around its magnificent four-teenth-century cathedral (Plate XXIX), heavily damaged in the war of 1914–18, since the town was taken by the German army before the battle of the Marne and then occupied a vital defensive salient;

FIG. 59.—THE SOUTHERN PART OF THE ILE DE FRANCE.
Spot-heights are in feet.
Based on *Carte de France au 200,000ᵉ*, sheet 25.

the cathedral was not completely restored until 1938. The town has long been a market-centre for the plains of Champagne to the east, as it lies on one of the main roads leading west to Paris, and today it is an important road and rail junction. Since the twelfth century Reims has had a flourishing textile industry based on the sheep of Champagne, and its fairs were renowned. Today it has grown into an important industrial town, with not only these old-established textiles (particularly flannels), but also food-processing industries, flour-milling, sugar-refining, confectionery, varied light engineering and glass-making. It is of course one of the two centres of the champagne wine industry, Epernay being the other. Reims has not grown appreciably since the nineteenth century, in fact its population dropped from about 100,000 in 1900 to a few thousands during the war of 1914–18, and was still only 76,000 in 1926. By 1938, however, it had risen to 116,687 and in 1962 this slight growth had been maintained to a total of 138,576.

The Vineyards.—Perhaps the best-known feature of the limestone escarpment is the famous vineyards, or at any rate the famous product of those vineyards, called after the old provincial name.[1] The slopes of the Montagne de Reims, the northern edge of the Marne valley (Plate XXX), and the Côte des Blancs (the main escarpment to the south of the Marne) are covered with long rows of vines. The vineyards, usually known after each neighbouring village— Verzenay, Verzy, Bouzy, Ay, Cramant, Vertus, Avize, Ambonnay and many more, cover about fifty square miles (Fig. 58).

Except for the southern aspect of the slopes, this district possesses no real physical advantages for the cultivation of the vine; the soils are rather poor, and the area is so near the northern limit of effective cultivation that bad or indifferent years are regrettably common as a result of too much rain, too little sunshine or late frosts. Both total yield and quality (as between a vintage and a non-vintage year) therefore vary considerably. It is to traditional skill and care in processing that champagne owes its reputation, although the uniform temperatures within the labyrinths of caves in the Chalk help in the maturing processes.

Until two centuries ago the Champagne grapes (almost all the *Pinot* variety) were used to make 'still' beverage wines, sold under the name of each particular vineyard. Then it was discovered by the renowned Dom Pérignon, of the Benedictine abbey of Hautvillers, that a delicate sparkling wine could be produced by means of carefully controlled fermentation. No longer is champagne sold under the name of the vineyard, since the final product is a blend, but under that of the firm which has processed it—*Clicquot, Heidsieck, Pommery* (whose capacious cellars on the outskirts of Reims consist largely of Roman chalk-pits connected by galleries), *Bollinger* and many other world-renowned names. The *cuvée* or blending of the juice from several vineyards after its first fermentation, followed by a lengthy maturing, clarifying and fortifying, are all most expert procedures.

The output of champagne wine is small, a mere 715,000 hectolitres out of the French total of 57·6 millions in 1963. But in a good

[1] P. Marres, 'La Champagne', in *La Vigne et le vin en France* (1950), pp 76-81.

vintage year its value is considerable, since it constitutes one of the best known 'export wines'.

II. THE NORTHERN PARIS BASIN

This comprises an area of low chalk-land which emerges from beneath the northern margins of the Tertiary strata of the Ile de France and continues northward to the Channel coast.[1] The gently undulating plateaus are largely *limon*-covered, and form one of the most important arable-farming areas in France, growing mainly wheat and sugar-beet. A number of distinct units can be distinguished : the coastal margins, Artois, Picardy, the Pays de Bray, the Pays de Caux, the Vexin, the valley of the lower Seine and its estuary.

THE COASTAL MARGINS

The coastline trends in a sweeping curve from the Straits of Dover to Cap de la Hève, the northern containing headland of the Seine estuary. Chalk forms the main element along this edge of the plateau (hence the name commonly applied to it of the '*Falaises de Craie*'), except in the Boulonnais where various Jurassic rocks are exposed. Since the formation of the Straits of Dover and the Flandrian transgression (see p. 24), marine erosion has severely attacked this cliffed coast, particularly in the south between the mouth of the Somme and Cap de la Hève ; it is estimated that the latter has retreated 1,500 yards during the last eight centuries. The action of the waves is emphasised by the fact that the Chalk overlies Gault marls and sands and Upper Jurassic clays, which are exposed at the base of the cliffs, so that masses of chalk constantly slump forward over these unstable 'lubricated' strata to the beach below.

One striking result of marine erosion is the formation of a type of 'hanging-valley' known as a *valleuse*. Wave action has cut back in places more rapidly than the small chalk-streams can erode their valleys, so that the mouth of each ends abruptly in a steep drop to the beach below (similar to the 'Seven Sisters' between Newhaven and Eastbourne). Many of the *valleuses* are now dry, the result of a lowered water-table. In places, however, the valleys open out to the coast at sea-level and the cliffs are completely interrupted, as at Dieppe where the Arques reaches the sea and at Fécamp near the mouth of the Valmont.

The cliffs thus vary in height ; to the west of Fécamp they rise for

---

[1] For a detailed, well illustrated and fully documented study of the Chalk in northern France, see Ph. Pinchemel, *Les Plaines de Craie du nord-ouest du Bassin Parisien et du sud-est du Bassin de Londres et leurs bordures: étude de géomorphologie* (1954). This contains a bibliography of 606 items.

250 to 300 feet but between Veules and Quiberville they are only 125 to 175 feet. The highest sections are formed by the headlands; Cap de St. Jouin rises to 400 feet, Cap d'Antifer to 381 feet and Cap de la Hève to 351 feet. The cliffs have been heavily undercut to form caves, and there are many magnificent isolated stacks (such as the Aiguille d'Etretat) and arches (notably the striking Porte d'Aval), both near Etretat to the north-east of Cap d'Antifer.

On the other hand, a considerable amount of material has accumulated through longshore drifting. To the east of Cap d'Antifer this drift is from west to east, although now somewhat reduced by the construction of groynes. The material consists of flints derived from beds in the eroded chalk-cliffs, and these have been built up as shingle-beaches across the bays, as at Dieppe.

In the angle where the direction of the coast changes abruptly from west-east to south-north, the chalk plateau falls back to form the wide funnel of the Somme estuary, where sand and mud have accumulated. Flint shingle moves as far as the mouth of the Somme and contributes to the growth of the hooked spit of Le Hourdel across the estuary. Beyond that point only lighter materials, such as coarse sands, are moved, and sand-spits backed by dunes have developed across the mouths of the Authie and the Canche. Between these spits and the edge of the chalk plateau are enclosed lagoons and marshland, much of which has been reclaimed and drained.[1] On the sand-spit projecting northward across the Canche estuary, terminating in the Pointe du Touquet, the modern luxury resort of Le Touquet has grown. From Ault, therefore, to near Cap d'Alprech, the old chalk-cliffs now lie well inland, fronted by reclaimed marsh (the *Marquenterre*), sand-dunes and low-water sands (Fig. 60).

From Cap d'Alprech to Sangatte is a most interesting section, where the dissected anticline of the Boulonnais (see p. 205) reaches the sea; as a result, a striking variety of formations is revealed. The Chalk of Cap Blanc Nez contrasts with the Jurassic limestone of Cap Gris Nez, which rises 180 feet from the sea. Pointe de la Crèche, a couple of miles north of Boulogne, exhibits in section the complexities of the structure; the Upper Jurassic strata, including clays, sandstones and limestones, reveal striking folds. The beach is covered with massive blocks of sandstone derived from the weathering of the cliffs. Several small streams, notably the Liane (at the mouth of which stands Boulogne), reach the sea through broad clay-floored valleys.

This coast is not naturally favourable for the development of ports,

---

[1] See A. Briquet, *Le Littoral du Nord de la France* (1930), for details and a number of maps. A more recent study is C. Prêcheur, *Le Littoral de la Manche de Sainte-Adresse à Ault. Etude morphologique* (1960).

FIG. 60.—THE COAST-LINE OF NORTHERN FRANCE.

The approximate edge of the Jurassic rocks, exposed by denudation of the
Boulonnais anticline, is indicated by a dotted line. The margin of the coast at
the time of the Flandrian transgression, before sedimentation and reclamation
had taken place, is shown by a pecked line. Heights are in feet.

Based on various maps in A. Briquet, *Le Littoral du Nord de la France* (1930).

but the proximity of England has encouraged the growth of the ferry terminals of Boulogne (connected with Dover and Folkestone) and Dieppe (with Newhaven); in 1963 about 558,000 passengers disembarked at Boulogne and 190,000 at Dieppe, and both ports have car-ferry facilities and a small commercial harbour. Coal was once by far the main import, but in these post-war years it is relatively unimportant. Oil, other hydro-carbons, timber and some iron and manganese ores for the Outreau blast-furnaces are now the main items imported into Boulogne. The neighbourhood is one of the chief manufacturing areas of cement in France, as lime and clay are found in convenient juxtaposition, and a considerable amount is exported. Bricks, tiles and earthenware are also made.

Boulogne is the largest fishing-port in France; of a total catch of about 385,000 tons in 1963, the port handled 118,000 tons. Dieppe was the fourth French fishing-port with 17,000 tons. Most of the Boulogne fishing-trade is in the hands of large trawler firms, and certain ancillary industries (curing, salting, packing, ice-making and the manufacture of fertilisers) are carried on. Fast night-trains of refrigerator cars serve the Paris markets. Dieppe handles rather the smaller vessels which return daily, and it has a large covered fish-market. Fécamp is still one of the centres for fitting-out the big *terre-neuviers*, the trawlers which visit the Grand Banks of Newfoundland, based on St. Pierre and Miquelon.

Finally, this section of coast has a considerable tourist importance and its resorts are thronged during the summer months, both sophisticated places such as Le Touquet and the innumerable quiet *plages* among the dunes.

ARTOIS

The *Collines de l'Artois* consist of a long anticlinal ridge of chalk trending from north-west to south-east, where it is usually known as the *Cambrésis*. The general level rises towards the north-west, reaching a maximum of 709 feet on the rim of the Boulonnais; the term *Haut-Boulonnais* is applied to this high chalk rim,[1] *Bas-Boulonnais* to the depression thus enclosed which opens on to the Channel. The surface of this breached anticline has a varied appearance, a result of the differential erosion of the diverse Jurassic and Cretaceous limestones, sandstones, marls and clays by the three small rivers Liane, Wimereuse and Slack. The residual hills, such as Mont Lambert (617 feet), stand up prominently from the clay-lands

[1] A detailed summary of the northern chalk cuesta of the Boulonnais, together with maps and a bibliography, is given by A. Coleman and A. M. Ferrar, 'Morphology of the North Boulonnais Chalk', in *G.J.* (1954), vol. cxx, pp. 62-80. There is a most interesting analysis of the mapped erosion surfaces.

of the valleys. The sands have an almost heath-like character, the clays carry pasture and copses, and the limestones have a cover of permanent grass. A small outcrop of coal at Hardinghen has been worked since the end of the seventeenth century, but only about 11,000 tons were produced each year in the decade before 1937, when mining ceased. However, this supply of fuel, together with some Jurassic iron-ores, initiated an iron-industry which survives as the present-day steel-works at Outreau, with a plant opened in 1951, including an electric furnace for making special alloy steels.

The Artois anticline itself is asymmetrical; the rocks dip gently south-westward towards Picardy but more steeply to the plain of Flanders. Many small streams flow down the southern slope to join the Canche and the Authie, and others cut deeply into the northern slope to water the Flanders Plain. A few have begun to develop valleys along the crest of the anticline parallel to the strike, notably the Ternoise (on which stands St. Pol), a tributary of the Canche. A right-bank tributary of the Ternoise flows from the north-west; it rises only two miles from the Lys, which flows to the north-west for about six miles also along the crest before swinging east down the slope to the Plain of Flanders.

Dry valleys are common, but there is also a surprising amount of surface water, largely because of the considerable *limon* covering. An undulating hill-and-dale relief is the result—open, with few trees, and with small nucleated villages and large farms growing wheat and sugar-beet on the loamy soils. About two-thirds of the *département* of Pas-de-Calais was under arable in 1963 (although this administrative unit of course includes part of the Flanders Plain); rather less than one-third of the total arable was under wheat. Formerly the chalk-lands were the grazing-grounds of large flocks of sheep, but now cattle (the *vache flamande*) are eight times as numerous, although some sheep are still folded on fodder-crops and grazed on stubble. A considerable area of fodder-crops is grown for the feeding of cattle kept mainly for milk production.

PICARDY

The name of the ancient dukedom of Picardy (*Picardie*) has survived as a regional term, and most of it lies in the *département* of Somme, which the river more or less bisects. The undulating chalk-lands rise to about 500 feet to the north of the Somme valley, but to 791 feet in the south on the rim of the Pays de Bray. The landscape is rather monotonous, consisting of sweeping expanses of chalk plateau interrupted only by dry valleys and by the larger marsh-floored valleys of the Somme, Authie and Canche.

The Chalk indeed appears on the surface comparatively rarely,

although newly ploughed land reveals its characteristic pale bloom, for
over much of the area lies the mantle of *limon*. Elsewhere, less usefully, are deposits of Clay-with-Flints; these often carry woodlands
or even uncultivated scrub-land. The loam soils are intensively
cultivated, for almost exactly two-thirds was under arable in 1958,
and a third of that grew wheat. The rest was devoted to sugar-beet
and to fodder-crops such as clover, colza and beet. A reflection
of this arable activity is that over 15,000 tractors were in operation
in 1963 in Somme; only two other *départements* (Seine-Maritime
and Pas-de-Calais) possessed more. More than a quarter of a million
cattle were kept, mostly stall-fed in large byres. The milk is sent to
Paris and the industrial north-east, and there is some cheese-making,
such as the attractive *Rollots* produced near Montdidier.

Another form of specialised agriculture is found along the alluvium-floored valleys, particularly that of the Somme, and on the
reclaimed marshes behind the estuaries of the Canche and the
Authie. Formerly they were used for peat-cutting, fishing and wild-
fowling, but today they are occupied by intensively cultivated
hortillons or market-gardens, utilising the heavily fertilised black
peat soils. The floor of the Somme valley is so intersected by the
braided channels of the river and irregular ponds formed by peat-
cutting that cultivators are obliged to use flat-bottomed boats to
visit their holdings and to take crops to the Amiens markets.

When one crosses Picardy, either by train from Boulogne via
Abbeville and Amiens on the way to Paris or by road (*NI*), there is a
remarkable impression of scanty population. One sees an occasional
isolated farm,[1] a large sugar-refinery standing among the fields, and
here and there a steeple projecting from a clump of trees in a hollow
or a valley. But numerous prosperous villages, many of them completely rebuilt since the wholesale devastation of 1914–18, are strung
out along the valleys. In the marshy Somme valley they stand on the
lower terraces away from the braided channels and ponds. Elsewhere they form small nucleated settlements in dry valleys, where the
water-table is near the surface and well-sinking is therefore less
laborious and expensive than on the plateau. The average density
of population in 1962 was 202 per square mile.

This average is as high as it is partly because of the presence of
Amiens, with its population of 109,869. The town stands mainly on
the left bank of the Somme, with its old citadel on a chalk hill across
the river near the junction of several tributary valleys. A settlement
has stood on this site since Roman times, and in the mediaeval period
it became an important focus of communications (notably on the

---

[1] R. Coque, 'L'Evolution de la maison rurale en Amiénois', in *A. de G.*
(1956), vol. lxv, pp. 401-17, traces the evolution of the 'courtyard farm' and its
relation to the rural economy.

route between Paris and Flanders), a commercial town and a centre for varied textile and metallurgical industries. Its superb Gothic cathedral, probably the finest in France, which remained almost unscathed in the 1914–18 war, is a testimony to its mediaeval splendour and importance. Today Amiens has textile, clothing and footwear manufactures and a wide range of food-processing industries.

Several other towns are located along the Somme valley; St. Quentin (almost wholly rebuilt since the war of 1914–18, and with a number of modern textile factories), Péronne and Abbeville are the only ones of any size.

THE OTHER CHALK-LAND PAYS

The Pays de Bray.—Although this small unit is on a different scale from Picardy, it is worthy of special mention. By road from Amiens to Rouen one traverses this *pays* transversely to the structure, from Dieppe to Beauvais the direction is longitudinal. In either case the contrast between the surrounding chalk-lands and this elongated ellipse of Upper Jurassic rocks is pronounced.

The Pays de Bray consists of an anticline from which the overlying Chalk has been removed, leaving infacing escarpments (Fig. 61). Within the anticline the Béthune flows north-west to the sea at Dieppe, the Epte first in a diametrically opposite direction then turning south to the Seine. The rim is also broken to the south by the Andelle, which has a short longitudinal upper course in the depression before bending south towards the Seine. As a result, a variety of rocks is exposed within the anticline. The infacing chalk slopes are underlain by Cretaceous Chalk Marl and Gault Clay, forming a clearly marked spring-line. Then follow Upper Jurassic clays and sands and in the centre some upstanding hillocks of Portland Limestone which rise to about 750 feet. Bray presents a varied landscape of woodlands, damp meadows, patches of sandy heathland and arable fields.

Several small hamlets lie along the floor of the depression, followed by the road and railway from Dieppe to Beauvais. Neufchâtel-en-Bray, Forges-les-Eaux (the name is a legacy of an ancient iron industry using local ores and charcoal), and Gournay-en-Bray are the largest.

The Pays de Caux.—This block of chalk forms a plateau extending westward towards Cap de la Hève as a blunted triangular upland between the chalk cliffs and the incised meanders of the Seine.[1] At

[1] A. Frémont, 'La Partie occidentale du Pays de Caux (La Région du Havre)', in *A. de G.* (1956), vol. lxv, pp. 98–122, deals in detail with the '*évolution économique*' of this area.

first sight it appears to have a fairly uniform surface-level at about
500 feet, swelling almost indistinguishably to a maximum of 673 feet.
It has been shown,[1] however, that although there is an overall general
slope towards the coast of about twenty feet per mile, this is not a
single surface but a series of broad shallow step-platforms, probably
of marine origin.   Many patches of impermeable Clay-with-Flints

FIG. 61.—THE PAYS DE BRAY.

The edges of the denuded anticline, within which are exposed Cretaceous marls,
Gault Clay and Jurassic clays, sands and limestones, are indicated diagrammatically by hachuring.   Some small hillocks of Portland Limestone rise to
758 feet to the north-east of Forges-les-Eaux.   Heights are given in feet.

Based on *Carte de France au 200,000ᵉ*, sheets 8, 9, 15, 16.

occur, sometimes extensive enough to bear small lakes.   Water
draining from these patches finds its way down fissures or joints in
the surrounding chalk, which it sometimes enlarges to form considerable sink-holes known locally as *béthunes* or *bétoires*.   Deeply
incised valleys are rare, except along the southern margins where

[1] B. W. Sparks, 'Erosion Surfaces around Dieppe', in *Proceedings of the
Geologists' Association* (1953), vol. 64, pp. 105-17, has a detailed map showing
eight distinct erosion surfaces.

short streams flow rapidly down the edge to join the Seine. The steep slopes of the Seine's incised meanders are heavily wooded.

The *limon*-covered surface of the plateau forms excellent farmland, and the land is divided into open hedgeless blocks of cultivation or permanent pasture. But for the tree-lined roads, so typical of northern France, the orchards around the compact nucleated villages, and an occasional large walled farm, the landscape seems rather bare (Plate XXXI). Villages and hamlets appear at much more frequent intervals than in Picardy, however.

The Pays de Caux corresponds closely to the *département* of Seine-Maritime (although this also includes the lower Seine valley and the Pays de Bray), and its land-use figures (for 1963) are indicative. Thirty-six per cent of the total area was under arable, the same proportion (a surprisingly high figure) was under permanent grassland, and 14 per cent under forest. Large strips growing wheat occupy rather more than half of the arable acreage, and the yield of wheat per acre is second only to that of Nord in France. Flax, sugar-beet, potatoes and fodder-crops make up the remaining acreage ; the area under flax amounted to about 47,000 acres in 1963, nearly a fifth of the French total.

This district is important for cattle-rearing, more so than any other area of the Paris Basin, for in 1963 there were 607,000 head. Nearly half of these were dairy cows, producing milk for the Paris, Rouen and other urban markets, and for cheese-making; *Suisse Bondon* cheeses are a well-known product.

No large towns stand on the plateau ; significantly Rouen, the *chef-lieu* of the *département*, lies below on the banks of the Seine. Numerous villages and hamlets are dotted around, some of them such as Yvetot along the main railway-line from Le Havre to Amiens, others (notably Pavilly, Bolbec and Montivilliers) near the heads of short valleys dropping down to the Seine.

Vexin.—The chalk plateau between Caux and the Tertiary rocks of the Ile de France to the south is known as Vexin. A division is sometimes made between *le Vexin normand* in the north-west and *le Vexin français* stretching south-east towards the Oise valley, although this has more historical than geographical significance.

Vexin differs from the other *limon*-covered chalk plateaus in the degree to which it is dissected by river valleys ; the tributaries of the Thérain and other Oise confluents in the east and south, and the Epte and the Andelle in the west, have cut quite steep valleys, leaving small tracts of plateau surface as interfluves. The cultivation of wheat and fodder-crops on the *limon* soils and dairying in the clay-floored valleys are the main agriculture activities. Vexin is crossed by the straight *N14*, the main road between Rouen and

Pontoise, and so to Paris. Many of the small market-towns through which it passes have, as might be expected, the suffix *Vexin*, such as Villers-en-Vexin, Les Thilliers-en-Vexin and Magny-en-Vexin.

THE LOWER SEINE VALLEY

The physical characteristics of the lower Seine valley [1] have been described above (p. 184). The steep chalk slopes are thickly wooded, and the reclaimed alluvial flats bordering the dyked course of the river are utilised either as meadow-land or for market-gardening. As the river meanders so these meadows occupy alternate sides of the river, becoming more extensive and seamed with drainage channels as the estuary is approached. The largest area is the *Marais Vernier*, which includes much land still of a marshy character and a large shallow lake (*la Grande Mare*). The marsh occupies a semi-circle ten miles across between two northward-projecting spurs of chalk ; the more westerly, the Pointe de la Rocque, is surmounted by a lighthouse, for it rises abruptly to over 150 feet a few hundred yards from the tidal flats. This semi-circle, bounded on the south by a steep chalk face rising to over 300 feet, represents the site of a former meander of the Seine, the cliff being the river-bluffs. On the opposite side of the estuary, a little lower down to the west of the Pointe de Tancarville, is another curve of chalk, the former complementary northward meander. The river current is now confined to a dredged channel leading directly through the *Embouchure de la Seine*, the 'estuary-funnel', and these former meander-sites lie well to the south and north respectively. The only bridge across the Seine below Rouen, at Tancarville, was recently opened.

Andresy, Poissy, Meulan, Mantes, Bonnières, Les Andelys, Elbeuf and many other towns are situated along the river.[2] They have wharves and quays, and a range of industries, using imported fuel and raw materials, has developed ; these include the manufacture of textiles, tobacco and cigarettes, paper, cellophane, cement (as at Gargenville, near Mantes, where chalk is quarried), bricks and chemicals. The two largest urban centres along the lower Seine are Rouen and Le Havre ; between them they contain a quarter of the entire population of Seine-Maritime.

Below Elbeuf the Seine makes a huge meander, leaving as a core the wooded spur of the Forêt de Rouvray (Fig. 62). Along the right bank of this meander on a terrace above the river (a position

---

[1] A. Vigarié, 'Observations sur les caractères structuraux et morphologiques de la Région de Rouen', in *A. de G.* (1954), vol. lxiii, pp. 22-32.

[2] E. Vigarié, 'L'Ensemble portuaire de la Basse-Seine', in *T.E.S.G.* (1959), vol. 50, pp. 136-51.

which has kept the city immune from all but exceptional flooding)
grew Rouen,[1] eighty miles from the sea and 150 river-miles from
Paris. It has been a town since pre-Roman times, and became
successively the seat of a bishopric, the capital of a powerful feudal
Normandy, an important centre of early industrial development,
and a base for French maritime expansion. In the mid-nineteenth
century, the threat to its mercantile interests by the growth of the size
of shipping, the progressive silting of the river below the port, and
the rivalry of Le Havre developing as an outport led to a programme
of engineering works after 1848. A dyked channel was constructed
through the estuary to the roadstead beyond Le Havre.. There is
an appreciable tidal range, and vessels drawing twenty-five feet can

FIG. 62.—THE LOWER SEINE AND ITS ESTUARY.
The heavy black lines along the river indicate embankments.

Based on *Carte de France et des frontières au 200,000ᵉ*, sheets 8, 15.

enter the port at mean high water springs, although the bulk of the
shipping using the port consists of medium-sized vessels drawing
twelve to twenty feet. The maritime port extends along both banks
of the Seine for about twelve miles to the Boïeldieu bridge in the
heart of the city, to which point the river is tidal. Above the bridge
the inland waterway port extends for a further eight miles to Oissel,
for the navigational improvements of the Seine between Rouen
and Paris, together with the development of the port of Paris, have
benefited river transport enormously. In addition to some miles
of river quays, numerous basins have free connection with the river.
If mineral oil is excluded, Rouen is the leading French port in

[1] F. Gay, 'La croissance de la région de Rouen et ses problèmes', in *Etudes
Normandes* (1964), no. 171, pp. 1-16.

terms of tonnage handled. If crude oil is included, however, both Marseilles (with 24·4 million tons of oil imported in 1963) and Le Havre (15·6 million tons) with their large refineries are of course far ahead. The following table summarises the main items imported in 1963:

Seaborne Trade of Rouen, 1963
(Thousand Tons)

	Imports	Exports
Oil	1,815	1,084
Coal	2,225	20
Other minerals	1,094	272
Grain	44	1,109
Others	1,616	1,191
	6,794	3,676

Source: *Annuaire statistique de la France*, 1964.

In the inter-war period the volume of these imports into Rouen was much greater, but two of the largest bulk commodities (coal and oil) have been considerably reduced; in 1930, for example, Rouen imported 5 million tons of coal and in 1938 about 3·1 million tons, of which two-thirds came from Britain. Similarly with oil; pre-war tankers delivered direct to the *Shell-Berre* refinery near Rouen, but today with their greatly increased size the oil is unloaded at Le Havre and piped to the refineries along the river.

Rouen is an inland waterway port second only in France to Strasbourg. In 1963 about 3·1 million tons of freight were loaded into barges, while 3·3 million tons were unloaded; in each case mineral oil was the dominant item.

The imported raw materials are used in the Rouen area, at factories along the lower Seine, and in the Paris region. Rouen itself is the centre of an important industrial district. Cotton manufacturing has been established since the eighteenth century when it was introduced into what had long been a textile district, first for wool then linen. Cotton factories now extend along both sides of the Seine and along tributary valleys, and a variety of other textile industries (rayon, nylon and clothing) has developed. A smelting works is situated on the lower Seine, the *Hauts Fourneaux de Rouen* at Grand-Quévilly on the left bank of the river below Rouen, using imported coke and ore. A great variety of metal-using industries is found at Rouen and downstream along the Seine at Duclair, Mailleraye, Caudebec and elsewhere to Le Havre itself—ship-building, ship-repairing, wire and cables, diesel engines and refrigerating equipment. Other industries include heavy chemicals (based on imports of phosphates and pyrites), and the production of paper at mills along the left bank at Grand-Quévilly and Oissel. Finally, the *Shell-Berre* refinery at Petit-Couronne above Rouen was the third largest in France in 1964 in terms of output (4·87 million tons).

Rouen has developed therefore as a port and industrial centre of considerable importance. From its original terrace-site on the north bank, the built-up area has spread up tributary valleys and (as a result of flood-protection and regularisation measures) on to the south bank within the meander. Its population in 1962 was 123,474, though if the fourteen adjacent communes in the official *agglomération* are included the total exceeds 250,000, the eighth largest in France. This is an indication of how the town's activities have expanded to draw neighbouring districts into its orbit.

Between Rouen and the sea are several small ports (Fig. 62), including Duclair, Jumièges, Le Trait and Villequier. Some have industries, but others are merely mooring-points for vessels negotiating the channel to Rouen. At Port-Jérôme, *Esso-Standard* have developed a refinery which (with a 1964 output of 4·0 million tons) is the fifth biggest in France (Plate XXXII). Crude oil is brought by pipe-line from the tanker terminal at Le Havre. Near by is a large petrochemical factory, owned by *Shell-St. Gobain*, which makes detergents. A few miles upstream of Port-Jérôme is the small Gravenchon refinery of the *Mobil-Oil* company; it had an output of 951,000 tons of hydro-carbons in 1964.

Le Havre, the second port of France in tonnage of vessels entered and cleared, is situated on the northern shore of the Seine estuary to the south-east of Cap de la Hève. Until the sixteenth century its site was an area of tidal marshes, from which its docks were excavated. Improvements have culminated in a deep-water channel leading into the port from the Carosse roadstead off Cap de la Hève; this enabled the ill-fated *Normandie* to enter at any state of the tide. Today the port accommodates Atlantic liners (handling over 40,000 passengers in 1963), ferry-steamers from Southampton and a large number of cargo-vessels. In bulk of freight handled, Le Havre is again second to Marseilles; the outstanding imports in 1963 were crude mineral oil (15·6 million tons), refined mineral oil (2·4 millions), coal (911,000), fruit (234,000) and oil-seeds (69,000). Apart from oil, which dominates the scene, the imports are neither so bulky nor so diverse as those of Rouen. Port industries include shipbuilding and repairing, engineering, flour-milling, oil-seed crushing and sugar-refining. A few miles upstream of Le Havre, on the banks of the Tancarville Canal, is the *Gonfreville-Seine* oil-refinery, built in 1933 and subsequently enlarged, with an output of 6·65 million tons of hydrocarbons in 1964; it is owned by the nationally sponsored *Compagnie Française de Raffinage*. A pipe-line has been constructed along the Seine valley from Gonfreville via the other refineries to Paris, and another pipe-line has recently been completed to the new Grandpuits refinery 40 miles south of Paris in the *département* of Seine-et-Marne.

Le Havre,[1] as a result of its multifarious commercial and industrial activities, has expanded inland from its site on the alluvial plain on to the surrounding chalk plateau. In 1962 its population had reached 184,133, or with its three neighbouring communes of Harfleur, St. Adresse and Sanvic, forming the official agglomeration, about 223,000. Considerable destruction occurred during the war of 1939–45, but much rebuilding has taken place, and numerous lofty ferro-concrete buildings, including a fine new station, have arisen behind the port area.

[1] F. Gay and J.-P. Damais, 'Le Havre, aspects géographiques et sociologiques de la croissance urbaine', in *Urbanisme* (1966), no. 93, pp. 35-49; and J.-P. Damais, *La Nouvelle Ville du Havre. Reconstruction et Repopulation, fascicule* 2, *tome* ix, of *Mémoires et Documents du Centre de Documentation cartographique et géographique* (1961).

CHAPTER 10

THE LOWLANDS OF NORTHERN FRANCE (2)

III. THE EASTERN PARIS BASIN

Beyond the edge of the Tertiary escarpment the eastern Paris Basin is occupied first by an outcrop of Chalk, then by a narrower tract of Gault Clay, and finally on the margins by the topmost Jurassic rocks. The last are at their narrowest in the extreme north, where they come up against the Palaeozoic rocks of the Ardennes massif and disappear completely near Hirson, but the exposures broaden as they swing southward in a great curve; the greater part are in Lorraine (Fig. 50). The same sequence appears in the south, although the belts of Chalk and Gault become increasingly attenuated, and it again culminates in the Jurassic limestone plateaus which in the east form a divide between the Seine and Saône basins and further west border the flanks of the Central Massif.

THE CHALK COUNTRY OF CHAMPAGNE

The *pays*-name of *Champagne pouilleuse*, indicating a dry, dusty and 'beggarly' type of country, has for long been applied to the outcrop of Chalk, at its widest thirty miles across, which sweeps in a curve for ninety miles from the Oise valley, where the Chalk actually comes up against the Devonian rocks of the Ardennes, to beyond the Yonne. In the north between the Oise and the Aisne the chalk-lands are known as *Laonnais*, after the town of Laon which lies on the edge of the Tertiary limestone to the west (see p. 192). Then follows the *Champagne pouilleuse* proper, succeeded southward by the *Pays d'Othe* between the upper Seine and the Yonne, and finally *Gâtinais* to the west of the Yonne. The last two are sufficiently distinctive to be considered separately.

The chalk country rises very gradually in altitude, from about 250 feet at the foot of the Falaise to 680 feet on its eastern rim, where a not very prominent escarpment descends to the Gault Clay plain. These chalk-lands are wide and open, and for centuries sheep-grazing has been their main utilisation; in 1961 there were still nearly a quarter of a million sheep in the two *départements* of Aube and Marne. Unlike the chalk country of the north-east, *limon* is almost completely absent, and the thin residues of *in situ* weathering are not of much value for arable farming. However, especially in the post-1945 years, heavy fertilisation has improved the meagre yields, and wheat and fodder-crops are cultivated in increasing quantities. In many ways this is one of the most monotonous and thinly populated parts of the French countryside.

The chalk country is crossed by river valleys—those of the Oise, the Aisne, the Marne, the Aube and the upper Seine (Fig. 53). These rivers are obvious misfits in their present valleys; broad trenches were eroded during Pleistocene times when their volume was much greater. The present streams wander over the flat valley-floors

FIG. 63.—THE SCARPLANDS OF THE EASTERN PARIS BASIN AND LORRAINE.

The escarpments are shown in generalised form by heavy lines, and are lettered as follows: **T**, Tertiary (Falaise de l'Ile de France); **UC**, Upper Chalk; **MC**, Middle Chalk; **G**, Upper Greensand (*gaize*) of the Argonne; **P**, Portland Limestone; **C**, Corallian Limestone; **O**, Oolitic Limestone; **L**, Lias; **M**, Muschelkalk (Trias). The Palaeozoic rocks are indicated by horizontal ruling.

Based on (i) *Carte géologique de la France*, 1 : 1,000,000, published by the *Service de la Carte géologique détaillée de la France*; and (ii) F. Machatschek, *Das Relief der Erde* (1938), p. 54.

which they have rendered almost impermeable by a lining of alluvium. The rivers, which formed numerous backwaters and braided sections, have been regularised to check flooding, but for navigation purposes it usually proved easier to build lateral canals, such as that of the Marne which follows the main stream for forty-two miles upstream to Vitry-le-François.

Nevertheless, the essential shortage of water within the chalk-lands has nucleated most settlement within these valleys, and villages usually lie along the foot of the chalk-bluffs at the spring-line. Some are little more than groups of farms, which possess both meadow-lands and damp pastures on which cattle are pastured and also sheep-grazings on the chalk-lands beyond the valley-bluffs.   These valleys are also route-ways, as they have been for many centuries, and the Marne is followed upstream by road, railway and canal from Châlons to Langres, the Seine similarly from Romilly through Troyes to Châtillon and thence to Dijon.   At Châlons the northward trend of the road along the Marne is continued by *N44* through Reims and Laon to the Channel coast; the chalk-land offers a line of easy movement from north to south which by-passes Paris on the east.   Some of the great mediaeval fairs were held at towns on these routes, notably at Troyes on the Seine and at Reims on the western edge of Champagne.

Troyes, the *chef-lieu* of the *département* of Aube, had a population of nearly 69,000 in 1962, and after Reims is the biggest town in this part of France.   It has a nodal position at the junction of seven railway lines and as many *routes nationales*, and has a port on the Seine Lateral Canal.   The town has developed a diversified industrial life, many of its activities (such as the manufacture of textiles and paper) being established for centuries; the earliest Saxton county-maps of England were printed on Troyes paper.   Châlons-sur-Marne, with a population in 1962 of 45,348, is almost as well placed in respect of communications, for it lies at the crossroads between the route from Lorraine and Metz which continues due west to Paris, and the north-south route already mentioned.   This town too has light industries, including food-processing.   Many other smaller towns stand along the valleys.   Rethel, for example, on the banks of the Aisne, has been a manufacturing town and market-centre for many centuries.   Indeed, its population has changed little from 7,500 in 1851 to 7,856, but it has breweries, saw-mills and small textile factories.   The town is the centre of a small valley-*pays*, known as *Rethelois*.

The Pays d'Othe.—The southern section of the *Champagne pouilleuse* between the upper Seine and the Yonne is known as the Pays d'Othe. It is diversified with irregular residual patches of the Lower Eocene *argiles plastiques*.   The south-facing chalk escarpment, overlooking the clay vale containing the Armançon, is covered with these sandy-clay deposits, and forms a prominent ridge rising at its highest to 912 feet.   This is one source of the water supply of Paris, for the Aqueduc de la Vanne, beginning in the Vanne valley near Rigny-le-Ferron, taps numerous springs and streams on the back-slope.   The ridge is much dissected by streams flowing both northwards down the back-slope to the Vanne (a right-bank longitudinal tributary of the Yonne) and southwards down the shorter slope to the Armançon.

Wooded spurs project in both directions between the deeply-cut valleys, long and tapering to the north, short and abrupt to the south. More patches of Eocene sandy-clays occur to the north of the Vanne, but much bare chalk is apparent.

This interesting *pays* has a pleasantly varied land-use and agriculture, the result of the differing geology and soils. The ridge is swathed with the Forêt d'Othe, while by contrast the open chalk country to the north provides sheep-pasture. Cattle are grazed on water-meadows along the streams, sugar-beet and cereals are cultivated on the plateau where the clay covering is present, vines are grown on south-facing slopes of the chalk escarpment, and orchards (particularly of cherries and cider-apples) cluster around the villages. Several attractive small towns are found, many of them with suffixes *-en-Othe*. One indication of a past activity is a series of names such as La Forge-à-l'Eau, Les Minières and La Charbonnière; beds of ferruginous sands in the *argiles plastiques* were worked and smelted with charcoal in the sixteenth and seventeenth centuries. The larger settlements are mostly along the Vanne and its tributaries; Sens, at the junction of that river with the Yonne, is the market-town for the district.

Gâtinais.—This *pays* lies mainly between the rivers Yonne and the Loing, but also extends west of the latter towards the plateau of Beauce. It represents a further section of the Chalk belt, but is still more masked than the Pays d'Othe with residual Eocene deposits of heavy clays. The surface is much wetter as a result of this impermeable cover, and large numbers of shallow lakes or *gâtines* (hence the name of the *pays*) lie in undulating hollows in the clay. The only Chalk appears at the sides of the numerous open valleys where streams have removed the clay cover.

Considerable drainage and reclamation of the *gâtines* have been effected and the clay soils now form useful pastures for cattle. Arable farming is concentrated on the gently sloping valley-sides, especially where the underlying fertile marls of the Lower Chalk are exposed in the Loing valley. Much of the district is under woodland, especially in the *étang* district between the Betz and Cléris valleys where the Bois des Haies covers a considerable area. There is no shortage of water, and small villages are widespread. Montargis, in the Loing valley where several tributary valleys converge to form an open fertile plain, is the regional centre. It is served by the Briare Canal, with which it is also connected to the Orléans and Loing Canals (Fig. 54); although these are only secondary waterways, they form a useful link-system in the heart of France. Montargis has several small rubber, chemical, leather and food-processing factories. Other towns along the Loing valley are Ferrières-en-Gâtinais and Nemours.

THE ARGONNE

To the north-east of *Champagne pouilleuse* lies the much dissected massif of the Argonne, consisting of a clay-sandstone of greenish-white colour known as *gaize* (Fig. 63). The massif has been defined by the erosion of two parallel longitudinal streams, the Aisne to the west and its tributary the Aire to the east. The latter rises in the Kimmeridge Clay belt not far from the Meuse and flows northwards, entrenched down through the clay; in fact it may disappear into the underlying porous Corallian Limestone for several miles, particularly during a dry summer. It reappears further north and crosses the Portland Limestone plateau in a trench which again is occasionally waterless in summer. It then turns sharply west near Grandpré through the northern part of the Argonne to join the Aisne, for here is an example of river capture (Fig. 64).[1] The Aire once continued its longitudinal direction northwards to join the Meuse, but an active west-flowing subsequent of the Aisne cut back into and finally through the Argonne, leaving the beheaded trunk of the proto-Aire to continue to the Meuse as the much reduced Bar.

Streams dissect each side of the Argonne, since there is much water in the valleys on these clay-sands although the ridges are dry. The southern Argonne is divided longitudinally into two by the deeply-cut valley of the Biesme, which flows northwards for about twelve miles until, like the Aire, it turns sharply west to join the Aisne. The steep-sided transverse valleys are given a number of names—*gorges*, *gorgeons*, *gorgettes*, *goulettes* and *chavées*, separated by sharp crests which rise to 750 feet in places.

The Argonne is still a well-wooded district, despite the age-old activities of wood-cutters and charcoal-burners and the vast devastation of the war of 1914–18. The ridges and valley sides are clothed with both deciduous trees and recently established plantations of conifers; the total area of woodland today is about 180 square miles. The valleys and depressions, where not cleared and drained, are either marshy or covered with thick scrub, while some of the higher drier ridges present a heath-like appearance, with silver birch, brambles, bracken and ling.

The Argonne is a zone of scanty settlement. Some small towns and villages are situated on the flanks of the uplands—Vouziers and Ste. Ménehould (near the junction of a dozen streams) on the west, Grandpré, Varennes-en-Argonne and Clermont-en-Argonne on the east. Smaller settlements lie within the upland in the more open valleys, such as the pleasant town of Florent-en-Argonne in

---

[1] J. L.-F. Tricart, *La Partie orientale du bassin de Paris. Etude morphologique* (1949), pp. 397–407, 'La Capture de l'Aire-Bar'.

the longitudinal valley of the Biesme. Some of the villages were once centres of iron industries, using local ferruginous sands, charcoal and water-power; small lakes were formed by damming streams (which resemble the 'hammer-ponds' of the Weald), but are now used only for fishing. Many men are employed in forestry and at the saw-mills and timber-yards. Today some mixed farming

FIG. 64.—RIVER CAPTURE IN THE ARGONNE.
The upper Aire once flowed north-north-westwards to join the Meuse. It was captured by an active subsequent of the Aisne, which cut back through the Argonne. The beheaded trunk is now the Bar, which joins the Meuse below Sedan. Heights are given in feet.

Based on *Carte de France au 200,000ᵉ*, sheets 10, 17.

is practised in the more open valleys, with an emphasis on dairying, and even cereals such as rye are grown.

The Argonne is still a zone of separation, as it has been for centuries, between Champagne and Lorraine, and it has long formed one of the outer defensive barriers of the Paris Basin. The upland is not a single cuesta like the Jurassic hills futher east but a much dissected upland, and the north-south trend of the ridges and valleys makes it difficult to cross transversely. One main road and railway run west from Verdun via Clermont-en-Argonne and Ste. Ménehould, but they have to pursue a circuitous route from one valley to the next, and the railway is obliged to tunnel. Another railway and road utilise the Aire gap by way of Grandpré. But between these two transverse routes twenty miles of forested ridges and valleys are crossed only by a single minor road.

THE PRE-ARDENNES REGION

A rather indeterminate region of Jurassic rocks, sometimes referred to as '*Plaines et Plateaux pré-Ardennais,*' lies in the extreme north-east between the chalklands and the Ardennes. The Meuse, after flowing through its long 'furrow' in the Corallian Limestone, continues in a series of large loops through a narrow Lias Clay vale before cutting north in a narrow gorge through the Ardennes. It receives two tributaries along the narrow outcrop of the Lias, the Chiers from the east which joins the main river below Sedan, and the short Sormonne which flows in a diametrically opposite direction to join the Meuse at Charleville. The Lias outcrop becomes progressively narrower to the north-west, finally vanishing against the Silurian rocks of the Rocroi massif in the Ardennes. To the south is a parallel band of Oolitic Limestone, forming a prominent cuesta overlooking the Lias vale, and then to the south again are narrow exposures of Oxford and Gault Clays, the Corallian being scarcely represented. Here the Jurassic rocks, sweeping to the north-west from Lorraine in an attenuating curve, end near Hirson.

The valleys of the Meuse and its tributaries form a prosperous farming area. The soils developed on the Lias Clay, enriched with calcareous downwash from the cuestas and with river alluvium, are used for the cultivation of oats, trefoil and fodder-beans, or are under short-ley meadow grasses. The emphasis is on livestock, including dairy- and beef-cattle, sheep and a large number of horses ('*la belle race ardennaise*'), and many large farms possess quadrangles of stables.

The *département* of Ardennes is included within the *Région Est I* of the *Chambre Syndicale de la Sidérurgie Française* (see Fig. 72). The Meuse valley from Sedan downstream to the Belgian frontier at Givet has metallurgical industries; such names as Neuve-Forge and Vieille-Forge are indicative of its old establishment. The initial advantages included charcoal from the well-wooded Ardennes and water-power from the Meuse tributaries. In the fifteenth century refugees from Liège introduced nail-making, which has survived to the present day. The war of 1914–18 caused widespread destruction and the industrial life had to be completely rebuilt. Today the district has no blast-furnaces, but a large steel-works, owned by the *Hauts-Fourneaux de la Chiers* company and built under the post-1945 modernisation plans, is situated at Blagny-Carignan on the banks of the Chiers ten miles upstream from its junction with the Meuse. Other steel-works at Mohon near Mézières, Vireux and Flize, utilising pig-iron from Lorraine, supply steel for the factories at Charleville, Monthermé, Vrigne-aux-Bois, Ville-sur-Lumes, Nouzon, Fumay and many other places (Fig. 65). These manufacture nails, hardware, boilers, wire and other metallurgical products in great variety. The northern branch of the Est Canal and the canalized Belgian Meuse afford relatively easy access to Lorraine and to the southern Belgian coalfield, while the Douai-Cambrai-Charleville line enables Nord coal to come by rail.

The chief town of the *département* of Ardennes is Mézières, on the south side of a meander of the Meuse, while its twin, Charleville, stands some miles downstream on the north side of the loop below the confluence of the Sormonne. Each is an old fortress town, with modern suburbs and factories engaged in various branches of metal-lurgical industry. Sedan, situated just below the junction of the Chiers, likewise consists of an old fortress town on the right bank of the river and new industrial suburbs on the left bank. It is the centre of a long-established woollen industry, originally based on wool from sheep both on the Ardennes and on the limestone plateaus to the south, and on the plentiful supplies of water from the flanks of the uplands. A number of factories, both in the suburbs of the town and in neighbouring villages such as Balan and Floing, still make fine woollens, velours and velvets.

This part of France has suffered grievously as a result of its strategic situation. Sedan was a fortified town as early as 1424. It was here that Napoleon III saw his army defeated in 1870, the whole area was devastated in the war of 1914–18, and much destruction occurred again in 1940–44. Ten years afterwards some of the towns still had a much smaller population than in 1938, but most of them have now recovered.

THE CLAY-LANDS OF CHAMPAGNE

A crescentic outcrop of Gault Clay flanks the chalk cuesta on the east, though it is much less extensive than the Chalk ; from the Aisne valley southward it forms a strip only a mile or two across, widening to twenty miles where it is crossed by the Marne flowing from Joinville almost to Vitry-le-François. The Gault then extends still further to the south as a narrow outcrop between the Chalk and the

Jurassic limestones, occupied by a section of the Armançon which flows through the clay vale to join the Yonne.

Further west, between the Yonne and the Loing, the Gault Clay

FIG. 65.—THE MEUSE VALLEY INDUSTRIAL AREA IN NORTHERN FRANCE.
Each town shown has metal-using industries.
Based on *Carte de France et des frontières au 200,000ᵉ*, sheet 10.

is diversified by outcrops of Upper Greensand. These form low sandstone ridges, known as the *Collines de Puisaye*, which trend east–west and rise to 1227 feet. This higher land causes a series of streams to flow north with a reasonable gradient both to the Loing and the Yonne, thus avoiding the marshlands found in other Gault districts. The clay outcrop crosses the Loire near Cosne, and can then be traced as a narrow band along the northern edge of Berry, where it finally disappears.

Except where each river in turn has cut an alluvium-floored valley across the outcrop and for residual patches of sand or outcrops of Greensand, the Gault forms a continuous sheet of heavy impermeable soils, hence the name '*humide*'. Originally it must have been an area of extensive swamps, lakes and thick forests, and many shallow interconnected lakes and marshy depressions remain, particularly in the source-region of the Aisne (*Belval*) and in the angle of the Marne to the south-west of St. Dizier (*Der*), where the Etang de Lahorre covers about 620 acres. Much reclamation, originally begun by religious houses in the Middle Ages, has been effected, and it has now a prosperous dairying (particularly for cheese-making) and mixed farming activity. The countryside is undulating rather than flat, and so while meadows are concentrated in damp depressions, arable land growing cereals and roots (particularly fodder-beet) is found on the better-drained lower slopes, and orchards occur on south-facing aspects or clustered around hamlets. The most prosperous arable part of *Champagne humide* is *Perthois*, where the Marne, the Saulx and the Blaize have deposited alluvium over the clays.

The small patches of sand form scattered higher areas of heathland among the clay-lands. Widespread afforestation has taken place, the Forêt du Der covers about 27,000 acres, the Forêt d'Orient about 40,000 acres, and between the Seine and the Aube the forests of Cussangy, Chaource, Rumilly and Aumont occupy another 15,000 acres.

Hamlets are small but widely distributed, since there is no problem of water supply. As in the Argonne, some of these settlements nurtured bygone iron industries based on patches of ferruginous sands within the clays. A few of the little towns still have metallurgical industries, now using Lorraine steel, as at St. Dizier (which makes nails and wire), Bar-le-Duc, Wassy and Vitry-le-François. Other activities include the manufacture of bricks and tiles, cement (at Frignicourt), textiles (the legacy of the wool sales at Troyes and elsewhere from the *Champagne pouilleuse* flocks), pottery (at Pargny-sur-Saulx) and crockery (at Couvrot). At Sermaize-les-Bains is one of the largest sugar-refineries in France. Both the Marne-Saône and Marne-Rhine Canals cross the central part of the region and so facilitate the movement of the bulky raw materials for these industries, as well as of agricultural products, and of fertilisers and lime for the heavy clay-soils.

XXV Quarry at Quenast in the valley of the upper Senne

XXVI The Maurits colliery, South Limburg

XXVII Paris. The Ile de la Cité

XXVIII Paris. The *Régie Rénault* at Billancourt

THE EASTERN JURASSIC MARGINS

The Jurassic outcrop swings south and south-west, forming an area which has been given by French geographers the collective name of *'Plateaux de la haute Marne et de la haute Seine'*. The succession of Jurassic rocks has been described in connection with the upper Seine and its several tributaries, which cross these outcrops more or less transversely (see p. 180 and Fig. 53). Several *pays* in this marginal area merit more detailed attention.

Barrois.—The *Plateau des Bars* consists of the western part of the Corallian plateau, a narrow belt of Kimmeridge Clay, and a low cuesta backed by the undulating plateau of Portland Limestone which dips gently westward towards *Champagne humide*. These various zones naturally display marked differences in land-use. The higher parts of the limestone plateaus are either wooded or afford poor grazing, although their lower slopes are ploughed. Cattle, kept both for dairying and for meat, graze on the clay-floored valleys.

The limestone slopes of Barrois have quite a reputation for wine, and its yield is included under the general classification of 'Burgundy'. A large amount of *vin ordinaire* is produced, but the vineyards along the river Serein, a tributary of the Yonne, in the neighbourhood of Chablis, yield a superb dry wine of a unique pale-gold colour. Another wine district extends north-east from Les Riceys across the Seine and Aube valleys; the best-known product is the *Vin Rosé des Riceys*. The vineyards of both Chablis and Les Riceys climb up the lower south-facing slopes of the limestone knolls and plateau edges.

Settlement is concentrated along both the main and side valleys. The three Bars, -sur-Seine, -sur-Aube and -le-Duc, stand in broad valleys cut by the Seine, the Aube and the Ornain respectively. They form prosperous market-towns and centres of communication, and have numerous light manufactures such as tanning, the preparation of leather-goods and food-processing. Further to the south Auxerre stands in the valley of the Yonne (the *pays*-name of *Auxerrois* is sometimes given to the surrounding district), and Tonnerre (similarly *Tonnerrois*) is on the left bank of the Armançon. These form a crescent of towns round the Jurassic rim of the eastern and south-eastern Paris Basin.

The Plateau de Langres.—This limestone upland forms the watershed of central France between the Seine and Saône systems. In the neighbourhood of Langres itself the plateau attains about 1,550 feet, but this increases south-west to heights of over 2,000 feet. The plateau is an asymmetrical anticline, with a steep and much faulted

R.G.W.E.—I

southern slope to the Saône valley and a more gentle gradient to the north, across which are trenched the upper Seine and its family of tributaries. The steep edge overlooking the Saône valley has a maximum altitude of 2,087 feet. The general name of *Côte d'Or* is applied where the cuesta-form becomes more pronounced further south, between Dijon and Beaune; this district really belongs to the Saône trough (see pp. 382–5).

The Langres plateau consists largely of Oolitic Limestone, though in some parts denudation has exposed the underlying Lias clays and marls. The Marne and the Armançon, as already emphasised, have cut back through the limestone on to these clays, where they take their rise. To the north-east of Langres the clay-lands are known as *Bassigny*, further to the south-west as *Auxois*, and on the northern flanks of the Morvan as *Terre Plaine* (Fig. 52). An outcrop of Lias Limestone forms a prominent escarpment to the south-east of Langres.

The plateau has a varied agricultural pattern, as evidenced by the land-use statistics for the *département* of Haute-Marne, in which much of the upland lies. Thirty-six per cent in 1963 was wooded, including most of the higher plateau where the rainfall is quite heavy (Langres has an annual mean of thirty-six inches, at an altitude of just over 1,500 feet). There are woodlands of beech, chestnut and oak, and some extensive coniferous plantations. Thirty per cent was devoted to arable cultivation, almost exactly half of this under cereals (oats and wheat), the rest under fodder crops and potatoes. Some vines are grown, but not on any scale; the great Burgundy vineyards of the adjoining *département* of Côte d'Or lie on the southern slopes of the plateau (see p. 382). About 22 per cent was under pasture, both the rather scrubby limestone grassland and the damp meadows on the Lias clays of the Marne valley; in 1963 there were 201,000 cattle (about half dairy animals) and some 43,000 sheep. In spite of the altitude and the appreciable rainfall, there is therefore quite a prosperous agricultural life.

Most of the small towns and villages are situated in the valleys— Auberive on the upper Aube, Recey on the Ource (a tributary of the Seine) and Alise Ste. Reine on the Oze (a tributary of the Armançon). Langres itself is an attractive walled town, standing boldly on a north-projecting limestone spur between the Marne and a small parallel headstream to the west, and serves as a market-centre for a considerable district.

The Langres plateau lies transversely athwart central France, so forming a distinct barrier to communications between Paris and the Mediterranean coast, but this is nevertheless crossed by several main railway lines. The most important line of the *Région Sud*, from Paris to Marseilles, follows the Yonne and Armançon valleys through the southern scarplands. It then climbs up the Oze valley through the Lias claylands to the summit at Blaisy-Bas (at a height of about 1,350 feet), and penetrates the watershed through a two-mile tunnel before beginning the steep descent of the Oolitic slope to the railway junction of Dijon, thence down the Saône valley. A second main line, that of the *Région Est* from Paris to Basel, follows in turn the valleys of the Seine to Troyes, then of the Aube beyond Bar-sur-Aube, and of the Marne from Chaumont to Langres; the watershed between Langres and Chalindrey is again negotiated by a tunnel. A markedly steep descent eastward down the Lias limestone edge, utilising the Amance valley, takes the line to Vesoul and so through the Belfort gap to Basel. Several main roads, none with any really severe gradients, focus on Langres from the north via the Marne valley, hence down to Vesoul and Besançon, and on Dijon from Paris and the west. Even two canals cross the divide. The Burgundy (*de Bourgogne*) Canal links the Yonne with the Saône via Dijon, although it requires 189 locks, and the Marne-Saône Canal, with 114 locks, passes to the east of Langres in a tunnel through a limestone spur.

Nivernais.—Although almost separated from the rest of the Jurassic rim by the projecting 'peninsula' of the Morvan, an area of Jurassic rocks with a distinct individuality is contained between the Loire and the edge of the Morvan. This is given the *pays*-name of Nivernais, after the regional centre of Nevers, and corresponds very closely to the *département* of Nièvre. The Loire flows across the western part, known as *Le Val du Nivernais* or as *Bas-Nivernais*. The central part is much higher, rising to 1,483 feet and is known as the *Plateaux* or *Côtes du Nivernais*. The eastern part, crossed by the Yonne, is *Bazois*.

Nivernais is structurally a complicated area, since it forms part of the northern end of one of the Tertiary rift-valleys which characterise the eastern flanks of the Central Massif (see pp. 527), and it is crossed by a number of roughly north–south faults. While Oolitic Limestone predominates, an ancient 'wedge' of granite appears in the neighbourhood of St. Saulge, while in the south a small downfaulted pocket has preserved Permian and Carboniferous rocks, including the Upper Coal Measures of the tiny Decize coalfield. Considerable overlying deposits of Pleistocene sands and gravels were deposited by the post-glacial Loire on leaving the Central Massif with its swollen volume and immense load.

Nivernais is therefore a district with varied landscapes, soils and land-use patterns. This is reflected by the figures for the land-use categories; 494,000 acres of arable, 496,000 acres of pasture and 520,000 acres of woodland were returned in the *département* of Nièvre in 1963. Agriculture is of a mixed character; cereals (wheat predominant) and fodder-crops occupy approximately the same acreage, and much permanent grass on the Lias clays and along the Loire valley supports 117,000 dairy-cattle and considerably more of the white Nivernais stock bred for beef and for draught-use. Vineyards on the terraces of the Loire below Nevers produce a light dry white wine which is mostly consumed locally, though a Nièvre wine with a more than local reputation is *Pouilly-Fumé*, produced in Pouilly-sur-Loire twenty-five miles downstream from Nevers.

Some of the areas of gravel and sand carry a heathland vegetation of bracken and gorse. Considerable tracts are under oak-birch woodland, and parts of the heaths have been planted with conifers.

Population is not dense, averaging about ninety per square mile over the region as a whole. There is no shortage of water and numerous villages occur along the tributary valleys of the Yonne and the Loire. Decize is a small mining town connected by a branch to the Loire Lateral Canal, by which coal is shipped to Nevers, the *chef-lieu* of the *département*, with a population of 41,051 in 1962. It has several light engineering industries, including the manufacture of aircraft parts. An ancient iron industry used the ferruginous ores of Berry and local charcoal, and today pig and raw steel are imported from Lorraine for light metal manufactures. Another old-established industry, the manufacture of crockery and earthenware, is still quite prosperous.

IV. THE MIDDLE LOIRE BASIN

The river Loire, after leaving its down-faulted basin in the north of the Central Massif, crosses the Oolitic Limestone and then swings in a curve through the south-western corner of the Paris Basin. The symmetrical arrangement of the strata, seen so clearly in the eastern part of the Basin, is here lacking, partly because the land is more low-lying (hence differential denudation has had less scope), partly because much is masked with unconformable sheets of Tertiary sands, clays and gravels.

This region may be described under the several sub-regions of the valleys of the Loire and its major tributaries; the *Sologne*, within the angle of the Loire; *Champagne berrichonne*, or Berry; the *Collines du Sancerrois*; and the districts of *Brenne* and *Boischaut*.

THE MIDDLE LOIRE VALLEY

From Nevers to the junction of the Maine near Angers, a distance of about 220 miles, the Loire flows in a broad trench usually varying in width from three to six miles, which rises by well-defined terrace-steps to the rolling plateau country beyond. In places this trench narrows to a mile or so, and to the east of Tours above the southern bank rise steep cliffs. The river meanders over the floor of this flood plain, and the vast loads of material brought down by the winter flood-waters from the Central Massif are spread out in ever-changing banks of sand and gravel, between which the river braids its course in a tangle of feeble water-courses and islets covered with osiers and willows. In summer it seems a placid river, with expanses of white gravel and sand, and quiet backwaters. In winter the many branches merge to form one swirling stream, covering the islets and filling the channel between the protective dykes built along almost its whole length through Touraine and Anjou, set far back from the summer course of the river. At times during these winter floods the waters spread out to form shallow lakes. Thus at Orléans the road and rail bridges are each more than a thousand feet long to cope with the flood-waters. At Tours the overall width of the river at flood is about 1,250 feet, and the road bridge crossing from the town on the bluffs on the south side is more than 1,400 feet in length.

The proto-Loire cut a much broader valley than the present river would seem to justify. In Pleistocene times it deposited vast quantities of sediment brought down from the Central Massif, but since then it has eroded its bed in stages within the old flood-plain, so forming a series of broad terraces. The present flood-plain is for the most part floored with sands and gravels, but the terraces are covered with alluvium on which fertile soils have developed. Below Blois, where chalk outcrops overlook the valley, downwash has produced a rich calcareous soil. Much drainage and reclamation of the valley-flats has been carried out.

The several sections of the Loire valley have sufficient identity to have received a whole series of *pays*-names. In the west of Nivernais it is known as the *Vallée Noire* or simply *Le Val*. Then succeed downstream the *Val d'Orléans*, the *Val de Blois*, the *Val de Touraine* and the *Val d'Anjou*.

Centuries of effort have made the terraces of the Loire valley one of the most attractive farming areas of France. It affords a pleasant agricultural landscape of rich meadows on the floor of the flood-plain, market- and nursery-gardens on the lower terraces (especially near the towns), larger fields of wheat on the broad upper terraces, and extensive orchards and vineyards. There are numerous local specialisations; thus Anjou is famous for its artichokes,[1] potatoes are grown along the south side of the Val d'Orléans, asparagus in the angle between the Cher and the Loire to the south of Blois, mushrooms along the lower Indre valley, and haricot-beans in Touraine. In fact, the term 'Garden of France' has been justly bestowed on

[1] An account of the specialised horticulture of Anjou is given by I. Deguil, 'L'Horticulture en Anjou', in *A. de G.* (1933), vol. xlii, pp. 601-9.

this valley, particularly on the Val de Touraine.[1]

The Loire valley has extensive vineyards on its slopes.[2] Touraine has long been famous for both white and red wines; the white wines of Vouvray, produced from grapes grown on the north bank between Blois and Tours, the red wines of Bourgueil also grown on the right bank but below Tours, and the Chinon vineyards on the north bank of the Vienne just above its confluence with the Loire, are all well known. The Val d'Anjou, in the neighbourhood of Saumur, produces a range of both sparkling and still wines.

The Loire valley has several large towns, each the centre of a valley-*pays*, each with an eventful history, with a lively industrial and commercial life superimposed upon the glories of the past. Orléans, the *chef-lieu* of Loiret, had a population of 88,105 in 1962; situated on the northern banks of the Loire, it has long been a bridge-town, helped by a string of islands. It is a gracious town, with broad streets and attractive squares. It has naturally developed as a market-town, lying as it does between Beauce and Berry, and several industries have achieved considerable importance; these include food-processing (flour-milling, the making of biscuits and confectionery, and the manufacture of vinegar), and numerous light engineering and metallurgical industries, mostly associated with agricultural machinery and tools. Further downstream is Blois, the *chef-lieu* of Loir-et-Cher, with a population of 34,426; its crowded houses rise steeply up the limestone slopes of the valley-side to the castle which has dominated the town for many centuries. It too is a bridge-town; five main roads converge from the north on the bridge, although only a single road from the south.

Tours is the largest town of the middle Loire valley. It has grown up on the south side of the valley within the long narrow triangle of level land between the Loire and the converging Cher. The town itself had a population of 96,472 in 1962; in recent years the built-up area has expanded over the interfluve and along the north bank of the Loire, and now the official *agglomération*, with a population of about 130,000, includes the contiguous communes of La Riche, St. Cyr-sur-Loire, St. Pierre-des-Corps, St. Radegonde-en-Touraine and St. Symphorien. The Loire is crossed by rail- and road-bridges, the latter carrying *N10*, the main road from Paris to Bordeaux. As centre of the 'Garden of France', its importance rests largely on agricultural produce; a famous agricultural fair (the '*Grande Semaine de Tours*') is held annually in May. Numerous industries [3]

[1] G. Lecointre, *La Touraine* (1947).

[2] P. Marres, 'Les Vignobles de la Loire et du Centre', in *La Vigne et le vin en France* (1950), pp. 59-75.

[3] Y. Babonaux, 'L'Industrialisation de Tours', in *A. de G.* (1948), vol. lvii, pp. 243-9.

have been established, mainly agricultural machinery, fertilisers and pharmaceutical chemicals, and some silk-works are a legacy of the past. Saumur, below the Vienne confluence, is important as a centre of the wine industry (Plate XXXIII). Two nuclear power-stations are in operation in the Loire valley near Chinon, a third at St. Laurent-des-Eaux on the loop of the Loire between Orléans and Blois.

These are the main towns, but a succession of small prosperous villages on either side of the river is situated on the terraces above flood danger. Some, such as Beaugency and Amboise, stand at minor Loire bridge-points.

One of the main features of the middle Loire valley is the remarkable number of *châteaux*, hence the popular term of 'château country'. This is partly due to historical and personal reasons, in that since the time of Charles VII the Bourbons had been particularly attracted by Touraine, and to the geographical features of this pleasant river-valley, with numerous prominent sites within easy distance of Paris. Some of the châteaux originated as mediaeval fortresses, but after the Renaissance they developed highly ornate, even flamboyant, architectural features. They succeed each other at intervals along the river-banks, each sited on some prominent bluff or spur—Amboise and the fortress-like Chaumont to the east of Tours, Chenonceaux (built on a bridge across the Cher), Valençay in the open country south of the Cher, Chambord (the largest of the Loire châteaux) and Cheverny away from the river to the east of Blois, and the Château de Blois. Another group is found below Tours—the fortress of Luynes, Langeais, Villandry (with its superb formal gardens), the great ruin of Chinon, and many more.

THE SOLOGNE

To the south of the angle of the middle Loire lies the Sologne,[1] a gently undulating plain 400 to 500 feet above sea-level and about 1,700 square miles in area, draining vaguely westwards to the Loire by way of the Loiret, Cosson and Beuvron, and to the Cher (hence again the Loire) by the Sauldre. The underlying rock is Chalk, but this is not visible except on sides of the valleys, for the region is covered with a thick mantle of Miocene clays and sands and in the south also with Clay-with-Flints and gravels, the immense *cônes de déjections* of the proto-Cher and -Loire. The heavy clays and gentle gradients have resulted in impeded drainage, so that this region has long been characterised by marshes and a vast number of lakes. The Sologne once carried an ancient forest, gradually destroyed during the Middle Ages, to be replaced by the *étangs* and by the

[1] A detailed study of the Sologne and its development is given by P. Guillaume, *La Sologne au cours des siècles* (1954).

landes, fougères, bruyères, genêts and *bremailles*. As a result, in the early part of the nineteenth century it formed one of the poorest parts of France; the few inhabitants were poverty-stricken, under-nourished and unhealthy, obtaining a bare existence by cultivating rye and buck-wheat and by keeping flocks of sheep. The density of population was probably less than twenty-five per square mile.

Many reclamation projects have been started, though not all were successfully carried out. In 1859 at La Motte-Beuvron, in the heart of the Sologne, '*Le Comité central de la Sologne*' was organised to systematise and co-ordinate the various efforts at improvement, which had considerable success. Some of the reclaimed land is now under cultivation, and cereals are grown, not much wheat but rye and malting-barley for the breweries of Orléans, and asparagus, potatoes and haricot-beans are cultivated on the sandy soils in the north. The reclaimed clay-lands afford grazing both for dairy- and beef-cattle. The breeding of '*basse-cour*', notably rabbits, geese and turkeys, has developed; the last are sent to Paris and even to England.

The most valuable improvements in the Sologne, particularly of the sands which in places overlie the clays, have been by afforesta-tion. Considerable progress had been made by 1914, in spite of a disastrously cold winter in 1879–80 which destroyed vast numbers of trees, notably the not too hardy maritime pine. Much of the woodland was of necessity felled during the 1914–18 war, so that despite renewed activity in the inter-war period, by 1939 the area planted was still less than in 1914. Since 1920 planting has been mainly of Austrian pine and Douglas fir, with some deciduous trees such as birch and oak. More felling was necessary in the 1939–45 period but more planting has since taken place. In all about half a million acres are under timber, but areas of heath still survive.

Population is scanty, concentrated in a number of small towns along the river-valleys—Romorantin, Salbris and Argent in the Sauldre valley; Bracieux, Neung-sur-Beuvron and La Motte-Beuvron in the Beuvron valley; and Montrichard, Selles and St. Aignan in the Cher valley. They are mostly market-towns, and possess industries connected with the exploitation of the forests; saw-mills prepare pit-props and sawn-timber, and an important cooperage activity serves the wine trade. Selles and St. Aignan each has a small pottery, while Romorantin possesses several small textile factories, the legacy of an activity based on the flocks of sheep that once grazed in the Sologne, and it also produces *lingerie*, foot-wear and ironmongery.

To the north of the Loire lies the Forêt d'Orléans [1] with an area of about two hundred square miles. It has developed on the same

[1] C. Milleret, 'La Forêt d'Orléans', in *A. de G.* (1963), vol. 72, pp. 426-58, with several maps and plates.

Miocene deposits as the Sologne, and is similar in many respects, although with only a few lakes.

Champagne Berrichonne.—The low undulating plateau of Berry slopes gently northward towards the Sologne from the edge of the Central Massif. It consists mainly of Oolitic Limestone in the south and Corallian Limestone in the north, with a narrow intervening strip of clay, and the plateau, 750 feet in altitude in the south, falls to 300 feet in the north. It is crossed by a number of rivers—the Cher and its tributaries in the east, the Indre and its head-streams in the centre, and the Creuse in the west. The whole region is sometimes divided into two—*la champagne d'Issoudun* to the west of the Cher in the *département* of Indre, and *la champagne de Bourges* to the east in the *département* of Cher, after the two main towns.

Much of the plateau carries a reddish-brown loamy soil, the product of limestone disintegration, and although somewhat dry this yields well when heavily fertilised. The *département* of Cher had actually 47 per cent of its area under arable in 1963, compared with only 21 per cent under pasture and 21 per cent under woodland; the figures for Indre were 58, 14 and 13 respectively. Rather more than half of this arable grew cereals (wheat, oats, barley for malting, and even some maize), the rest fodder-crops. There were also in the two *départements* about 410,000 cattle, 257,000 sheep (the long-legged *mouton berrichon*), 93,000 goats and 146,000 pigs, evidence of a mixed agriculture; some famous goat-milk cheeses from Berry can be bought in the Paris markets. Vineyards are common on the limestone slopes, but these rarely produce wine other than *vin ordinaire*; *Reuilly* is one of the few quality wines.

Some quite extensive woodlands consist mostly of oak with an admixture of beech, hornbeam and birch; the Forêts de Châteauroux, de Meillant and de Bommiers are notable tracts. These woods once supplied charcoal to small local iron-works, but they now provide timber for furniture-making at Châteauroux and St. Amand.

The agricultural population of these open limestone plains is not dense; Cher averages 104 people per square mile, Indre about 93. Population is distributed in large villages along the river valleys. The regional capital is Bourges, with a population in 1962 of about 64,000. Situated at the convergence of two Cher tributaries (the Auron and the Yèvre), it has long been a major route-centre; nine main roads and a number of railways converge on it, but the Berry Canal which passes through its western outskirts is now disused. Bourges is one of the old-established, if minor, centres of metallurgical industry, and its present activities include foundries, ordnance works, an aircraft factory, textile and clothing factories[1] and several concerns making agricultural implements and hardware. Other industries include tanning and leather working based on hides from local herds at Levroux and Issoudun, milling, brewing at Châteauroux and Issoudun, and the manufacture of linoleum. Such towns as Vierzon, Mehun and Foëcy have brick, tile and porcelain industries; a modern development is the manufacture of electrical insulators using Jurassic fire-clays. Châteauroux has textile industries, now making cloth for uniforms, and in the neighbourhood of Argenton the manufacture and embroidery of *lingerie* is still carried on, largely as a domestic industry.

Sancerrois.—The Collines du Sancerrois, of Portland Limestone, rise to 1,424 feet in the Massif d'Henrichemont, and drain north by rivers flowing to the Sauldre, which have cut deeply into the underlying rocks. Where surface deposits of Clay-with-Flints and residual Eocene clays occur (the so-called *terres froides*), there are extensive woodlands of oak and birch, and the higher parts are covered with a scrub of brushwood and brambles. The most favoured areas for agriculture and settlement occur in the valleys, where the Chalk has been exposed and the slopes are covered with a veneer of *terres chaudes*, a warm limy downwash-soil. Here grow pleasant orchards of pear, plum and cherry, and a profitable specialisation on the higher slopes is provided by the cultivation of walnuts, producing about 700 tons of nuts per annum. Sancerrois has been a vine-growing region since Roman times, producing some light white wines, although it was badly hit by phylloxera. Sancerre itself stands well to the west of the Loire on a limestone knoll overlooking the marshy valley of the Vauvise.

Brenne and Boischaut.—These districts lie to the south and west of Berry, between it and the Limousin crystalline plateau. They rise to about 500–850 feet, and are mostly covered with Middle and Lower Jurassic sandstones and clays. Some masses of reddish sandstone form low conical hills, known locally as *butons* and covered with pines and broom-scrub, but the greater part is a gently undulating erosion surface heavily plastered with impermeable clays. Brenne, like the Sologne, has numerous small lakes, marshes and peat-bogs (in fact it is sometimes referred to as ' *Brenne marécageuse* '), of which only a little has been drained. About 350 of these reedy sheets of water survive, totalling 10,600 acres, of which the largest, '*la Mer Rouge*', covers nearly 450 acres. Boischaut is higher, better drained and more wooded, though with considerable areas of rather bleak

[1] A. Douguédroit, 'L'Industrie du vêtement dans le Berry', in *A. de G.* (1960), vol. 69, pp. 584-93, with a detailed map.

moorland (known as *brandes*) and scrubby heath (*varennes*). Some mixed farming is practised on the better-drained clay soils, but population is inevitably scanty.

V. THE WESTERN PARIS BASIN

The difficulty of demarcating a boundary between the Paris Basin and Armorica has already been stressed (see p. 7). Much of the western part of the Paris Basin forms part of the old province of Normandy,[1] which today broadly comprises Seine-Maritime on the east bank of the lower Seine, and Eure, Calvados, Orne and Manche to the west (Fig. 1). These *départements* form in fact a transition zone between the central Paris Basin and Armorica. Only Eure, Orne and Calvados are under consideration here, since Seine-Maritime has been described as the Pays de Caux, and Manche is included in Armorica.

The coast between the Seine estuary and the Baie des Veys (the joint estuary of the Vire and the Taute) represents a section across the northern margins of the Cretaceous and Jurassic rocks in France. From Honfleur to Trouville at the mouth of the river Touques, the Chalk and Upper Jurassic limestones reach the sea ; the cliffs are generally steep, though wooded in places, and are fronted by an offshore wave-cut platform, the Rochers des Creuniers. From Trouville to the mouth of the Dives the cliffs are still prominent, consisting of Cretaceous clays rising inland to over 300 feet. Then follows a break where the Dives has worn a broad valley, forming an estuary encumbered with sand-banks and a broad sandy beach backed by dunes, which continues to the marshy estuary of the Orne near Ouistreham. From here to the Pointe de Maisy, the eastern 'corner' of the Baie des Veys, the Oolitic Limestone of the Campagne de Caen reaches the sea, forming a low rocky coast with cliffed sections culminating in the 130-foot Cap Manvieux to the west of Arromanches, alternating with valleys opening on to the shore. Offshore lies a wave-cut platform, known as the Plateau du Calvados in the east and as the Rochers de Grand-camp in the west, with numerous boulders, rocky islets and shingle-banks in places appearing above high-tide level.

No section of coast has ever been studied in such detail, nor has one seen such vital military events, as this part of Normandy. It was here that the liberation of Europe began, when the operation 'Overlord' was launched on June 6th, 1944. Indeed, a little plaque on a wall at Ranville, to the east of the lower Orne, records it to be '*le premier village de France libéré*'. Devastation was inevitably immense

[1] R. Musset, *La Normandie* (1960), a detailed survey of 220 pp.

from these military operations; such villages as Villers-Bocage were shattered and Caen itself was terribly damaged. Today the rebuilding is complete, but the 'Mulberry harbour' off Arromanches still survives, and a plaque on a monument near its seaward end records the name of 'Port Winston' bestowed on it.

THE RELIEF REGIONS

The Chalk Plateaus.—The chalk outcrop extends across the valley of the lower Seine to form an area of open and gently undulating plateau-land at an altitude of 450 to 600 feet. It is, however, dissected by the steep-sided valleys of various Seine tributaries, forming a number of broadly similar *pays*—Lieuvin, Neubourg, Evreux, Ouche, Thimerais and other smaller ones (Fig. 52). The surface of the plateaus is patchily covered with residual tracts of Lower Eocene sands and clays, and *limon* in some parts lies over both the Chalk and these newer deposits. The valley-floors are broad and inclined to be marshy, although for the most part they have been reclaimed to form excellent pasture. Between Evreux and Louviers the Campagne du Neubourg is covered with the beech-woods of the Forêt de Bord.

Perche.—The land rises westward to Perche, where a short west-east anticline has produced the swelling ridge of the Collines du Perche, attaining a height of 1,014 feet in the north in the Monts d'Amain. The surface of this anticline has been planed off, exposing the underlying Jurassic rocks, notably the Oxford Clay, although the highest part of the ridge actually consists of Cretaceous sandstones. The Collines du Perche form a watershed rising above the otherwise uniform unbroken level. The Blaise, Avre and Iton flow northwards across the chalk-lands to the Seine; the Rille, Touques, Dives and Orne also drain northwards direct to the English Channel; and the headstreams of the Sarthe and the Loir flow away south-west ultimately to the Loire. This watershed is very indeterminate and many streams rise within a few hundred yards of each other and flow away in opposite directions. The various Mesozoic rocks—chalk, limestone, sandstone—are largely covered with residual clays.

The Pays de la Sarthe.—To the south-west of Perche the varied Mesozoic rocks extend to the edge of the Palaeozoic massif. The river Sarthe flows in a south-westerly direction to its confluence with the Mayenne near Angers, hence the general name *Pays de la Sarthe*. Here once again is apparent the absence of a distinctive boundary between the Paris Basin and Armorica. The *Institut National de la Statistique* in its official map of the geographical regions of France distinguishes a single area, the *Pays de la Mayenne et de la Sarthe*, for although the Pays de la Mayenne is of Palaeozoic rocks and the

Pays de la Sarthe of Mesozoic rocks, the considerable overlying areas of residual clay result in a remarkably similar landscape and land-use, a *bocage* country (see p. 460) of small fields of pasture, wooded hedges and copses, and orchards. The same transitional character is indicated by the regional name of *Maine*, one of the old provinces (Fig. 1) ; *Haut-Maine* is the basin of Le Mans in the Sarthe valley, *Bas-Maine* the basin of Laval in the Mayenne valley within the slate-country of eastern Armorica (see p. 470).

The regional unity of the Pays de la Sarthe then is due to the fact that it occupies the basin of the Sarthe and its main headstream the Huisne, though three distinct types of landscape can be distinguished. The '*pays argileux*' is the *bocage* country referred to above. Areas of limestone, the '*pays calcaire*', form the higher interfluves between the valleys and resemble the *campagnes* further to the north described below. Thirdly, a considerable cover of Cretaceous sands extends between the Sarthe and the Loir, forming the '*région des sables du Mans*' or '*le pays manceau*' ; names such as Sablé-sur-Sarthe are indicative of its character. Much consists of heathland, though tracts of conifers have been planted, mostly maritime pines, exploited for resin since the beginning of the nineteenth century. Near Le Mans these light soils, when heavily fertilised, are used for market-gardening. Occasionally the sands are more compact and form a reddish stone known locally as '*le roussard*', which has been used for churches and other buildings in Le Mans. Among these Cretaceous sands a small isolated patch of Jurassic clays appears around the town of Ecommoy to the south-east of Le Mans. This covers the floor of a former dome from which the overlying Cretaceous rocks have been denuded. Its damp rich soils form such a contrast to the dry hungry sands of the surrounding country that it is actually known as the *Oasis du Belinois* ; [1] '*des ruisseaux jaseurs coulent en minces filets ou se brisent en cascatelles*'.[2]

The Pays d'Auge.—A narrow strip of Oxford Clay between the Chalk and the Jurassic limestones has been eroded by the river Dives flowing north to the Baie de la Seine, so forming the broad valley, with gently sloping sides, of the Pays d'Auge. The river wanders across this plain, which is thickly covered with alluvium.

The Campagnes Bas-Normandes.—To the west of the Oxford Clay of the Pays d'Auge is a long north-south outcrop of Oolitic Limestone. It forms in the north the low plateau of Caen (the *Campagne de Caen*), which reaches the coast to the west of the mouth of the

---

[1] J. Bienfait, 'Le Belinois', in *Norois* (1954), vol. iii, pp. 219-30.
[2] E. Bruley, *Géographie des Pays de la Loire* (1937), p. 146.

Dives at Ouistreham. This gives rise to the rocky coastline already described, which contrasts with the earthy cliffs of Cretaceous clays to the east of the Dives. The limestone extends southward, interrupted in the neighbourhood of Falaise by an easterly projection of Cambrian slates; the limestone here forms a quite prominent escarpment. Further south the Oolite follows the eastern edge of the Palaeozoic rocks, rising as the *Campagne d'Argentan* to the north of the town of that name, and forming a watershed between the north-flowing Orne and Dives and the south-flowing headstreams of the Sarthe. Further south the limestone plateau is known after the chief town of the upper Sarthe basin as the *Campagne d'Alençon*. The Oolite exposure trends away southward along the edge of the Palaeozoic rocks, becoming more attenuated until it disappears in the Sarthe valley near Saldé-sur-Sarthe.

The term *campagne* which has been applied to these limestone plateaus is akin to the word *champagne*, indicating an open gently undulating surface mainly given over to large fields and arable cultivation.

The Plaine du Bessin.—The river Aure and its long headstream the Dromme rise in the limestone country of the Campagne de Caen, and flow northwards in well-defined valleys to within two miles of the coast near Port-en-Bessin. The Aure then makes a remarkable right-angled bend and flows westwards for nearly twenty miles parallel to the coast, though separated from it by a limestone spur. This lowland, where the Lower Jurassic clays outcrop, is known as the Plaine du Bessin. Further west these clays are covered by the sediments deposited by the rivers Vire and Taute, which enter the south-eastern and south-western angles respectively of the Baie des Veys. Both the sediments and the clays have been largely drained and reclaimed by a close network of channels.

LAND-USE

It is clear from this description of the physical features of central Normandy that a great variation appears in the agriculture practised on the damp valleys and claylands, the *limon*-covered Chalk, and the limestone plateaus both with and without an appreciable clay cover. Climatically this part of Normandy has distinct maritime tendencies. Ste. Honorine-du-Fay (to the south-east of Caen) experiences a range of only 24° F. between the mean January (39° F.) and July (63° F.) temperatures, while on the coast this range is still less marked and the January temperature is about 44° F. Rainfall averages 28 to 30 inches, two or three inches less than that received by the more exposed Breton peninsula to the west, and it is evenly distributed throughout the year.

Central Normandy forms an agricultural transition area between Armorica and the Paris Basin proper. The *limon*-covered Chalk and the clay-covered limestone grow cereals and roots, as in the eastern Paris Basin, but with an emphasis on oats as the main cereal and on potatoes as the chief root-crop. The clays and the reclaimed marshlands of the river valleys provide excellent pasture for dairy cattle, and in places they are intensively cultivated under market-gardens, growing early vegetables. Large orchards of cider-apples are found, especially in the Pays d'Auge; cider is the *vin du pays* of Normandy, although less so, it is said, than in the past, for both beer and wine are gaining ground at its expense. A potent liqueur, *Calvados*, is distilled locally from apple-juice.

The two *départements* of Calvados and Eure are included in the region under discussion, and the following figures are revealing:

Land-Use, 1963

(*Percentages of Total Area*)

	Arable	Of which Cereals	Permanent Pasture	Woodland
Eure. . .	41	60	27	19
Calvados . .	23	58	58	6

Source: *Ministère de l'Agriculture*, quoted by *Annuaire statistique de la France*, 1964.

The significant facts are that Eure, the more easterly *département*, has twice as much arable as Calvados but less than half the proportion of pasture. This progressive transition westward towards the pastoral economy of Brittany is further demonstrated by the fact that the next *département* to the west, Manche, had 73 per cent of its area under permanent pasture and only 12 per cent under arable.

Mixed farming is therefore characteristic of central Normandy, but with an emphasis on arable in Eure and on livestock in Calvados, though in the latter the limestone Campagne de Caen forms an exception, for it is almost wholly under the plough. In 1963 there were 476,000 cattle in Calvados and 340,000 in Eure, notably the famous *race normande*, producing milk for the Paris market and for cheese-making. This is the area of origin of the three well-known Normandy cheeses—*Camembert*, *Livarot* and *Pont-l'Evêque*, each called after the original village of production. *Camembert* was first made in the village of that name in 1761 by Madame Marie Harel, to whose memory a monument fittingly stands in the main

square. Various fresh cream-cheeses are also processed here—
Gournay, Petit-Suisse, Bonde, Neufchâtel and others. Poultry and
pig-rearing (162,000 pigs in the two *départements*) are obvious concomitants of the dairying industry, and horses are still bred in considerable numbers in this area; Perche is the home of the famous
Percheron.

POPULATION AND SETTLEMENT

Population is dispersed widely in small villages along the river
valleys in the chalk-lands to the east, and near the coast where breaks
occur in the cliffs. The only place of any size in the eastern chalk-
lands is Evreux in the valley of the Iton, a pleasant town of 40,158
people in 1962, a market-centre and the *chef-lieu* of Eure. A few
small ports, notably Port-en-Bessin, Grand-Camp and Isigny, carry
on inshore fishing and the collection of lobsters and shell-fish. The
numerous seaside resorts include the fashionable Deauville; the
suffixes *-sur-Mer*, *les-Bains* and *-plage* are freely bestowed along this
coast. Bayeux stands some distance from the sea on the river Aure,
serving as the market-town for the Pays de Bessin, with some old-
established industries such as pottery and lace-making. Lisieux in
the valley of the Touques has been a little market-town for centuries,
but the canonisation of Ste Thérèse in 1923 made it a famous place
of pilgrimage.

Further west several towns lie along a natural route way running
from the Loire valley to the coast of Normandy east of the Cotentin
peninsula, utilising the Sarthe valley in the south and the Orne valley
in the north. The most important town in the south is Le Mans, the
regional centre of the middle Sarthe basin, once capital of the duchy
of Maine, now *chef-lieu* of the *département* of Sarthe. The old town
stands upstream of the confluence of the Sarthe and the Huisne,
dominated by the cathedral on a prominent hill; the new town has
expanded southward along the right bank of the main stream. Le
Mans is now a regional centre of some importance for the Sarthe
basin and for much of western Normandy; its population in 1962
was 136,083. It has a variety of industries, including the manufacture of automobiles and aircraft, agricultural machinery and light
metallurgical articles. A large chemical factory produces pharmaceutical drugs and fertilisers, and there are also a tobacco factory,
clothing factories and an old-established works which makes stained
glass. Le Mans is a major route-centre, for here cross the north-
south Caen–Angers and east-west Paris–Rennes routes, and the town
is famous for its motor-racing circuit. Further north are the towns
of Alençon (with about 27,000 inhabitants), which is a market-centre
and also has nearby granite and kaolin quarries, and Argentan in
the upper Orne valley.

The chief town of Calvados is Caen (with 95,238 people in 1962), a place of lengthy historical antecedents; it was indeed the residence of William the Conqueror. The town was grievously damaged during the initial heavy fighting following the Allied landings in the summer of 1944. It has been triumphantly rebuilt in modern style; symbolically, its new university buildings were opened in the summer of 1957. It is linked to the sea at Ouistreham by the lateral *Canal Maritime*, nine miles in length. Caen combines the functions of a prosperous market-centre for the varied agriculture of the *campagne* with modern large-scale industry, notably the production of steel.

The Normandy Iron and Steel Industry.—The iron-ore fields of north-western France (Fig. 72) occur for the most part near the western margins of the Armorican massif. Much of the ore is smelted near Caen, so it is convenient to describe the ore-fields here. The ferruginous rocks, mainly Ordovician oolites, are preserved for the most part in synclines within the Pre-Cambrian sandstones and quartzites. Where the iron-bearing beds were exposed on the surface by denudation, the carbonates were oxidised into hematites; most of these have been worked out as a result of their accessibility, tolerable richness (over 60 per cent metal in places) and non-phosphoric quality. Elsewhere the ore is a granular calcareous *minette*, with some 30 to 40 per cent iron, though less phosphoric than the Lorraine ores.

Four individual synclines containing these ferruginous rocks can be traced; their trends stand out even on the small-scale map (Fig. 72). To the south of Caen is the May syncline, where mines are worked at May itself, St. André, Maltot and Bully. Then following in order from north to south are the Urville syncline, with Soumont as the chief mining centre, the Falaise syncline containing the mines of Jurques, Ondefontaine, St. Rémy and Mont Pinçon, and then a series of interrupted deposits along the syncline of Mortain-Bagnoles, worked at Mortain, Halouze, La Ferrière-aux-Etangs and elsewhere.

The ironstones were worked as early as pre-Roman times, and on a small scale almost continuously until the mid-nineteenth century, by which time the readily accessible ores had been exhausted. In 1875 geological research revealed the presence of further deposits near May, later at Halouze and La Ferrière-aux-Etangs, with the result that several mining concessions were granted before the end of the century. Little development took place in this predominantly rural and agricultural area, where both capital and labour were unwilling, until foreign interests, notably German, were attracted by the proximity of the deposits to the coast. By 1914 twenty concessions had been granted, of which eleven were controlled by German groups.

By 1913 production had reached an annual output of 800,000 tons, the whole of which was sent out of the district. In that year 490,000 tons were exported by sea from Granville, St. Malo and Caen, of which Rotterdam took 262,000 tons (then sent up the Rhine by barge to Duisburg and the Ruhr), Emden received 66,500 tons (which also went to the Ruhr via the Dortmund-Ems Canal), and the rest, mostly haematite, went to Great Britain—to South Wales, Middlesbrough and Workington.

The outbreak of war in 1914 had a notable effect on the French iron industry, when the north-eastern industrial area, including the Briey and Longwy *minette* regions, were enemy occupied. France had to turn to other supplies of ore, and Normandy became of considerable importance. Output of ore reached a million tons in 1917, and although in the period of post-war reconstruction the recovery of *Lorraine Annexée* dwarfed the Normandy ore-fields, production has continued steadily. Between 1929 and 1937 the yield varied from 1·3 to 1·9 million tons, of which about a third was used locally, rather less than a third went elsewhere in France, and the rest was exported by sea from Caen, mostly to Britain.

During the occupation of 1940–4 the ore-fields were at first prosecuted vigorously, but of course production ceased following the invasion of Normandy and the ore-handling installations were seriously damaged. Production was at first small after the liberation, but this rapidly increased until by 1952 seven mines were yielding 2·5 million tons, a figure which after a slight drop in 1953 has been maintained (2·64 million tons in 1963). About half this ore is exported to Great Britain, the Belgo–Luxembourg Union and West Germany.

Before the war of 1914–18 all the ore produced in the Normandy fields was sent to other consuming areas. In 1910 the industrialist Thyssen established the German-controlled *Société des Hauts Fourneaux de Caen* to erect coke-ovens, by-product plant and six blast-furnaces at Mondeville, to the north-east of Caen. The outbreak of the 1914–18 war intervened, but with the desperate need for munitions it was decided to go ahead, and the company, taken over by the French Government at the outbreak of war, was re-incorporated by the *Schneider* company of Le Creusot as the *Société Métallurgique de Normandie*. In 1916 the coke-ovens and a first blast-furnace were put into operation. In 1920 about 54,000 tons of pig-iron were produced for export. Between the wars the *S.M.N.* extended the works into an integrated steel-making plant, and by 1940 there were six batteries of forty-two coke-ovens, two blast-furnaces, with Bessemer and open-hearth steel-furnaces, and a large rolling-mill producing about a quarter of a million tons of steel. Half of this output was used locally at the shipbuilding yards at Blainville on the banks of the Canal Maritime between Caen and the sea, and at other engineering works in the neighbourhood. During the invasion of the continent in 1944, the Mondeville works were very heavily damaged, but most of the rebuilding was completed by 1951, and production now exceeds that of pre-war years.

CHAPTER 11

THE SCARPLANDS AND VALES
OF LORRAINE

It is not easy to define Lorraine as a geographical region, largely because it forms a transition zone between the outer cuestas of the Paris Basin and the massif of the Vosges.[1] The name has for long had a political connotation; for centuries it was a dukedom on France's eastern frontiers, not formally incorporated into that country until as late as 1766. In 1871 the eastern part (now the French *département* of Moselle) was absorbed with Alsace (Haut- and Bas-Rhin) into Germany, the annexed area being known as the *Reichsland* and to the French as *Lorraine Annexée*. This did not include all Lorraine; the part left in French hands consisted of the *départements* of Meuse, Meurthe-et-Moselle and Vosges. The annexed territory was returned to France in 1918, but it was again occupied by Germany in 1940 and it was clear that the conqueror's intention was to integrate the area within the Reich. Although in the period 1871–1918 the two provinces had been administered as a unit, in 1940 Alsace was added to Baden and Lorraine to the *Saar-Pfalz* (the Saar-Palatinate). The latter territory became after 1941 the *Gau Westmark*. Strong measures were put into effect to assimilate Alsace and Lorraine within the Reich, but the spirit of resistance burned strongly among those remaining in the provinces and among the many exiles; the cross of Lorraine symbolised the resistance of Free France. In 1944 the provinces returned to France.

On an administrative basis, therefore, contemporary Lorraine comprises the four *départements* of Moselle, Meuse, Meurthe-et-Moselle and most of Vosges. Geographically, however, it is more convenient to adopt the compromise suggested on pp. 8-10, which takes the watershed between the Aire and the Meuse as the western boundary, the narrow but prominent outcrop of the *Muschelkalk* as the eastern. Lorraine, using this definition, consists of an area of Triassic and Jurassic rocks, with alternating outcrops of limestone and clay. The more resistant limestones form a series of cuestas (the *Côtes*), each with an eastward-facing slope dissected by deep valleys into spurs and outlying fragments, and a plateau-surface sinking gently to the west. Between them occur strata of clays and

[1] A. Blanc, E. Juillard, J. Ray and M. Rochefort, *Les Régions de L'Est* (1960), in the series *France de Demain*, gives a well illustrated survey of Alsace and Lorraine.

marls; where their dip is gentle the outcrop is extensive, forming broad undulating vales with abundant surface drainage and heavy clay soils. The valley of the Meuse is entrenched in the Corallian

FIG. 66.—THE REGIONAL DIVISIONS OF PART OF EASTERN FRANCE.

The neighbouring regions of the Paris Basin and the Saône Basin are not sub-divided (see Figs. 52 and 95 respectively). The numerals I to VIII refer to the sub-regions of Lorraine listed in the text (Chapter 11).

Based on a variety of sources, including (i) *Carte géologique de la France*, 1 : 1,000,000, published by the *Service de la Carte géologique détaillée de la France*; and (ii) map of *Régions géographiques de la France*, 1 : 1,400,000, published by the *Institut National de la Statistique et des Etudes Economiques.*

Limestone of the *Côtes de Meuse*, with its main escarpment beyond the right bank of the river. It is succeeded eastward by the Oxford Clay plain of the *Woëvre*, and then the extensive Oolitic Limestone upland, the *Plateau de la Moselle*, terminating in the dissected edge of the *Côtes de Moselle* overlooking the Moselle valley. To the east again is the '*Plateau Lorraine propre*', continued in the south by the '*Hautes plaines de la Lorraine méridionale*'; the terms '*plateau*' and '*plaine*' are here rather misleading, since the surface of the latter is generally at a higher altitude than that of the former. Both are covered with Lias Clays in the west and with Keuper Marls in the east as far as the *Muschelkalk* scarp.

This distinctive Lorraine region is not limited to France. The northern margin is indicated by the edge of the Ardennes, demarcated by the sudden outcrop of Lower Palaeozoic rocks. Between this clear geological demarcation and the French frontier are two areas of similar Triassic and Jurassic rocks—the *Bon Pays* of Luxembourg and the *Côtes Lorraines* of the Arlon district of south-eastern Belgium. These eight subdivisions are defined in Fig. 66.

I. THE MEUSE VALLEY AND THE CÔTES DE MEUSE

The Upper Jurassic rocks, notably Corallian Limestone, with some Kimmeridge Clay and Portland Limestone further west, form a broad curving outcrop. This appears on the surface to the south-west of Mézières, swings southward to where it attains a maximum width of thirty-five miles in the neighbourhood of Commercy, and then trends south-westward along the flanks of the Central Massif to the neighbourhood of Châteauroux (Fig. 67).

The River Meuse.—The Meuse rises in the Lias district of Bassigny, and receives a number of headstreams across the plain of Lorraine, both from the Triassic ridges of the Monts Faucilles and from the clay-lands, in spite of some encroachments by the Moselle (see p. 260). It then cuts through the Oolitic Limestone in a steep-sided valley, to enter for a short distance the Oxford Clay vale near Neufchâteau. But from just below this town it flows northwards for ninety-five miles, almost to Stenay, in a trench-like valley incised in the Corallian Limestone, parallel to but five to ten miles west of the escarpment (Fig. 68). During this long section the Meuse receives no surface tributaries other than a few streamlets which emerge as springs on the sides of the limestone valley. Formerly the river received tributaries both from the Lower Cretaceous ridges and valleys to the west, now captured by active Seine headstreams such as the Aire (see p. 219), and from the Woëvre to the east, now captured by the Moselle. The Meuse was obviously once much larger, as its deeply-cut valley, with a flood-plain nearly a mile wide, can testify. No longer is it an actively eroding but rather a depositing river; it wanders across its flood-plain, with braided sections, stagnant backwaters and abandoned loops.

FIG. 67.—SIMPLIFIED GEOLOGICAL MAP OF PART OF EASTERN FRANCE.

The numbers in the key are as follows: **13**, Quaternary, Tertiary; **12**, Upper Cretaceous (including Chalk and Upper Greensand); **11**, Lower Cretaceous (Gault Clay); **10**, Upper Jurassic (including Portland Limestone, Kimmeridge Clay, Corallian Limestone and Oxford Clay); **9**, Middle Jurassic (including Oolitic Limestone); **8**, Lower Jurassic (including Lias clays and limestone); **7**, Upper and Middle Trias (Keuper and Muschelkalk); **6**, Lower Trias (sandstones); **5**, Permian, Upper and Middle Carboniferous; **4**, Lower Carboniferous, Devonian, Silurian, Ordovician, Cambrian; **3**, Pre-Cambrian; **2**, eruptive rocks; **1**, granitic and gneissic rocks.

A few towns, inserted to help location, are indicated by initials, as follows: **A**, Arlon; **B**, Briey; **Ba**, Basel; **Be**, Belfort; **Ch**, Chaumont; **Co**, Colmar; **Cs**, Châlons-sur-Marne; **E**, Epinal; **L**, Luxembourg; **Me**, Mézières; **Mu**, Mulhouse; **Mz**, Metz; **Na**, Nancy; **Sb**, Sarrebourg; **Sg**, Sarreguemines; **St**, Strasbourg; **Th**, Thionville; **To**, Toul; **Tr**, Trier; **Ve**, Verdun.

Based on *Carte géologique de la France*, 1:1,000,000, published by the *Service de la Carte géologique détaillée de la France*.

In its natural state the Meuse would be of little use for navigation, but it has been regularised and improved from Troussey, where it is linked to the Marne-Rhine Canal, to the Belgian frontier (Fig. 85). Part of the river has been incorporated into the northern section of the Est Canal; loops have been cut through to straighten the course and four tunnels have been constructed through meander-cores. Its natural régime is very variable; heavy rains on the impermeable clays of the Lorraine plateau formerly caused rapid run-off and serious flooding downstream, both in winter and in late summer, while conversely after a long spell of drought in early summer the river would degenerate in places to shrunken trickles among the gravel-banks. The bed has been deepened by dredging, and fifty-nine locks were constructed in order to maintain an effective depth of seven feet. The river flows not on the Oolite but on a layer of its own alluvium, in places as much as thirty feet thick, deposited in its more active days. This has produced an impermeable bed, and there is little loss by infiltration.

Despite difficulties, the French section of the Meuse and the Est Canal carries annually about 2·4 million tons of freight, including coal, pit-props, building-stone and bricks. It passes through such important towns as Verdun (where it is contained in a tunnel under the fortifications), Stenay, Sedan and Mézières-Charleville (see p. 222). Moreover, there is a useful trans-frontier traffic; about three-quarters of a million tons of freight moves in each direction.

The Côtes de Meuse.—To the east of the Meuse valley is the line of the Côtes de Meuse. While the floor of the valley near Verdun lies at 670 feet, on the ridge-line only a mile or two to the east heights of 1,270 feet are attained; the highest point of the Côtes de Meuse is actually 1,352 feet. The summit level of this ridge is remarkably uniform, but several deep dry valleys eroded by former Meuse tributaries from the east dissect it into a number of steep-sided flat-topped hills, particularly in the south. A clearly defined gap, utilised by the Marne-Rhine Canal, lies west of Toul (Fig. 71).

Much of the ridge is thickly forested, mostly planted by the Government department of *Eaux et Forêts*. The concentrated devastation of the war of 1914–18 destroyed about 35,000 acres of forest in the neighbourhood of Verdun, most of which had been replanted by 1938. The Forêt d'Amblonville to the south-east of Verdun continues unbroken southward as the Forêt de la Montagne and the Forêt d'Apremont.

Settlement.—Several towns situated along the Meuse valley have functioned as fortresses for much of their existence—Neufchâteau, Void, St. Mihiel and Verdun itself. The Corallian ridge, with its outward escarpment backed by the Meuse trough, formed a definite transverse obstacle, a major defensive line against any thrust into

FIG. 68.—THE CÔTES DE MEUSE AND MOSELLE, AND THE WOËVRE.

The steep edges of the east-facing *Côtes* and of the western edge of the Meuse valley are indicated in a generalised way by hachures. Heights are given in feet. The map stresses (i) the limited narrow trench of the Meuse, with only a few short tributaries from either side; (ii) the damp surface of the clay-covered Woëvre, with numerous small lakes and a dense pattern of streams, draining either east to the Moselle or north to the Chiers and so to the Meuse; (iii) the dissected edges of the *Côtes*.

A few of the many villages along the foot of the Côte de Meuse are shown (-*sous-les-Côtes*). Note, however, the misleading Rupt-en-Woëvre and Savonnières-en-Woëvre, which are not in the Woëvre as here defined.

Based on *Carte de France et des frontières au 200,000ᵉ*, sheets 17, 18.

the Paris Basin. The greatest of these fortresses—Verdun—stands at the crossing-point of the Meuse valley route through eastern France

Mézières, Sedan, Verdun, Toul, Dijon) and the vital east–west line from Metz via Reims or Châlons-sur-Marne to Paris. Limestone bluffs project westward to north and south of the town, and the old citadel was built on a massive hillock. Verdun has been a fortress since before Roman times; it was greatly developed by Vauban in the reign of Louis XIV, and was immeasurably strengthened between 1871 and 1914. As a result, Marshal Pétain's successful defence in 1916–17 ('*Ils ne passeront pas*') cost the lives of over half a million men. The fortified hills surrounding the town were the scene of constant assaults and repulses; the grim name of one hill, le Mort Homme, bears testimony to this.

Settlements to the east of the Meuse are confined to the deeper valleys which have been cut down through the Corallian into the underlying clay, where water is obtainable and where meadows and small patches of arable land occur. Examples of these dip-slope valley villages are Sommedieue, Dompierre-aux-Bois and Lamorville in the section of the Côtes between St. Mihiel and Verdun. Economically the Côtes have little value, other than as a source of timber (notably pit-props), of building-stone which is quarried at Euville, Commercy and elsewhere, and of agricultural lime and cement. The proximity of the Est Canal is useful for the export of these bulky commodities.

II. THE OXFORD-CLAY VALE

Between the underlying Oolites and the overlying Corallian Limestone occurs a considerable thickness of Oxford Clay, dipping gently westward. Its outcrop can be traced from near Mézières, trending south-eastward to the Meuse at Stenay, then swinging southward to Neufchâteau. It is of no great width, varying between twelve and fifteen miles, while to the south of Toul it forms only a narrow strip of two or three miles, where it is known as *Soulossois* (Fig. 71). Nevertheless, it makes a distinctive contribution to the Lorraine landscape, forming a gently undulating vale about 650 feet above sea-level.

The *pays*-name *Woëvre* is applied to this clay-vale, derived from the Latin word *wabra*, meaning a thicket. This element appears commonly in the local place-names, as in Fresnes-en-Woëvre and St. Benoît-de-Woëvre. Unfortunately, the generic 'Woëvre' is used outside the present accepted limits of the *pays*; thus Rupt-en-Woëvre and Savonnières-en-Woëvre each lie in the valley of a short Meuse tributary, well to the west of the Corallian crest-line (Fig. 68). But the Woëvre in its present *pays*-sense is restricted to the Oxford-Clay vale.

The Oxford Clay consists of a heavy blue clay well over 650 feet in thickness, overlain by some calcareous marls known as *terrain à chailles*. Much of this superficial cover is derived from both the Oolitic and the Corallian Limestones, providing a soil which is inherently fertile, although heavy, rather cold and often waterlogged as a result of the impermeable sub-stratum. The vale is characterised by abundant surface drainage, a multiplicity of wandering streams and shallow lakes ; the latter increase considerably in size during the winter (Fig. 68). The largest is the Etang de Lachaussée in the south, drained by the Yron, thence to the Orne.

It is probable that the waters of the Woëvre once drained westwards to the Meuse, as evidenced by the several high-level dry valleys through the Côtes de Meuse. The more active Moselle to the east, flowing in a much lower valley, has gradually captured the greater part of the Woëvre drainage. The streams rise near the eastern edge of the Côtes de Meuse at the junction of the Corallian and the clay, wander vaguely eastwards against the dip of the strata (and indeed against the general slope) until they converge to form a few larger rivers—Ache, Rupt de Mad, Orne (the master-stream of the district), and Fentsch, which then cross the Oolitic plateau in several striking gorges (see p. 253). The northern part of this clay-vale drains by way of the Crusnes and the Othain to the Chiers below Montmédy, and so to the Meuse.

Land-Use and Agriculture.—The Woëvre has some importance for agriculture, particularly in the slightly higher areas flanking the Côtes de Meuse, where calcareous downwash has enriched the soil. Considerable artificial drainage has extended the area of arable land, notably for the cultivation of wheat, oats and potatoes, and permanent grassland supports dairying activity. Vineyards are found on the lower slopes of the Côtes de Meuse and their eastern outliers, producing *vin ordinaire*, and there are orchards, particularly of stone-fruits such as plums and cherries. But much of the Woëvre is too wet for farmland, and considerable tracts of woodland survive among the small lakes and marshes. The Etang de Lachaussée is surrounded by the extensive Bois des Haudronvilles.

Settlement.—On a population map much of the Woëvre stands out with an average density of less than fifty people per square mile. Villages are small and somewhat scattered, usually on the higher eminences of the Corallian outliers, such as Loupmont on the lower slopes of a hillock named simply Le Mont. Other settlements occur along the foot of the Corallian slope, including a long string of villages with the suffix '*sous-les-Côtes*', especially along the steep continuous section between Verdun and St. Mihiel. Sometimes a village lies quite up the escarpment in a south-facing hollow, such as

Moulainville, while at the foot of the escarpment near the spring-line is Moulainville-la-Basse. An example of a hamlet named from its location is Le Mont Sec, fifteen miles east of St. Mihiel; the village perches on the north-eastern side of a prominent little hillock, over-looking the depression containing the Etang de la Perche.

III. THE PLATEAU AND CÔTES DE MOSELLE

Rocks of Middle Jurassic age, mainly Oolitic limestones, clays and marls, appear on the surface near Hirson in northern France as a narrow belt between the chalk-lands of the Paris Basin and the Palaeozoic rocks of the Ardennes. This outcrop trends in a direction south of east, and is crossed by the alluvium-floored Meuse valley just above the Chiers confluence. To the east of Montmédy, however, the outcrop widens and swings away southward, forming a triangular plateau, the base of which lies along the Belgian and Luxembourg frontiers for a distance of about twenty-five miles, while its apex is situated sixty miles to the south near Nancy. The northern part is known as the Plateau de Briey, then comes the Plateau de Jarnisy, and in the south the Plateau de Haye. A small portion of the upland, isolated by the right angle of the Moselle to the east of Toul, is known as the Forêt de Haye, and other outlying portions survive to the east of the Moselle between Nancy and Metz (Fig. 71). From where the valley of the Moselle cuts across the Jurassic plateau, the outcrop trends south-westward, first as a narrow belt, then widening to form the Plateau de Langres, the southern boundary of the Seine basin.

This Oolitic plateau, with an undulating surface of flat-topped ridges a thousand feet above sea-level, rises slowly eastward to a prominent escarpment (the *Côtes de Moselle*), overlooking in the north the Lias plateau of the southern Bon Pays of Luxembourg, and in the east first the Moselle valley as far south as the Meurthe confluence and then the clay-plain of Lorraine. The escarpment in the north rises to a height of 1,388 feet, falling within a distance of only three or four miles to the Moselle valley at about 500 feet. To the south of Toul the highest point on the main ridge rises to 1,660 feet, although in point of fact the maximum elevation attained in the *Côtes* is provided by an Oolitic outlier in the plain of Lorraine to the east, the prominent Butte de Vaudémont or de Sion (1,788 feet).

Both the plateau and the escarpment are deeply trenched by rivers. In the south a number of Meuse headstreams (Mouzon, Anger, Frézelle, Vair, Vraine), which rise in the Keuper or Lias plain of Lorraine, cut right across the Oolitic plateau. The Meuse itself traverses the outcrop just above Neufchâteau, and the Moselle not only crosses it between Pont-St. Vincent and Toul but also recrosses between Toul and Frouard. A remarkable river-capture is responsible for this seeming anomaly (Fig. 71, and see p. 260). The Plateau de Haye is seamed with dry valleys which once drained north-westwards to the Meuse from the clay-plains of *Xaintois* (see p. 275). The lowered water-table, the result of the much lower level of the Madon (a left-bank tributary which joins the Moselle at Pont-St. Vincent), has left these valleys dry, except where they have been cut right down into the Lias clays. Here as a result springs have been formed, the waters of which mostly find their way north-eastwards to the Madon.

Further north the plateau and escarpment are cut across by several left-bank Moselle tributaries, which rise in the claylands of the Woëvre, as already described, and flow eastwards. The Ache and the Rupt de Mad are both contained in steep-sided valleys which become increasingly prominent as the escarpment edge is approached, their floors lying at 50 to 250 feet below the plateau-surface, and further north still the Orne (Fig. 74) and the Fentsch flow in deep almost gorge-like valleys. In the extreme north, near the frontier, the escarpment is incised by the northward-flowing Alzette and its tributaries the Kayl and the Dudelange (Fig. 80). The Chiers pursues an unusual course, for it rises in Luxembourg and flows westwards before cutting south-westwards through the Oolitic escarpment, then picking up its tributaries the Othain and the Crusnes, and finally joining the Meuse.

Land-Use and Agriculture.—The soils vary considerably. Over the southern Plateau de Haye a kind of reddish sandy-clay is found, known as *terre-rouge*, which tends to be dry and 'hungry'. On the lower valley-sides calcareous downwash provides a much better soil, and the valley bottoms are covered with alluvium. In the north the more extensive occurrence of marls and clays allows the development of quite reasonable soils, used for arable farming. Some areas of coarse gravel and sand, often containing quite large sandstone fragments, are the remains of diluvial deposits of the former consequent rivers flowing north-westwards from the Vosges before the present scarp-and-vale drainage system evolved.

Extensive forests occur, particularly in the south where a large part of the Plateau de Haye is wooded, and also the Forêt de Haye lies in the angle of the Moselle-Meurthe confluence. Less continuous patches of woodland are found in the north, particularly on the gravels.

Much of the Briey plateau is under arable, growing wheat and potatoes. Vineyards appear both along the south-east facing slopes of the Côtes de Moselle and on the sides of the valleys which cut across the plateau. Hops and stone-fruits such as plums and cherries grow well in these calcareous soils.

The Iron-Ore Deposits.—The major significance of the Middle Jurassic plateau results from the fact that between the overlying Oolites and the underlying Lias occurs a considerable thickness of iron-ore, known as *minette*, the largest deposits in Europe. The ore consists of either a *chamosite* (a silicate of iron) or a *siderite* (a carbonate of iron), of oolitic structure with minute spherical concretions within a calcareous matrix, except in the Nancy basin in the south where the matrix is markedly siliceous. The iron content varies considerably in the different beds from 24 to as much as 40 per cent, although the richer ores have been largely exhausted; the average content of ores now worked is of the order of 33 per cent. They contain from about 1·7 to 1·9 per cent of phosphorus, and so before the introduction of the Gilchrist-Thomas process neither wrought iron nor steel could be successfully made. The term '*minette*' was therefore contemptuously applied to these ores.

The overall thickness of the ore-bearing strata varies from 80 to 130 feet, within which as many as seven distinct beds may be distinguished. Near the top of the deposit is a bed of ore which has a relatively high iron content of 40 per cent or more, but is sandy or gravelly and exceedingly friable. Below this is to be found the 'calcareous red' bed (a ferruginous limestone), the best *minette* ore, with an iron content of 40 per cent; unfortunately these deposits are approaching exhaustion and indeed have been worked out in many areas. Beneath this again lies the 'calcareous yellow' bed, not quite so rich, but actively worked in the Orne valley. The most widespread bed is the 'grey', which is usually calcareous in France. It has a lowish iron content varying from 24 to 32 per cent, but today it is the most extensively worked for it occurs in layers of up to twenty feet thick. Beneath this are the 'brown bed', the 'black bed' which is markedly siliceous, and the underlying 'green bed' three to nine feet in thickness but highly pyritous; these are but little worked.

The Jurassic and underlying strata dip gently south-westward; as a result, while the ore-beds appear at the surface on the scarp-faces and valley-sides in the north and east, they occur at progressively greater depths to the west. Ore has in fact been proved as far west as Verdun at about 1,900 feet below the surface. The low iron content obviously makes deep mining uneconomic, and the area shown on Fig. 69 represents the limit of the worked areas and concessions at the present time. Apart from the low iron content and phosphoric character of Lorraine ore, further geographical drawbacks are the difficult terrain with steep-sided valleys and escarpments, the distance from adequate supplies of coking coal, and its vulnerable European position near the meeting-place of four countries.

On the other hand, the ore-field has some positive advantages, apart from its estimated reserves of 8,000 million tons in France and a further 200 millions in Luxembourg.[1] The dip of the strata is gentle, there is usually little structural disturbance so that the beds are continuous, and mining is highly mechanised and cheap. The deeply trenched valleys enable much ore to be won by horizontal galleries driven into the hill-sides and even in some districts by open quarries, although in places shaft-mining is used. A large proportion of the ore is calcareous and therefore self-fluxing in the blast-furnaces, while the juxtaposition of various qualities enables the siliceous and calcareous ores to be mixed to form self-fluxing charges. Finally, the geographical position which has brought travail to Lorraine three times in seventy years has paradoxically meant that at the heart of the industrial complex of western Europe it has shared in its development. The contribution of Lorraine to the French iron and steel industry is shown by the following table:

Output of Iron-Ore in France

(*Million Tons*)

	1929	1937	1952	1958	1963
Lorraine	48·00	35·42	37·75	55·91	54·38
Normandy	1·88	1·94	2·47	2·83	2·64
Anjou-Brittany . . .	0·53	0·38	0·58	1·03	0·77
Others	0·32	0·08	0·38	0·40	0·10
France	50·73	37·82	41·18	60·17	57·89

Source: Successive volumes of *Annuaire statistique de la France* (Paris) and publications of the *Chambre Syndicale de la Sidérurgie française.*

The Ore Basins.—The *minette* field is divided by faults and intervening barren ground into four individual districts: those of Nancy, Briey, Longwy and Moselle. Administratively the whole field comes under two regions of the *Chambre Syndicale de la Sidérurgie* (Fig. 72), namely *Est I*, which comprises the Longwy, the greater part of the Briey, and the Nancy basins in the *département* of Meurthe-et-Moselle, and *Est II*, which includes the Moselle field in the *département* of Moselle. Output is dominated by Briey and Moselle, as the following table shows:

[1] The estimates produced by the Economic Commission for Europe in 1949 gave the *iron content* of the total French reserves (of which about 10 per cent lie outside Lorraine) as 2,277 million tons, and of the Luxembourg *minette* field as 63 million tons. A later estimate gives the French total as 2,692 million tons.

Output of Iron-Ore

(Million Tons)

	1929	1937	1952	1958	1963
Briey	21·35	16·53	18·28	27·78	26·25
Longwy	3·78	2·26	2·26	2·88	3·23
Nancy	1·49	1·00	0·93	1·93	1·95
Moselle	21·37	15·63	16·28	23·32	22·95
Lorraine	47·99	35·42	37·75	55·91	54·38

Source: For 1929 and 1937, *Statistique de l'Industrie minérale*; for 1952 *Mémento de Statistique*, published by the E.C.S.C., Luxembourg; for 1958, 1963, *Chambre Syndicale de la Sidérurgie française*.

The detached Nancy basin in the south, the first to be worked, produces rather low-grade siliceous ores, which moreover are sandy and friable and so are mostly smelted locally, using as fluxes calcareous ores brought from further north.   Nevertheless, the ore is cheaply mined by adits driven into the steep eastern slope of the Forêt de Haye and along the edge of the outlier of the Bois de Faulx (Fig. 69); about a million tons have been produced annually in recent years.   Some ore is shipped by barge from Maxéville, the port of Nancy, by the Marne-Rhine and Sarre Colliery canals to the Saar.

The main mining areas in the Briey basin occur in the upper parts of the Orne valley between Jœuf and Conflans, in the upper parts of the Woigot valley to the north-west of Briey near Tucquegnieux, and further west in the upper Othain valley between Landres and Domremy.   Most of the mining here is by shafts as much as 300 feet in depth.   Its isolated situation, together paradoxically with the transportable quality of the ores and their calcareous nature which makes them valuable for mixing, has resulted in an absence of iron- and steel-works in this plateau area, and much ore is sent away by rail.

The plateau of Briey ends abruptly in the north more or less along the international frontier, and is bounded on the north-west by the Chiers valley.   The headstreams of this river and its neighbour the Alzette have dissected the scarp-edge, where the ferruginous sandstones of the Chiers basin outcrop.   These ores consist mainly of the sandy 'Upper Red' beds, which are particularly friable.   The important centre of Longwy, which has given its name to the whole northern industrial basin, lies in the Chiers valley near its junction with that of the Godbrange.   The ore is worked mainly by galleries opening out into the steep-sided valleys, although at Hussigny it occurs so near the surface that it is obtained by open-cast methods. Mining activity in this northern basin is continuous with that of Luxembourg; mineral-lines and cable-railways cross the frontier in

XXIX Reims

XXX Champagne vineyards near Epernay along the Marne Lateral Canal

XXXI Part of the Pays de Caux

XXXII The Port-Jérôme oil-refinery on the Seine between Le Havre and Rouen several places, and several French mines are owned by Luxembourg companies.

The Moselle basin occurs in what was formerly German Lorraine. While ore-beds have been proved from north of Pont-à-Mousson continuously to the Luxembourg frontier, mining is concentrated in certain districts. Two of these follow the narrow lower valleys of the Orne and the Fentsch, where galleries can be driven into the steep hill-sides. South of Jœuf, in the Orne valley, deep mines are sunk into the plateau surface itself, as near Montois-la-Montagne, Ste. Marie-aux-Chênes and St. Privat-la-Montagne (Fig. 74). Much of the ore is siliceous, hence the need for supplies of calcareous ore from mines further west in the Briey basin.

Two groups of mines near Redange and Russange belong geographically and geologically to the Longwy region, but are in the *département* of Moselle (*Région Est II*). The reasons for this date back to 1871, when Germany defined the new frontier.

Settlement.—A major iron- and steel-producing region based on these ore-fields has developed in Lorraine, for the most part along the foot of the eastern escarpment between Maizières and Thionville ; it is therefore convenient to describe this industrial development as a whole in the next regional section (the Moselle valley). It must not be forgotten, however, that the steel industry has also developed along the narrow valleys of the Orne and Fentsch and within the Plateau de Briey, and along the northern valleys of the Chiers and its headstreams. A continuous succession of modern integrated steel-works and coke-oven plants has grown up, with crowded towns which have expanded chaotically from small villages, and modern well-planned housing-estates. It is estimated that the population of the Orne and Fentsch valleys trebled between 1891 and 1906, the results of industrial expansion following the introduction of the Gilchrist-Thomas process, and there was further rapid growth after the war of 1914–18. The large labour requirements were met in part by the introduction of foreign workers, notably of Poles and Italians, as elsewhere in the mines and factories of western Europe ; the results of this immigration during the years following the war of 1914–18 are shown by the fact that of the total population of 147,074 in the *arrondissement* of Briey in 1926, no less than 60,278 were foreigners.[1] After the war of 1939–45 another great influx of foreign and stateless workers took place to help meet the demands of the expanding steel industry. Today long lines of dense industrial settlements are separated by thinly populated plateau surfaces, with their arable farms and woodlands. While

[1] See A. Sömme, *La Lorraine métallurgique* (1938), chapter xvii, 'Les Italiens et les Polonais sur le Plateau de Briey', pp. 146-50.

R.G.W.E.—K

FIG. 69.—THE IRON-ORE BASINS OF LORRAINE.

The map indicates the *département* boundary between Moselle and Meurthe-et-Moselle, i.e. the Franco-German boundary in 1871–1919 and 1940–4, when *Lorraine Annexée* (the *département* of Moselle) was included in Germany. Iron-ore mines in Luxembourg are not shown.

Based on: (i) *Carte industrielle de la Lorraine* (1930); (ii) *Atlas de France*, 'Richesse minérales concessibles' (sheet 44) (1933); (iii) *Cartes de France et des frontières au 200,000ᵉ*, sheets 11, 18, 27; (iv) post-1945 information from various official sources.

FIG. 70.—THE LORRAINE IRON AND STEEL INDUSTRY.

Minor steel-works and steel-using industries are not shown. The boundary of the Saar before January 1st, 1957 is indicated.

Based on (i) *Carte industrielle de la Lorraine* (1930); (ii) *Cartes de France et des frontières au 200,000ᵉ*, sheets 11, 18, 27; (iii) post-1945 information derived from *Statistical Bulletin*, vol. 28, no. 2 (1953), and *ibid.*, vol. 30, no. 8 (1955), published by the British Iron and Steel Federation.

some drain of population has gone on from these intervening agricultural districts, the small villages on the plateau have continued their placid existence, though obviously benefiting from the expanding markets in the adjacent crowded industrial areas.

IV. THE MOSELLE VALLEY

The Moselle valley is shown as a unit-region on Fig. 66, extending from the Meurthe confluence northward to the point where it leaves France. The Moselle, which flows for 319 miles through west-central Europe, takes its rise in a number of small headstreams on the north-western flanks of the granitic Ballon d'Alsace in the High Vosges (Fig. 118). The river flows more or less north-westwards, first over the crystalline rocks, then across the Triassic sandstone country (see p. 513) where it is enclosed for some distance within a forested gorge, over the undulating plain of Lorraine, and so reaches the Oolite outcrop at Pont-St. Vincent.

It seems that the Moselle once continued its westerly trend across this Oolitic plateau, the narrow Oxford Clay belt and the Corallian cuesta in turn, so forming one of the main headstreams of its neighbour to the west, the present Meuse. The Meurthe and the lower Moselle then formed a single consequent stream, which was more active than the proto-Meuse, partly because its volume was greater, partly because its gradient was steeper, for the Meuse rises at a much lower altitude. Fifty miles from their sources the Meuse and the Moselle are descending at a rate of about three and twelve feet per mile respectively, and where the rivers approach most closely the floor of the Meuse is more than 150 feet above that of the Moselle. The original Meurthe-Moselle consequent developed an active subsequent tributary which cut back through the Oolitic Limestone into the Oxford Clay vale and captured what is now the upper Moselle at Toul, forming a magnificent 'elbow of capture' (Fig. 71). The result is that the Moselle now flows across the Oolite to Toul on the edge of the Oxford Clay, but then turns abruptly north then north-east across the Oolite again to the Meurthe junction at Custines. A small obsequent, the Ane or Asne, occupies the 'Toul Gap' or the Val de l'Ane, the former course of the river, which is now utilised by the Marne-Rhine Canal (Fig. 71), and by the main railway-line between Paris, Nancy and Strasbourg. Toul, at the eastern end of the gap, and dominated to the north by the twin Corallian buttes of the Côte St. Michel and Côte Barine, was for long a fortress town, utilising these steep-sided hills for fortifications.

From the Meurthe confluence the Moselle winds northwards along the edge of the Lias plain in a broad alluvium-floored valley closely bounded on the west by the steep dissected edge of the Côtes de Moselle. Outliers of Oolitic Limestone cap the Grand Couronnée de Nancy, and the Côte de Delme forms a prominent little ridge rising to 1,322 feet to the east of the river Seille. In the angle of the Moselle-Seille confluence stands the old fortress-town of Metz.

FIG. 71.—THE TOUL GAP.

The abbreviations of towns are as follows: **C**, Commercy; **Cu**, Custines; **Dom**, Dombasle; **Fr**, Frouard; **G**, Gironville; **J**, Jouy-sous-les-Côtes; **P**, Pompey; **PM**, Pont-à-Mousson; **P.St.V**, Pont-St. Vincent; **Ros**, Rosières-aux-Salines; **St.N**, St. Nicolas-du-Port; **Tr**, Troussey; **V**, Varangéville.

Based on *Carte de France et des frontières au 200,000ᵉ*, sheets 18, 27.

Thirty miles downstream near Thionville the river again changes direction towards the north-east, cutting through the well-marked north-south Virine cuesta of Liassic limestone in a distinct gap, and so it reaches the point of convergence of the French, West German and Luxembourg frontiers near Schengen.

The river is unnavigable above the Meurthe confluence, although from near Epinal to Toul its valley is utilised by the southern branch of the lateral Est Canal, which runs first on one side of the river, then on the other, and from Toul to Frouard it is paralleled by fifteen miles of the Marne-Rhine Canal. Between Frouard and Metz the river is canalised, and from Metz to Thionville sections of its course are utilised by the lateral *Canal des Mines de Fer de la Moselle* (Fig. 74). Below Thionville, to its junction with the Rhine at Koblenz, the Moselle has been canalised to take 1500-ton barges, by means of barrages.[1] The scheme, including hydro-electric stations, was completed in 1964 (see p. 492).

The Lorraine Steel Industry.[2]—It has already been shown that Lorraine contributes almost 93 per cent of the total French iron-ore output; in addition the district was responsible for four-fifths of French pig-iron, two-thirds of the crude steel, and just over half of the finished steel products. *Est I* and *Est II* (as delimited on Fig. 72) contained at the end of 1963 72 of the 97 active blast-furnaces in France, 83 of the 99 Thomas converters and 25 of the 60 Martin open-hearth furnaces. The total output of crude steel from the two regions in 1963 was 11·30 million tons out of a French total of 17·56 millions.

Even before the war of 1939–45 the production of steel in Lorraine, as indeed elsewhere in France, was dominated by a few large integrated concerns,[3] which contrasts with the considerable number of dispersed individual steel-using firms. Since 1945 this tendency has increased; grouping and consolidation have taken place in order to enable development schemes envisaged under the Monnet Plan

[1] A. A. Michel, 'The canalisation of the Moselle and West European integration', in *G.R.* (1962), vol. 52, pp. 475-91; and F. Chanrion, *Une Victoire européenne: la Moselle* (1964).

[2] There is an extensive literature on the Lorraine iron and steel industry. The 'classic' account is Axel Sömme, *La Lorraine métallurgique* (1930). See also J. Bichelonne and P. Angot, *Le Bassin ferrifère de Lorraine* (1939); J. Chardonnet, *La Sidérurgie française* (1954); and N. J. G. Pounds and W. N. Parker, *Coal and Steel in Western Europe* (1957). A very useful account is provided by J. E. Martin, 'Location Factors in the Lorraine Iron and Steel Industry', in *Transactions and Papers: The Institute of British Geographers* (1957), Publication No. 23, pp. 191-212. Two publications by the British Iron and Steel Federation are 'The French Steel Development Plan', reprinted from *Monthly Statistical Bulletin* (1953), vol. 28, No. 2, and 'Steel Developments in France', *ibid.* (1955), vol. 30, No. 8. The High Authority of the European Coal and Steel Community publish much statistical material, reports and bulletins from Luxembourg. See also C. Prêcheur, *La Sidérurgie française* (1963), a most valuable survey.

[3] A review of the progress of industrial grouping and consolidation before the war of 1939–45 is provided by R. de Fou, *Le Mouvement de concentration dans la sidérurgie lorraine* (1943).

to be implemented.   The huge *Sidelor* (the *Union Sidérurgique Lorraine*) was incorporated in 1950; it operates works at Micheville near the Luxembourg frontier, at Rombas, Homécourt and Auboué in the Orne valley, and at Pont-à-Mousson in the Moselle

FIG. 72.—THE FRENCH IRON-ORE FIELDS AND THE CENTRES OF THE
IRON AND STEEL INDUSTRY.

The towns are shown in which major steel-making and steel-using industries are located, with the exception of those in Lorraine, which are shown in detail on Figs. 69, 70.   The boundaries of the seven regions into which the industry is grouped under the *Chambre Syndicale de la Sidérurgie* are shown.   Ore-fields are in black.

Based on : (i) *Atlas de France*, sheet 44, 'Richesses minérales concessibles' (1933) ; (ii) post-1945 information derived from *Statistical Bulletin*, vol. 28, no. 2 (1953), and *ibid.*, vol. 30, no. 8 (1955), published by the British Iron and Steel Federation.

valley.   *Sollac* (the *Société Lorraine de Laminage Continu*), also formed in 1950, controls steel-works and rolling-mills at Hayange, Sérémange and Ebange in the Fentsch valley.   The long-established *De Wendel* firm owns integrated works at Hayange in the Fentsch valley and at Moyeuvre in the Orne valley; this firm was founded as long ago as 1805 by the Marquis François de Wendel, and it was one of his descendants who in conjunction with *Schneider* of Le Creusot bought the rights of the basic process of steel-making from Gilchrist and Thomas.

Three steel-making areas can be distinguished: the Longwy and Nancy districts within *Est I*, and the Moselle-Briey districts mainly included in *Est II* (Fig. 70).

The Longwy District.—In the Longwy district the industry is situated

FIG. 73.—THE IRON AND STEEL INDUSTRY IN NORTHERN LORRAINE.

Details of the Luxembourg iron and steel works, not shown on this map, appear on Fig. 80. The built-up areas are generalised.

Based on: (i) *Carte de France au 50,000ᵉ*, sheets XXXII/10, 11; XXXIII/10, 11; (ii) post-1945 information derived from various official sources.

in several narrow steep-sided valleys. *Sidelor* have an integrated plant at Micheville in the upper Alzette valley near the Luxembourg frontier, but the greatest concentration of industry is around Longwy, in the Chiers valley near the junction of several tributaries. Not far from the Belgian frontier is the Mont-St. Martin works, owned by the *Société des Aciéries de Longwy*, and further down-valley are the Chiers, Senelle and Réhon works (Fig. 73). Several blast-furnace plants are located in this frontier region, for, as was noted above, the friable ores cannot stand transport and are mostly smelted locally.[1] The pig-iron is sent out of the district, much of it to the *Nord* and Ardennes industrial areas. Thus the *Hauts Fourneaux de Saulnes* operates a blast-furnace plant near the Luxembourg frontier, the *Arbed*-controlled *Société Minière des Terres-Rouges* (see p. 289) has blast-furnaces at Audun-le-Tiche, and others are at Godbrange, Redange, Villerupt and Ottange (Fig. 73). Several of these have been rebuilt under post-war modernisation plans. A number of steel-using industries has developed in the Longwy district, and further down the valley, at the junction of the Chiers and the Crusnes, boilers, tubes and a wide range of hardware are made.

The Nancy District.—The chief integrated plants in the Nancy region are at Pompey, Frouard, Maxéville and Neuves-Maisons (Fig. 70). These are served by rail and inland waterway transport, the first three by the Marne-Rhine Canal and the canalised Moselle, the last by the southern branch of the Est Canal. Further north *Sidelor* operates blast-furnaces at Pont-à-Mousson, which is incidentally one of the main centres in France for the production of cast-iron pipes. It is interesting to note that the steel girders for the Eiffel Tower were made at Pompey. Numerous steel-using and -finishing industries have developed in the Nancy region, notably light engineering, electrical equipment and electric locomotives.

The Moselle District.—The metallurgical industry of the *département* of Moselle expanded tremendously between 1871 and 1914; the Treaty of Frankfurt brought *Lorraine Annexée* (known to the Germans as the *Reichsland*) into the German empire, and it shared vast industrial developments. France thus inherited a thriving industrial region in 1919. The industrial district extends along the left bank of the Moselle near the foot of the limestone escarpment from Metz to Thionville, and along the lower Orne and Fentsch valleys. The several large integrated plants produce annually about 5·6 million tons of steel, that is, over a third of the whole French output. In the Moselle valley itself are the integrated works of the *Union Consommateurs des Produits Métallurgiques et Industriels* at Hagondange, the neighbouring steel-works of the *Société des Aciers Fins de l'Est*, the blast-furnaces of Uckange, and the rolling-mills of the *Laminoirs à Froid* to the north-east of Thionville. Along the narrow floor and sides of the Fentsch valley are concentrated blast-furnaces, steel-works, coke-ovens, old towns and new *cités-ouvrières*, roads and railways—a continuous alignment of heavy industry from Knutange downstream to Florange and Ebange. Similarly, further south in the Orne valley (Fig. 74) there is continuous industrialisation from Auboué to *Sidelor's* huge plant at Rombas (Plate XXXIV). At

---

[1] Modern methods of sintering, designed to utilise the fines and enrich the iron-content, are overcoming this difficulty.

K 2

Jœuf, incidentally, the Gilchrist-Thomas basic process was first used in France.

Other Industries.—The main preoccupation of the towns of the lower Moselle valley from Nancy to Thionville is therefore the production of steel and a variety of steel-using industries. Nancy has a wide range of other industries, many of long establishment; these include glass-making, textile manufactures brought by Alsatian refugees after the Franco-Prussian War of 1870, electrical engineering, tanning and the manufacture of leather goods, some chemical industries,

FIG. 74.—THE IRON AND STEEL WORKS IN THE ORNE VALLEY, LORRAINE.
Note the deep shaft-mines on the plateau as well as the adit-mines on the steep sides of the valleys.
Based on *Carte de France au 50,000ᵉ*, sheet XXXIII/12, with later information.

brewing, the making of furniture and musical instruments, and food-processing industries; in short, a most intensively developed and varied industrial life. As a result, the population of the Nancy commune in 1962 was 133,532, but with the nine other communes which make up the official *agglomération urbaine* the total is about 180,000. Such suburban communes as Essey-les-Nancy, Vandœuvres-les-Nancy and Villers-les-Nancy have grown rapidly, particularly in the inter-war years. Nancy has considerable administrative importance as the *chef-lieu* of Meurthe-et-Moselle, and was for long the capital of the duchy of Lorraine.

Metz, the *chef-lieu* of the *département* of Moselle, is the only large town in this part of Lorraine not concerned directly with the iron and steel industry. Its position has resulted in its function as a fortress town since Gallo-Roman times. Under the direction of Vauban, it formed one of the strongest defence-points on France's eastern frontier, and after it became German in 1871 it was made still more powerful, so that it remained in German hands until occupied by Marshal Pétain's forces in November 1918. Today the town has spread far beyond the narrow picturesque streets around the cathedral. While its communal population was 109,678 in 1962, with the contiguous residential and industrial suburbs of Ban-St. Martin, Longeville-les-Metz and Montigny-les-Metz the agglomeration total was about 157,000. A variety of light industries is carried on in and around Metz. It is an agricultural centre for the Moselle valley, for the neighbouring *côtes*, and for the district of Messin to the east. As a result, the food-preserving industries supply Parisian food-shops with numerous '*fabriqué-en-Metz*' products (tinned and bottled fruit and vegetables, preserves and tinned meats). On the fertile soils of the flood-plain extensive market-gardens and orchards grow asparagus, strawberries, peas and beans, yellow plums, pears and cherries, and hop-gardens to the south serve several large breweries in Metz. Although this part of the valley does not yield the famous Moselle vintages, vineyards have been cultivated on the limestone slopes since Roman times, and quantities of *vin ordinaire* are bottled in Metz. Other enterprises in the neighbourhood include lime-kilns, cement-works and plaster-works (using the raw materials from adjacent quarries), tanneries, flour-mills, tobacco factories and timber-using industries.

V. THE PLATEAU OF LORRAINE

This sub-region, known to French geographers as the *plateau Lorrain propre*, extends eastward from the outliers of Oolitic Limestone along the right bank of the Moselle to the Muschelkalk outcrop (see p. 513) on the flanks of the Vosges. The central part of this plateau, the upper Nied and Seille basins, is given the *pays*-name of *Saulnois*. The surface rocks consist mainly of clays—Keuper in the east, Lias in the west; a slight escarpment of Rhaetic Limestone affords a surface manifestation of the margin between these Triassic and Jurassic rocks. The Lias outcrops are rather more varied, consisting of clays, marls, shales and some gritty limestones (the Mid-Lias Grits), while the Keuper comprises more uniform impermeable heavy clay-marls, but these differences do not really detract from the geographical unity. The surface of the plateau is diversified by deposits of diluvial gravels washed down from the Vosges by the swollen Pleistocene streams, and now forming a north–south zone of irregular hillocks mostly covered with woodland.

In the extreme north a small upfold of Triassic rocks (the Saar-louis Anticline) projects south-westward across the frontier from the Saarland into France. The newer rocks have been denuded from its upper surface, so revealing the Bunter Sandstone. This forms the forested Plateau de St. Avold, consisting of a series of ridges which rise to 1,398 feet. This sandstone upland is bounded on its perimeter by an escarpment of Muschelkalk.

Drainage.—The Lorraine plateau is crossed by a number of rivers, the floors of which lie between about 600 and 800 feet, while in places the higher intervening levels attain 1,100 feet. The Sarre rises on the northern slopes of Mont Donon in the Vosges and flows northwards over the forested Bunter Sandstone. It then follows the Muschelkalk outcrop northwards from Sarrebourg to Sarre-Union. Here it crosses the strip of Pleistocene gravels, flowing in a narrow valley among undulating hills, and then wanders on to the clay plain, diversified by patches of the gravels and coarse sands. Finally it re-enters the Bunter Sandstone country, marking the frontier for about seven miles before it becomes wholly a German river in the Saarland. The Nied, formed by the union of its two headstreams, the Nied Française and Nied Allemande, curves right round the southern and western rim of the Triassic upland of St. Avold, draining the central part of the plateau. It is a slow-flowing river with a flat-bottomed valley, and is marshy and liable to flood in places. The Seille, which joins the Moselle at Metz, also pursues a sluggish course over the clay-lands. Much of its former swampy flood-plain has been reclaimed and the river is regularised, but the valley is still liable to inundation in wet winters.

One result of the cover of impermeable Keuper Marl and the gently undulating surface of the plateau is the presence of many irregular-shaped lakes (Fig. 75). Some to the west of Sarrebourg lie on the Keuper Marl among the forested hillocks of diluvial gravels; the largest of these, the Etang de Gondrexange, acts as a reservoir for the Marne-Rhine Canal and the Canal des Houillères de la Sarre (Fig. 85). Other lakes in Saulnois are contained in hollows formed by subsidence due to the removal of underlying beds of common salt and gypsum from the Keuper. Many have been artificially enlarged and are used for pisciculture. The Etang de Lindre, for example (shown on Fig. 75), is an *étang périodique* formed by damming the river Seille above Dieuze.

Land-Use and Agriculture.—The climate of the Lorraine plateau, mainly because of its altitude, is rather cool and damp, with rainfall totals of 28 to 32 inches. Nancy, for example, just outside the south-western corner of this sub-region, has mean temperatures of

FIG. 75.—THE 'LAKE-DISTRICT' OF NORTHERN LORRAINE.

This map gives some impression of the confused relief of the north-central part of the Lorraine plateau. The lakes lie in the hollows among the irregular hillocks of diluvial gravels resting on the Keuper clays. Many have been dammed and are used for fish-rearing, some (notably the Etang de Lindre) are *étangs périodiques*, and are drained at intervals for cultivation. The Etang de Gondrexange lies near the watershed and acts as a feeder to the Marne-Rhine and Sarre Colliery Canals.

Some of the *étangs* are shown by abbreviations as follows : **G,** E. de Gondrexange ; **L,** E. de Lindre ; **M,** Grand E. de Mittersheim ; **S,** E. du Stock ; **Z,** E. de Zommange.

Based on *Carte de France au 50,000ᵉ*, sheets XXXV/14, 15 ; XXXVI/14, 15.

31° F. and 62° F. in January and July respectively, and a mean
annual rainfall of 31 inches; an appreciable early summer maximum
is indicative of the approach in eastern France to continental conditions. The soils vary considerably, the result of the diverse nature
of the parent rocks. Considerable tracts of woodland cover the
gravel ridges and notably the Bunter Sandstone uplands of the
Forêts de St. Avold, de Warndt and de la Houve.

Mixed farming is widespread, with a dominance of permanent
pasture on the Lias Clays and of arable land on the Keuper Marls.
The best arable soils are developed on the Muschelkalk, where
Sarrebourg is the market-centre of a prosperous area. As in many
rural areas adjacent to industrial populations, the pasture has
strikingly increased since the war of 1914–18 at the expense of arable.
Not only do the industrial districts require milk, which the farmers
find profitable to produce, but the better wages obtained in industry
have drawn labour from the land. As a result, the area under
permanent pasture forms rather more than half of the total farm-
land. But cereals are still grown, oats for fodder and wheat for
human consumption each occupying about two-fifths of the cereal
acreage, and barley for brewing the remainder. Vineyards grow
on some south-facing slopes in the Seille valley, particularly near
Château-Salins and Dieuze, but conditions are not really favourable
and the wines produced are rather rough *vins ordinaires*.

The *département* of Moselle corresponds roughly with the Lorraine
plateau, and the official statistics for 1963 give some indication of
the land-use.

Département of Moselle, 1963

(Square Miles)

Total area	2,399
Woodland	622
Permanent pasture	743
Arable land	677
Cereals	383
Fodder crops	141
Potatoes	35
Fallow	66

Source: Figures from *Ministère de l'Agriculture*, quoted in *Annuaire statistique
de la France*, 1964.

The importance of animal-rearing is shown by the fact that in
the *département* there were 139,000 head of dairy cattle and about
185,000 pigs, the usual concomitant of the dairying industry.
Poultry are widely kept, notably immense numbers of geese, whose
livers are destined to be the raw material of the unforgettable
delicacy of the *pâté de foie gras Strasbourgeois*.

The Salt-Deposits.—The plateau of Lorraine has two sources of mineral wealth. The Triassic and older Jurassic rocks are notable for their deposits of salts, as in Cheshire and Worcestershire in England and on an enormous scale in the North German Plain, as a result of evaporation in gulfs of the sea or in enclosed lagoons. The Lorraine salt-deposits have been exploited for many centuries, certainly since Roman times. Numerous place-names contain salt-elements, including Château-Salins, Rosières-aux-Salines, Salonnes, Salival, Marsal, and possibly Sauinois itself. More than 1·9 million tons of sodium chloride were produced in 1963 from three main districts (Fig. 76).

In the north the salt-field of Sarralbe occurs in the Muschelkalk, and is exploited by brine-pumping at Sarralbe itself, Salzbronn and Haras. The salt provides the raw material for the *Solvay* chemical works at Sarralbe.

The output of the Seille basin comes from salt-beds in the over-lying Keuper; until about 1866 rock-salt was mined and brine was obtained from surface springs. Since then it has been necessary to pump the brine from deep borings at Dieuze, Château-Salins, Moyenvic and Chambrey. The first of these has a large chemical works.

The third producing-area lies in the valley of the Sanon, which joins the Meurthe at St. Nicolas-du-Port. These salt-deposits occur in the Lias marls, and while a few rock-salt mines still operate, most of the extraction is by pumping of brine-solutions. The centres of production include Varangéville, Dombasle and Rosières-aux-Salines. There are several purifying and packing plants, and the *Solvay* works at Dombasle uses salt as its major raw material.

The Moselle Coalfield.[1]—In the extreme north the Coal Measures of the German Saar Basin are continued across the frontier into Lorraine (Fig. 77). Though exposed in the Saarland, the relatively undisturbed Coal Measures to the south of the river Saar are overlain by progressively thicker deposits of Triassic rocks. After an interruption due to downfaulting south-west of Falquemont in the Nied valley, where as a result the seams lie at unworkable depths, coal is again found fairly near the surface in the Moselle valley. It has in fact been proved at a depth of 2,587 feet near Pont-à-Mousson, and while no development has so far taken place the proximity of this coal to the iron deposits of Lorraine may be of value in the future.

The Saar coalfield was first worked by France during the Napoleonic era, but almost the whole district passed to Rhenish Prussia in 1815 and exploitation steadily progressed in the nineteenth century. A certain amount of prospecting took place and concessions were

[1] R. Haby, *Les Houillères lorraines et leur région* (1965).

granted on the French side of the frontier, but little development took place there.   After the disastrous Franco-Prussian War, when the

FIG. 76.—THE MINERAL RESOURCES OF ALSACE AND LORRAINE.

The navigable waterways are shown as solid lines (for their names see Fig. 85). The iron-ore fields are shown in more detail on Fig. 69, and the Saar-Moselle coalfields on Fig. 77.   The disused canal to Dieuze (see Fig. 75) is shown by a pecked line.

A small oilfield has recently been discovered at Staffelfelden to the north-east of Mulhouse.

Based on (i) *La France: géographie-tourisme* (1952), edited by D. Faucher, vol. ii, p. 345 ; and (ii) *Carte industrielle de la Lorraine* (1930).

whole basin became German, the field was vigorously prosecuted as German industrialisation proceeded apace.   By 1913 the Saar had an annual output of seventeen million tons, of which *Lorraine Annexée* contributed almost a fifth.

Between 1920 and 1935 the Saar Territory was placed under a council appointed by the League of Nations, and the coalfield was granted to France for fifteen years. The collieries and coke-ovens were operated by an administration controlled by the French government, known as the *Mines Domaniales de la Sarre,* with its headquarters at Saarbrücken.

The portion of the field which lies in the *département* of Moselle, returned to France in 1919, was also actively prosecuted. There are three separate districts. The chief mining area is in the valley of the Rosselle (a left-bank tributary of the river Saar), particularly in

FIG. 77.—THE MOSELLE AND SAAR COALFIELDS.
The former boundary between the Saarland and West Germany is shown. German collieries in the Saarland are not marked.

Based on (i) *Saaratlas* (1934), sheets 4, 23 ; (ii) C. C. Held, 'The new Saarland', in *Geographical Review* (1951), vol. 41, p. 599.

the angle to the north-west of Forbach. This district is known as *Petite-Rosselle,* and six large collieries (one of which, situated just over the frontier at Warndt, is operated on lease from Germany) are in production. Further west is the Merlebach-Spittel district with four deep collieries near L'Hôpital, Merlebach and Heiligenbronn, whose workings extend into the Saarland itself. These sub-frontier workings have been one of the main stumbling-blocks to Franco-German agreement. The third district lies further to the north-west in the valley of the Bisten, another left-bank tributary of the Saar, where the colliery of La Houve produces low-grade coal used in pithead thermal-generators.

Although the coal occurs at depths much greater than in the

Saarland, the seams are relatively undisturbed and one in the Petite-Rosselle area exceeds twelve feet in thickness. Output rose steadily in the inter-war years from 3·8 million tons in 1913 to 6·7 millions in 1938. Since 1945 the output of the Moselle portion has soared ; in 1963, 13·16 million tons, almost twice as much as the pre-war figure and nearly a quarter of France's total, came from the eleven collieries. The yield per underground worker averaged 2·70 tons per shift, compared with 1·90 for France as a whole, an indication of the thick uninterrupted seams and the degree of modern mechanisation. This is in fact the highest output per worker in Europe, and compares favourably with that in the Ruhr (1·68) and in Belgium (1·15). Unfortunately for the metallurgical industry, the Moselle field produces none of the *demi-gras* (semi-bituminous coal) so well suited for metallurgical coking ; in 1963, 62 per cent of its output consisted of *flambant gras* (free-burning gas coals), 15 per cent of *flambant sec* (dry steam-coal), and 24 per cent of *gras* (bituminous coal). About 2·4 million tons of metallurgical coke were made from locally produced coal in 1963, the bulk of the coal being shipped by canal and rail to many parts of eastern and central France for domestic use, locomotive fuel and steam-raising. France's very real need of metallurgical coke has led to continuous post-war research ; as was stated in 1952 by the official *Chambre Syndicale de la Sidérurgie*, '*Des recherches, déjà avancées, tendent à utiliser le charbon lorrain à cette fin* (*cokéfaction*)'. Two modern cokeries were completed in 1952, one owned by the *Houillères nationales* at Carling, the other by a group of steel firms at Marienau. These cokeries are now producing metallurgical coke from mixtures of various Saar and Moselle coals without using a proportion of Ruhr coal. Two large thermal power-stations are owned by the *Houillères nationales*, at Carling and at Grossbliederstroff. At Carling too is a large chemical plant, part of a carbo-petroleum complex which straddles the border, including integrated plants at Fürstenhausen and Perl in the Saarland.

The long, weary Franco-German negotiations concerning the future of the Saar ended in June 1956. A number of major issues was settled, notably the French agreeing to the incorporation of the Saar into West Germany on January 1st, 1957. In this agreement the French made concessions about the future development of the *Grand Canal d'Alsace* (see p. 299), the Germans about the canalisation of the Moselle. The problem of the frontier coalfield was settled by allowing France to continue to work the Warndt colliery from French territory until 1980.

Settlement.—The distribution of population on the Lorraine plateau manifests the variety of relief, soils and economic development.

The rural population lives in small villages, often on south-facing slopes above the clay-vales. Market-towns usually stand at bridge-points on the rivers, such as the trio of Sarrebourg, Sarralbe and Sarreguemines on the river Sarre, Bouzonville on the Nied, and Noményy on the Seille. The salt industry and the northern coalfield have resulted in the growth of a number of small industrial centres. There is no dominating regional centre; the two main towns of this part of France are Nancy and Metz on the western margins.

VI. THE HIGH PLAIN OF LORRAINE

The plain of Lorraine shares the same geological characteristics as the plateau to the north, a similar broad pattern of a western Liassic and an eastern Keuper section, with the outcrops curving south-westward in conformity with the concentric pattern of the Paris Basin. Its southern boundary, the watershed between the Meuse-Moselle drainage to the north and the Saône headstreams to the south, consists of a south-westerly prolongation of the Triassic rocks surrounding the High Vosges, known as the Monts Faucilles, with a double escarpment of Muschelkalk.

The plain of Lorraine lies at an average elevation well above 1,100 feet, diversified by a series of valleys occupied by the Moselle and its tributaries as they converge on the Nancy–Toul area. The rivers—Meurthe, Mortagne, Moselle—and their numerous headstreams rise on the western slopes of the Vosges (Fig. 118), and then cross the flanking Bunter Sandstone in gorge-like valleys. They trend north-westwards across the Muschelkalk, Keuper and Lias in turn, now flowing in broad rather marshy valleys, but with steep bounding slopes lying well back from the river. None of these rivers is much used for navigation, but the flat-floored Moselle valley provides room for the lateral Est Canal (Southern Branch). The Moselle receives only one left-bank tributary, the Madon, which drains the clay-lands to the south-west. These river valleys dissect the Lorraine plain and introduce a certain variety into the landscape.

Several individual districts have received *pays*-names; thus *Xaintois* lies around Mirecourt in the Madon valley, and *Vermois* is in the converging angle between the Meurthe and the Moselle. The Rhaetic outcrop of calcareous sandstone, which separates the Lias from the Keuper in the Lorraine plateau, is present also in the plain, and can be traced south-south-westward as the escarpment of *Virine*, cut through in prominent valley-gaps by the Moselle tributaries. Irregular patches of diluvial gravels (the *terre blanche*) occur here and there, and strips of recent alluvium cover the floors of the valleys.

Land-Use and Agriculture.—The character of the agricultural land-scape is very similar to that of the Lorraine plateau. The patches of gravel and sand are wooded, the limestone-derived loams and some of the clays are under arable, the rest of the clays and the damp valley-floors carry permanent pasture, some of which is irrigated as water-meadows. Wheat, oats and potatoes are widely grown, and dairy cattle are numerous. Vineyards cover some south-facing slopes, particularly near Lunéville, although the rather high altitude, exposure and rainfall make this an unfavoured area for viticulture.

Settlement.—Small towns and large villages are strung out along the lower slopes of the valleys. Thus in the Moselle valley below Epinal are Thaon, Igney, Châtel-sur-Moselle, Vincey, Charmes and Bayon, and along the Mortagne are Rambervillers, Magnières, and Gerbéviller. Many of these have small factories, often long-established from the days of water-power, engaged in textile-spinning, embroidery, leather-work, timber-using industries, the manufacture of glass-ware, pottery and chemical products. The chief town is Lunéville at the confluence of the Meurthe and the Vesouze; its activities include engineering (notably rolling-stock, made by a branch of the firm at Graffenstaden near Strasbourg), and the manufacture of textiles, embroidery and straw hats.

VII. BELGIAN LORRAINE

This area of about four hundred square miles lies in the extreme south-east of Belgium, known as the *Côtes Lorraines*. In the east a narrow tongue of a rather clayey red Bunter Sandstone extends for fifteen miles along the southern margin of the Ardennes. Then follows a succession of Jurassic calcareous sandstones, limestones, shales and marls, trending in roughly parallel outcrops from west to east. The Muschelkalk and Keuper, though well represented in the Grand Duchy of Luxembourg further to the east, are not present on the surface in Belgian Lorraine except in an insignificant area in the north-east adjoining the frontier.

As elsewhere in the scarplands, these rocks offer a varied resistance to denudation. The most northerly escarpment consists of yellowish Lower Lias Sandstone, known further east as the Luxembourg Sandstone. This escarpment, to which is given the name of the Sinemurian Cuesta by geologists, trends eastward across the country to the north of Arlon (Fig. 78).[1] It is much dissected, rising

[1] R. Souchez, 'A propos de reliefs résiduels gréseux au nord de Virton (Lorraine belge)', in *Revue belge de Géographie* (1963), vol. 87, pp. 171-6; and R. Souchez, 'Influences paléoclimatiques sur le modèle du plateau gréseux de Lorraine belge', in *A. de G.* (1966), vol. 75, pp. 401-9, with a detailed bibliography.

to a number of minor wooded summits, the highest being the Hirtzenberg (1,526 feet) near Arlon. A few miles further south is the Charmouthian Cuesta, trending eastward from near Virton into the Grand Duchy, and consisting of Mid-Lias calcareous sandstones, known as the Habergy Sandstones from their extensive development near the small town of that name. Although a less prominent feature than the Luxembourg Sandstone escarpment, it rises towards the east to form several quite noticeable hills, one near the frontier reaching 1,348 feet. The third escarpment, in the south, comprises a short section of Oolitic Limestone, here known as the Bajocian Cuesta. This is one of the best defined of the Jurassic escarpments, for it can be traced for about ninety miles from the Chiers valley almost to the Moselle. The Franco-Belgian frontier in the west runs to the south of the scarp-edge, but elsewhere lies to the north of it. This anomaly in fact gave Belgium a tiny portion of the *minette* ore-field, which small though it was did originally help to establish an iron and steel industry. The summit point of this escarpment within Belgium attains 1,322 feet south of Halanzy, but it is appreciably higher in Luxembourg and France.

Between these sandstone and limestone ridges occur the various clays, marls and shales of the Middle and Upper Lias, within whose less resistant outcrops river systems have developed their east–west vales. The valley of the Semois lies between the edge of the Ardennes and the Luxembourg escarpment; this river rises near Arlon, and flows westwards over the clays and marls until it crosses on to the Palaeozoic rocks of the Ardennes. Most of the remainder of Belgian Lorraine drains to the Chiers and so to the Meuse. The Ton drains the vale between the Luxembourg and Habergy cuestas, the Vire occupies the vale between the Habergy and Longwy cuestas; the two streams meet just below Virton and flow south-west into France and so to the Chiers. One interesting river is the Messancy, which rises on the southern slopes of the Hirtzenberg and flows due south, cutting through the Habergy escarpment to join the Chiers just inside Belgium near Athus. The Chiers itself cuts right through the Oolitic scarp near Longwy on its way westwards.

Climate.—Belgian Lorraine ranges in altitude from 850 feet in the lower western vales to about 1,500 feet at a few points in the eastern parts of the escarpments. Although generally lower than the Ardennes and with a southerly aspect, winters are quite severe, as is indicated by an annual average of 103 days with frost at Arlon. The marked seasonal range is shown by the mean monthly temperatures for Arlon of 34° F. and 62° F. in January and July respectively. The mean annual precipitation for the region as a whole is about 39 inches, with a distinct maximum between November and

Fig. 78.—The Bon Pays of Luxembourg and Belgian Lorraine.

The Palaeozoic rocks of the Ardennes are stippled, and the trends of the main *Côtes* are indicated by hachures. Heights are given in feet, prominent summits by black triangles. The three escarpments are no longer referred to by these names, but are called the Sinemurian, Charmouthian and Bajocian Cuestas, in order from north to south.

Based on *Carte de France et des frontières au 200,000ʹ*, sheets 10, 11.

February, not appreciably less than that of the Ardennes to the north, though summers are markedly warmer and drier.

Land-Use and Agriculture.—The whole of Belgian Lorraine was once under forest, and even today almost half is wooded. Fig. 112 shows that the major woodlands, mainly of birch and pine, occur on the sandy soils of the escarpments, although small patches of beech and oak survive on the heavier clays.

Belgian Lorraine is regarded as a unit-area (*la Région jurassique*) by the Belgian *Ministère de l'Agriculture* and the *Institut National de Statistique*, and agricultural statistics are therefore conveniently available. In 1961 just 35 per cent of the total area was classified as farm-land. Of this almost exactly two-thirds was under pasture (including both long- and short-leys), 3 per cent under fodder crops, and 10 per cent under oats. These figures indicate the importance of stock-rearing; of the 48,000 cattle a third were dairy animals, and in addition there were about 11,000 pigs. The clay and marl soils are somewhat intractable and require heavy fertilising for arable crops, but nevertheless about 22 per cent of the farm-land was under cereals (10 per cent oats, 7 per cent wheat), and a further six per cent grew potatoes. Some fruit is cultivated, usually by means of 'grass-orchards'. Thus Belgian Lorraine, while not being of outstanding agricultural significance (as shown by the fact that in 1961 only 2·2 per cent of Belgium's farm-land was returned in this region), has a certain limited importance.[1]

Iron-Ore.—The extension of the Lorraine *minette* across the Belgian frontier in the neighbourhood of Musson and Halanzy was appreciated early in the nineteenth century. But the Belgian portion of the field covers only a little over a square mile and the yield is small; still, it stimulated developments in this southern district, and blast-furnaces were built at Musson and Halanzy and a steel-works at Athus near the Luxembourg frontier, which are still active. The *minette* has been mined in small quantities—a peak of 248,000 tons in 1900, about 176,000 tons in 1938, but only 96,000 tons were obtained from the single mine in operation in 1963, and the bulk of the ore used comes from French Lorraine.

Settlements.—The total population of the two *arrondissements* of Arlon and Virton, which coincide with the official *région agricole*, was 90,286 in 1964, with a population per square mile of about 225, compared with 775 for all Belgium. This population is mostly grouped in small nucleated villages in the clay-vales, and the only

[1] 'L'Aménagement du Sud-Luxembourg; aperçu des synthèses et conclusions de l'enquête préparatoire', published by the *Ministère des Travaux Publiques* (1961).

place of any size is Arlon (13,721 people in 1964). It is a pleasant town, situated at a height of 1,350 feet, the administrative centre of the *arrondissement* and a prosperous market-centre. It is an important route-focus, for no less than eleven main roads converge upon it, and it is the frontier-station for the Brussels-Namur-Luxembourg railway-line. The little town of Athus (7,075 people), the only other place with a population exceeding five thousand, is chiefly important for the integrated steel-works of *S.A. d'Angleur-Athus*.

VIII. THE BON PAYS OF LUXEMBOURG

The regional name of the *Bon Pays* is given to the outcrop of Triassic and Lower Jurassic rocks which covers the southern two-thirds of the Grand Duchy of Luxembourg. The geological map (Fig. 67) shows that the Lower Palaeozoic rocks here recede to the north-east, forming a triangular embayment extending into Germany beyond Trier. This re-entrant indicates the line of the broad Luxembourg Syncline, a downfold parallel to and contemporaneous with the Hercynian folding of the Ardennes, Eifel and Hunsrück (see pp. 483-6 and Fig. 108). Its surface reveals a much greater variety of Mesozoic rocks than in Belgian Lorraine to the west, where the Trias is scarcely represented. The Triassic and Jurassic rocks were subjected to a long period of differential erosion, and the several outcrops present the pattern of an acute angle pointing north-east, with successively younger rocks occurring towards the south-west. The oldest, the Bunter Sandstone, follows the edge of the Devonian rocks, but only the north-western 'limb' of the outcrop appears in Luxembourg, the south-eastern in Germany to the east of the river Sarre. The next formation, the Muschelkalk, is represented both in the north, where it succeeds the Bunter along the edge of the Ardennes, and in the east along the Moselle valley. The Muschelkalk here differs from its usual shelly limestone character, for it consists rather of sandstones and marls in the lower beds and of dolomitic limestones and sandstones in the upper beds. Within the angle of the Muschelkalk, and broadly parallel to its two outcrops, occur the Keuper rocks, consisting mainly of clays and marls, but including also layers of sandstone, dolomitic limestones, and some gypsum which is quarried for plaster and cement. At the top of the Keuper are occasional outcrops of yellow Rhaetic Sandstone.

The central part of the Bon Pays, enclosed to the north and east by these older Triassic outcrops, consists of an extensive area of yellow calcareous Lower Lias Sandstone. This forms a triangular plateau, interrupted in the north by the valley of the Alzette, deeply eroded into the underlying Keuper rocks. To the south-west succeed the Middle and Upper Lias clays, shales and marls, and occasional beds of calcareous sandstones. Finally, in the extreme south-west, part of the northern edge of the Oolite escarpment just appears in Luxembourg; limited though it is, it does provide the Grand Duchy with appreciable deposits of *minette*.

Mention must be made of the quite extensive Quaternary deposits, both the diluvial Pleistocene gravels and coarse sands and the narrow strips of newer alluvium. The Pleistocene deposits are found on the high lands along the Ardennes margins, where they cover both the Bunter Sandstone and the lower parts of the Devonian rocks. They occur too on the higher areas in the west of the Bon Pays and along the foot of the Oolitic cuesta in the south-west. These gravels formerly contained workable quantities of alluvial iron-ore (hydrated oxide of iron) in nodules or grains, redeposited from the *minette* ore-beds to the south. The early Luxembourg iron industry in fact developed because of the accessibility of these non-phosphoric alluvial ores, which could be smelted with charcoal.

Relief Features.—A pattern of drainage has developed in the Bon Pays which (except for the headstreams of the Chiers in the extreme south-west) focuses on the Moselle in the eastern angle of the country. In the north, flowing eastwards within a broad trough cut in the Bunter Sandstone, are the Attert and its parallel tributary the Wark, which join the Sûre flowing in the same direction. In the east such streams as the Syre flow direct to the Moselle, and the broadly parallel Ernz Blanche and Ernz Noire join the Sûre.

The central and western parts of the Bon Pays are drained by the Alzette and its numerous left-bank tributaries. This river rises in France, deriving headstreams from the Oolitic plateau, and then flows north across the central Bon Pays to its junction with the Sûre near Ettelbruck. As a result the river crosses each of the varied outcrops in turn. First it cuts through the Oolitic escarpment above Esch, next it flows over the Mid-Lias Clay in the broad Vallée de Roeser, and continues for ten miles deeply entrenched in the Luxembourg Sandstone (Fig. 79). As the river approaches the city of Luxembourg, its valley becomes virtually a gorge with sinuous winding loops; the surface of the sandstone plateau lies almost 200 feet above river-level. It was on the rocky peninsula between the Alzette and its western tributary the Pétrusse that the tenth-century fortress was built which formed the nucleus of the city. One result of the deep meanders is that the railway from Liège to Metz and Strasbourg has to cross the Alzette three times, requiring a viaduct 850 feet in length, and to pierce a meander-core by means of a tunnel. To the north of the city the Alzette passes on to the Keuper Marls, and its valley broadens out as the Vallée de Mersch, although the dissected slopes of the sandstone rise steeply away from the valley floor.

Several streams, notably the Pétrusse, the Mamer and the Eisch, flow in a general easterly direction to the Alzette.

FIG. 79.—THE MIDDLE ALZETTE VALLEY AND THE CITY OF LUXEMBOURG

The northward-flowing Alzette leaves the broad Vallée de Roeser, eroded in the Mid-Lias Clays, for a winding gorge cut across the Luxembourg (Lower Lias) Sandstone. A few miles downstream from the capital city, the valley widens out as the steep sandstone slopes recede from the river, leaving the wide Vallée de Mersch eroded from the Keuper Marls and floored with recent alluvium. Heights are given in feet.

Based on (i) *Carte de France au 50,000ᵉ*, sheets XXXIII/10, XXXIV/10; and (ii) *Geologische Übersichtskarte des Luxemburger Landes*, edited by J. Robert.

The development of this complex river-pattern upon a varied series of geological outcrops has produced a diverse landscape. In the north the so-called 'Sub-Ardennes Depression', a broad trough eroded in the Bunter by the Attert, Wark and Sûre, lies along the margin of the Ardennes. Near its southern edge the Muschelkalk escarpment trends north-eastward, although cut through completely in one place by the broad Alzette valley, and in the east it forms some prominent little peaks of 1,200 to 1,300 feet in height overlooking the Sûre valley. This cuesta is again interrupted by the Ernz Blanche and the Sûre, but is continued into West Germany.

The central part of the Bon Pays consists of a low undulating plateau of Luxembourg (Lias) Sandstone, flanked both to the north-west and to the south-east by the lower but equally undulating surface of the Keuper Marls. Most of this plateau lies between about 1,000 and 1,300 feet, the highest point occurring in the Grunenwald at 1,434 feet to the north-east of Luxembourg city. The northern edge of the Luxembourg Sandstone forms a distinct out-facing cuesta, which has already been traced across Belgian Lorraine as the Sine-mutian Cuesta, and a less marked cuesta borders the Triassic outcrops in the Moselle valley in the east. In several places this sandstone forms striking relief features. The gorge of the Alzette near Luxembourg city has already been mentioned, and the winding valley of the Sûre between Reisdorf and Echternach (where the outcrop continues into Germany) is also spectacular. The most impressive scenery is in the valley of the Ernz Noire (known as the Mœllerdall or Müllerthal), a right-bank tributary of the Sûre in the extreme north-east. Not only has stream erosion cut deep gorges, but rainwater percolates into the fissures of this calcareous sandstone, enlarging them by solution and forming chasms (such as the famous Gorge du Loup), grottoes and caverns alternating with steep buttresses and fantastic rock pinnacles. The rocks vary in resistance to denudation, and in places strata of siliceous sandstones are much less easily attacked than the calcareous sandstones, so stand out boldly. Where harder strata outcrop across streams, rapids and falls occur, notably the famous Schiessentümpel on the Ernz Noire itself. These sandstones are densely wooded with beech, and the whole district, known as the 'Petite Suisse', is a much visited tourist area.

Towards the south-west the surface rocks consist of Middle and Upper Lias clays and shales, forming undulating country between 800 and 1,000 feet high. The valleys occupied by the Alzette's headstreams have open cross-profiles, with gentle interfluves, though occasional bands of limestone and sandstone form steep escarpments. The Habergy Sandstone, mentioned above as forming the Charmouthian Cuesta in Belgian Lorraine, can be traced as a low cuesta, with a maximum altitude of 1,309 feet, from the Belgian frontier to the Alzette valley.

In the extreme south is the prominent north-facing Oolitic escarpment, forming heights which overlook the Chiers and Alzette valleys; the Gintzenberg near Dudelange, on which stands Luxembourg's radio-station, attains 1,394 feet, and the Hatschenberg, also near Dudelange, is about thirty feet less. A small detached mass of Upper Lias limestone, standing prominently on the watershed between the sources of the Chiers and an Alzette headstream, a mile to the north of the Oolitic escarpment, is known as the Zolver Knapp or the Butte de Soleuvre (1,385 feet).

The Moselle valley is sufficiently distinct to be mentioned specifically, since it forms a depression along the south-eastern frontier; the official lowest point in the Grand Duchy is found in its valley at the Sûre confluence at 423 feet. The flood-plain is covered with alluvium and gravels, and the valley-slopes cut in the Keuper rise gently to the west. Where the Muschelkalk approaches the river the slopes are steeper, but faults have resulted in step-like south-east facing terraces, each backed by a prominent escarpment.

Climate.—Considerable climatic variations are experienced over the Bon Pays, in spite of its limited size. The Moselle valley in the south-east lies to some degree in a rain-shadow and has a south-easterly aspect; as a result it usually experiences a pleasant climate, with a mean annual rainfall of 26 to 28 inches, monthly temperatures varying from about 65° F. to 35° F., and long sunshine hours. The rest of the Bon Pays has a higher rainfall varying from about 32 to 38 inches, and is cooler and cloudier than the Moselle valley. Indeed, the highest mean rainfall figures for Luxembourg are found not in the much higher Ardennes, but in the south-west on the exposed Oolitic escarpment where the total is over 40 inches. Great local variations occur; sheltered south-facing valleys experience more pleasant conditions than do the open plateau surfaces.

Land-Use and Agriculture.—The Bon Pays is, in proportion to its area, almost as much under woodland as the Ardennes (Fig. 112), even though there was extensive felling in the eighteenth and early nineteenth centuries by the charcoal-burners to provide fuel for the iron-furnaces. The Luxembourg Sandstone carries considerable woodland, notably in the neighbourhood of the capital—the extensive Grunenwald to the north-east and the Baumbusch to the north-west. Another forest is the Marscherwald to the east of the Ernz Noire valley. As Fig. 112 shows, woodland is widespread on the uplands but it has been cleared from the valleys for cultivation. Beech is the most common tree, though oak and oak-beech woods are still found. Conifers are planted extensively, especially on the sandstones, by the *Administration des Eaux et Forêts*.

The Bon Pays is a region of mixed farming, mainly practised on a subsistence basis, although the local variations in relief, soils and climate are reflected in differences in emphasis. The damp alluvial valley-floors and the heavier marls and clays in the west and south-west tend to be under permanent pasture. Gentle slopes with well-drained soils developed on the calcareous sandstones are devoted to arable, with strips under various crops, and in favoured areas to orchards and vineyards. Over the Bon Pays as a whole the land is divided more or less equally between grain crops, roots, and green fodder with permanent pasture. Oats for fodder make up almost half the grain crops, with winter wheat and some rye for human consumption. Potatoes, fodder-beet, turnips and swedes comprise the root-crops, the first occupying two-thirds of the total area, while red clover and lucerne are grown to supplement the permanent meadowlands which are cut for hay. The most significant changes which have taken place since the war of 1940–5 have been a marked decrease in arable land and an increase in pasture and meadowland. While the area under cereals has declined but little, root-crops occupied in 1960 only half the area in 1938 and fodder-crops have decreased by a quarter.

Both dairy and beef cattle, mostly Frisians, are kept in the Bon Pays; this is the most important aspect of agriculture. Every small-holding and farm has a few animals and large herds are rare; in the Grand Duchy as a whole (separate figures are not available for the Bon Pays) in 1960 only 307 farms out of 9,058 units which kept cattle had herds exceeding fifty animals, and more than a thousand holdings had only one or two animals.

Milk is produced for the capital city and for the industrial towns in the south, as well as for sale to the dairy co-operatives which separate the cream to supply the butter factories at Saeul and Ettelbruck. The skimmed milk returned to the farms is fed to pigs, which share with dairy-cattle the responsibility of being the 'cash-crops' in the otherwise subsistence arable economy. There is not only a considerable demand within Luxembourg, for pork is one of the main items of diet, but also from neighbouring countries.

Many fruit-trees are grown, including apples, cider-apples, plums and damsons; most of these are scattered through the Bon Pays in every village for local needs, but some orchards are owned by commercial growers, mainly on the south-eastern valley-slopes. Rose-bushes are cultivated, notably on the heavy marls and clays of the Vallée de Mersch, though the area devoted to roses has considerably declined. About 185 acres were so used before 1914, producing six million bushes a year, but in the years before 1939 output fell to well below a million, and since the war less than half a million have been grown annually, though they are still exported.

The Moselle valley is famed for its vines, and although the bulk of the well-known Moselle wines are produced below Trier, Luxembourg yields quite a range both of light dry white wines and also of some sparkling wines. The vineyards are situated on the south-east facing slopes of calcareous Keuper and Muschelkalk rocks, on natural or artificially constructed terraces above the river valley. The valley is very marginal for wine production, for the altitude is considerable, bitter winds from the uplands in the north are experienced despite the sheltered slopes, and both late frosts and wet summers with sunshine below average are regrettably common features. Both total yield and quality fluctuate considerably.

The Iron and Steel Industry.—The basis of the iron and steel industry of Luxembourg is the extension of the Lorraine *minette* field for a few miles across the French frontier into the Grand Duchy (Fig. 69). As a result of this geographical accident the country is the ninth steel producer in the world,[1] and is the present headquarters of the High Authority of the European Coal and Steel Community. Moreover, its economy is predominantly dependent on steel, for this accounts for from 65 to 75 per cent of the country's total productivity and exports by value; the actual percentage of exports in 1960 was 68. Even more eloquent is the fact that about 21,000 people, or one in every five of the working population, were employed in the iron and steel industry in 1960.

Ore-Mining.—The *minette* area in Luxembourg extends over little more than fourteen square miles, but the deposits are estimated to comprise 300 million tons of exploitable ore, with an iron content of 63 million tons. The field is divided into three basins (Fig. 80) by the river valleys. In the western basin, within the triangle of Rodange, Pétange and Differdange, and bounded on the south-west by the French frontier, the ore produced is mainly siliceous, with an iron-content of about 28 per cent. Between the rivers Alzette and Kayl lies the Esch field, and east of the Kayl the eastern field; these two deposits are calcareous, with an average iron-content of only about 24·6 per cent. In 1960 the average iron-content of ore obtained was 26·0 per cent, distinctly lower than that of French Lorraine; before 1939 the average varied between 30 and 31 per cent. This reduction over only fifteen years indicates partly the working-out of the richer

[1] A useful publication by the British Iron and Steel Federation is 'The Luxemburg Iron and Steel Industry', reprinted from *Monthly Statistical Bulletin* (1952), vol. 27, no. 8. See also A. Kipgen, 'The Luxembourg Iron Industry', in *Journal of the Iron and Steel Institute* (1934), vol. cxxx, (ii), pp. 11-23. Historical aspects are dealt with by K. C. Edwards, 'Historical Geography of the Luxembourg Iron and Steel Industry', in *Transactions of the Institute of British Geographers* (1961), no. 29, pp. 1-16. See also M. and G. Steffes, *La Sidérurgie luxembourgeoise* (1962), 181 pp., published in Luxembourg city.

upper beds, such as the 'Esch red bed', partly post-war technological improvements which have enabled the poorer ores to be utilised. There is wide variation in the colour and thickness of the individual beds, which are similar in nature and occurrence to those in French Lorraine. The 'grey' and 'yellow' beds comprise today the main exploited deposits; in the Esch basin the workable beds total 150 feet in thickness.

FIG. 80.—THE IRON AND STEEL INDUSTRY OF SOUTHERN LUXEMBOURG.

Details of the French iron- and steel-works, not shown on this map, appear on Fig. 73. The built-up areas are generalised. Only the active plants are shown.

T.R. *Terres-Rouges* (a subsidiary within the *Arbed* group); **S.M.M. de Rodange,** *Société Minière et Métallurgique de Rodange.*

Based on: (i) *Carte de France au 50,000ᵉ*, sheets XXXIII/10, 11; XXXIV/10, 11; (ii) *Carte topographique du Grande-Duché de Luxembourg*, sheets 11, 13, 14; (iii) information derived from *Monthly Statistical Bulletin* (1952), vol. 27, no. 8, published by the British Iron and Steel Federation.

In 1963 some 6·99 million tons were produced, of which just over half was calcareous. This output does not equal the highest ever, achieved in 1926 and again in 1957, when 7·8 million tons with an iron-content of 30 per cent were obtained. Only twenty-four individual mines are now in operation, indicating a steady reduction in number from eighty-one in 1926. Sixteen of these are wholly open-cast, where the ore is worked in large shallow quarries, but many of the former profitable open-cast mines, particularly those in the upper 'Esch red beds', are now exhausted, for thirty-eight were being operated in 1937. The remaining mines are exploited by galleries driven more or less horizontally at different levels into the *minette* escarpment and into the sides of the river valleys. The dip of the strata is for the most part gentle and there is little structural disturbance, so that mining costs are relatively low. Eleven of the mines, producing three-quarters of the total, are owned by three big Luxembourg steel companies, six others by four Belgian steel companies, and the remainder are small independent concerns.

The calcareous ores are almost wholly self-fluxing, and the Luxembourg smelters blend them with siliceous ores in the proportion of two to one. Although rather more calcareous ore is produced this is still not sufficient, and moreover the more easily accessible calcareous 'grey' and 'yellow' beds are being rapidly worked out. A considerable amount of calcareous ore is therefore imported from French Lorraine, and in the post-war period some high-grade ore has been obtained from Sweden. Between 1946 and 1954 the latter sent a total of over five million tons, the peak of 1·3 million tons occurring in 1948, since when a considerable reduction has been effected; a mere 56,000 tons were imported in 1960.

Apart from the particular requirements of metallurgical practice, Luxembourg is unable to produce sufficient ore to feed her own furnaces; consumption totals 12 to 13 million tons, and about 6 to 7 million tons are imported annually from France. The Grand Duchy also exported 1·2 million tons, mostly to Belgium, the result both of geographical proximity and of industrial collaboration and financial relationships. In other words, the Luxembourg furnaces actually consumed rather more foreign than home-produced ore, although in the three preceding years the balance was slightly in the opposite direction. The balance-sheet for 1960 is summarised in the following table:

(Thousand Tons)

Consumption in Blast Furnaces			Exports to				Imports from		
Home-produced	Foreign	Total	Germany	France	Belgium	Total	France	Sweden	Total
5,901	6,883	12,784	—	136	1,070	1,206	6,870	56	6,926

Source: *Chambre de Commerce* and *Inspection du Travail des Mines*, quoted in *Annuaire statistique, 1960*.

XXXIII The River Loire at Saumur

XXXIV The *Sidelor* steel-works at Rombas, Lorraine

XXXV The Rhine and the port of Strasbourg

XXXVI The Garonne and Bordeaux

This table represents fairly adequately the post-war pattern, except that Luxembourg until 1957 exported some ore to West Germany and imported more from Sweden. In 1953, too, the Saar took over 600,000 tons but none in 1954. The table indicates both the central position of the Grand Duchy in Europe, and the present inadequacy of home production of the ore which was the basis of her iron and steel industry.

Steel Production.—The industrial pattern, as in other west European countries, had been dominated by the gradual integration of individual enterprises. The largest is the *Société Anonyme des Aciéries Réunies de Burbach, Eich et Dudelange*, known generally as *Arbed*, which was created in 1911 by the merging of three independent companies. The *Terres-Rouges* company, incorporated in 1919 to take over various installations and properties owned and operated in Luxembourg by German interests, entered into association with *Arbed* in 1926, and they have now merged to form one of Europe's largest combines.[1] *Arbed* has five plants in operation (Fig. 80), together with the Schifflange plant which is at present closed down. These include blast-furnaces and Bessemer converters at Belval, Esch and Dudelange, blast-furnaces at Terres-Rouges to the north-west of Esch (from which molten iron is conveyed through conduits to the Belval and Esch converters), and electric furnaces at Dommeldange to the north of Luxembourg city which produce mainly alloy steels. This vast *Arbed* group has a total capacity of over 3 million tons of pig-iron, the same amount of crude steel, and 2·5 million tons of rolled steel products. In addition to its ore-mines in Luxembourg, *Arbed* owns others across the frontier in France, connected with its blast-furnaces by electrified mineral lines and in places by overhead cables. It operates another integrated steel-plant at Burbach near Saarbrücken in the Saar, it owns collieries and coking-plant in the Aachen field, it has financial interests in the Kempen and South Limburg coalfields, and it controls a number of metal-using industries in Belgium, French Lorraine, the Saar and the Rhineland.

The second industrial corporation in Luxembourg is the *S.A. des Hauts-Fourneaux et Aciéries de Differdange, St. Ingbert et Rumelange*, known as *Hadir*, formed in 1920 to take over and integrate a number of mainly German interests. The Rumelange works, comprising three small blast-furnaces, stood idle during the inter-war period, and was dismantled during the 1940–4 period by the Germans. *Hadir's* main plant is at Differdange (Fig. 80), where its nine furnaces have a capacity of a million tons of pig, its six Bessemer converters

[1] *La Sidérurgie au Grande-Duché de Luxembourg et les origines de l'Arbed* (1960), published by the Arbed company.

R.G.W.E.—L

can produce 800,000 tons of crude steel, and its rolling-mills can process 700,000 tons of semi-finished steel.   While not of the industrial stature of the *Arbed* group, *Hadir*'s interests are wide, and include iron-ore mines in the district and at Ottange in French Lorraine, and also a large rolling-mill at St. Ingbert in the Saarland.[1]

The third company is a subsidiary of the Belgian *Cockerill-Ougrée-Marihaye* group, the *Société Minière et Métallurgique de Rodange*, whose works are situated north of Rodange near the Belgian frontier, adjacent to the Luxembourg-Pétange-Paris railway-line.   Five blast-furnaces and four Bessemer converters are in operation, each with an annual capacity of half a million tons, several rolling-mills specialising in rails, iron and steel foundries, and a brick-making plant.   The company owns ore-mines both in the Grand Duchy near Rumelange and in French Lorraine, with which the works are connected by overhead cable.

The Steinfort works in western Luxembourg, situated five miles east of Arlon, and owned by the Belgian *Angleur-Athus* group, closed down in 1931 as a result of the world depression, reopened just before the war, but have now permanently ceased operation.

In 1963 these three steel companies, operating seven individual groups of plant (Fig. 80), produced 3·6 and 4·0 million tons of pig-iron and of crude steel respectively.   The industry consumed 13·0 million tons of ore, more than half of which was obtained from abroad, and used 3·5 million tons of coke in the blast-furnaces.   There are no coke-ovens in Luxembourg, as it has always been considered more economical to import fuel in the form of coke ; no outlet is afforded in the Bessemer steel-converters for the use of coke-oven gas.   While Belgium and the Netherlands supplied some coke before the war of 1939–45, since then Germany has provided almost all of Luxembourg's requirements.

A large proportion of Luxembourg's steel enters into world commerce, but it is difficult to give precise details since figures are published for the *Union Economique Belgo-Luxembourgeoise* as a unit.

Steel-using Industries.—A number of important steel-using firms are active in the Grand Duchy.   The largest is the *Paul Wurth* works at Hollerich in the southern suburbs of the capital ; a proportion of its share-capital is held by *Arbed-Terres-Rouges*.   This firm has a wide range of interests, developed over the years from a small foundry and boiler-works ; it builds and erects bridges all over the world, it specialises in installations and equipment for iron- and steel-works, it has a high reputation for the construction of cranes, and it manufactures a variety of factory machinery and railway rolling-stock.   The

[1] *Hadir*, owned by the vast French company of *Pont-à-Mousson*, was sold in 1966 to *Arbed*.

long-established firm of *Duchscher*, with its works at Wecker near Wasserbillig on the German frontier, manufactures agricultural implements and machinery, serving the farming country of the Bon Pays and the Moselle valley. From its situation in the Moselle wine-country, it has for long made wine-presses for local use; this industry has developed so that the works now export wine-presses to wine-making centres of central and southern Europe and also to the vine-growing areas in the southern hemisphere. The firm manufactures other presses and extractive machinery, as for cider and for vegetable oils. Lesser centres of engineering and metal manufacturing include Lintgen and Keispelt to the north of Luxembourg city, where tools and kitchen implements are made, and Hünsdorf which manufactures mining equipment for the Luxembourg ore-fields, for Lorraine and for further afield.

Other Industries.—Other industries are much less important, most of them concentrated in the capital. They include textile factories (survivors of a widespread domestic industry) making woollen cloth, hosiery and knitted goods, leather-tanning for shoes and gloves, brewing and distilling, and the manufacture of cigarettes. Small brick-works, cement-works and saw-mills are found in most towns and villages. Luxembourg city has many small-scale industries, particularly in the suburb of Hollerich to the south.

Finally, mention must be made of the 'tourist industry'. This attractive little country, situated in the heart of western Europe and the focus of several trans-continental lines, is visited by a large number of tourists every year. Deliberate State encouragement and propaganda have fostered this. The chief tourist centre is the capital, partly because of its own interest as a charming and historic city, partly because it is an excellent centre for the country as a whole. Many small towns and villages cater extensively for visitors— Echternach for the Sûre valley and the 'Petite Suisse' district, Remich and Wormeldange for the Moselle valley, Vianden, Diekirch, Ettelbruck and Clervaux for the Ardennes, Mondorf-les-Bains in the extreme south for its mineral springs. The number of hotels, pensions, etc., has risen from 681 in 1950 to 1,143 in 1959. In addition, the excellently organised youth hostels attract large numbers of younger visitors; there were 91,000 '*nuitées*' in 1960, including nearly 10,000 from Great Britain.

Settlement.—The density of population over the Bon Pays was 365 per square mile at the end of 1960, comparing notably with the Ardennes (126 per square mile). This figure for the Bon Pays is as high as it is because the total population includes both the capital city (71,653 people) and the industrial area, notably Esch-sur-Alzette, the centre of the steel industry, which had a population of 27,954 in 1960. Differdange (17,637), Dudelange (14,617), and Pétange (11,623) were other towns almost exclusively preoccupied with iron and steel manufacture. The Bon Pays, occupying two-thirds of the area of the Grand Duchy, contains 92 per cent of its total population of 315,000, the result of a diverse agriculture and a highly developed iron and steel industry.

CHAPTER 12

THE PLAIN OF ALSACE

The valley of the Rhine from Basel to Mainz consists of a broad trench bordered by parallel step-faults which demarcate each edge of a rift-valley.[1] The formation of this rift-valley and in particular of its western containing wall, the Vosges, is described on pp. 513-14.

During much of Tertiary times the rift-valley formed a long arm of the sea opening southward, which later became a brackish inland lake draining through what is now the Porte de Bourgogne (see p. 366) to the south-west. Vast amounts of sediment, chiefly Oligocene clays, were deposited on its floor. Probably during the Pliocene period, earth-movements caused depression further to the north, and the proto-Rhine, which had previously formed a headstream of what is now the Saône draining to the plain of Bresse (see p. 370), was forced to develop a remarkable right-angle bend near Basel and to flow northwards through the rift-valley. Thus not only was the river's direction reversed, but its base-level was lowered and so its erosive power was increased; as a result it cut deeply into the Tertiary deposits. During interglacial and immediately post-glacial times, great thicknesses of sands and gravels were deposited on the floor of the rift-valley by torrents flowing from the Vosges, the Jura and the Black Forest. There were also considerable and very significant deposits of wind-blown *loess*, similar in origin and character to the *limon* of Picardy and southern Belgium (see p. 23). The Rhine and its tributaries have continued to deposit material on the present flood-plain; in the neighbourhood of Kembs in the south this Recent alluvium is more than thirty feet in thickness.

Only occasionally are the underlying rocks, mainly Oligocene clays, revealed in the floor of the valley by removal of the newer sediments. The most notable of some small outcrops of Jurassic rocks is a bar of limestone which crosses the Rhine transversely near Kembs, causing the Istein rapids.

THE PHYSICAL FEATURES

The plain of Alsace forms the south-western portion of this rift-valley floor, extending northward for ninety miles from the foothills

[1] Two sound, well illustrated accounts are E. Juillard, *L'Alsace: le sol, les hommes et la vie régionale* (1963); and A. Blanc, E. Juillard, J. Ray and M. Rochefort, *Les Régions de l'Est* (1960), in the series *France de Demain*.

of the Jura (the *Jura alsacienne*) to the German frontier along the
river Lauter, and varying in width from ten to twenty-five miles
between the Rhine's regulated channel and the foothills of the Vosges.
Three relief divisions may be distinguished: the higher terraces
sloping gently eastward from 600 feet above sea-level along the
Vosges foothills, the *Sundgau* in the extreme south of the rift-valley,
and the flood-plains of the Ill and the Rhine in the south and of the
Rhine alone to the north of Strasbourg.

The Higher Terraces.—The foothills of the Vosges, composed of
Triassic and Jurassic sandstones, form stepped terraces (the so-called

FIG. 81.—THE PLAIN OF LOWER ALSACE.

The large number of minor streams and drainage channels flowing across the
plain to the Rhine are omitted. The Franco-German frontier follows the centre
of the Rhine. The Bien Wald, Forêt de Haguenau and Forêt de Vendenheim,
developed on sheets of sand and gravel, separate the fertile *loess*-covered areas.
Heights are given in feet.

Based on *Carte de France et des frontières au 200,000ᵉ*, sheets 19, 28.

'*collines sous-vosgiennes*'), gashed through by deep, almost gorge-like,
valleys of rivers descending eastwards or north-eastwards from the
High Vosges until they are picked up by the northwards-flowing Ill.

These are torrential streams actively eroding into the flanks of the Vosges, and they are heavily laden with débris, particularly during the snow-melt floods of early summer and following late summer storms. As a result, extensive deposition takes place on the plain immediately beyond the foothills, where the gradient abruptly lessens and the rate of flow is checked. The confluence of each of these Vosges streams with the Ill forms an acute angle marked by the deposition of gravels, among which the waters flow in braided streams, sometimes below the surface.

Much of this area consists of marsh (where the water-table is high), alternating with dry pebble-banks covered with scrubby vegetation. The Thur in particular flows across a large arid gravel-fan (the Ochsenfeld), where it leaves its deeply-cut valley below Thann. Parts of it have, however, been improved by irrigation to provide meadow-land of sorts. North of Sélestat lies another area of gravels and marsh, for which the river Scheer is responsible.

To the north of Strasbourg, beyond the Ill confluence, rivers flow down to the Rhine from the Low Vosges, notably the Zorn, the Moder, the Sauer and the Lauter (Fig. 81). Each of these has deposited a fan of coarse sandy deposits, broadening eastward towards the Rhine.

Loess-soils in places swathe the surface of both the gravels and the Tertiary clays, forming a widespread '*manteau limoneux*'. A distinction is drawn in Alsace between the '*loess ancien*', which has been reworked by running water and redeposited in stratified layers though retaining many of its original characteristics, and the '*loess récent*', the true wind-blown material lying at all levels. The *loess* weathers to form a friable yellowish loam, warm and easily worked, and is for the most part under arable cultivation. The soils are rather dry, the result of their high porosity, but the underlying clays are usually adequately damp.

The Sundgau.—One part of the plain of Alsace, in the extreme south of the rift-valley, merits special attention. The name Sundgau, which means 'the southern region', is applied to this district situated between the limestone foothills of the Jura and the river Ill above Mulhouse. Its undulating surface ascends from about 850 feet above the Ill valley to 1,400 feet in the south, most of it lying between 1,250 and 1,350 feet. The underlying rocks consist of Oligocene clays, and in the south (in the district known as *Ajoie*) these clays appear on the surface. Elsewhere the country is covered with irregular sheets of fluvio-glacial sands and gravels, laid down by the powerful inter-glacial and post-glacial tributaries of the proto-Rhine. The present rivers crossing the Sundgau have dissected these sheets of gravels, forming broad shallow valleys in many places cutting down into the

Oligocene clays, and leaving flat-topped interfluves still covered with the gravels. The present rivers are much smaller than those of late glacial times, and wander vaguely across their floors as misfits. Many of their tributary valleys are now dry, the result of a lowered water-table, others contain temporary streams which run down the valleys after heavy rain, to lose themselves in the gravel-sheets where they open out into the more level plain. Small patches of good loam-soils have developed on a sporadic cover of *loess*.

The western Sundgau is characterised by more than 200 lakes with an aggregate area of only about 1½ square miles (Fig. 82). They

FIG. 82.—THE SUNDGAU OF SOUTHERN ALSACE.
Heights on the map are given in feet.
Based on *Carte de France au 50,000ᵉ*, sheets XXXVI/21, 22; XXXVII/21, 22.

occur in the flat valley-bottoms, strung out in lines along depressions in the irregular gravel cover, their floors underlain by impermeable clays. Some are maintained artificially by dams.

The Ill and Rhine Flood-plains.—A distinct step (of twenty feet or so) at the eastern edge of the river terraces marks the descent to the flood-plains of the Ill and the Rhine. Especially in the south these flood-plains are almost horizontal from west to east, but have a distinct northward slope. As a result the Ill, which rises on the flanks of the Jura, flows northwards for some eighty miles almost parallel to the Rhine, until the easterly slope of the plain becomes rather more marked, causing the tributary to converge upon the Rhine and finally to join it ten miles north of Strasbourg.

The flood-plains of the Ill and the Rhine were composed of gravel-sheets deposited by the swollen rivers towards the end of the Pleistocene. A lowering of base-level to the north (see p. 21) resulted in renewed down-cutting into these gravel-sheets, and so now the Ill and the Rhine each occupies a broad flood-plain separated by a distinct terrace formed of these gravels.

The flood-plain of the Ill, three miles in width, is intersected by the braided water-courses of the river and its gradually converging tributaries. This flood-plain was formerly covered with swamp, interspersed with islands of gravel and clumps of trees, known as the *Ried*. Much of this *Ill-Ried* has been reclaimed, as evidenced by the network of drainage channels and the carefully maintained water-meadows, though parts, notably in the angle between the Scheer and the Ill, are still marshy, and most areas even though protected with dykes are liable to flooding in winter. Settlements are notably absent, even in the reclaimed districts.

THE RIVER RHINE

The Rhine winds over the floor of a flood-plain which varies in width from a mile or so just below Basel to nearly three miles near Strasbourg. Its current is swift, for between Basel and Strasbourg there is a fall in altitude of some 330 feet; during times of high water, particularly in early summer, the river swirls powerfully down-stream. Much of this Rhine water comes from its Alpine head-streams, and the river carries an enormous amount of gravel, sand and silt. Much of this is deposited on the floor of the flood-plain, largely as a result of the sudden decrease in gradient and hence in the speed of the current; at the Istein rapids at Kembs in the south the rate of flow is about eleven knots, but the average rate between Basel and Strasbourg is only five to six knots.[1]

Before extensive works of regularisation were carried out in the nineteenth century (discussed below), the Rhine meandered over its flood-plain among an ever-changing series of braided channels and gravel islets, and the flood-waters extended over an area several times as wide as at the present. The main river is now contained between reinforced banks, usually cutting across meanders to provide a more direct channel. But on either side of this channel remain part-silted backwaters, cut-offs and minor channels, where patches of alder, willow and poplar alternate with reed-swamps. This area is known as the *Rheinwald* or the *Rhein-Ried*. Parts have been reclaimed to form tolerable summer pasture, particularly

[1] A. Demangeon and L. Febvre, *Le Rhin* (1935), p. 158.

where the old gravels are overlain with sand and mud. But much of this *Ried* still remains unreclaimed, for the gravel-sheets are too unrewarding to merit the effort involved. Sometimes the lower layers of the gravel-banks have compacted into intractable conglomerates, which dry out into a concrete-like mass. Even in the main regularised channel, new gravel-banks still form and change their positions during flood times.

The volume of Rhine water is exceedingly variable. The following graphic figures have been quoted [1] for three points within the rift-valley section:

(*Cu.m. per Second*)

	Low Water	Average Flow	High Water
Basel . . .	330	865	4,624
Kehl . . .	380	956	4,685
Lauterbourg . .	465	1,106	5,010

During much of winter, the Alsatian Rhine experiences low water because of the freezing of its Alpine headstreams, and a further period of low water occurs in late summer, with a maximum in late May or early June. Floods may take place at any time, but they are most pronounced in early summer and can still be dangerous should there be a sudden and concentrated thaw.

The Rhine Navigation.—The navigation of the Rhine is obviously handicapped by these many physical disadvantages. Yet because of its situation, the river has been used for centuries and much effort has been expended in schemes of regularisation. During the nineteenth century, as a result of works begun in 1817, the main river was gradually confined to a straightened dyked channel. This regularisation was completed as far upstream as Mannheim by 1866, and in the decade after 1906 the Mannheim-Basel section was also straightened and embanked. The dyked course between Basel and Mainz is about fifty miles shorter than the natural channel, thus resulting in a steeper gradient, and this, combined with the confining of the waters to a narrowed channel, produced a much swifter current and made upstream navigation extremely difficult. In addition, the development of railways along the Rhine valley, linking Basel directly with the lower Rhineland and the North Sea ports, caused navigation above Mannheim virtually to cease until the twentieth century. From 1907 to 1914, however, further regularisation was carried out in the section between Mannheim and Strasbourg, and more improvements in the Alsatian section took place

[1] *Op. cit.* (1935), p. 155.

in the inter-war years, notably in the Istein section below Basel. Developments by the French authorities involved the improvement of the river-port of Strasbourg, and the construction of the initial section of the *Grand Canal d'Alsace*. In 1928, moreover, the Swiss began a considerable development and extension of the river-port of Basel.

The result of these developments is that at the present time an effective minimum depth of about eight feet is maintained as far upstream as Strasbourg-Kehl, unless an exceptional period of low water should occur. Between Kehl and Basel the river is negotiable by barges of from 1,000 to 1,500 tons towed by powerful tugs and with expert pilotage, but this is normally only for about ninety days in the year between the beginning of June and the end of August.

The Grand Canal d'Alsace.—Since Alsace returned to France after the war of 1914–18, that country has been very interested in a left-bank lateral canal, with the dual function of overcoming the navigational difficulties of the Rhine and of utilising its hydro-electricity potential. In 1919 the State-sponsored *Société des Forces Motrices du Rhin* was formed, which produced a most ambitious multi-purpose project involving a lateral canal of seven sections. One of the clauses in the Treaty of Versailles empowered France to divert water from the Rhine, providing that navigational facilities were not thereby impaired. France was in the strong position of having five members on the post-war Rhine Commission compared with Germany's four, and despite protests by Germany and also by Switzerland she decided to go ahead.[1]

The first stage was designed to overcome a serious obstacle on the river near Kembs below Basel, the transverse Istein Bar of resistant Jurassic limestone. The concentration of the current in a more direct channel had caused serious erosion below the bar, forming rapids extremely difficult of negotiation and impassable for much of the year. The French first constructed the Kembs barrage, completed in 1927, designed to raise the level of the main river and so provide water for a new lateral canal, as well as for the Huningue Branch Canal which links, with the aid of five locks, the river-port of Basel with the Rhône-Rhine Canal to the north-west (Fig. 85). The next stage was to cut a Kembs by-pass loop of four miles, rejoining the Rhine below the Istein rapids by means of a locked connection. A power-station was built at the northern end of this canal to utilise the head between the level of the canal and that of the river. The scheme was completed in 1933, and all traffic to or

---

[1] J. Ritter, 'L'Aménagement du Rhin français', in *A. de G.* (1953), vol. lxii, pp. 365-8, gives an account of the installations at Ottmarsheim. See also J. Labadié, 'Le Grand Canal d'Alsace', in *Géographia* (1953), no. 27, pp. 28-31; this includes a useful map.

from Basel then utilised the canal, negotiating the sets of locks at each end; the section of the Rhine thus by-passed was in future neglected for navigation.

No further progress took place before the war of 1939–45, but in 1950 the French Government authorised the nationalised company of *Electricité de France* to go ahead with a second stage. A further loop was constructed between Kembs and Ottmarsheim; traffic then passed through the Kembs locks along both new sections, and so by a further set of locks to rejoin the Rhine, where a second power-station was built. This stage was completed in 1952. The third loop between Ottmarsheim and Fessenheim was then commenced, and the Fessenheim station was completed in 1956. The whole position was, however, altered in June 1956, when agreement was reached in Luxembourg between West Germany and France concerning the future of the Saar (see p. 274), in which one of the terms involved the *Grand Canal d'Alsace*. The French Government agreed not to proceed with this canal beyond Marckolsheim, the northern end of the fourth loop. Beyond that point the river itself is being improved by means of three stabilising barrages at Rhinau-Sundhouse, Gerstheim and Strasbourg, and hydro-electricity plants are being installed. By 1966 six power-stations were completed: Kembs (1932), Ottmarsheim (1952), Fessenheim (1956), Vogelgrün (1959), Marckolsheim (1960) and Rhinau (1964).

The six Rhine power-stations now afford a considerable contribution of electricity to the French grid. In 1963 the five in operation produced between them 4·48 milliard kwh.

The importance of the post-war contribution of electricity to the French energy requirements is shown by these figures:

Production of Electricity in France

(1000 million kwh)

	1938	1944	1949	1954	1956	1958	1965
Hydro .	10	10	11	24	26	32	44
Thermal .	9	7	19	21	28	29	45

Source: *Direction de l'Electricité, Ministère de l'Industrie et du Commerce*, published in various volumes of *Annuaire statistique de la France*.

LAND-USE AND AGRICULTURE

Climate.—Climatically the plain of Alsace is well favoured for agriculture, at any rate compared with Lorraine to the west. The mean annual rainfall varies from 19 inches at Colmar, which is very much in the rain-shadow of the Vosges, to Strasbourg with 26 inches.

The continental influences in this eastern part of France are manifested in a marked summer maximum of precipitation, July usually being the wettest month. The summers are warm, the mean monthly temperature at Strasbourg being 65° F., and sunshine hours are long. Strasbourg has in fact recorded a maximum temperature of 102° F., while the tendency to continentality is also indicated by a record minimum of –16° F. and by the fact that the mean January temperature is 31° F. In severe winters the Rhine may freeze, as in 1952, and a navigable channel may be difficult to maintain even with ice-breakers. As many as eighty days with frost may be experienced.

The Vosges do, however, provide a surprising degree of shelter (see p. 517); spring comes appreciably earlier than in Lorraine, and the south-easterly aspect is of great importance to such crops as the vine. The fact that grapes and tobacco flourish, and that even peaches, apricots and almonds grow in favoured localities, is evidence of the pleasant summer climate.

Agriculture.[1]—The main agricultural variations in the gently sloping Alsatian plain are largely the result of differences in soil-types—whether the soils are developed on *loess*, on recent alluvium, or on diluvial sands and gravels. The first tend to be under arable cultivation, the second under permanent pasture, the third under woodland, scrub-forest or marsh.

The warm well-drained *loess*-soils form an 'apron' over the lower slopes of the foothills and extend in places into the plain itself. To the south of Sélestat, in Haut-Rhin, the *loess*-cover is uneven and patchy, but in Bas-Rhin it is quite extensive. To the north of Strasbourg these fertile loam-soils occupy most of the Saverne 'embayment', which forms a broad re-entrant into the Vosges (see pp. 521-2 and Fig. 119). From this, three 'promontories' of similar soils extend eastward, almost to the edge of the Rhine flood-plain, between the 'sand-deltas' of the Zorn, Moder, Sauer and Lauter (Fig. 81). These undulating plains form a very fertile part of Alsace. The most prosperous district is that which lies to the north-west of Strasbourg, crossed by the main road and railway running westward to Nancy and by the Marne-Rhine Canal; this district is known as the *Kochersberg*, after a prominent hill on which stood a castle built by the bishops of Strasbourg. Holdings have been subdivided through generations of *parcellement*; indeed, in some cantons the average unit is a mere 700 square metres and cultivation is on a garden scale.

Wheat, maize, barley (for brewing), sugar-beet, tobacco, potatoes and oats (for fodder) are grown wherever these loamy soils occur.

[1] E. Juillard, *La Vie rurale dans la plaine de Basse-Alsace: essai de géographie* (1953).

Dairying is widespread; in 1963 there were 98,000 dairy cattle in Bas-Rhin and 52,000 in Haut-Rhin. Large numbers are grazed in summer on the *Ried* pastures and stall-fed in the winter on locally grown trefoil, lucerne and fodder-beet.

Hops are widely grown, usually on a small family-holding; indeed, this is one of the world's chief producing areas, supplying the many Rhineland breweries in both France and Germany. To the south of Strasbourg numerous orchards of apples, plums, cherries and even peaches and apricots flourish on the south-facing slopes covered with calcareous down-wash; this fruit cultivation is a tribute to the long hours of summer sunshine and to a freedom from spring frosts on the slopes. The vineyards on the slopes of the foothills and in the valley re-entrants are described on p. 519, as they belong to the Vosges rather than to the plain; the vine-growing area is officially described by the *Ministère de l'Economie Nationale* as the '*Zone sous-vosgienne du Vignoble*'.

The reclaimed alluvium of the *Ried* of the Ill plain is mostly under permanent pasture, but in places there are market-gardens, growing peas, potatoes, carrots and asparagus both for the urban markets and for the canning industry. In the northern part of the Rhine *Ried* tobacco and hops are grown on small-holdings cultivated by families.

Woodland.—Much of the Alsatian plain, especially in the south, is not reclaimed, and consists either of marshes along the Rhine flood-plain and to a less extent along that of the Ill, or of forest on the *loess*-free gravels and coarse sands. In the Sundgau about a quarter of the surface is wooded (Fig. 82). In the south of the Rhine plain itself the forest of the Harth extends over the gravel-flats from north-west of Basel for nearly twenty miles as far as Ensisheim. This is a poor scrub-forest, of little value except for cutting vine- and hop-poles from the stunted oak-coppice. Further to the west between the rivers Doller and Thur is the Forêt de Nonnenbruch (Fig. 83), an even poorer area of scrub-woodland. Some smaller woodlands are found in Middle Alsace, notably the Thurwald in the lower Thur valley, the Niederwald in the Fecht valley and the Illwald to the south-west of Strasbourg. Woodlands also occur on the sandy areas in Lower Alsace to the north of Strasbourg—the Forêt de Vendenheim in the Zorn valley, the extensive Haguenau forest which covers the 'sand-delta', seamed with distributaries, of the Moder and the Sauer (Fig. 81), and the Bien Wald in the lower Lauter valley, although most of this lies across the frontier in West Germany. These sandy areas have been carefully planted with pines, and provide timber of much better quality than does the scrub-forest on the gravel-sheets south of Strasbourg.

Some indication of the land-use distributions which have been described is given by the statistics of the Alsatian *départements* of Haut-Rhin and Bas-Rhin. Admittedly the former includes the eastern flanks of the High Vosges and the latter a part of the Low Vosges, but they do provide some indication of the order of magnitude involved.

Land-Use, 1963

(*Percentage of Total Area*)

	Pasture	Woodland	Arable Land
Bas-Rhin . . .	20	35	31
Haut-Rhin . . .	23	37	29

Source: *Ministère de l'Agriculture*, published in the *Annuaire statistique de la France, 1964*.

MINING AND INDUSTRY

Agriculture represents only one aspect of the economy of Alsace, for this is a considerable industrial region. Deposits of minerals include potash in the south and petroleum in the north, the latter being substantially less important (Fig. 76).

Potash.—In 1904, when this territory was in German hands, borings were sunk to the north of Mulhouse in quest of mineral oil. Deposits of potash in the form of *sylvite* (*KCl*) were discovered in the Oligocene strata, deposited when the rift-valley was a gulf of the sea in early Tertiary times. One stratum of potash, about four feet thick, lies at 2,057 feet, another nearly three times as thick is seventy feet lower. The extent of the deposits, covering nearly eighty square miles, was revealed by some hundreds of borings put down through the sandy soils of the Forêt de Nonnenbruch. The deposits contain between 12 and 22 per cent of pure potash, in places as much as 30 per cent, and the estimated reserves are 1,500 million tons, of which half are readily exploitable by present techniques. Before 1918 the great German *Kalisyndikat* was mainly concerned with the exploitation of its own vast deposits between the rivers Weser and Elbe, the chief centre being Stassfurt; this was the only major potash resource worked in the world at that time and the monopoly was jealously guarded. The Nonnenbruch deposits were therefore exploited only slowly and the annual output was deliberately limited to a mere 4 per cent of the German total, or about 50,000 tons of pure potash. As a result, until after the war of 1914–18 relatively little development took place. With the reacquisition of Alsace by France the Stassfurt monopoly was broken, and within three years the Alsatian output had trebled as compared with pre-war figures. Several companies are now operating the field, one of which (the

Mines Domaniales de Potasse d'Alsace) was acquired by the French State in 1924. Seven individual groups of deep mines are situated in the angle between the Doller in the south and the Ill in the west

FIG. 83.—THE POTASH-MINING DISTRICT OF SOUTHERN ALSACE.

The outlines of the built-up areas and woodlands are generalised. The large area of woodland north-west of Mulhouse is the Forêt de Nonnenbruch.

Based on *Carte de France au 50,000°*, sheet XXXVII/20, with additional information.

(Fig. 83); each is served by mineral-lines, branching from the main Strasbourg-Mulhouse railway. A number of pleasant *cités-ouvrières* house the 12,000 workers; the large *Cité Ste. Barbe* was built a mile north of Wittenheim to serve the neighbouring *Eugène* and *Théodore* mines, five housing estates in the extreme west house the labour for the *Amélie* mines near Wittelsheim, and there are several more. These mines and housing estates are dispersed among the woodlands of the Forêt de Nonnenbruch.

Development after 1919 proceeded apace, and by 1926 competition with German potash necessitated an agreement between the two countries concerning the amount which might be put on the world market, although several other countries (notably the U.S.A. and the U.S.S.R.) were also increasing their output. This agreement was actually soon scrapped. By 1937 France was producing annually just over three million tons of crude potash, or 16 per cent of the world total, compared with Germany's 63 per cent and the U.S.A.'s 9 per cent. After the end of the war of 1939–45, the enormous demand for fertilisers resulted in a considerable increase of output; in 1963 France produced 10·3 million tons, nearly four times her highest pre-war output, of which 40 per cent was exported. Several processing factories have been built near the groups of mines. Much of this potash, crude and refined, is shipped from Strasbourg by barge down the Rhine to Antwerp, hence to the Benelux countries (her main customers), Great Britain and even the U.S.A.

Petroleum.—Petroleum occurs on a small scale in northern Alsace. Oil-seepages were known and utilised in this district as early as the fifteenth century, especially near the village of Pechelbronn (which means 'pitch-spring'), and from 1735 small patches of oil-sands occurring near the surface were worked. As late as 1888 these sands (the '*lentilles de sable*') were mined by a German company by means of shafts and the oil extracted from the sands. In 1881 the first borings were sunk, and oil was pumped from depths between 650 and 3,000 feet. Today a series of oil-wells operates along a line parallel to the Rhine. The company working the oilfield is the *S.A. d'Exploitation Minière de Pechelbronn*, with its subsidiary the *Société Française Alsacienne des Carburants*. Further research and prospecting is being carried out by the *Société de Prospection et d'Exploitation Pétrolières en Alsace*, and a little oil has been found elsewhere, notably in the triangle between Erstein, Barr and Sélestat, to the west and north-west of Mulhouse, and near Altkirch in the Sundgau. The Alsatian output of oil is, however, small. In 1963 the Pechelbronn and the Staffelfelden fields produced only 34,000 tons out of a French total of 2·5 millions. This was only a small contribution to the 46·7 million tons through-put of French refineries.

Industry.—The most important aspect of industry is the manufacture of textiles, which began in mediaeval times on a domestic scale in the foothills of the Vosges, where it still continues (see p. 520). The introduction of steam-power during the Industrial Revolution resulted in a certain degree of concentration in Mulhouse, Colmar and Belfort, and two-thirds of the operatives in this eastern textile region now live in and around these three towns. Although the emphasis is on the production of cotton cloth, a wide range of other textile products is made—sewing-thread, printed calico, woollens, silk and rayon. Other industrial activities are concentrated at these three towns and especially at Strasbourg (see below).

POPULATION AND SETTLEMENT

The distribution of population and settlement shows some interesting features. Several areas are virtually uninhabited, notably the higher parts of the Sundgau among the lakes and woodlands, the *Ried* along the floor of the Rhine flood-plain, the gravel-sheets on the higher terrace-plains, and the forested sandy 'deltas' of Lower Alsace. The aridity of the higher gravels and the waterlogged character of the lower gravels are alike inimical to anything but poor forest growth.

The *loess*-areas on the terraces are occupied by a quite dense agricultural population, spread out in a close pattern of prosperous villages and individual small-holdings. This is particularly noticeable in the Kochersberg district to the north-west and west of Strasbourg. To the south of Strasbourg the pattern of settlement takes on a linear character, reflecting the parallel belts of land-use. One string of villages lies on the higher ground between the respective *Ried*-districts of the Rhine and the Ill, another follows the Rhône-Rhine Canal, and a third is situated along the main-line railway between Strasbourg and Basel (via Sélestat, Colmar and Mulhouse) following the edge of the terrace to the west of the Ill. A further series of towns lies at the zone of contact between the Vosges and the Alsatian plains, where each upland valley opens on to the high terrace; many have textile industries, long-established because of water-power, or are centres of wine production (see p. 519) and agricultural market-towns. A few of these places, specially favoured as route-centres, have developed a considerable urban life.

Mulhouse (111,000 people in 1962) is the commercial and industrial, although not the administrative, capital of Haut-Rhin and of southern Alsace. It stands on the northern edge of the Sundgau at an altitude of about 800 feet, overlooking the upper Ill valley. It has a basin, equipped with wharves and railway-sidings, opening into the Rhône-Rhine Canal, which is especially valuable for bringing coal from the Strasbourg *dépôts*. As a railway route-focus it has considerable importance, for the main line following the left bank of the Rhine from Basel to Strasbourg passes through the town, from it a line proceeds westward through the Belfort gap to Besançon and Lyons, and another runs north-eastward across the Rhine to Freiburg and western Germany. Mulhouse was only a small town of 5,000 people at the beginning of the nineteenth century; it had been an autonomous city in alliance with the Swiss Confederation until it became French in 1797. The industrial developments of the nineteenth century caused a rapid growth. Some pioneer efforts here in the housing of workers sought to cope with the increase of the industrial population in the mid-nineteenth century. In 1853 the mayor of the town, with the co-operation of the *Société Industrielle de Mulhouse*, inaugurated the *Société des Cités-Ouvrières* to build residential blocks in the north-west of the town near the Ill-Doller confluence. The society built about a thousand houses (together with schools, bath-houses and other amenities) for sale to workers by means of long-term mortgage schemes. This district, known as the '*Arbeiterstadt*' during the periods of German sovereignty, represented a remarkable social achievement for the mid-nineteenth century.

The industrial life of present-day Mulhouse is varied, although there is still an emphasis on textiles—cotton cloth, sewing-thread, calico, linen, silk and rayon, together with ancillary industries such as printing, dyeing and finishing, and hosiery. The potash deposits to the north of the town have resulted in chemical industries, notably the production of refined potassium salts, dye-stuffs and explosives. Some of these factories lie outside Mulhouse along the main road between the town and Ensisheim. The several engineering concerns include a branch of the *Société Alsacienne de Constructions Mécaniques* (which has its main works near Strasbourg), manufacturing locomotives and rolling-stock, textile machinery, etc.

Colmar (54,264 people in 1962) is the *chef-lieu* of Haut-Rhin, standing on the Lauch a few miles above its confluence with the Ill. The narrow irregular streets of the old Alsatian town, with its interesting timbered houses with fanciful façades, contrast remarkably with the unattractive industrial and residential suburbs. One feels, indeed, that this town has much of a German atmosphere, despite its undoubtedly strong pro-French sentiments. A German dialect is widely spoken, and place- and family-names are mostly in the German forms. It is an important textile centre, with some factories in the town itself, particularly dyeing and finishing works, and many more along the Fecht and Logelbach valleys.

Strasbourg.—The dominance of Strasbourg in Alsace is indicated by the fact that the population of the city in 1962 was 233,549, which with its three contiguous communes of Bischheim, Hoenheim and Schiltigheim made up the official '*agglomération urbain*' of about

307,000, or one-third of the total of Bas-Rhin. The city stands at an altitude of between 450 and 500 feet, the inner part enclosed by the divided channel of the Ill, and situated about two miles from the Rhine on the terrace above the flood-plain (Fig. 84).

The location of Strasbourg is one of fundamental geographical importance. To the north-west, where the High and Low Vosges meet, the edge of the upland leans back to the west to form the low-land 'bay' of Saverne. Beyond this is the lowest pass over the Vosges, the Col de la Saverne, reached by the deeply-cut re-entrant of the Zorn valley (Plate LVI and Fig. 119); this is the main 'gate-way' between the Rhineland and Lorraine. Beyond the Rhine, some forty miles further north, is a similar gap, the Kraichgau, between the northern end of the Black Forest and the Odenwald. Here then is a transverse route-way crossing the Rhine valley (it is significant that one of the Orient Express lines between Paris and Istanbul uses the Saverne-Kraichgau gaps). Strasbourg has long dominated these crossroads. It has functioned as a Gallic settle-ment, as a Roman military camp and as a Frankish town, and its history has been one of many vicissitudes, the inevitable result of its situation in the Franco-German marchlands. For nearly four centuries it prospered as a powerful imperial city until its annexation by France in 1681; then it became one of the fortress towns protecting France's eastern frontier, and like so many others was strongly fortified by Vauban. In 1870 the city was besieged by the German army; the fortifications, though strong by eighteenth-century standards, could not withstand a sustained bombardment which destroyed the citadel and other defensive works, and the city surrendered after six weeks' valiant resistance. During its German sovereignty, between 1871 and 1918, it was still more heavily fortified by concentric defensive works. It was returned to France in 1919. In 1939 many of its citizens were evacuated and it stood during the winter of 1939–40 as a silent outpost of France beyond the Maginot Line. A large part of the city was damaged before its surrender in the summer of 1940, but it was liberated in 1944. The German port of Kehl, on the opposite side of the Rhine, was captured and occupied by the French in 1944, and many of the returning inhabitants of Strasbourg were rehoused there until the destroyed portions of the French city were rebuilt. The river-port of Kehl was put under joint Franco-German administration in July 1952, but in April 1953 it was returned wholly to West Germany.

The heart of Strasbourg lies on an island within the main branches of the Ill, dominated by the magnificent red sandstone Gothic cathedral whose spire rises to a height of 464 feet. Beyond the island, with the narrow streets and picturesque houses with carved gables, the suburbs of Strasbourg now spread for several miles. In the north are the industrial suburbs of Robertsau and Schiltigheim, and to the south-west is Graffenstaden, in each of which a variety

FIG. 84.—STRASBOURG.

Based on (i) Plate 56, *Atlas de France* (1936); (ii) W. Seghers, *Kaart der Binnencheepvaartwegen van N.-W. Europa* (n.d.); and (iii) additional information derived from local town-plans, etc.

of engineering industries has developed; others have grown up around the port district. Other activities include several chemical works (producing fertilisers, drugs, soap and perfumes), rayon-textile factories, and works which manufacture a variety of electrical equipment including refrigerators, radio and television sets. As a result of Strasbourg's position on the Alsatian plain it has many food-processing industries—the canning of fruit and vegetables, the production of the famous *pâté de foie gras Strasbourgeois*, tobacco processing, chocolate-making, brewing and distilling. Tanning, paper-making and printing have been carried on for centuries; Gutenberg made his first experiments in printing in Strasbourg in the year 1436, and the celebrated Johann Mentel established himself as a master printer in the city in 1458 only a few years after Gutenberg's Bible was published at Mainz.

Two large oil-refineries in the suburbs of Strasbourg, at Reichstett and Herrlisheim, were completed in 1963. They are linked by the South European Pipeline with Lavéra on the Mediterranean (see p. 418). In 1964 these refineries had an output of 2·7 and 3·2 million tons respectively.

Strasbourg is an inland port of considerable importance (Plate XXXV). It has been a small river-port for centuries, but the construction of the Rhône-Rhine Canal in 1832 and of the Marne-Rhine Canal in 1842 made it the chief canal-port in eastern France (Fig. 85). The first of these has a length of just over 200 miles, and links Strasbourg with the Saône at St. Symphorien by a complex route necessitating no less than 166 locks. It is not a large waterway, although it was reconstructed after 1918 to accommodate 300-ton barges; nevertheless, it conveys about a million tons of freight annually, including about half a million tons of coal which moves southward from Strasbourg. A major project is in progress (with a completion date of 1975) to turn the Rhône-Rhine Canal into a modern water-way, forming a link between the North and Mediterranean Seas. The section of the old canal north of Mulhouse is now virtually disused, since traffic uses the loops of the *Grand Canal d'Alsace* (pp. 299–300) and the Rhine. A new canal is under construction across the watershed through the Belfort gap, with a new Port de Bourgogne, near Belfort. The thirteen locks of this section of the old waterway will be replaced by a ship-lift. The new waterway will be called the *Grand Canal du Rhin au Rhône*.

The Marne-Rhine Canal, 197 miles in length, runs westward from Strasbourg through the industrial districts of southern Lorraine and joins the Marne-Saône and Marne Lateral canals at Vitry-le François. It was difficult to construct, since it has to negotiate first the northern part of the Vosges through the Saverne Gap (Fig. 119) and then in succession the Jurassic escarpments. This necessitated 178 locks, of which fifty-two are used between Strasbourg and the Vosges water-shed, which it pierces in two tunnels. Maintenance of navigation is

FIG. 85.—THE WATERWAYS OF EASTERN FRANCE.

Towns are indicated by abbreviations, as follows: **A**, Arlon; **B**, Bingen; **Ba**, Basel; **Be**, Besançon; **Bel**, Belfort; **C-M**, Charleville-Mézières; **Col**, Colmar; **Cor**, Corre; **Di**, Dijon; **Do**, Dole; **E**, Epinal; **F**, Frouard; **Gi**, Givet; **Go**, Gondrexange; **Gr**, Gray; **K**, Kembs; **Ke**, Kehl; **Ko**, Koblenz; **L**, Lauterbourg; **Lux**, Luxembourg; **M**, Mainz; **Ma**, Mannheim; **Me**, Metz; **Mo**, Montbéliard; **Mu**, Mulhouse; **N**, Nancy; **O**, Ottmarsheim; **P**, Pont-à-Bar; **PM**, Pont-à-Mousson; **S**, Sedan; **Sa**, Saarbrücken; **Sar**, Sarreguemines; **Sav**, Saverne; **St**, Strasbourg; **St.J**, St. Jean-de-Losne; **St.S**, St. Symphorien; **T**, Toul; **Th**, Thionville; **Tri**, Trier; **Tro**, Troussey; **V**, (Est Canal) Verdun; **V**, (Marne-Saône C.) Vitry-le-François. **Hun.B.**, Huningue Branch; **C.M.H.S.**, Canal de Montbéliard à la Haute-Saône (projected).

Based on W. Seghers, *Kaart der Binnenscheepvaartwegen van N.-W. Europa* (Antwerp, n.d.).

not easy, for the water supply is sometimes inadequate, and some sections supplied from torrential streams are liable as a result to silting. Nevertheless, this waterway links Strasbourg with Lorraine, and as a result conveys between 1 and 2 million tons annually.

As a Rhine port Strasbourg has developed only in this century. The improvement of river navigation before 1914 primarily benefited Mannheim, and while Alsace was still part of Germany constant demands came from the citizens of Strasbourg for further improvements upstream to their city. A port area has developed east and north of the town, facing Kehl across the river (Fig. 84). These developments have gone on since the *Bassin du Commerce* was opened in 1892; two link-canals were built directly from the Rhine into the canal-port and several new basins have been constructed, including the *Bassin aux Pétroles* to the north of the port. The *Nouveau Port* to the south has been developed since 1928.

In 1964 the port of Strasbourg handled 9·2 million tons of freight, of which 8·5 millions moved along the Rhine, the remainder via the two canals. The city imports coal, cereals and oil by water, and exports potash from the Nonnenbruch mines, much of which goes directly by water to the fertiliser factories and chemical works of Antwerp. The value to France of the Rhine as a navigable waterway is shown by the fact that about 12 million tons of freight are transported annually in French barges, irrespective of freight carried in Dutch, West German and Swiss vessels. Approximately two-thirds of this freight moves upstream.

CHAPTER 13

THE BASIN OF AQUITAINE

The Basin of Aquitaine[1] forms a roughly triangular lowland occupying about one-seventh of the area of France. For long periods of geological time it was affected by extensive marine transgressions and the deposition that took place has contributed appreciably to the present surface features. The Jurassic sea extended over the Basin and indeed over what is now the Central Massif, and so Jurassic limestones form a continuous outcrop from the Biscayan coast of southern Vendée as far south as the valley of the Aveyron. The Cretaceous sea, though less widespread, also covered the whole Basin and was indeed continuous with the transgression over the Paris Basin by way of the straits now indicated by the 'Gate of Poitou' and with Languedoc by the 'Gap of Naurouze'. The Upper Cretaceous limestones now appear widely in the north and north-east and also again in the south along the Pyrenean flanks (Fig. 140), in each area dipping gently inwards under the Tertiary rocks. They are more sandy than the rocks of corresponding age in the Paris Basin, a result of the shallower waters in which they were deposited.

These Jurassic and Cretaceous rocks in the north-east are diversified by a number of minor folds running more or less from north-west to south-east, an apparent resurrection of Armorican trends as a result of the mid-Tertiary Alpine orogeny. The strata are also slightly inclined towards the west, the result of the *en masse* tilting of the Central Massif.

The still more reduced Eocene and Oligocene seas occupied most of the gulf between the edge of the Central Massif and the slowly uprising folds of the Pyrenees. Accordingly, extensive deposits of older Tertiary (particularly Oligocene) rocks form the surface cover over the northern part of the Basin between the Garonne and the edge of the Cretaceous outcrop. They are also represented in the Gap of Naurouze, indicating the maintenance at that time of the marine link between Aquitaine and Languedoc. Unlike the Paris Basin, where these Upper Tertiary rocks mainly consist of limestones laid down in deep clear water, the seas in Aquitaine were shallow and the predominant deposits consist mainly of sands and clays, although frequently of a calcareous nature.

[1] Useful texts include P. Barrère and R. Heisch, *La Région du Sud-Ouest* (1962), a well illustrated volume in the series *France de Demain*; and H. Enjalbert, *Les Pays aquitains, le modelé et les sols*, vol. 1 (1960), with 618 pp.

In mid-Tertiary times, however, the Naurouze Gap was closed through a slight uplift, and the margins of the sea withdrew to what is now the south-western part of the Aquitaine Basin. Great thicknesses of Miocene deposits worn from the uprising Pyrenees, forming a soft calcareous sandstone known as *molasse*, together with shelly sands (*faluns*), were laid down to the south of the Garonne. Occasional beds of limestone are intercalated among the *molasse*. In Pliocene times occurred the last stages in the infilling of this 'gulf of Aquitaine', the deposition of a fan of pebbles and coarse sand along the northern flanks of the Pyrenees, derived from their continued wastage.

Further diversification of a superficial character has subsequently occurred. The Quaternary Pyrenean glaciers, while not so extensive as those of the Alps, were responsible for the deposition of glacial drift over the northern foreland. More effective has been the continued work of the series of rivers flowing into the Basin both from the Central Massif and from the Pyrenees, and (with the exception of the Charente in the extreme north and the Adour in the south-west) focusing on the Gironde estuary. On leaving the upland courses where erosion is still trenchant, their work has been primarily depositive and vast loads of alluvium have been laid down over the flood-plains. The swollen rivers of the Pleistocene period did, however, cut down into the underlying rocks, thus forming broad valleys bordered with distinct terraces and separated by gentle interfluves. The rim of limestone plateaus in the north-east has been especially deeply trenched. The multitude of streams with their fluctuating régimes still modify the landscape. During the floods of winter and spring much erosion of the valleys takes place; vast loads of material are swept down, the coarsest gravels to encumber the flood-plains, the finest materials to the Gironde or the Bay of Biscay.

Another contribution to the surface features of Aquitaine was the result of a minor Quaternary transgression of the sea, during which sheets of fine marine sands were laid down in the extreme south-west. These materials are the main source of the Landes, although additional sand has been derived from weathering in the Pyrenees by way of the Garonne and the Adour.

The net result has been the production of an extensive, rather monotonous, lowland of gently undulating hills and valleys, as D. Faucher expresses it, '*ce pays aux lignes molles, aux larges horizons*'.[1] Though some low ridges appear in the east and south-east, the prominent concentric cuestas and vales which characterise the Paris Basin are absent.

Climatically this area is one of the most pleasant parts of France. Bordeaux has mean monthly temperature figures of 41° F. in

[1] D. Faucher, *La France: géographie-tourisme* (1951), vol. i, p. 423.

January and 69° F. in August, an equability due in large part to the proximity of the ocean. Toulouse, though at a higher altitude and almost halfway between the Atlantic and the Mediterranean, has figures very little different (40° F. and 70° F. respectively). Rainfall is distributed throughout the year, and although Mediterranean tendencies are indicated by a July minimum, no month is really dry. Indeed, the Basin is so open to the ocean in the west that Mediterranean influences are really slight. The Naurouze Gap is in fact a climatic as well as a hydrographic divide; the olive is absent from Aquitaine and only appears so far east as Carcassonne. Bordeaux has a mean annual total of 30 inches, Toulouse of 26 inches, and both have quite humid autumns and springs. These figures do of course mask considerable variations; long periods of drought may be succeeded by rainfall of considerable intensity with widespread flooding, especially in the Pyrenean foothills and in the bordering low plateaus, where violent summer thunderstorms are experienced. Cases are on record of an annual total at various stations amounting to twice that received during the previous year. The Basin is liable to the effects of wind, especially to cold, dry air-streams from the Central Massif in spring, and to the *autan* which may blow northwards in the same season from Spain over the crest-line of the Pyrenees, in cause and character very similar to the *föhn*. These winds may have a desiccating effect during the critical spring growing season, particularly on the vine.

The way of life over most of Aquitaine is primarily rural and agricultural. The plains are traditionally the scene of cereal cultivation, and more than half of the arable is still so used; wheat and maize are predominant, the latter being well suited by the damp springs and warm summers. In this century the area of temporary and irrigated grasslands, of fodder-crops such as lucerne and red trefoil and of hybrid maize[1] has increased, and so have livestock. In the northern part of the Basin, in Charente, co-operation in the dairy industry has developed more than anywhere in France. Horses, pigs and sheep are bred, many of the last involved in transhumance movements to and from the Pyrenean pastures, and small stock (especially geese and turkeys) are widely reared. The general character of the polyculture is emphasised by the market-gardens on the lower valley-terraces and by widespread orchards. Vineyards are extensive, and while *vin ordinaire* is produced almost everywhere, the superb wines of the Bordelais and the brandies of Cognac and Armagnac have a wide reputation.

The unit of cultivation tends on the whole to be small, much

[1] S. Lerat, 'L'Introduction du maïs hybride dans les pays de l'Adour', in *R.G.P.S.-O.* (1961), vol. 34, pp. 97-117; the area of maize has doubled, its yield quadrupled, during the last decade.

more so than in the Paris Basin, and rather resembling the pattern
of things in the Rhône valley and along the Mediterranean coastlands. A farm is often still worked by a *métayer* or share-tenant,
with a few cows, poultry, some permanent pasture, an orchard and
a vineyard, and a block of arable land under cereals and fodder-
crops. On the other hand, several large domains still exist, and
métayage is decreasing.

Not all the land is under cultivation. The sandy surface of the
Landes has little to offer, except on its margins where limited
schemes of drainage and improvement have been effected, and it
is now mainly under pine-woods. The southern fans of gravels,
though often flooded after heavy Pyrenean rains or snow-melt, are
for much of the year a scene of bleached aridity, and some of the
river flood-plains are encumbered with sheets of gravel and braided
streams. The higher parts of the sandy or gravelly interfluvial
plateaus carry heath and gorse, other areas once wooded with oaks
are now fern-brakes, and some of the limestones bear a scrub-vegeta-
tion. The former forests now survive only as fragments, mainly
along steep valley-sides, though copses of evergreen oak and chestnut survive in the east, beech on the higher ground generally, and
cork oak especially along the Garonne valley to the north-west of
Toulouse. There are also scattered patches of other varieties of oak,
groves of cypresses near villages, lines of poplars along the valleys,
and willow thickets bordering the streams.

Aquitaine is one of the less densely populated parts of France,
despite its prosperous and well-developed agriculture. Only the
département of Gironde of the twelve occupying the Basin has an
average density (225 per square mile in 1962) exceeding that of France
as a whole, and some districts are very scantily populated. Approximately a third of the population is concentrated along the lower
Garonne and Dordogne valleys and the Gironde estuary, where
Bordeaux and its agglomeration are situated, and the areas of denser
population continue inland along the well-cultivated valleys with
their prosperous towns. The low overall average is mainly due to
the absence of any large industrial regions, yet even so the rural
population has been declining since the mid-nineteenth century.
This is partly the result of a falling birth-rate and an ageing population; between the wars deaths appreciably exceeded births in several
départements, and even in the post-war years when the position has
improved somewhat the balance is still precarious. In 1961 there
were for example only 5,166 births in Dordogne compared with
4,685 deaths, and in Ariège (which includes part of the Pyrenees)
there was an actual adverse balance (1,833 births, 1,922 deaths). In
the twelve *départements* an overall excess of only about 2·3 per
thousand of the population compares unfavourably with 7·6 per

thousand for France as a whole. Another general cause of decline has been the attractions of urban life and of better paid employment in industry. Other specific reasons include the phylloxera crisis in the '80s, the fall in price of wheat at the turn of the century, and the increase in livestock-farming at the expense of arable which needs more labour. The decline has become so marked that paradoxically an appreciable shortage of agricultural labour has developed, remedied in part by an influx of Spanish and Italian workers. At times agricultural workers have even come from less favoured parts of France itself, such as Savoy, the Central Massif and Brittany; between 1922 and 1929, for example, over 8,000 people from the last region established themselves in Dordogne alone.

This rural population lives in dispersed and sometimes widely scattered settlements. Small towns are distributed fairly evenly over the Basin, each serving as a market- and servicing-centre for a particular district. Such are Angoulême and Périgueux in the north-east, Bergerac and Cahors in the east, Agen in the middle Garonne valley, Montauban and Albi in the Tarn lowlands, Tarbes and Pau in the south at the junction of mountain and plain, and Bayonne in the extreme south-west, towns of from 15,000 to 45,000 inhabitants. Most have a long history as bridge- or fortress-points, and have added to their market functions and old-established industries (mostly dealing with local agricultural products) a variety of modern manufactures, based on such factors as hydro-electricity and local natural gas and a deliberate location in the part of France furthest from her eastern frontier. Some discoveries of mineral oil and gas have been made in recent years.

One paradox is the fact that in this predominantly rural part of France are situated two of her seven largest cities, Bordeaux and Toulouse. The former, with nine contiguous communes, had 472,000 people in its agglomeration in 1962; for long a great port, it is also the centre of a manufacturing district and of the Bordelais vineyards, and is indeed the commercial focus of south-western France. Toulouse is a route-centre at the other extremity of the Garonne valley, of '*la longue avenue garonnaise*' (D. Faucher). It is the 'economic capital' of south-eastern Aquitaine, a commercial and industrial centre with over a quarter of a million people.

Regional Divisions.—Within the overall unity of these lowlands, with, at any rate to the casual traveller, a uniformity of aspect that seems to verge on the monotonous, it is possible to distinguish a number of *pays* with a certain individuality (Fig. 86). The *Garonne valley* itself, from the junction with the Ariège above Toulouse to the Gironde estuary, forms an axis lying diametrically across the lowlands. Between the Gironde and Vendée to the north is the *Charente*, drained by the river of the same name. The limestone margins in the east may be conveniently divided into the low Cretaceous plateaus of *Périgord*, and the Jurassic plateaus of *Quercy* crossed by the Lot. In

FIG. 86.—THE REGIONAL DIVISIONS OF AQUITAINE AND THE PYRENEES.
Rouss., Roussillon.

Based on a variety of sources, notably the map *Régions géographiques de la France* ; 1 : 1,400,000, published by the *Institut National de la Statistique et des Etudes Economiques.*

the south-east are the low Tertiary plateaus of *Albigeois* and *Lauraguais*, leading via the Gap of Naurouze into Languedoc. Then to the south-west of the curve of the middle Garonne is an area of low plateaus covered with sediments and crossed by a fan of rivers, comprising the higher *Lannemezan* and the lower *Armagnac*. In the south-west, occupying the angle between the Pyrenees and the Bay of Biscay, is a region which, largely drained by the river Adour, is known generally as the *Pays de l'Adour*. Finally, to the south-west of the Gironde estuary is the sand-region of the *Landes*.

THE GARONNE VALLEY

From above Toulouse to the Gironde estuary, the Garonne pursues its course more or less along the axial line of the Basin of Aquitaine. The valley-floor lies at only 450 feet above sea-level near Toulouse, and the gentle descent of the river below this point contrasts with the markedly steep drop down the Pyrenean slopes in its upper course. The heavy winter rainfall and the rapid runoff from the impermeable rocks of the Pyrenean massifs can cause extensive winter flooding, with widespread deposition of gravel and alluvium.[1] The record flood at Castets, thirty-three miles above Bordeaux, occurred in 1770 when the waters rose forty-two feet above mean level. Floods still occur, despite measures of regularisation effected since 1830, when systematic efforts were first made to confine the river within a single dyked channel. As a waterway, therefore, the Garonne is of little value (see p. 331).

The valley of the Garonne comprises a shallow trench, within which the river meanders among gravel-banks and sheets of fine alluvium. Successive phases of rejuvenation have caused the river to erode a series of terraces standing above the present flood-plain. Between Toulouse and the Tarn confluence, for example, the terrace-surfaces are well defined at about 500, 600 and 650 feet, and they are traceable downstream, decreasing in altitude, almost to Bordeaux.

The Garonne receives numerous tributaries, and the 'delayed' nature of their junctions, where the confluents flow almost parallel to the main river for some distance, helps to account for the width of the main valley-floor. Above Toulouse, near the Ariège confluence, the valley-floor is twelve miles across between the lowest terrace-bluffs. Further downstream below Castelsarrasin, where the Garonne turns westwards, it receives the Tarn (itself joined but a few miles higher by the Aveyron); their converging valleys form an extensive area of deposition, '*une sorte de delta intérieur*', sometimes referred to as the *pays montalbanais* from the location of Montauban in the south-east of this lowland. Still further downstream are numerous other right-bank confluents, the largest being the Lot which joins the main river near Aiguillon. Most of the Garonne's

[1] M. Pardé, *Le Régime de la Garonne* (1935). See also H. Enjalbert, 'Les Inondations de Bordeaux en 1952', in *R.G.P.S.-O.* (1953), vol. xxiv, pp. 258-68, which describes the floods on the Garonne and the effects on the Bordelais in December of that year.

left-bank tributaries rise on the higher parts of the Plateau de Lannemezan. These tributaries—Save, Gers, Baïse and a multitude of others—spread loads of silt over the plain of the Lomagne as they approach their successive confluences with the main river.

Below the Lot confluence the Garonne continues north-westwards through its flood-plain, bordered by low Oligocene plateaus on either side; at times the limestone bluffs approach quite closely, as between St. Macaire and Langon where they are only half a mile apart. Towards Bordeaux the valley widens again and is floored by the *palus*, marshlands now mostly drained. Fifteen miles below the city the Garonne unites with the Dordogne, at the beak-like tip (the Bec d'Ambès) of the Entre-deux-Mers peninsula.

The Dordogne, after crossing the Périgord plateau of Cretaceous limestone, enters the low Tertiary sandstone country near Bergerac. It too winds over its broad flood-plain; its meanders are especially well developed above and below Libourne, where it receives the waters of the Dronne and the Isle from northern Périgord. The northern edge of its valley above the Garonne junction is bordered by a prominent though interrupted escarpment, known as the *Côtes de la Dordogne*. The régime of the Dordogne is extremely variable. In late summer the depth in the main channel below Bergerac may be little more than a foot, with bleached shingle-banks separating the braided streams. In winter, by contrast, its surging waters may be six feet or more in depth.

The estuary of the Gironde extends north-westward towards the Bay of Biscay for fifty miles; at its mouth between the Pointe de la Coubre and the Pointe de Grave it is six miles in width. The river is bordered on the south by dyked and drained areas of alluvium known appropriately as *Petite Flandre*.[1] Along the north bank, however, cliffs of Upper Cretaceous limestone come right down to the shore. Near Royan at the Pointe de Vallière these horizontally bedded limestones have been worn into steep cliffs fronted by wave-cut platforms from which rise rugged stacks.

The Gironde estuary is an immense area of deposition, for not only do the two main rivers contribute a continual aggregation of alluvium, particularly during the floods of autumn and winter, but much silt is brought in from the Bay of Biscay with each flow-tide. Constant dredging is necessary to maintain a navigable channel to the port of Bordeaux.[2]

While the region of the Garonne valley possesses a distinct unity,

[1] H. Enjalbert, 'Les Formations alluviales de la Gironde', in *Comptes-Rendus du Congrès International de Géographie* (Lisbonne, 1949, published in 1950), vol. ii, pp. 461-81.

[2] L. Glangeaud, 'Etudes océanographiques et géologiques pour l'aménagement de l'estuaire girondin', in *A. de G.* (1937), vol. xlvi, pp. 509-12.

XXXVII Jarnac in the Charente

XXXVIII Besançon within the loop of the River Doubs

XXXIX The city of Lyons

XL The Donzère-Mondragon by-pass canal and power-station

the distance from Toulouse to the sea makes it inevitable that several individual *pays de Garonne* can be distinguished. The upper section is known as the *Garonne toulousaine*, then in turn downstream is the *pays montalbanais* in the neighbourhood of the Tarn junction, succeeded by the *Garonne agenaise*, the middle section of the river, and then above Bordeaux the *Garonne bordelaise*. Finally, the lands bordering the estuary are referred to as *les pays girondins*. The influence of the city makes it convenient and justifiable to describe the last two together as the Bordeaux region.

The Valley of the Garonne Toulousaine.—In the Garonne valley, in the neighbourhood of Toulouse, sheets of quartzite pebbles alternate with layers of tough clay overlying the *molasse*. Percolating water has heavily leached these gravels, and in some areas this has caused the formation of an impermeable hard-pan, known locally as *le grepp*. Much of this area, particularly the upper terraces, is wooded.

Despite the not very favourable gravelly soils, known as *les boulbènes*, agriculture is varied and quite prosperous. Some of the upper gravel-terraces are vine-covered, and villages such as Villaudric, Longages, Tournefeuille and others produce wines in considerable quantity, mostly for local consumption. Orchards of peaches, cherries and plums grow around the villages or in lines along the roads. On the broad middle terraces are hedgeless strips of arable cultivation, mainly of maize and wheat. The lowest damp terraces are usually under permanent pasture, often improved by the sowing of grasses and by the use of fertilisers, on which are reared dairy cattle (supplying milk for the urban population of Toulouse), beef-cattle of the *race gasconne*, and horses to be sold off in the markets of Toulouse. Sheep from the Pyrenean pastures are grazed during winter and spring. Along the valley-terraces to the north and south of Toulouse market-gardens cover a considerable area ; [1] besides the usual vegetables two interesting specialities include the production of gherkins (of which over 600 acres are grown) and near Lalande of flowers, particularly violets. Tobacco is cultivated on the better soils.

Toulouse.—The *pays toulousain* is of course dominated by Toulouse, which (with its 330,570 people in 1962) is the fourth city of France,[2]

[1] J. Odol, 'La Banlieue maraîchère au nord de Toulouse', in *R.G.P.S.-O.* (1952), vol. xxiii, pp. 189-232. This is an immensely detailed account of the holdings, types of crops, methods of cultivation, etc. See also C. Couffin, 'L'Influence de la ville de Toulouse sur l'agriculture des terrasses garonnaises de la rive gauche', in *R.G.P.S.-O.* (1957), vol. xxviii, pp. 359-72.
[2] J. Coppolani, *Toulouse : étude de géographie urbaine* (1954), affords an account of the origin, development, industrial activity and rôle as a regional capital of the city of Toulouse. A special edition of the *R.G.P.S.-O.* (1961) was devoted to Toulouse. See also P. Pechoux *et al.*, 'Les grandes villes françaises, Toulouse', in *La Documentation française* (1966), 53 pp.

though (with 336,000 people) only the seventh agglomeration. Most of the town stands on a low plateau above the right bank of the Garonne, although on the other side of the river have grown the suburbs of St. Cyprien. Despite the regularisation of the river, these built-up areas on the low-lying left bank are subject to winter flooding.

Toulouse is a striking example of a French city with well developed regional functions. The town stands at the western approach to the Gap of Naurouze between the Montagne Noire and the foothills of the Pyrenees, in the corridor between Aquitaine and Languedoc. It is therefore an important road and rail focus; four main lines and several light railways converge on the town, and the Canal du Midi joins the Garonne Lateral Canal. Toulouse has grown rapidly in the last century, for its population was only 83,000 in 1846. During the years of the war of 1939–45, when it was a refuge in south-west France, its population increased by some 50,000. The town centre is surrounded by a closely settled district of large villages, linked by an intensive autobus service, emphasising its importance as a market- and servicing-centre for a considerable region; the city is in fact a veritable *métropole commerciale*, with its enormous markets and shopping districts.

Toulouse is also an industrial centre. Some of its activities are based on the processing of local agricultural produce, such as grain-milling, leather-tanning, fruit- and vegetable-canning, the making of pickles and tobacco-curing. In 1919 the French Government established a company, the *Office National Industriel de l'Azote*,[1] which took over the buildings of an explosives factory in order to manufacture a variety of nitrogenous materials from atmospheric nitrogen, with hydrogen obtained variously from coke-oven gas, later from the fractional distillation of mineral oil, and now from the natural gas found at St. Marcet (see p. 323). The installation, situated on the banks of the Garonne in the southern outskirts of Toulouse, has expanded enormously; in 1964 it employed nearly 3,250 workers, and besides ammonia and nitric acid it produced sulphate of ammonia, ammonium nitrate, nitro-chalk and a wide range of other products, totalling 824,000 tons. Several other fac-tories make explosives and cartridges, some produce agricultural implements and electrical apparatus. Several branches of the textile industry have long been established, notably the production of ready-made clothing, *lingerie* and millinery. A small aircraft factory was established in Toulouse in 1917. Today France's largest aviation company, *Sud-Aviation*, has three plants near the city; it makes the *Caravelle* jet-liner and is co-operating with the *British Aircraft Cor-poration* in the *Concorde*. The company employs about 11,000.

[1] A. Taillefer, 'L'Office National Industriel de l'Azote', in *R.G.P.S.-O.* (1957), vol. xxviii, pp. 5-34.

Three other aircraft firms have plants near the city. In all, the commercial and industrial life of the city is varied, well developed and prosperous.[1]

This activity has been helped in recent years by the development of power supplies, and electricity is obtained by high voltage transmission lines from the Pyrenean stations. A most interesting development has been the piping of natural gas from a small field at St. Marcet,[2] discovered in 1939 about forty-four miles to the south-west, and operated by the *Régie Autonome des Pétroles*. By 1961 the output had been increased to 303 million cubic metres. A pipeline was completed between the field and Toulouse in 1942, and after the war this was extended westward to Pau and down the Garonne valley to Bordeaux, with branches to other towns.[3] The gas-grid has been extended to include the very much larger Lacq field (see p. 360), and *La Société Nationale du Gaz du Sud-Ouest* has been formed to distribute the gas.

Finally, the importance of Toulouse as a regional centre is shown by its cultural life, for it has a famed university, numerous academies and schools, libraries and museums.

The Pays Montalbanais.—The junction of the valleys of the Garonne, Tarn and Aveyron forms a broad lowland region sufficiently distinctive to be regarded as a *pays*, occupied largely by the modern *département* of Tarn-et-Garonne. The land varies in height from 250 to 200 feet above sea-level, and is covered with alluvium seamed by the meandering courses of the three rivers and their tributaries. The flood-plains, known as *ramiers*, are liable to inundation; they are lined with willows and in places covered with plantations of poplars cut at intervals, as to the west of Castelsarrasin. The damp pastures are used for summer grazing.

About 48 per cent of the total area of Tarn-et-Garonne was under arable in 1963, and 13 per cent each under pasture and woodland. Most of these woods are on the higher interfluves, such as the Forêt de Montech between the converging Garonne and Tarn. The terraces away from the flood-plain are characterised by a polyculture, with small fields of wheat, maize, potatoes, beans and lucerne, orchards of peaches and pears, vineyards both for wine and for table-grapes on the higher gravel terraces, and market-gardens producing asparagus, tomatoes, gherkins, melons and artichokes.

[1] J. Coppolani, 'Esquisse géographique de la banlieue de Toulouse', in *R.G.P.S.-O.* (1964), vol. 35, pp. 218-41, 347-67.

[2] D. Schneegans, 'Gas-bearing Structures of Southern France', in *Bulletin of the American Association of Petroleum Geologists* (1948), vol. 32, p. 206.

[3] G. G. Weigend, 'The Outlook for the Gas and Oil Industry of South-west France', in *E.G.* (1953), vol. 29, pp. 315-18.

Many of the labourers, both seasonal and permanent, and indeed some of the *patrons-propriétaires*, are Spaniards or Italians. There are many villages, neat and prosperous, but the market-centres are Montauban (on the right bank of the Tarn some eight miles above its junction with the Aveyron), Moissac, Castelsarrasin and Montech. The first of these, the capital of Tarn-et-Garonne, had a population of 43,401 in 1962 ; it is essentially a rural centre, with large markets, widely radiating autobus services, and industries based on agricultural products.

The Agenais.—The Agenais in its broadest sense includes both the valley proper of the Garonne (the *Garonne agenaise*) and the low limestone plateau extending northward to the Lot valley, sometimes referred to as *Bas-Quercy*.[1] The flood-plain of the river (known locally as *la bassure*) is covered with gravel and alluvium, and in places the river forms complicated braidings, though the main channel is regularised. Above the flood-plain rise three distinct terraces : the lowest covered with rich alluvium (the *boulbène chaude*), the middle with quite fertile gravels, and the highest with poor leached gravels. In places occur some fertile patches of *limon*, and over the low plateau there is much clay soil with a high lime content, rather dry but quite productive.

As in the upper parts of the Garonne valley, market-gardening and fruit-growing have replaced to a large extent the traditional cultivation of hard wheat on the better soils and rye on the poor ones. Some small-holdings use irrigation, raising water from wells by electric pumps to ensure good crops on the dry soils. Thousands of tons of vegetables are sent to the markets of Bordeaux, Toulouse and Paris or to local canneries.

The limestone slopes descending gently towards the river are covered with orchards of peaches, apricots, cherries and plums, for these stone-fruits do well on the calcareous soils. Much fresh fruit is exported, canning and the manufacture of *pâtes de fruits* and jam are carried on, and the drying of prunes is notable at Granges-sur-Lot.

Towns such as Agen itself (the *chef-lieu* of Lot-et-Garonne, with a population of 35,000), Valence d'Agen, Aiguillon, Port-Ste. Marie and Tonneins are market- and processing-centres for this charming orchard country. This part of the Garonne valley contains a number of immigrants, not only from other parts of France where opportunities are limited but also from Spain and Italy.

The Bordeaux Region.—The valley of the lower Garonne from St. Macaire downstream to Bec d'Ambès can be called *la Garonne*

---

[1] A detailed account is provided by P. Deffontaines, *Les Pays de la moyenne Garonne* (*Agenais, Bas-Quercy*) (1932).

bordelaise, a prosperous agricultural area. The lowest terraces and the drained *palus* are the scene of intensive market-gardening,[1] which developed particularly after 1870 when phylloxera attacked the vines of the Bordelais. Again much specialisation occurs, notably on the former marshland of Grattequina to the north of Bordeaux, where 550 acres are under artichokes alone, and in the communes of Eysines and Le Taillan which grow early potatoes. Further away from the river valley, large fields of wheat and maize become dominant, and in fact 40 per cent of the whole arable area of Gironde was under cereals in 1961. The wheat-fields of the *pays de Bénauge* and the *Bazas* to the south of the Garonne are especially important, supplying the flour-mills of Bordeaux.

The demands of Bordeaux for milk are met by numerous though small herds kept on the permanent pastures of the flood-plain; there were 98,000 dairy cattle in 1963 in the *département* of Gironde. The area of fodder crops has increased.

The Gironde Vineyards.[2]—Notwithstanding this varied agricultural activity and despite the past ravages of phylloxera,[3] the proportion of Gironde under vines in 1963 (12 per cent) still exceeded that under general arable cultivation (10 per cent). In some communes, in fact, more than half of the total area is vine-covered, and the total of just under 440 square miles of vineyards in 1963 was third to Hérault and Aude for an individual French *département*.

The Bordeaux region has been a major producer of wine for centuries. Output reached about 1·3 million hectolitres in 1870, but fell to about 0·8 millions as the result of phylloxera during succeeding years. Recovery has been steady, and in 1963 the yield amounted to

---

[1] A detailed account of market-gardening in the Bordeaux area, with maps, plans and photographs, is provided by P. Barrère, 'La banlieue maraîchère de Bordeaux', in *Cahiers d'outre-mer* (1949), vol. 2, pp. 135-72. See also C. Caste-vert, 'Problèmes de la polyculture en Entre-deux-Mers', in *R.G.P.S.-O.* (1965), vol. 35, pp. 23-37.

[2] G. G. Weigend, 'The Basis and Significance of Viticulture in Southwest France', in *Annals of the Association of American Geographers* (1954), vol. xliv, pp. 75-101; G. Lafforgue, *Le Vignoble girondin* (1947); and G. Mergoil, 'La structure du Vignoble girondin', *R.G.P.S.-O.* (1961), vol. 34, pp. 119-40.

[3] The phylloxera is an aphid, of American origin, which first appeared in Languedoc in 1863, and had spread to the Bordeaux district by 1868. It multi-plies prodigiously, living in galls on the leaves and the roots, where it cannot be reached by spraying. The affected vines become stunted and die. By 1884 every vine-growing part of France was affected, and no remedy had been found. In 1891 it was discovered that vine-stocks from the eastern U.S.A. were almost immune, and a vast programme of grafting European scions on to these stocks was begun. While not wholly resistant, these vines are affected much less seriously. Other scourges of the vineyards are *oïdeum*, a white mildew, which can be checked by dusting with sulphur, and blue mildew, checked by spraying with copper-sulphate solution.

about 5·0 million hectolitres, over four times as much as in the pre-phylloxera period, a circumstance which is unique in France.¹ More important is the fact that 94 per cent of this huge output consisted of quality wines, a quarter of the French output of these grades. The wines are of remarkable variety, partly the result of soils which vary from river alluvium to terrace gravels, calcareous clays and sandy marls, partly the result of different altitude and aspect, and partly the various traditions and age-old practices of individual producers; most famed are the *château* vineyards, some with world-renowned names. Many of the holdings are small; indeed, only 3 per cent of the total area is in units exceeding seventy-five acres, and five-sixths of the estates are less than five acres each. The co-operative movement has made progress, especially since 1932, and over sixty co-operatives are now active in the Gironde with 8,000 members. These operate not so much in the areas of the individual high-quality producers, but in the large-yielding districts of medium and lower quality wines.

Of the several main wine-producing districts (Fig. 87), three are outstanding. Along the left bank of the Gironde estuary, north of Bordeaux, is the *Médoc*, producing for the most part red wines, the southern part of which (the *Haut-Médoc*) yields the outstanding clarets. The second major district is *Graves*, extending along the left bank of the Garonne above Bordeaux as far as Langon. Two-thirds of these Graves wines are réd, though the white varieties are particularly popular in England. Further south comes a group of five communes whose vineyards yield the sweet white wines known generally as *Sauternes*. The third famed district is *St. Emilion* and *Pomerol*, situated near Libourne on the northern side of the Dordogne valley. Some three hundred vineyards produce considerable quantities of red wine of a heavier quality than claret.

Special mention has been made of these superlative districts, but other extensive vine-growing regions are found on the *palus* or riverside alluvial flats, on the gently undulating hill-slopes or *côtes* in the Entre-deux-Mers (which produce quantities of dry white wine), and on the Côtes de Blaye along the right bank of the Gironde estuary. Quite apart from the amount consumed in France, large quantities of wine are shipped from Bordeaux, more than four times the amount before 1939 and nearly half the total French export.

¹ Unfortunately, the year 1956 was climatically very adverse for the Bordeaux vineyards. Cold chilling mists and frosts persisted in the valleys during almost the whole period from January to April, and only the vineyards on the upper terraces and slopes escaped. Many of the vines died, and vast areas have had to be replanted. Output fell by a third to 2·1 million hectolitres in 1957, but recovered somewhat to 2·98 in 1958, and by 1963 had reached as much as 5·0 million.

FIG. 87.—THE BORDEAUX WINE-PRODUCING AREA.

The main *appellations* are numbered as follows: **1**, Entre-deux-Mers; **2**, Bourgeais-Côtes de Bourg; **3**, Côtes de Fronsac; **4**, Lalande de Pomerol; **5**, Ste. Croix-du-Mont; **6**, Côtes Canon Fronsac; **7**, Pomerol; **8**, Loupiac; **9**, Région de Sauternes et Barsac; **10**, Blayais: Côtes de Blaye; **11**, Premières Côtes de Bordeaux; **12**, Ste. Foy-Bordeaux; **13**, Néac; **14**, Sables-St. Emilion; **15**, *Appellation* 'Bordeaux'; **16**, Graves; **17**, Graves de Vayres; **18**, Cérons; **19**, Haut-Médoc; **20**, St. Emilion; **21**, Médoc; **22**, Côtes de Bordeaux: St. Macaire.

Based on *La France vinicole: carte publiée sous le haut patronage de l'Institut National des Appellations d'Origine*, in the *Atlas de la France vinicole L. Larmat* (80, Boulevard Haussmann, Paris, 8e).

Bordeaux.—Bordeaux is the sixth city and, in terms of tonnage handled, the fifth port of France.[1] Its long rather difficult estuary-approach for large vessels, its position away from the main shipping routes, and its limited and primarily agricultural hinterland have made it progressively less able to compete with its rivals; Le Havre has taken most transatlantic traffic and is the gateway for the Paris Basin, Marseilles dominates trade with North Africa, the Middle East and beyond, and Rouen and Dunkirk have outstripped it because of their large industrial hinterlands.

The city of Bordeaux lies mainly on the left bank of the Garonne at its lowest bridge-point, sixty miles up the estuary (Fig. 88). The river at this point makes a pronounced bend to the west (Plate XXVI), where firm banks overlook the deep water on the outside of the curve, and the town has gradually developed in a semicircle westward. Little urban growth took place along the right bank within the river-curve until the beginning of this century, since when factories, power-stations and marshalling-yards have been built.

Since Roman times Bordeaux has been the commercial metropolis of south-western France. For three centuries it was the capital and outlet of the English possessions of Guyenne, and its trade (particularly in wine) throve exceedingly, but it suffered during the tribulations of the sixteenth and seventeenth centuries. The colonial activity of the eighteenth century gave the port a renewed prosperity similar to that of Nantes, but in the nineteenth century the town continued to grow more rapidly than the port, which suffered from competition with its more advantageously placed rivals. Its population reached 100,000 by 1841 and a quarter of a million by 1891, as a result of its multifarious commercial and industrial activities. Neighbouring communes to the west were gradually absorbed into the conurbation, so that by 1954 while the population of the *ville* itself was 254,122, the nine communes included in the official *agglomération* brought up the total to 471,540, a figure exceeded only by Paris, Marseilles and Lyons.

Until the mid-nineteenth century the Gironde estuary, though requiring navigational care, presented no real obstacle to the ships of the time. In 1869 the first dock-basin was constructed, succeeded by others, together with river-quays and improved port facilities. Further developments were effected during the war of 1914–18, when

[1] The following articles on Bordeaux are useful: (i) A. Grange, 'Le Port de Bordeaux après la Libération', in *Cahiers d'outre-mer* (1948), vol. 1, pp. 14-27, containing photographs of vessels wrecked in the channel; (ii) Y. Deler, 'Le Port de Bordeaux', in *Information géographique* (1949), vol. 13, pp. 138-42; (iii) G. G. Weigend, 'Bordeaux: An Example of Changing Port Functions', in *G.R.* (1955), vol. 45, pp. 217-43; (iv) Y. Deler, 'Progrès et avenir du port de Bordeaux', in *Information géographique* (1957), vol. 21, pp. 53-61; (v) M. Cassou-Mounat, 'Le port de Bordeaux', in *R.G.P.S.-O.* (1965), vol. 36, pp. 420-7.

FIG. 88.—BORDEAUX AND THE GIRONDE ESTUARY.

The edge of the low Oligocene plateau in the north-east is indicated approximately by a heavy pecked line; spot-heights are in feet. The built-up area of Bordeaux is shown by a fine stipple. The *Shell-Berre* refinery at Pauillac and the *Caltex* refinery at Bec d'Ambès are marked. *Note.* The *Esso-Standard* refinery was opened in 1960 near the *Caltex* plant; it had an output of 2·18 million tons of hydrocarbons in 1964.

Based on *Carte de France au 200,000ᵉ*, sheets 50, 56.

M 2

the American forces in Europe made much use of the port. Plans were put forward in the closing years of the war for the extension of the dock system, linked by the projected Canal de Grattequina (shown on Fig. 88) to the river about six miles below the city. But with the growth of outports, traffic using the port declined during the inter-war period and these projects have never been realised. Although Bordeaux was spared the destruction suffered by many French harbours during the war of 1939–45, the channel between the city and Lagrange was blocked by the wrecks of eighteen vessels, some deliberately sunk by the Germans. The first ship managed to enter the port in August 1945, but it was two years before the main channel was clear. Since then some new quays have been constructed at Marquis to handle imports of American coal. The Germans built some submarine-pens alongside the docks; these have been retained for ship repairs and storage.

The development of an outport is inevitable when a main port lies far up a difficult estuary. The first was Pauillac-Trompeloup, completed in 1894, situated halfway between Bordeaux and the sea. The Avant-Port du Verdon was constructed in 1933 just inside the Pointe de Grave, consisting of a liner-pier with an approach channel affording a low-water depth of forty-two feet, linked to Bordeaux by means of an electrified railway. Unfortunately the liner-pier and other facilities were destroyed by the Germans during the occupation, and so far reconstruction has not been considered worth while in view of the cost involved and the probable limited usage in the future. Other estuary ports include Mortagne and Blaye on the right bank, and the oil-port at Bec d'Ambès at the apex of the Entre-deux-Mers peninsula.

The shipping and freight returns for *Le Port Autonome* of Bordeaux include these subsidiary estuary ports. The year of greatest activity in modern times was 1918, when it was used by the American forces in Europe, and 6·9 million tons of freight passed through. In 1929 the total handled was 5·2 million tons, and after a marked decline during the depression years it rose again to 4·1 million tons in 1938. Following the war of 1939–45 it was not until 1947 that the channel had been cleared, but in that year the total freight handled recovered to the extent of 3·3 million tons, and by 1963 the figure totalled 7·02 million tons, of which 4·17 millions consisted of imports. A big proportion (2·3 million tons of imports and 1·5 million tons of exports) consisted of crude and refined oil handled at the oil-jetties at Pauillac and Bec d'Ambès. About 390,000 tons of coal were imported, much less than the million tons annually before the war, mostly from Britain and Poland, although in the immediate post-war years American coal came in great quantities (in 1947 exceeding the pre-war figure). About 157,000 tons of oil-seeds made a useful contribution, then followed foodstuffs (wheat, sugar, coffee, rice, cocoa-beans, rum, bananas), timber, cellulose and chemical raw materials (mainly phosphates and pyrites). Exports are dominated by petroleum products, pit-props from the Landes, and wines and spirits.

The Garonne has few of the qualities of a navigable river, as might be deduced from the description of its physical characteristics above. It is officially classified as navigable for a distance of about 290 miles up to Roquefort, but it is really only effectively navigable to Castets, where the lateral canal takes off (Fig. 89), to run parallel to the river for about 120 miles to Toulouse. The 'port fluvial de Bordeaux' nevertheless has some activity, and in 1963 the Port Autonome handled 1·95 million tons of river-borne freight.[1] If the small subsidiary ports upstream of the city (Cambes, Langoiran, Cadillac and others) are included, the total handled in 1963 was about 3·0 million tons. Much of this is short-distance traffic. Rather more than half consisted of hydrocarbons, for Shell, Antar, B.P., Caltex and Esso all have riverside oil-dépôts. The rest of the freight consists of sands and gravels, dredged from the river bed.

Bordeaux is an important industrial centre[2] with a variety of activities. Many are situated within the city to the west of the river, particularly those dealing with agricultural or 'colonial' products— sugar-refining from beet imported coastwise from Boulogne, oil-seed-crushing (particularly ground-nuts), chocolate and tobacco manufacturing, rum-refining, the distillation of liqueurs, and fruit- and vegetable-preserving. The specialised 'consumer-goods' include the processing and manufacture of leather, paper, wood (ply-wood, tropical veneers and furniture), electrical apparatus, glass bottles, corks, dyes and agricultural implements. The newer heavy industries are sited along the right bank opposite the city (an area developed when the first terminal of the railway from Paris was located there in 1852 before the rail-bridge was constructed), on the left bank to the north of the dock basins, and at the outports. These include chemical factories (making fertilisers and vine-sprays), timber-yards, briquette-plant, small shipyards and repair-works, and a flour-mill. Three large cement-works at Lormont on the right bank a few miles downstream use lime brought by rail from St. Astier near Périgueux. An engineering works has foundries at Lormont, and several government-sponsored aircraft, chemical and explosives factories are deliberately sited in the south-west of the country. The industries of Bordeaux use imported coal and oil, electricity brought by high-tension cable from the Pyrenees via the Lannemezan

[1] J. P. Sourbes, 'Le Port fluvial de Bordeaux', in R.G.P.S.-O. (1958), vol. xxix, pp. 134-57; this contains several maps and tables of statistics.

[2] J. Dumas, 'Les zones industrielles de l'agglomération bordelaise', in R.G.P.S.-O. (1965), vol. 35, pp. 415-20.

transformer-station, and (since the war of 1939–45) natural gas piped from the field at St. Marcet (see p. 323).

FIG. 89.—THE WATERWAYS OF WESTERN FRANCE.

Abbreviations are as follows: **I.R.C.**, Ille-Rance Canal; **M.C.**, Midi Canal; **N.B.C.**, Nantes-Brest Canal.

Navigable portions of rivers are indicated by a heavy line; some of these are used only seasonally, and are of little importance.

Based on *Atlas de France*, sheet 56.

Three oil-refineries, at Pauillac, Bec d'Ambès (Fig. 88) and Bordeaux, are in operation.[1] The first, on the left bank of the Gironde halfway between Bordeaux and the sea, is owned by the

[1] G. G. Weigend, 'The Outlook for the Gas and Oil Industry of Southwest France', in *E.G.* (1953), vol. 29, pp. 307-19.

Compagnie Raffinage Shell-Berre, and had an output of 303,000 tons in 1964. The Ambès refinery, at the tip of the Entre-deux-Mers peninsula, is operated by the *Société Caltex*, an associate of the big American firm; it had an output of 1·67 million tons in 1964. Both were virtually destroyed during the war, but have been rebuilt.[1] The *Esso-Standard* refinery, opened in 1960 near the *Caltex* plant, had an output of 2·18 million tons of hydrocarbons in 1964.

THE PAYS DES CHARENTES

The northern part of the Basin of Aquitaine, between the Gironde and the Vendéan margins of Armorica, is drained by the river Charente, except for the extreme south where the Seudre flows parallel to the Gironde. The Charente rises on the crystalline rocks of western Limousin, and crosses the *pays* known as *Confolentais* after the town of Confolens in the neighbouring valley of the upper Vienne. The river flows north-westwards towards Civray through the Lias vale flanking the edge of the Central Massif, then winds in loops southwards across low plateaus of Middle and Upper Jurassic limestones to Angoulême. It again changes direction to flow towards the sea beyond Rochefort. The main river and its tributaries thus drain a considerable area of these limestone and marl plateaus, and the general name of *Pays des Charentes* or *Pays charentais* is fully justified;[2] the region more or less comprises the two *départements* of Charente and Charente-Maritime. Several minor *pays* can be distinguished. In the east is *Angoumois*, the district around the city of Angoulême; in the centre is the *Champagne charentaise*, sub-divided into the *Grande Champagne* to the south of Cognac and the lower *Petite Champagne* further west; bordering the coast between La Rochelle and Rochefort is *Aunis*, and in the south-west lies *Saintonge*.

In the north-east of Charente the Middle and Upper Jurassic limestones continue into the south-western Paris Basin between the ancient uplands of Vendée and Limousin, through the broad 'Gate of Poitou', deriving its name from the province which extended westward to the sea. The 'gate' forms a watershed at 650 feet between the westerly-flowing Charente, the Sèvre-Niortaise and their headstreams, and the Vienne's tributaries which ultimately join the Loire. The limestones in this area are purer than those to the south-west in Aquitaine, and furnish a freestone worked at a number of places, including the famous quarries of Tercé.

[1] P. Arqué, 'Bordeaux, port pétrolier', in *R.G.P.S.-O.* (1956), vol. xxvii, pp. 98-101.

[2] H. Enjalbert, 'La Vallée moyenne de la Charente', in *A. de G.* (1952), vol. lxi, pp. 16-33, gives a full account of the physical features of the valley, with numerous maps and photographs.

The Coast.—The coastline between the mouth of the Sèvre Niortaise and the Pointe de la Coubre reflects the submergence of an irregular but low-lying land-margin modified by subsequent deposition. The coastal scenery includes low rugged cliffs and isolated rock-masses of limestone rising from sand- and mud-flats, salt-marsh and sand-dunes.

The structural lines of Armorica can be traced south-eastward across the Jurassic and Cretaceous limestone country. The anticline of La Rochelle (or Angoumois) forms a low ridge reaching the coast to the north of that port, and then continuing in a north-westerly direction as the 'back-bone' of the Ile de Ré. Similarly the anticline of Marennes (or Saintonge) is continued seawards as a string of rocks (les Palles and l'Estrée) protruding from the tidal marshes, to form the nucleus of the Ile d'Oléron. Between these ridges, a rise of sea-level contemporaneous with the Flandrian transgression along the North Sea coast (see p. 24) created broad estuaries and shallow bays. Protected by the islands, sedimentation has proceeded apace, helped by the development of vegetation, and thus creating extensive salt-marshes (Fig. 90).

Since the twelfth century, the natural processes of salt-marsh accretion have been accelerated by the construction of dykes and palisades. Some of this effort has been devoted to producing the *prés salés* or salt-pastures, and at times Dutch engineers have been employed in the work, as in the reign of Henry IV. Much of the reclamation was the indirect result of the flourishing salt-industry; the Salines d'Aunis and Salines de Saintonge for many years provided salt for the fisheries of northern Europe, later for those of the Newfoundland Grand Banks. The marshes were subdivided by low dykes into a rectilinear pattern of 'pans' or *salines*, into which sea-water was allowed to flow through sluices and left to evaporate during summer. By the beginning of the seventeenth century many of these *salines* had fallen into disuse, partly because of the extortionate methods of the gatherers of the notorious salt-tax (*gabelle*), partly because of competition elsewhere. The neglected marshes became the home of malarial mosquitoes, and were commonly referred to as the *terres maudites*. Towards the end of the eighteenth century, efforts were made at reclamation by cutting a series of drainage channels; the rivers were regularised, canals (the St. Agnant, Broue, Mérignac and others) were constructed, and syndicates of land-holders were established. Today much of the former marshland is under market-gardens or pasture, though the river estuaries are still bordered by mud-flats and sand-banks at low tide.

The honeycomb patterns of the enclosures surrounded by dykes still exist, for the *marais salants* have in places been transformed into *claires à huitres* or oyster-breeding grounds. This is notably the case at Marennes and La Tremblade on each side of the muddy estuary of the Seudre in the shelter of the Ile d'Oléron. Mussels are bred in the former *salines* on the seaward side of the Marais de Brouage and along the east coasts of Oléron and Ré, while eels are trapped in the canals.

FIG. 90.—THE MARSHLANDS ALONG THE BISCAY COAST.
Based on *Carte de France et des frontières au 1: 200,000*, sheets 37, 43, 44, 50.

The Interior of the Pays des Charentes.—An area of low limestone plateaus slopes gently westward from 450 feet on the borders of Limousin towards the coast. The landscape is open and somewhat monotonous, only slightly trenched into platforms by the rivers. In places, however, the limestones of differing degrees of resistance form low *côtes* and residual hillocks with quite steep slopes. Some of the towns, such as Angoulême and Rochefort, have taken advantage of these limestone bluffs and promontories as sites for defence.

Soils vary from lime-rich clays and marls to thin rather dry reddish soils on the plateaus formed by limestone disintegration. Some sandy soils are developed on residual patches of Oligocene sands to the north-west of Cognac and in the Saintonge. Along the floors of the valleys swampy and peat-filled areas of alluvium and marine sands thickly cover the underlying limestones; these are known as '*pays-bas*', such as the Pays-Bas de Matha to the north-east of Cognac. The calcareous soils are rather dry, but the water-table is rarely far below the surface, and the light warm character of the soils is recognised by their name of *terres chaudes*.

Land-Use and Agriculture.—The two *départements* of Charente and Charente-Maritime correspond so conveniently with the Pays des Charentes that their land-use figures may be usefully quoted.

Land-Use, 1963

(*Percentage of Total Area*)

	Arable Land	Pasture	Woodland	Vines
Charente	51	17	17	7
Charente-Maritime . .	53	14	12	6

Source: *Ministère de l'Agriculture*, quoted by *Annuaire statistique de la France, 1964.*

The areas of woodland are small on these limestone plateaus, although patches of oak-forest grow on areas of clay soils, the remnants of a more continuous cover. Maritime pines have been planted on the coastal sands (notably the Forêt de la Coubre between the mouths of the Seudre and Gironde), occasional lines of poplars form wind-breaks, and juniper-scrub covers part of the plateaus.

Pasture-land includes water-meadows along the alluvium-lined valley-floors, the *prés salés* bordering the sea-coast and estuaries, and the poor grassland on some of the drier parts of the plateau (in parts used for military training grounds and race-horse stables). In 1963 about 42,000 horses and 302,000 sheep were in the two *départements*, the latter kept both on the limestone pastures of the interior and on the coastal salt-grazings. One of the most striking changes in the last thirty or forty years has been the increase in dairying in the Charente, replacing the arable systems. In 1963, of the 559,000 cattle 341,000 were dairy animals. This development has been furthered by the large-scale inclusion of short-ley grass within the arable rotation and by the increase in the acreage under fodder-crops. In 1963, a million acres were under clover, fodder-beet, mixed grains, legumes and kale. The improvement in short-ley grassland has been made possible by increased supplies of superphosphate and other fertilisers from the factories near Tonnay-Charente and elsewhere, which the leached soils badly require. Water-meadows along the valley-floors have been improved by both fertilising and irrigation. On the other hand, the dairy industry has been stimulated by the increase in co-operative methods, which are in fact better developed than anywhere else in France.[1] The first co-operative dairy was established in 1888 in the commune of Surgères, with ninety members owning about 300 animals. By 1900 there were 98 societies with 48,850 members, and by 1938 this had further increased to 134 societies with nearly 80,000 members. Today the individual societies are organised within the *Association Centrale des Laiteries des Charentes et du Poitou*, handling nearly five million hectolitres of milk each year. The emphasis is on the production of butter; '*beurre des Charentes*' has a widespread reputation in France. In addition to dairying, young beef-stores are bought in Limousin and fattened in the Charente, and the pig population totalled 181,000 in 1963.

The ancient basis of agriculture in the Charente was the cultivation of cereals, and much of the plateau-land grew wheat, usually with an alternate year's fallow. The poorer sandy soils were used for rye, while further south maize made its appearance. In 1963 the area under cereals had, however, fallen to under 40 per cent of the total arable, to be replaced by fodder-crops and by potatoes.

Market-gardening has developed especially in the neighbourhood of Tonnay-Charente and on the sandy soils and reclaimed marshes along the coasts of the mainland and islands. The heavily fertilised soils yield excellent crops of asparagus, carrots, tomatoes, peas and garlic. The Tonnay-Charente district specialises in cauliflowers and early potatoes, and near Angoulême artichokes are cultivated.

The Vine.—Before phylloxera struck the Charente in 1876, the vine occupied one-sixth of the farmed area. Since the sixteenth century grapes have been grown for the distillation of brandy, and the name *Cognac*, derived from the town of nearly 20,000 people on the south bank of the Charente in the heart of the *pays*, has become world-renowned. After the phylloxera attack, which caused almost economic disaster to the district, planting with imported American

[1] An account of the early development of the dairy industry is given by G. Reverseau, 'Les Industries laitières dans les Charentes', in *A. de G.* (1925), vol. xxxiv, pp. 210-18.

stocks using local scions proceeded slowly, and today 185,000 acres are under grapes, only a quarter of the pre-phylloxera area. Some grapes make red and white wines for local consumption and for the manufacture of vinegar, but the emphasis is on the production of high quality brandy. Organisation and control are rigorous to maintain the standards; in 1936 strict *Appellation Contrôlée* decrees were instigated, defining the specific districts with their soils, types of grape, and methods of distillation for each of the seven famous grades of *Cognac*. These districts are more or less concentric, with the *Grande Champagne* area in the centre between Cognac, Jarnac and Segonzac. The yields of the high-quality *eaux-de-vie* are not great, but their value is considerable, especially as about three-quarters of the total is exported.

Population and Settlement.—Numerous settlements are found along the coast, many of them fishing-villages, others seaside resorts. On the mainland are Châtelaillon to the south of La Rochelle, Fouras on the rocky point north-west of Rochefort, and Ronce-les-Bains on the sand-dune coast south of the Seudre; St. Martin is on the Ile de Ré, and St. Denis, Boyardville and St. Trojan on Oléron, now linked to the mainland by a bridge nearly 2 miles long, the longest in France. These are pleasant resorts, with sandy beaches backed by dunes and pines.

The chief port is La Rochelle,[1] situated in the north-eastern corner of a small bay sheltered by the Ile de Ré to the west and by a low limestone ridge to the north. It was one of the leading French seaports until the sixteenth-century wars of religion, during which as a centre of Protestantism it suffered several sieges (notably that of 1628 by Richelieu's forces) and much destruction. Its fortunes revived in the eighteenth century, for it became one of France's colonial ports, trading with her American possessions. In the nineteenth century, however, La Rochelle was faced with the problem of coping with the increased size of vessels; two wet-docks were constructed, but rapidly became inadequate. In 1873 it was decided that the only solution was the construction of an outport where the limestone ridge on which the town stands ends abruptly at a deepwater roadstead, and between 1881 and 1890 the port of La Pallice was constructed, the works including a liner-mole and a large dock-basin. Its installations were heavily damaged during the war of 1939–45, but restoration was complete by 1950. Today La Pallice is the commercial port, while La Rochelle's chief importance is as

---

[1] See (i) F. Gay, *Le Port de La Rochelle-La Pallice: évolution récente* (1949); (ii) Y. Deprez, 'Le Grand Port de La Rochelle-Pallice et la liaison routière Océan-Suisse', in *Norois* (1955), vol. 2, pp. 419-22; and (iii) C. Chaline, 'Le Port de commerce de La Pallice', in *Norois* (1956), vol. 3, pp. 427-38.

a fishing-harbour. In 1963 the two ports (their returns are not separately distinguished) handled 4·4 million tons of shipping, the ninth in France in this respect, though this activity is only half that of pre-war years. La Rochelle is the fourth fishing-port of France both by weight of catch and by value. A new fish-quay was built in 1925, equipped with storage sheds, refrigerator plant and railway-sidings, and 21,000 tons of fish were handled in 1963. The town in 1962 had a population of about 68,000, and forms the administrative centre of Charente-Maritime. It has a variety of industries, mostly connected with the processing of food products, the preparation of fertilisers from imported phosphates and fish-residues, ship-building and repairing, and the construction of aircraft and railway rolling-stock.

Further south, ten miles up the estuary of the Charente, Rochefort was developed in the mid-seventeenth century by Colbert as a naval port and arsenal. It continued these functions until the Napoleonic wars, but as the size of warships grew, Rochefort, so far up a winding river, suffered by comparison with Brest and Toulon, and its functions slowly declined; in 1928 the naval dockyards and arsenal were finally closed. Its present population is only about 33,000, some 5,000 more than before the war of 1939–45. Further still up the river is Tonnay-Charente, the head of maritime navigation, whose wharves handle coal and phosphates for a large chemical factory nearby. It was for long one of the brandy-exporting ports, and until 1939 the spirit was taken by barge down the Charente to Tonnay, but during the war the river gradually became unnavigable through neglect and it has not been restored. Two-fifths of the Cognac exported is railed or sent by road-tanker to Tonnay and shipped from there.

The interior of the Pays des Charentes is a region of fairly uniform population dispersed over the countryside; the average density per square mile in Charente and Charente-Maritime in 1962 was 142 and 168 respectively. The larger towns are situated along the main river-valleys, notably that of the Charente itself; Angoulême, Châteauneuf-sur-Charente, Jarnac (Plate XXXVII), Cognac and Saintes succeed downstream. Other small towns are in tributary valleys, such as St. Jean-d'Angély and Tonnay-Boutonne in the valley of the Boutonne river. Most of these are market-towns and agricultural centres, situated where north-south routes cross the west-east lines of communication through the valleys. Cognac and Jarnac, as has been emphasised, have special functions 'grâce aux eaux-de-vie'.

The chief town of Charente is Angoulême, with a population in 1962 of 51,000, or if the whole *agglomération* is included, of 60,000. It is situated in a strong defensive position on a low limestone plateau, partly surrounded by the Charente and its confluent the Arguienne.

Today Angoulême is a pleasant city, very much the regional centre of the *pays*, '*le centre d'une région tres animée, un véritable entrepôt commerciale*'.[1] Its industrial activity includes large paper-mills, breweries, flour-mills, leather-works and metallurgical manufactures, including agricultural implements.

PÉRIGORD

It is not easy to ascribe limits to Périgord, although on Fig. 86 an attempt has been made to do so. Structurally this region consists of a low plateau of Upper Cretaceous limestone, with cappings of Oligocene sandstones on the interfluves. These strata are separated from the crystalline rocks of Limousin by a narrow belt of Middle Jurassic limestone, by a depression floored with Lias clays, and in the neighbourhood of Brive by a low-lying Permian-floored basin occupied by the Vézère and its headstreams. These rocks were affected by the earth-movements of early Tertiary times associated with the uplifting of the Pyrenees, and several folds and fault-lines can be traced south-eastward from the Charente.[2] Briefly, the anticline of Mareuil continues from near Angoulême into the Permian basin of Brive. Parallel to this and some ten miles to the south is the anticline of Périgueux, with folds represented most clearly in the '*dôme de St. Cyprien*' where the limestone forms a broad ridge to the east of the angle of confluence of the Vézère and Dordogne. The folds are revealed in places as undulations in the limestone strata; near La Boissière d'Ans, for example, the strata form '*les molles ondulations*'. Further south again is the anticline of Ribérac, which can be traced intermittently south-eastward across the Lot valley near Fumel into Quercy.

The present relief of Périgord is the result of prolonged though interrupted periods of denudation, a '*relief cyclique périgourdin*' in the words of P. Fénelon. He has determined six distinct erosion surfaces, ranging from the '*surface stéphanienne*' of the Carboniferous age to that of the Mio-Pliocene.[3] The heights of the individual peneplains vary considerably, since the late Tertiary uplift and tilting of the Central Massif affected these marginal areas also. Thus, for example, the Mio-Pliocene surface can be traced from about 1,350 feet near the confluence of the Dordogne and the Diège to

[1] D. Faucher, 'Le Bassin d'Aquitaine' in *La France: géographie-tourisme* 1951), vol. i, p. 440.

[2] P. Fénelon, *Le Périgord* (1951), pp. 29-39, describes these structural features, with a number of detailed sections; the lines of folding are traced on a map on p. 113.

[3] P. Fénelon, *op. cit.* (1951), has a detailed table (pp. 190-1) and a corresponding map (pp. 193-4) showing these surfaces. He indicates their correlation with the work of H. Baulig and others in the Central Massif and its western margins.

600 feet near Feugerolles, though most of it lies at 700 to 600 feet, sloping gently to the south-west.

Périgord is crossed by converging rivers flowing from Limousin and Cantal south-westwards to the Gironde estuary—the Dronne, Isle, Vézère and the Dordogne itself. The uplift and tilting of the Central Massif caused a complex series of rejuvenations of these rivers, so that they now flow in trench-like valleys dividing the plateau into individual blocks. Several terraces can be distinguished, and Fénelon has proposed a classification (which accords well with the work of geomorphologists on the valleys of the western Central Massif), comprising four distinct erosional terraces and two aggradational terraces.[1] The rivers pursue extremely winding courses, with acute meanders enclosing meander-cores, and limestone cliffs in places rise steeply on the outside of the curves.

The régime of the rivers is extremely variable. Many of the smaller tributaries are unable to maintain their courses across the permeable limestone during the long months of drought; even the Dordogne may shrink to depths of as little as a foot as far down as Bergerac. In winter, however, the run-off from the crystalline rocks over which the headstreams flow may cause a rapid rise, producing extensive flooding lower down the main river.

The surface features of Périgord are thus varied. The limestone plateaus (which occasion the name *Périgord blanc*) show certain karstic features (hence another appellation of *le karst périgourdin*). Parts of the plateau are peppered with shallow solution hollows, called locally *eygues* or *crozes*, much the same as the *cloups* of Quercy and on a smaller scale as the *sotchs* of the Grands Causses. At the most 150 feet in diameter and 30 feet in depth, they often lead by vertical shafts (*avens*) into complex cave systems below, such as the well-known Gouffre de Proumeyssac near La Bugue and the Trou de Granville near Rouffignac. Conversely, small elongated hummocks known in the *Sarladais* district (on either side of the Dordogne between Sarlat and Gourdon) as *pechs*, are the residual results of differential erosion of heterogeneous limestones, and from the fact that their long axes show a distinct alignment they may represent the dissected remains of once continuous ridges. The various groups of *pechs* are separated by shallow depressions known as *plaines*.

Several examples of subterranean rivers occur, and on the lower slopes of the valleys powerful resurgences burst out, such as the Fontaine de Troby near Cadouin in the valley of a small left-bank tributary of the Dordogne. Many cave-systems have been dry for millennia as a result of the lowering of the water-table as the rivers

[1] These terraces are clearly tabulated, with the corresponding ones worked out by other authorities along other rivers in the western Central Massif, by P. Fénelon, *op. cit.* (1951), pp. 275-6.

deepened their valleys. Others are produced by differential solution ; a much fissured but resistant horizontal cap of limestone commonly overlies a more soluble calcareous marl which has been eaten back under the overhanging hard stratum, forming caves opening on to the valley-sides. Some of these are renowned as the homes of early man, as along the sides of the Vézère valley near Les Eyzies above its junction with the Dordogne, where occur the caves of Cro-Magnon, La Madeleine, Le Moustier, La Mouthe, Laugerie-Basse and -Haute, Font-de-Gaume, Lascaux and many more, with their remarkable wall-paintings, the legacy of primitive art.

By contrast with the limestone country, some areas of plateau are covered with Tertiary sands, sandy clays and gravels. These superficial deposits survive patchily on the interfluves in eastern Périgord and more continuously in the west and south-west. To the south of the Dordogne valley near Bergerac, the Tertiary siliceous sands, which are darker in colour than the limestones, have given to the district the local name of *Périgord noir*.

Land-Use and Agriculture.—Périgord corresponds closely to the *département* of Dordogne, which was created with Périgueux as its *chef-lieu* more or less in the centre. In 1963 about 33 per cent of the total area was under woodland, 26 per cent under arable cultivation, and 15 per cent under permanent pasture.

This high proportion of woodland is at first sight surprising, but most of it is found on the Tertiary sands and clays. Chestnuts have long been widespread, and form part of the economy ;[1] they are used for human consumption, they are fed to pigs and even sheep, and they are sent to the Bordeaux markets. Several varieties of oaks are found, sometimes growing in considerable though now reduced woodlands such as the Forêt de Barade to the north-west of the lower Vézère valley, others in copses on the plateaus or on the valley slopes. For centuries herds of swine have been pannaged in these oak-woods. The trees yield the renowned Périgord truffles (*Tuber melanosporum*), which grow on their roots a foot or so beneath the ground, and are harvested during the winter with the help of pigs or dogs to locate them by the aid of scent. In addition to these deciduous woods, conifers (particularly maritime pine) have been planted on the sands since the mid-nineteenth century and especially since the war of 1914–18. These woodlands supply constructional timber and pit-props, tanning materials are obtained from the oaks, and much charcoal-burning is still carried on. This last was one of the bases of the long-established metallurgical industry ; forges and furnaces, situated along the river valleys to utilise water-power,

[1] M. Depain, 'La Châtaigneraie périgourdine', in *R.G.P.S.-O.* (1936), vol. vii, pp. 340-65.

smelted the haematite ores found sporadically in the Tertiary sands.
The variety of relief, soil and aspect is reflected in the variety of
agriculture; the polyculture is striking even for Aquitaine, a region
of agricultural diversity. The countryside is a veritable '*paysage
mixte*', with patches of woodland and heath, small fields with
hedgerows, occasional larger fields divided into hedgeless strips,
orchards, groves of nut-trees, and vineyards on sunny slopes.
Almost half of the arable in Dordogne grows cereals (actually 48
per cent), chiefly wheat with some maize and barley, and almost a
third is under fodder crops. In 1963, 281,000 cattle were present,
bred both for milk under the influence of the neighbouring Charntee
and for veal, and fed on the valley water-meadows and on fodder-
crops. About 185,000 sheep grazed on the poorer limestone pastures,
and 252,000 pigs were reared on skim-milk from the dairies and in
many places still pannaged on acorns and chestnuts in the woods.
The breeding of capons, ducks, turkeys and geese is widespread, and
fattened and truffle-stuffed birds are exported to the markets of
Paris and elsewhere. The *foie gras de Perdrix* is considered by some
to equal the product of Strasbourg.

Orchards are an important item in the economy, and the usual
stone-fruits are grown, particularly cherries, peaches, greengages
and plums (the last especially in the Bergerac district where prunes
are dried, and near Périgueux where the potent *eau-de-vie de prunes*
is distilled). Apples rather unexpectedly are grown for cider-
making. Chestnuts have already been mentioned, and another
special item is the walnut, notably in the Vézère valley, of which
more than 11,000 tons a year are produced.[1] Some of the nuts are
crushed for oil, some exported green, others shelled and dried,
others pickled, while the walnut wood is used by furniture makers
in the local towns and in Bordeaux.

Finally, vineyards covered 4 per cent of the total area of the
département in 1963; this is only half of the pre-phylloxera acreage.
Still, 1·08 million hectolitres of wine were produced in 1963, of
which a third was of *appellation contrôlée* quality; some, such as
the white wines of Monbazillac and the Sauternes-like wines of
Brantôme, are widely known in France.

Population and Settlement.—The population is rather thinly and
unevenly distributed, with an average density per square mile for
the *département* of Dordogne of only 106. Small isolated farms
and hamlets are found on the Tertiary sands and occasional larger

---

[1] O. Lavaud, 'La Vallée périgourdine de la Vézère', in *A. de G.* (1931), vol. xl,
pp. 144-52, gives a full account of walnut production. A more recent account is
C. Laugénie, 'La culture du noyer en Périgord', in *R.G.P.S.-O.* (1965), vol. 36,
pp. 135-58.

nucleated villages on the limestone plateaus, but most settlements are situated along the valleys. Small prosperous market-towns include Ribérac on the Dronne, Sarlat on the Cuze, Domme on the upper Dordogne and Terrasson on the Vézère. On a larger scale are the attractive Bergerac (26,000 people), and the *chef-lieu* of the *département*, Périgueux itself (41,134), situated on gentle slopes rising from the banks of the Isle. Some industries are supplied with electricity from power-stations in the neighbourhood (as at Tuilières a few miles above Bergerac, where a barrage has been constructed across the Dordogne, and at Manzac on the same river), or from the stations in the Central Massif. The processing of agricultural products includes the crushing of walnuts for oil, the milling of wheat and maize, the preparation of tobacco and the preserving of fruit. The manufacture is long established of footwear at such towns as Bergerac, Terrasson and Nontron, of textiles at Mussidan, of paper at Couze, Lalinde, Thiviers and St. Paul-de-Lisonne, of feltings at Ribérac, and of glass-ware near Terrasson. Timber-yards are situated along the river-banks where water-power is still used, and much sawn timber is exported. Numerous lime- and cement-works are also located along the rivers, where limestone can be worked in quarries on the valley-sides.

THE CAUSSES DU QUERCY

The name Quercy is derived from a Gaulish tribe, the *Cadurques*, from which comes also the name of the main town of the region, Cahors. Its wider connotation as an ancient province of France included the districts of both Haut- and Bas-Quercy, although the latter to the south belongs to the Pays de Garonne. A small part of Haut-Quercy on the borders of Aurillac consists of the crystalline rocks of the Central Massif, known as the *Ségala du Quercy* (see p. 573). The greater part of Haut-Quercy proper comprises limestone plateaus of mainly Upper Jurassic age ; indeed, these plateaus are sometimes known as the *Causses Aquitaines* or as the *Petits Causses* in contradistinction to the *Grands Causses* of the Central Massif. Four distinct *Causse*-units can be distinguished within this region, the names and locations of which are indicated on Fig. 121.

The limestone strata dip gently westward, the result of Tertiary tilting, from 1,500 feet above sea-level on the margins of the Central Massif to 850 feet in the west and south-west, though the Causse de Martel has on the whole a rather lower elevation, sloping from 1,100 to 500 feet. The surfaces of the plateaus have been planed by the forces of subaerial erosion, and R. Clozier [1] has distinguished

[1] R. Clozier, 'Les Surfaces d'aplanissement des Causses du Quercy (Petits Causses)', in *Comptes Rendus du Congrès Internationale de Géographie* (Paris) (1931), vol. ii, pp. 461-8 ; and *Les Causses du Quercy* (1940).

surfaces of three distinct ages, with traces of at least one still older in the extreme east.

The plateaus are deeply trenched by the steep-sided valleys of the Dordogne and the Lot; limestone cliffs drop abruptly in places to the river edge on the outer curves of meanders. The valley-floors are, however, quite wide, sometimes as much as a mile, as the ingrown meanders swing from one side to another. A considerable extent of alluvium-covered flat usually lies on the inside of each meander, beyond which several gravel-covered terraces rise in low steps towards the bounding limestone bluffs.[1] There is an extraordinary ramification of valleys. Most of the higher ones, known as *combes*, are dry, while others contain seasonal streams draining from the individual plateau-blocks into the main rivers. Many complex systems of subterranean drainage occur, and powerful resurgences break out near the base of the valley-sides; the flow from the Fontaine de Chartreux practically doubles the volume of the Lot within the town of Cahors.

The plateaus show in detail a diversity due to the differential denudation of the limestones, shales and marls, and to the solution features of the calcareous rocks. Broad shallow depressions or *cloups* often contain reddish *terra rossa* clays. Deep vertical chasms, sometimes called *igues* or *avens*, lead into extensive cave-systems, and many of them have been explored. Perhaps the most famous is the Gouffre de Padirac in the Causse de Gramat not far from Rocamadour, descended by the *doyen* of French speleologists, E.-A. Martel, in 1889;[2] its mouth is about 100 feet in diameter and its vertical shaft falls for 325 feet. The water-table in this cave-system fluctuates violently, and a vertical rise of 115 feet above the usual low-water level has been recorded.[3]

Land-Use and Agriculture.—The surface of the plateau reveals areas of bare limestone, greyish tracts of stony soil and residues of *terra rossa* in the depressions. Much scrubby vegetation consists of juniper, blackthorn and box. About 30 per cent of the total area of the *département* of Lot (which occupies the greater part of this region) was classified in 1963 as under woodland. Much of this consists of oak, usually forming a scrub-forest known variously as *garrissade, garric* or *garouille*, though in some parts a careful forest policy has produced a growth of well-developed trees. Areas of poor seasonal pasture (*grèzes*), usually scorched and brown in

---

[1] Terraces can be distinguished along the Lot valley (and very similarly along that of its tributary the Cère) at 950, 575, 460 and 310 feet, corresponding closely to those defined by P. Fénelon in Périgord *op. cit.*, (1951), pp. 275-6.

[2] E.-A. Martel, *Les Abîmes* (1894).

[3] N. Casteret, *Ten Years under the Earth*, p. 191 (English translation, 1940).

summer, are found on the plateau, and meadows (*glèbes*) appear in hollows and valleys where the ground-water is not far below.

The arable lands, which amounted to only 20 per cent of the total area of Lot in 1963, are found in the *cloups* where a down-wash of *terra rossa* has accumulated and along the floors of both the dry valleys and the river valleys. Much has gone out of cultivation in the last century; indeed, the official land-use category of '*territoire agricole non cultivé*' occupied in Lot about 10 per cent in 1963, and none of this was deliberate fallow.

Nevertheless, a well-developed agriculture is found in more favourable areas, especially on south-facing slopes; it is interesting to find in this district the terms *souleillan* and *hiversenq*, which correspond to the *adret* and *ubac* in the Alps. The broad floors of the main valleys provide the most important arable lands; the Lot plain near Cahors, for example, presents a variegated pattern of fields of cereals, strips of improved pasture, and well-kept orchards and vineyards. More than half the arable produces wheat, grown either with an alternate year of fallow or in rotation with maize, potatoes and fodder-beet. Small patches of rye can still be found, especially in the higher depressions, but the total area has declined. The vine is grown on south-facing slopes near Cahors, lavender on the plateaus south of the Lot,[1] walnuts in groves or as individual trees, and small orchards of plums, apricots and peaches on the river-terraces near the villages, while strawberries are a local speciality in the Dordogne valley. Tobacco is cultivated in small patches, and market-gardens are intensively worked on valley-floors near the towns.

Pastoral farming is important, and about 190,000 sheep were in the *département* in 1963, mostly grazing on the high limestone pastures, although the animals are commonly turned on to the wheat-stubble after the harvest. The richer valley-pastures are the scene of dairying activity, especially along the Lot valley near Cahors. Of 106,000 cattle in the *département* in 1963, nearly half were dairy animals (some milk is used for cheese-making, notably the famous *Rocamadour* variety) and others (the *Salers* breed) were reared for farm work. About 57,000 pigs were kept, pannaged on acorns in the oak-woods for part of the year, and most farms kept poultry.

The agricultural scene in Haut-Quercy is therefore one of contrasts, ranging from poor grazing on the limestone plateaus to the varied and intensive activity on the valley-floors and south-facing slopes of the more fertile depressions.

Population and Settlement.—Although there are a few local concentrations, the population as a whole over Haut-Quercy is rather low;

---

[1] R. Lacaze, 'La Culture de la lavande dans le Quercy', in *R.G.P.S.-O.* (1965), vol. 35, pp. 39-52.

in 1962 the *département* of Lot had about 150,000 people, with an average density per square mile of only 75, approaching indeed the sparseness of some of the Alpine and Central Massif *départements*. This is one of the regions where rural depopulation has proceeded steadily, for at the end of the eighteenth century the density in Quercy was probably of the order of 300 per square mile.

Most of the population in the Petits Causses proper live in villages and hamlets, clustered on the south-facing slope of a *cloup* or at the lower end of a *combe* near a permanent spring. Some large villages stand on the plateaus, acting as market- and servicing-centres, such as Martel in the Causse of the same name, Gramat, Labastide-Murat and Gourdon in the Causse de Gramat, and Limogne and Montpezat in the Causse de Limogne; most of these contain two to four thousand inhabitants. The larger towns are situated in the valleys, although perched on the upper terraces away from the danger of flooding, or occasionally on the isthmus formed by a meander-neck, as in the case of Cahors around which the Lot swings in a sweeping curve. Rocamadour, in the valley of the Alzou, is an attractive little town clinging incredibly to the side of a steep limestone cliff crowned by a church. These towns—Cajarc, Puy-l'Evêque and Fumel, as well as Cahors, in the valley of the Lot, and Gourdon on the Bleu (a tiny Dordogne tributary)—are the main centres of Quercy's prosperity. Fumel on the borders of Périgord has old-established metallurgical works, originally based on local charcoal and iron-ore, later on coke once brought by river from St. Aubin, but now transported by rail from the ovens of Le Boucau near Bayonne and even from the Nord coalfield. But otherwise there is little industry except for saw-mills and tanneries, a few limestone quarries and cement-works, and some food-producing activities such as the canning of vegetables, the milling of wheat, the processing of tobacco, and the manufacture of various macaroni-like *pasta*.

Cahors, with its 19,000 people, is the chief town of the *département* ;[1] its function, as D. Faucher succinctly puts it, is as '*un marché et une petite ville de fonctionnaires*'. It has long been a bridge-town, as its superb fourteenth-century bridge with three arch-pierced towers indicates, and the old walls across the Lot meander-neck testify to its rôle as a stronghold during the troubled past.

ALBIGEOIS AND LAURAGUAIS

In the triangular area between the Aveyron on the north, the *Garonne toulousaine* on the west, and the Monts de Lacaune and Montagne Noire on the east lies a low undulating plateau region. The northern part, drained by the Tarn and centred on Albi, is given

[1] E. Baudet, *Une Evolution de ville, Cahors en Quercy* (1928).

the *pays*-name of *Albigeois*. To the south of the Agout (a left-bank Tarn tributary) a further series of plateaus extends south-eastward into the Col de Naurouze; these include the *pays castrais* in the Agout valley around the town of Castres and the *Mirepésis* near Mirepoix in the south, but they are commonly referred to collectively as *Lauraguais*.

The rocks are varied in this region, testifying to the fluctuating conditions of deposition in early Tertiary times. Some of them are so similar to the true *molasse* of Miocene age that they are called *molasse gréseuse* and *molasse argileuse*, according to their content of sand and clay. The clay character tends to dominate, and the resulting soils are referred to, especially in Lauraguais, as *terrefort*, *terre grasse* and *terre luisante*. The clays are occasionally interrupted by sheets of gravel, often of a quartzitic character, derived from the crystalline rocks of the Central Massif. Limestones intercalated among the *molasse* are widespread in the north of Albigeois, and elsewhere are deposits of coarse sandstones and conglomerates.

The present relief is largely the result of the differential erosion of these sediments by running water, for many streams flow westwards from the Central Massif and from the watershed in the Col de Naurouze further to the south. Most of their valleys form trenches two or three miles wide, with the present rivers meandering across their clay-covered floors. The Tarn is particularly winding, especially in the section between Ambialet and Albi; near the former the river turns almost completely back on itself, leaving an attenuated meander-neck. In other places, by contrast, the rivers are contained in steep narrow trenches, particularly where they have cut through bars of resistant limestone to form small *cluse*-like valleys. The Cluse du Mas-d'Azil-Sabarat, for example, has been eroded by the Arize, and the valley of the Agout has in places a gorge-like character, as at Lavaur where the little town is perched on a steep hill overlooking the river. Dry valleys are common, cutting through the sheets of *molasse*, and probably eroded by powerful Pleistocene streams swollen by the heavier rainfall of those times and by the abundant melt-water from the Pyrenean glaciers.

The plateau-landscape is subdued, sloping from 600 or 650 feet in the east to 400 feet as the Garonne valley is approached. Minor diversifications of the surface include long but irregular *côtes* of limestone in the south and east; near Fanjeaux, for example, over-looking the Col de Naurouze, appears a triple line of these *côtes*. Again, particularly in Albigeois, the Oligocene limestone sometimes forms low plateaus between the valleys, to which the name *causse* is given; they reveal narrow *crêts* of limestone, broader whale-backed ridges of calcareous sandstone, and occasionally flat-topped buttes (known as *éperons*) where the interfluves have been cut into by transverse valleys.

The Quaternary rivers deposited over their valley-floors vast amounts of gravel derived from the wastage of the Central Massif and the Pyrenees. The rapid run-off from the autumn and winter rains still brings down material, coarse and fine, to be deposited on the valley-floors. Flooding is common, occasionally attaining serious proportions following heavy periods of rain, as in March 1930; near the confluence of the Tarn and Agout at St. Sulpice the waters rose more than sixty feet and caused widespread destruction among villages on the river-terraces.

Land-Use and Agriculture.—Both Albigeois and Lauraguais are prosperous agricultural areas, the result of reasonably fertile soils (especially where derived from the lighter clays and loams), the modest elevation, and the warmth of these southern latitudes. In the *département* of Tarn, which occupies much of the region, 45 per cent of the total area was under arable in 1963; of this about two-fifths was devoted to cereals, mainly maize and wheat, about a third to fodder-crops, and a tenth was left fallow. Market-gardening is found especially in the Tarn valley near Albi and at Gaillac, Arthez and St. Juéry where the terraces are intensively cultivated; specialisations include onions in the neighbourhood of Lescure and strawberries at Gaillac. Nearly a fifth of the *département* carried permanent pasture, including both poor winter pasture on the limestone and sandstone plateaus, and better meadows in the floors of the valleys. These pastures, supplemented by fodder-crops, enabled 166,000 cattle (of which about 107,000 were dairy animals, the rest bred for beef or draught-use), 142,000 sheep and 144,000 pigs to be maintained. The sheep, mainly the *Lacaune* breed, are kept both for wool and for milk to be made into cheese. Mules are bred in considerable numbers. Nearly 6 per cent of Tarn (70,000 acres) was occupied by vineyards in 1963. A large proportion of the wine output is *ordinaire*, both red and white, but the wines of the Gaillac district (the *vins rouges du Gaillacois*) and some white wines of a '*graves*' character in the Tarn valley have a certain reputation. Mulberries and orchard-fruits are also widely grown.

The landscape is thus pleasantly varied, with low hills and gentle valleys, fields of maize and wheat, orchards and vineyards, and villages on the valley terraces. The numerous isolated tile-roofed farms are known as *bordes* or *métairies*, the latter after the system of *métayage* which is still prevalent. Probably much of the district was once tree-covered, but only 17 per cent of Tarn is now under woodland. Though some continuous stretches of forest still exist, most of the oak woodland, including also chestnuts, hornbeams, cypress and pines, occurs as small copses around villages.

Industry and Towns.—Rather surprisingly, the district between Albi and Castres forms one of the minor industrial regions of France, an activity long established on a domestic basis, manufacturing cloth from local wool. Today Castres is still an important textile town, using electric power from Central Massif stations and manufacturing both woollen and cotton cloth. Other towns in the valleys of the Thoré (Labruguière, Mazamet and Labastide-Rouairoux) and of the upper Agout (Brassac and Vabre) are similarly occupied. The wool-dressing and textile industries of these towns in the Thoré valley, an extension of the lowland into the Central Massif between the ancient uplands of the Montagne Noire and the Lacaune, are described on p. 576. A large rayon factory operates in Albi. Tanning and leather-dressing, using local hides, is important at Graulhet on the banks of the Dadou, a tributary of the Agout. There is a considerable specialisation in furniture-making and cabinet-work generally at Revel, and Castres has a number of engineering and metallurgical industries, including the manufacture of machine-tools, automobile bodies and parts, electrical machinery and equipment, and various types of pumps.

To the north of Albi and between the valleys of the Tarn and the Cérou is situated the coalfield of Carmaux-Albi, consisting of two small concealed basins separated by a barren area. This field is grouped administratively with Decazeville to the north as the *Houillères d'Aquitaine*[1] ; the two produced jointly 1·96 million tons in 1962, more or less equally divided between them. This coal is a valuable contribution to the economy of south-western France, for it is used at the large Pinet power-station near Carmaux and at another near Albi, in several local coke-ovens, and in the glass-, lime- and cement-works in the neighbourhood of Albi and Carmaux. Associated with the coke-ovens are chemical works at the two last towns, making benzene, sulphate of ammonia and acids. Some coke is consumed at the steel-works of St. Juéry, situated on the banks of the Tarn a few miles upstream from Albi, which use pig-iron from St. Etienne and even from Lorraine, and supply the metal-using industries of Albi (notably tools and agricultural implements). The labour for this industrial activity is supplied partly by the local population (many men own small farms and work in a factory too, their women-folk in the textile-mills), partly by foreigners such as Poles.

Albi and Castres have dual functions as market-centres for a large agricultural area and as the foci of this industrial activity. Albi, with its administrative function as *chef-lieu* of the *département* of Tarn, had a population of 41,000 in 1962, and has several industrial

[1] L. Brunet-Le Roisic, 'L'Evolution récente des houillères du bassin d'Aquitaine', in *R.G.P.S.-O.* (1965), vol. 36, pp. 193-201.

neighbours, such as Carmaux (15,000 people) and St. Juéry. Castres, with 40,000 people, is also the centre of the small industrial towns along the Thoré valley.

An undulating region of low plateaus slopes gently northward from a height of about 2,000 feet in the foothills of the central Pyrenees to the margins of the Garonne valley at 600 feet. The *molasse* is covered for the most part with an alluvial fan crossed by a series of diverging rivers, each only a few miles from the next. Those in the east flow to the upper Garonne—the Louge, Nère, Touch, Save and Gimone; those in the centre flow northwards to the *Garonne agenaise*—the Arrats, Gers and Baïse, and the rivers in the west flow to the Adour—the Douze, Midouze, the Adour itself, Lées, Luy de France and Gave de Pau (Fig. 91).

These streams laid down this joint alluvial fan in late Tertiary times, building out into the 'Gulf of Aquitaine' a delta of sand and gravel worn from the uprising Pyrenees. The apex of the fan consists of coarse Pliocene pebbles, forming the small triangular plateau of *Lannemezan*, deposited by the powerful river Neste which rises near the crest-line of the Pyrenees. Further to the west are similar though smaller Pliocene fans—the *Plateau de Cieutat* in the neighbourhood of Bagnères-de-Bigorre, formed by the ancestor of the Adour, and the *Plateau de Ger*, the product of the streams which now join the Gave de Pau. These fans, or as the French geologists call them, *anciens cônes de déjections*, form in truth '*les plateaux à débris*'.[1]

To the north of these stony plateaus the lower *Plateau d'Armagnac* (sometimes called *la Gascogne gersoise*) slopes away towards the Garonne valley. It too is crossed by many rivers, and although their valleys are cut down into the *molasse*, deposits of Pleistocene and Recent alluvium cover much of the interfluves and the river terraces. Further variety is introduced by patches of glacial clay and of *limon*.

The southern plateaus therefore owe their present form primarily to the past and present work of the multitude of rivers. The valleys are markedly asymmetrical, with the steep side in each case facing the west; rivulets flow down the longer east-facing slopes, as is evident on Fig. 91. Various theories seek to account for this asymmetry. Possibly exposure to the westerly winds has caused more rapid weathering and erosion of the west-facing valley-sides as

[1] An immensely detailed survey of these formations is given by F. Taillefer, *Le Piémont des Pyrénées françaises, contributions à l'étude des reliefs de Piémont* (1951).

compared with the eastern slopes in a comparative lee. Another
suggestion is that fine wind-blown deposits, probably derived from
the Quaternary sands of the Landes, have been blown eastwards,
accumulating on the leeward side of each valley and thus compelling

FIG. 91.—THE DRAINAGE PATTERN IN WESTERN LANNEMEZAN
AND THE PAYS DE L'ADOUR.

The map shows the extraordinary fan of streams flowing northwards over the
gravel plateau of Bigorre, situated about 20 miles west of Lannemezan. Long
narrow ridges separate the valleys, their sides furrowed with short rivulets. The
asymmetrical nature of the valleys is shown by the large numbers of these
rivulets flowing down the gentler east-facing slopes. Heights are in feet.

Based on *Carte de France au 200,000ᵉ*, sheet 70.

its stream to move further to the east, so cutting into and steepening
the western valley-side.

The valleys are separated by gentle ridges, in the north composed
of Oligocene limestone capped with *molasse* or sands, and known

generally as '*les coteaux de Gascogne*'. In some of these limestone outcrops the gentle folds of the outer Pyrenean zone can be traced. For the most part, however, the Armagnac plateau is an area of only slight variations in relief.

Land-Use and Agriculture.—The stony plateaus in the south consist for the most part of dreary moorlands, wind-swept and usually snow-covered in winter, and rather arid in summer. The soils are thin and coarse, leached and acid, and bear a poor pasture or a scrub of gorse, ling, broom and other shrubs. The valley sides and floors are wooded, especially in Cieutat where oaks and chestnuts grow. The chief value of Lannemezan and its neighbouring plateaus is as pasture for sheep and beef-cattle, and some improvement of the moister valley-pastures has been effected by irrigation and fertilisation.

Further north, with a milder climate, lower elevation and tractable soils, the countryside assumes a more genial aspect. A large part of Armagnac lies administratively in the *département* of Gers; in 1963 exactly 60 per cent of the total area was under arable, 14 per cent under permanent grassland, 9 per cent under woodland (oak and chestnut) and 7 per cent under vines. Here again is the polyculture so characteristic of Aquitaine, although the basis of life is the cultivation of cereals (principally quick-ripening hard wheats, maize and a little oats), which occupy almost two-thirds of the arable land. A further quarter of the arable is under fodder-crops, which together with the improved irrigated pastures in the valley bottoms enable the *département* to maintain over 200,000 cattle, of which half are dairy animals, the *race gasconne*. Others are bred for draught-purposes (for which they are more widely used than horses) or for veal, and between 30,000 and 40,000 animals are shipped away each year to markets elsewhere in France. Pigs too are widespread, 88,000 in the *département* in 1963, fattened on maize and skimmed milk. Mules are reared, many of them to be sent over the Pyrenees for sale in Spain. Large numbers of poultry make Gers one of the main producers of eggs, and it is a famous rearing area for geese. Sheep, however, declined from about 100,000 in Gers at the turn of the century to 10,000 during the war of 1939–1945, although by 1963 there had been some recovery to about 33,000. They are brought down in summer from the Pyrenean foothills or from Lannemezan to graze on the wheat stubble.

About 114,000 acres of Gers were under vines in 1963, yielding a large output of wine. Although none is of high quality, much pleasant *vin rouge* is produced near Lectoure and Mirande in Haut-Armagnac, and white wines, known collectively as '*Côtes du Gers*', come from Bas-Armagnac. The district is best known for its brandy, regarded by many as little inferior to Cognac; around Condom are the specified zones which produce *Grand-Armagnac*, *Fin-Armagnac* and *Petit-Armagnac* in order of quality.

Population and Settlement.—In spite of this agricultural prosperity, the density of population is well below that of France as a whole; the average for Gers was only 75 per square mile in 1962, which represents a big decline since 1846, when the figure was 132. Rural depopulation has proceeded steadily, and but for the fact that nearly 30,000 foreigners, mainly Italians and Spaniards, are settled on the land, comprising a sixth of the population of Gers, the density would be lower still. Towns are small, with few industries other than food-processing; their main function is as markets and shopping-centres. One old-established feature is the frequent occurrence of fairs, each a focus not only of economic but also of social activity, and usually held in conjunction with religious festivals.[1] The most important centre is the *chef-lieu* of the *département*, Auch (situated in the valley of the Gers at a height of about 400 feet), but which had a population of only 20,834 in 1962. Other towns—notably Condom, Nérac and Lectoure—had less than 7,000, with a peaceful charm and an air of a subdued prosperity. The small town of Lannemezan, with its 7,600 people, stands on the northern edge of the gravel-plateaus; it is the market-centre for a considerable district and holds important sheep- and cattle-fairs. Here is situated the main transformer-station for the central Pyrenean hydro-electric stations, from which 150,000-volt transmission lines run to Pau, Dax and Bordeaux, and others to Toulouse, while a recently constructed 220,000-volt line runs to Verlhaguet (near Montauban) and beyond to link up with the main Dordogne transformer-station at Le Breuil.

THE PAYS DE L'ADOUR

The river Adour rises on the eastern flanks of the Massif du Néouvielle in the central Pyrenees, and flows northwards across Bigorre as one of the streams which have built up the detrital fan already described. It maintains this northward direction as far as Riscle, near which it turns westwards, and continues in this direction as far as Dax, then south-westwards to reach the sea three miles beyond Bayonne.

The valley of the middle Adour is bordered on the south by gravels and coarse sands and on the north by the sheets of fine sand of the southern Landes. The river wanders among its deposits, with a maze of meanders, braided channels and gravel islets, the last

[1] H. M. Kendall, 'Fairs and Markets in the Department of Gers, France', in *E.G.* (1936), vol. 12, pp. 351-8.

especially pronounced during summer. In winter and spring, however, the headstreams bring down so much water that widespread flooding occurs, sometimes occupying the whole floor between the lowest terraces.[1] This zone of sand- and gravel-banks is known as the *graves* or *barthes*,[2] and is covered in places with alder-thickets, willows and poplars, though drainage has improved the valley-pastures in some places. The main river is joined by a succession of tributaries flowing down in a north-westerly direction from the gravel-plateaus of Bigorre and Ger which cover the frontal zone of the Pyrenean flanks. The chief confluents are the Gave de Pau and the Gave d'Oloron. A few right-bank tributaries drain the southern Landes, notably the Midouze, with its feeders issuing vaguely from shallow lakes and marshes.

This curve of the Adour encloses several sub-regions of considerable variety, though known collectively as the *Pays de l'Adour*. Along the northern edge of the Pyrenees are the low plateaus and ridges of *Béarn*, *Basse-Navarre* and *Labouard* (these three are sometimes referred to generally as the *Collines basques*), sloping gently northward and north-westward from 1,100 to 600 feet. These plateaus consist of Upper Cretaceous limestones, marls and conglomerates with occasional exposures of Upper Triassic sandstones, flanked on the north with varied Tertiary and newer rocks and an uneven layer of younger sands and gravels. The superficial cover is largely the result of the powerful action of the swollen rivers of glacial times, which have also cut into the underlying rocks and in part removed the newer deposits (even revealing in places the pre-Pyrenean fold trends). Several of the valleys form minor *pays*, such as the *Plaine de Tarbes* in the upper Adour valley and the *Pays de Soule* in the valley of the Saison (see p. 671). The rounded 'coteaux' and '*pays mamelonnés*' forming the interfluves are of the order of 1,000 to 1,100 feet above sea-level.

To the north of these plateaus and within the curve of the Adour is the district of *Chalosse*,[3] very similar in character to Bas-Armagnac further east. In the east and centre lies a subdivision known as the *Chalosse de Geaune*, where the interfluves form whale-backed ridges scored by a multitude of rivulets, and the valleys are bordered by broad terraces at levels ranging from 30 to 200 feet above the present rivers. The landscape is gentle, indeed D. Faucher describes it as '*les coteaux aimables*'. The western part of the *pays*, the *Chalosse de Pouillon*, consists of sands of Miocene age (the *sables fauves*).

[1] J. Fischer, 'Le Régime de l'Adour et de ses affluents', in *R.G.P.S.-O.* (1930), vol. i, pp. 75-97.
[2] M. Richard, 'Les Barthes de l'Adour', *ibid.* (1937), vol. viii, pp. 101-63 and 237-66.
[3] L. Papy, 'La Chalosse', in *A. de G.* (1931), vol. xl, pp. 239-58.

The Coast.—Between the mouth of the Adour and the Pointe-St. Martin (just north of Biarritz) the coast is a continuation of that of the Landes, with a belt of forested dunes and a broad sandy beach. For a short distance to the south the Tertiary strata actually reach the sea, forming low cliffs subject to intense erosion, and at Pointe-St. Martin the undercutting action of the waves has produced a steep cliff capped with an overhanging cornice from which falls are frequent. Further south the low cliffs of Eocene clays, gashed with ravines, are constantly receding as the result of *en masse* slumping on to the beach.

Still further to the south, however, the 'frontal zone' of the Pyrenees (see p. 667), represented by the Upper Cretaceous limestone plateau of Labouard, reaches the sea, and the coastline cuts transversely across these structures. A slight marine transgression has produced an indented coast, and limestone cliffs alternate with coves referred to as *les rias basques*. In some places, notably near Socoa on the shores of the Baie de St. Jean-de-Luz, the strata dip seawards at an angle of about forty-five degrees, and from a wave-cut platform at the base of the cliffs project sharp saw-tooth ridges of the more resistant strata. The coves are being slowly filled in by long-shore drift of fine sand in a southerly direction, although groynes and dykes have been built to protect the approaches to the harbour of St. Jean-de-Luz at the mouth of the estuary of the Nivelle. Hendaye is not backed by cliffs, and its broad bay (the Baie de Chingaudy) is flanked by sandy beaches.

Land-Use and Agriculture.—Taking the *département* of Basses-Pyrénées as an indication, 40 per cent of the total area in 1963 was uncultivated, 23 per cent under arable, 15 per cent under permanent pasture and 19 per cent under woodland. The forested area was once much greater, but continued cutting and grazing have converted much into scrub or rough pasture. Such a district is the *Landes de Hasparren et de Mixe* in the undulating country between the valleys of the Nive and the lower Adour. A few continuous areas of woodlands still survive, such as the Forêt de Bidache of oak, beech and chestnut, and pine forests have been established in the Chalosse de Pouillon. Hedges of stunted oaks and lines of poplars are common on the terraces and plateau.

The waste land is extensive; it includes bracken-brakes covering former woodland, poor grassland and heathland on some of the gravels and sands, and the scrub-covered *graves* and *barthes* of the Adour valley. Along the flood-plains of the *gaves* are found *saligues*, scrubby thickets of willow, hawthorn and alder.

The category of permanent pasture includes both poor grasslands on the low plateaus between the rivers and on the rounded ridges of the Chalosse, and also the verdant valley-floors of the *gaves*, which in places are irrigated. Feeders take off from the swiftly flowing streams and supply lateral irrigation canals running along the lowest terraces; in the plain of Tarbes the Canal d'Alaric, for example, runs along the right bank. On these pastures are kept cattle (which have increased rapidly in number during the last half-century), the *tarbais* breed of horses, and large numbers of pigs. The most important animal reared on the poor pastures is, however, the sheep; in 1963 Basses-Pyrénées had 341,000, and only Aveyron and Haute-Vienne of the other *départements* had more. In addition, Pyrenean sheep are brought down to graze in the valleys during winter and spring. Poultry are widespread, especially turkeys and geese; a side-line is the manufacture from goose-down of *duvets* (down-quilts, climbing-jackets, etc.) at Hagetmau.

The traditional cultivation of the Adour basin has long consisted of cereals—wheat, millet and barley; these are still important, especially on the sandy loams, with the more recent addition of maize (see p. 315 n.) and of oats for fodder, and the area under cereals in 1963 was still as high as 55 per cent of the arable. One major change has taken place in this century, for almost exactly a third of the farmland is under fodder-crops, including lucerne grown with the aid of irrigation. The area under potatoes has also increased, there is much more market-gardening, and some tobacco cultivation. The area of vineyards has never recovered from the phylloxera ravages; only about 22,000 acres of vines were cultivated in 1963, producing almost entirely *vin ordinaire*, and brandy is distilled and sold in Bayonne, though not of a quality comparable with that of Armagnac to the east. Orchards of peaches and apricots are grown on the slopes of the *collines*.

Population and Settlement.—The population of the Pays de l'Adour is unevenly distributed, with an average density of about 150 per square mile. The majority of people live in villages and isolated farms along the river valleys on the upper terraces away from flood-danger.[1] The way of life is pre-eminently rural, depending on a varied agriculture and the raising of stock. A few larger towns and some more densely populated rural areas are situated in the upper basins of rivers near the point of contact between the plain and the mountains to the south. Such is Tarbes (51,000 people in 1962), the chief town of Hautes-Pyrénées, situated in a basin on the upper Adour (Fig. 91). Its animal fairs are well known, and it is a commercial and industrial centre with old-established tanneries and

[1] See, for example, J. Loubergé, 'Villages et maisons rurales dans la vallée moyenne du Gave de Pau', in *R.G.P.S.-O.* (1958), vol. xxix, pp. 21-50; he discusses the siting of villages relative to the river terraces and the valley edge, with a map.

leather-working industries, notably the manufacture of patent-leather harness and footwear. There are also long-established furniture factories, and a specialisation in stone-carving, especially marble. As a result of the developments of Pyrenean power-stations, some new industries have developed in recent years, including the manufacture of electrical apparatus and machinery, turbines, dynamos and locomotives.

Further to the west is Pau, situated on the right bank of the turbulent Gave de Pau ; with its 61,000 people it is the *chef-lieu* of Basses-Pyrénées. Not only is it one of the tourist-gateways to the Pyrenees, but it is a prosperous market-town. As an industrial centre it has grown as a result of the availability of hydro-electricity and, since the war, of natural gas piped from St. Marcet. Numerous factories were built in the years before 1939 in this 'safe' area, including metallurgical and engineering works, tanneries and shoe factories, the manufacture of textiles and of the famous *bérets*, and the processing of agricultural commodities. Another important valley town is Oloron-Ste. Marie (14,000 people), also with a diverse industrial activity : the manufacture of woollen, linen and cotton cloth, *bérets*, sandals and other foot-gear, wooden articles, and bells of all shapes and sizes. Towns with similar functions are Nay and Orthez, both in the valley of the Gave de Pau, Maubourguet in the Adour valley, and Salies-de-Béarn, which as its name would imply has long exploited the rock-salt found locally in the Triassic rocks. A few small towns are situated along the middle Adour valley (Riscle, Aire, St. Sever, Mugron and Dax), but the poverty of the *graves* along the valley-floor limits their importance.

The most important town on the Adour is Bayonne, situated at the confluence with the Nive, with a population of about 41,000. Much of the built-up area lies along the left bank of the Adour below the confluence, but the newer part of the town has been built on the triangular peninsula between the two rivers. Bayonne began life in the fifth century as a point on a main route into Spain, and in the twelfth and thirteenth century during English rule it became important for the wine trade. But situated three miles from the open sea up a winding river with a difficult entry, the port of Bayonne was faced in the sixteenth century with serious problems of silting. By the beginning of the seventeenth century the river outlet had been stabilised at the southern side of Cap Breton (instead of as previously to the north), and further movement has been checked by the construction of moles on either side of its mouth. Regular dredging maintains a channel across the Barre shoal outside the estuary.

The modern port of Bayonne[1] includes both quays at Le Boucau

[1] P. Duchemin, 'Le Port de Bayonne et les industries de l'Adour', in *R.G.P.S.-O.* (1954), vol. xxv, pp. 144-56.

along the right bank midway between the town and the open sea, and others within the town as far upstream as the bridges at the Adour-Nive confluence. Its trade grew steadily in the late nineteenth century, particularly after the opening of the steel-works of *Les Forges de l'Adour* at Le Boucau[1] in 1882, and a peak of a million tons of freight was handled in the years preceding the war of 1914–1918. A considerable decline was experienced during the inter-war years, particularly in the tonnage of exports, and by 1938 the figure was only about 610,000 tons. Bayonne is handicapped by its somewhat remote position in a corner of France and by the limited rail communications serving its own hinterland. Since 1945 the freight handled has fluctuated between 600,000 and 800,000 tons, predominantly imports, and in 1963 it accommodated 1,582 vessels with a net tonnage of about 843,000. The steel-works at Le Boucau were responsible for much of the freight handled; in 1963, 231,000 tons of iron-ore were imported from Algeria and northern Spain and 310,000 tons of coal and coke, while nearly 120,000 tons of steel and steel products were shipped away. The town also has food-processing industries (notably wheat-milling), fertiliser factories and an aircraft factory established in the 'thirties.

Bayonne is a centre for the flourishing tourist industry of the extreme south-west, and especially for the attractive *Côte des basques*. A series of resorts extends from the Adour to the Spanish frontier, ranging from the sophisticated charm of Biarritz (now a town of 26,000 people) to villages such as the promisingly named Chambre d'Amour and Costa Aldia.

This coast was once one of the most active centres of the French fishing industry; Bayonne, Biarritz, Bidart, Guéthary, Ciboure and St. Jean-de-Luz have been important for centuries. Fishing-vessels from these ports went to Newfoundland and Arctic waters, and the Basque fishermen were second only to the Bretons, but since the mid-nineteenth century this activity has declined. St. Jean is still the most important centre for the French sardine fisheries, and anchovy, tunny and mackerel are also caught. Along the coast at various towns are fish-preserving and -canning factories.

The Oil-fields.[2]—The right to search for mineral oil over most of the Pays de l'Adour and adjacent areas in the upper Garonne basin was leased to the Government-sponsored *Société Nationale des*

[1] S. Lerat, 'La Sidérurgie du Boucau est-elle à la veille d'une reconversion?', in *R.G.P.S.-O.* (1960), vol. 31, pp. 113-22.

[2] (i) G. G. Weigend, 'The Outlook for the Gas and Oil Industry of South-West France', in *E.G.* (1953), vol. 29, pp. 307-19; (ii) R. Brunet, 'Le Sud-Ouest et le problème pétrolier', in *R.G.P.S.-O.* (1957), vol. xxviii, pp. 60-78; (iii) A. Guilcher, 'Le Pétrole et le gaz naturel en France', in *T.K. Ned. A.G.* (1956), vol. lxxiii, pp. 245-59.

Pétroles d'Aquitaine in 1941, although little was done until after the war, when in 1949 oil was located at Lacq, to the north-west of Pau; this field yields an oil with an asphalt base and a low petrol content. At first production rose steadily to 308,000 tons in 1954, but since then there has been a disquieting decline to only 86,000 tons in 1963, possibly an indication of approaching exhaustion. The crude oil is sent by rail either to the Shell-Berre refinery at Pauillac or to the La Mède refinery near Marseilles.

It seems that the major importance of Lacq lies in the production not of oil but of natural gas, which has been found below the oil-field at great depths.[1] The output during 1963 totalled 45·3 milliard cubic metres from numerous producing bores, the deepest of which exceeds 17,000 feet. The significance of this development is that by 1964 the gas furnished the equivalent of seven million tons of coal or 4 per cent of France's total consumption of energy. A completely new town, Mourenx, has grown near Lacq, now with over 12,000 people. A vast amount of gas is stored underground at Lussagnet. Much gas is used locally in the nearby Artix thermal power-station, opened in 1961–2; in 1963 it had the largest output (2·51 million kWh) of any French station. A gas-grid has been constructed in conjunction with the St. Marcet field; mains have been built from Lacq to Bordeaux, Nantes, Vannes, Besançon, Lyons and Paris. Plans have been prepared for the extension of the chemical works at Pierrefitte in Hautes-Pyrénées, and for the erection of several factories for fertilisers, plastics and other by-products in both the Pyrenean and Bordeaux regions. The gas is highly sulphurous, and about 1·5 million tons of sulphur are extracted each year, making France the second world producer. A large thermal generator is in operation at Ambès. Further discoveries of gas were made in 1965 at Meillon and Mazières, near Pau, and several wells have been completed.

THE LANDES

The Coast.—The straight coast of the Landes extends from the Pointe de Grave to the mouth of the Adour, unbroken for a distance of about 140 miles save for the Baie d'Arcachon (Fig. 92). This shore-line has developed through the formation of an offshore bar by south-flowing long-shore currents, thus straightening off former estuaries.[2] Extensive sand-dunes accumulated on this bar and so

[1] S. Lerat, 'La Mise en valeur du gisement de gaz de Lacq', in *A. de G.* (1957), vol. lxvi, pp. 260-7; J. P. Fouchier, 'Considerations économiques sur Lacq', in *Revue française de l'Energie* (1955), p. 360; and K. Suter, 'Das Erdgas und Industriezentrum Lacq', in *Geographica Helvetica* (1965), vol. xx, pp. 8-13.

[2] A. Guilcher, A. Godard and E. Visseaux, 'Formes de plage et houle sur le littoral des Landes de Gascogne', in *R.G.P.S.-O.* (1952), vol. xxiii, pp. 99-117; this deals with tidal and other influences on the form of the Landes beaches.

created a continuous barrier which has converted the indentations into a string of large shallow lagoons, for the most part reed-margined and dotted with islets and sand-banks.[1] The dune-belt is so continuous that the northern lagoons are obliged to drain southwards, each linked with the next by a channel roughly parallel to the coast and leading ultimately into the Baie d'Arcachon. Some of the smaller southern *étangs* do drain directly to the sea.

The dune-belt, in places six miles in width, consists of several longitudinal crest-lines separated by parallel depressions and fronted by shelving beaches of fine white sand. Many of the dunes exceed 150 feet in height, and one, the Dune de Sabloney (or de Pilat), attains 300 feet, probably the largest in Europe. The winds from the sea constantly blow sand inland, and there is some movement within the dune-belt,[2] although the *étangs* check this, as does the planting of pines and marram grass, and the construction of wicker fences.

The Baie d'Arcachon forms the only major breach in the dune-line. Across its mouth the long spit of Cap Ferret is still extending southward, built up by south-flowing currents. At low tide the water area of the bay shrinks to less than a third, leaving stretches of mud intersected by a labyrinth of channels (*esteys* and *rus*) separating mud-flats and sandy islets, with areas of salt-marsh around the margins of the bay. Into its south-eastern corner wanders the Leyre, the main drainage stream of the Landes.[3]

The Interior Landes.—Behind the dune-lagoon margin from the Gironde to the Adour lie the Landes proper, covering 6,000 square miles in the *départements* of Gironde and Landes. This area represents the Quaternary *dépression landaise*, into which marine clays and fine sands were deposited. The surface now consists of a gently undulating cover of fine siliceous sands, heavily impregnated with oxides of iron, which have been reworked and re-deposited by numerous small streams, and sometimes even re-sorted by the action of the wind. They are underlain by a dark-coloured hard-pan (*alios*), in some places reinforced by the *garluche*, an iron-pan of complete impermeability formed by the leaching and downward percolation of water impregnated with ferruginous compounds. Shallow meres and swamps covered much of the Landes in the past, and despite measures of reclamation much remains as dreary reed-

[1] J. Filliol, 'Aspects physiques de la région des étangs landais d'Arcachon à Soustons', in *R.G.P.S.-O.* (1955), vol. xxvi, pp. 28-43; this discusses the results of vegetation and sedimentation on the *étangs* of the Landes.

[2] J. J. Wolff, 'The Dunes of Sabloney near Arcachon', in *G.J.* (1929), vol. lxxiii, p. 453; this includes a series of interesting photographs illustrating the changing features of the dunes.

[3] J. Weulersse, 'Le Bassin d'Arcachon', in *A. de G.* (1928), vol. xxxvii, pp. 407-27, gives a full account, with numerous maps and photographs.

covered waste; in former days herdsmen on their stilts were a familiar sight and they are still occasionally to be seen. In their primitive state the Landes consisted of *étangs* and marshes,[1] *bruyères* and

FIG. 92.—PART OF THE LANDES.

The *étangs* are abbreviated as follows: **A.**, Aureilhan; **B.P.**, Biscarosse-Parentis; **C.S.**, Cazaux-Sanguinet.

Based on (i) *Carte de France et des frontières au 1: 200,000ᵉ*, sheets 56, 63; (ii) a map in the *Esso Magazine* (1955–56), vol. v, no. 1, p. 19, which locates oil wells sunk to that date.

[1] J. Filliol, 'Aspects physiques de la région des étangs landais d'Arcachon à Soustons', in *R.G.P.S.-O.* (1955), vol. xxvi, pp. 28-43; this deals with the '*rôle morphologique de la végétation*' in the evolution of the *étangs*.

fougères, thickets of broom and gorse, tangles of brambles, expanses of ling and coarse grass; at one extreme were small groves of ever-green oak and pine, at the other bare sand. The whole district com-prised in fact '*le grand désert landais*', and the word '*lande*' is used elsewhere in France and Belgium to denote a waste area.

The afforestation of the Landes began along the coastal dune-margin in the years immediately preceding the French Revolution.[1] During the first half of the nineteenth century, however, progress was slow, and it was only after 1857, when the government department of *Eaux et Forêts* took over, that any adequate drainage schemes were effected. Some of the marsh has been drained and the hard-pan broken by deep ploughing. The main species used for afforestation is the maritime pine (*Pinus pinaster*), of which many millions have been planted. The forest has to be carefully preserved, insect pests (particularly crickets) must be combated, and drainage systems maintained, while the tinder-dry nature of the woodland and the high resin-content of the trees make fire a constant threat. Between 1930 and 1948 more than 900,000 acres of plantation were ravaged by fire; in the hot dry summer of 1949 occurred the grievous con-flagrations which destroyed over 300,000 acres to the south-west of Bordeaux, with considerable loss of life. Though the pine dominates, other trees have been deliberately planted, notably willows in the damper depressions, cork-oak in the south, and in places groves of carob-trees. In 1963, notwithstanding the fire-damage of previous years, the Landes forests amounted to about 2,200 square miles, more than a third of the total area.

Several sub-regions can be distinguished within the apparent uniformity of the Landes. In the centre are the *Grandes Landes*, still the wildest and most thinly populated part. This is bordered on the north-east by the rather higher *Petites Landes*, the *Pays d'Albret* and *la Marsan*, where the sand is less extensive and in many places replaced by Tertiary clays and limestones, wooded with evergreen oaks or covered with pasture. To the south of the Baie d'Arcachon is the *Pays de Born*, and to the south of this again the coastal region of *Marensin*, where grow extensive groves of cork-oak. Finally, to the north-east of the Baie d'Arcachon is the *Pays de Buch*.

Economic Development.—For long the Landes formed one of the most scantily populated, unproductive and unhealthy regions of France. As D. Faucher says, '*Le peuple, sous-alimenté, dévoré de*

---

[1] A very detailed account of the reclamation of the Landes is provided by A. Larroquette, *Les Landes de Gascogne et la Forêt landaise. Aperçu physique et étude transformation économique* (1924). See also C. Angus, 'La Forêt landaise', in *Géographia* (1954), no. 28, pp. 25-31, which contains a detailed map of land-use.

paludisme, menait une vie chétive et précaire'. Agriculture was carried on in a humble way in clearings, forming minute *oases agricoles* where rye, later maize, melons and other vegetables could be cultivated. As late as 1932 more than half the arable land was worked by *métayers*. In the mid-nineteenth century considerable flocks of sheep were kept, indeed at that time Landes with 650,000 had more than any other *département* in France, and many more animals wintered there from the Pyrenees.

The reclamation and drainage measures intended primarily for the pine-plantations also helped agriculture. So too did the extension of the railways into south-western France; the line from Bordeaux to Arcachon was opened in 1841, the straight line south through Labouheyre and Dax to Bayonne in 1855, and the line across the eastern Landes via Mont-de-Marsan to Tarbes in 1859. Numerous roads were constructed and the region was in some measure opened up.[1] By 1963 about 17 per cent of the *département* of Landes was under arable, but only 2 per cent was permanent pasture. Two-thirds of the arable grew cereals, chiefly maize, and 20 per cent was under fodder-crops. Cattle (142,000) and pigs (75,000) have now largely replaced sheep (29,000). The same tendencies are discernible in the neighbouring *département* of Gironde.

The main economic importance of the Landes continues to be in the exploitation of the forests. For many centuries the poor woodlands were cut and burnt for charcoal to provide fuel for several small glass-works (long since abandoned) and for furnaces which smelted local bog-ores. Today the carefully grown trees are systematically cut for pit-props (150,000 tons a year), telegraph-poles, railway sleepers and sawn timber, much of which is exported from Bordeaux. In spite of the development of synthetic substitutes, the pines are still tapped by the *gemmeurs* for resin, from which terebenthine and other products are distilled at factories within the forests. But the annual production of resin is now of the order of 700,000 hectolitres, compared with a peak of more than twice as much; the fires of 1949 destroyed many mature trees and hit the industry seriously. Until recently the high resin-content had precluded use of the wood for pulping, but technical improvements have made this possible, and paper-mills have been built at Mimizan,[2] Bègles and Facture.

Lignite is extracted from large open-cast workings near Hostens

[1] A detailed account, with maps, of the development of communications in the Landes and its effect on the economy is given by H. Cavaillès, 'Le Problème de la circulation dans les Landes de Gascogne', in *A. de G.* (1933), vol. xlii, pp. 561-82.

[2] M. Preuilh, 'La Papeterie de Mimizan (Landes)', in *R.G.P.S.-O.* (1962), vol. 33, pp. 398-400.

and Arjuzanx, yielding about 1·5 million tons annually. Near each field is a large modern thermal generator, producing together over 500,000 kwh annually.

There has been some development along the coast in respect of the tourist industry, making use of the fine sandy beaches and a pleasant sunny climate. Lacanau-Océan in the north, Arcachon, Biscarosse-Plage, Mimizan-Plage and Hossegor have grown considerably as resorts. In 1963 Arcachon landed 2,900 tons of fish, mostly sardines and also sole and turbot, though its chief importance is for oysters; with La Tremblade and Marennes further north it has virtual monopoly of the Portuguese variety, which is cultivated in vast numbers in small enclosed culture-beds (*parcs* or *parquers*).

The Parentis-Born Oilfield.—The *Société Esso-Standard* had considered developments in the area south-west of Bordeaux since before the war of 1939–45 and was granted an exploration permit in 1951, but serious development only started in 1954. Oil was reached in a bore sunk on the southern shores of the Etang de Parentis, and since then twenty-eight further wells have been drilled (Fig. 92), of which several have proved to be dry.[1] In 1954 only 132,000 tons of oil were produced, but in the following year this had increased to 576,000 tons and in 1963 it totalled 1,870,000 tons, an appreciable supplement to France's imported supplies. Exploration is continuing in the area and other discoveries have been made. The oil is piped to a small storage-dépôt at Parentis, then conveyed by rail-tankers to the *Esso-Standard* refinery at Bordeaux.

[1] (i) 'Oil Strike in France', in *Esso Magazine* (1955–6), vol. v, no. 1, pp. 15-19; (ii) H. Enjalbert, 'Parentis', in *R.G.P.S.-O.* (1957), vol. xxviii, pp. 35-59; and (iii) R. Brunet, 'Le Sud-Ouest et le problème pétrolier', *ibid.*, pp. 60-78.

CHAPTER 14

THE SAÔNE-RHÔNE VALLEY

The valley of the Saône, continued to the south of Lyons by that of the Rhône, forms such a distinctive elongated feature that it is often referred to as '*le Fosse Saône-Rhône*' or '*le Couloir entre les Montagnes*'. It consists of a structural depression, clearly defined in the west by the edge of the Central Massif. The Saône valley is demarcated on the east, though not quite so prominently, by the edge of the Jura. The eastern wall of the Rhône valley below Lyons is still less clearly defined, for the outlying uplands of the Fore-Alps project intermittently between the Rhône's left-bank tributaries.

The Plateau de Langres, which lies across the northern end of the corridor, is easily crossed from the Paris Basin and Lorraine by road, rail and canal. Another route-way leads into the valley from the Rhineland by way of the Porte de Bourgogne (the 'Gate of Belfort') between the Vosges and the Jura, and others, though more difficult, enter the corridor from the east from Switzerland and Italy. Thus despite the inadequacy of the Rhône as a waterway and the series of gorge-like sections within its valley, the corridor has formed for many centuries an obvious line of communication between north-western Europe and the Mediterranean lands, or, as D. Faucher puts it, '*un vestibule du Nord pour le Midi, du Midi pour le Nord*'. Roads and railways follow each bank of the river, although in places with considerable difficulty. The gorge-sections had to be negotiated with the aid of cuttings and tunnels, as at Cruas where two roads, two railways and the river occupy a narrow valley. As most of the tributaries have braided their courses through broad gravel-fans across the main valley-floor before they join the Rhône, each bridge is necessarily many times longer than the width of the stream (particularly in summer) would seem to require. It was not until 1855 that the Lyons-Valence left-bank railway was opened, and extended during the following year to Avignon. The right-bank line was completed even later, and the Lyons-Nîmes section was not finally opened until 1879. Today the left-bank railway is one of the most heavily used routes in France, carrying a considerable passenger and freight traffic between Paris and the lower Rhône-Marseilles-Riviera region. Freight traffic includes coal moving southwards, lime and cement going northwards from the large works along the valley, and wine from the Midi and Algeria. Many of the imports of Marseilles, France's Mediterranean entry, are sent north by rail, including wheat, flour, oil-seeds and hydro-carbons, as well as a range of manufactures from its industrial hinterland. Most interesting is the specialised north-bound traffic in vegetables (*primeurs*), fruit and flowers from the climatically favoured Midi and lower Rhône valley, carried in insulated or refrigerator vans.

The more important of the valley roads is *N7* along the left bank from Lyons to Avignon, thence continuing south-east to Aix-en-Provence, Cannes, Nice and the Italian frontier; this carries an immense tourist traffic of cars and coaches to the coastal resorts throughout the year, as well as lorries transporting agricultural produce. *N86* along the right bank follows the Rhône to Pont-St. Esprit, and then trends away south-westward to Nîmes, Montpellier and Perpignan as the mouth of the Rhône valley opens out. Finally, many of the regular air-services use the 'air-space' between the lofty mountains on either side.

The south-bound traveller is conscious within a short distance of a distinctive change in the landscape from the green meadows, arable fields and woodlands of western Europe to a bright sun-drenched Provençal scene of bare limestones and silvery shrubs, with a rather harsh summer aridity. These changes are summarised botanically on Fig. 93, where the northern limits of certain Mediterranean species and the southern limits of species more characteristic of northern Europe are indicated. A diverse and often specialised agriculture varies from the cultivation of wheat, maize and fodder-crops in the broad Saône trough, to mulberries, olives, early vegetables, sub-tropical fruits and flowers nearer the Mediterranean coast. Many of the valley-slopes carry vineyards, the most famed on the Côte d'Or, on the east-facing slopes of the Central Massif further south, and along the Rhône terraces. An active industrial life has developed in many of the towns, particularly at Lyons, the third city of France, and at Dijon. A string of small towns is aligned along the Rhône valley, each in a fertile basin commanding a crossing-point of the river, and often dominated by an ancient fortress; some indeed were Roman strong-points and developed an early civic life.

THE STRUCTURAL EVOLUTION OF THE CORRIDOR

The structure of the Saône-Rhône valley is one of considerable complexity, since it forms a marginal region between the Hercynian uplands of the Central Massif and the mid-Tertiary folds of the Jura and the Alps, thus affected by both periods of earth-movement. The resulting region has only, as one might say, '*une unité de surface*'.

It is probable that the depression was at any rate vaguely outlined

FIG. 93.   FIG. 94.

FIG. 93 (left).—LIMITS OF CRITICAL BOTANICAL SPECIES IN THE RHÔNE VALLEY.

A, Northern limit of the olive and the holm oak ; B, northern limit of the holm oak alone ; C, northern limit of thyme ; D, southern limit of pedunculate oak ; E, southern limit of hornbeam.

Based on D. Faucher, *La France: géographie-tourisme* (1951), vol. i, p. 14.

FIG. 94 (right).—THE REGULARISATION OF THE LOWER RHÔNE.

The seven schemes of derivations, barrages and power stations are shown.

Based on (i) D. Faucher, *op. cit.*, p. 238 ; (ii) various large-scale maps.

by the end of the Hercynian earth-movements of Carbo-Permian times. During the Jurassic and Cretaceous great thicknesses of limestone were deposited over much of what is now southern France. In Miocene times the earth-movements which produced both the folding of the Alpine ranges to the east and also the bodily upheaval and tilting of the Central Massif to the west, defined the corridor in more or less its present form. Moreover, the gentle synclinal folding of the sediments laid down in what is now the Paris Basin, together with faulting along its southern margins, were responsible for the formation of the Plateau de Langres, a kind of bridge or '*liaison sédimentaire*', between the Morvan and the Vosges. The Saône-Rhône valley suffered down-faulting, although more unilaterally (along the edge of the Central Massif) than in the case of the Rhine depression. Geological borings have for example revealed a continuation of the coal-basin of St. Etienne away to the north-east, down-faulted progressively more deeply; at Torcieu in the Ain valley to the north-east of Lyons coal has been reached at 4,600 feet. In fact beneath the sediments of the Rhône valley the surfaces of the Hercynian blocks lie at such varying depths that it has been said that '*le soussol profond était assez chaotique*'.[1]

The lines of fracture are less defined on the eastern side of the Rhône valley in the Fore-Alps, although the lower courses of the Isère and the Drôme seem to follow groups of faults. Some small Hercynian horsts project through the newer cover, as in the Plateau de Crémieu to the east of Lyons where ancient igneous and meta-morphic rocks form the 'prow' of a peninsula of middle Jurassic limestones. This happens again further up the Saône valley in the '*petit massif de la Serre*' to the north of Dole. Most of these faulting movements were completed by the end of the Miocene.

The history of the Saône-Rhône corridor involved deposition under fluctuating marine and lacustrine conditions. Eocene deposits occur to the north of Montpellier and on the other side of the Rhône near Aix-en-Provence. Oligocene limestones and clays flank the edge of the Cévennes and overlie the Lower Cretaceous rocks to the east of Alès, and occur again on either side of the Durance. Many of these Eocene and Oligocene limestones have been gently folded, and the landscape is markedly undulating. Further north the lime-stones are buried by newer Tertiary rocks, but another considerable outcrop appears to the north-east of Dijon.

In late Eocene or early Oligocene times an eastward extension of the Pyrenean folding into Provence (see p. 621) probably confined a lake extending far to the north. These southern confining ridges, sometimes known as '*l'isthme durancien*', were broken through in

[1] D. Faucher and A. Gilbert, 'Le Couloir entre les Montagnes', in *La France: géographie-tourisme* (1951), vol. i (p. 206).

Miocene times by *en bloc* down-faulting movements which formed
the Golfe du Lion. A narrow gulf of the sea thus extended during
the Miocene along the valley to Lyons and north-eastward across
what is now the Swiss Plateau, as evidenced by the present widespread Miocene deposits. Later in the Miocene or early Pliocene,
changes of sea-level substantially reduced this elongated gulf, so
that the Swiss Plateau became first a lake, still draining southwards,
and in due course dry land.

This reduced gulf of the sea in the lower Rhône valley was separated from the Saône valley by another transverse barrier, the 'sill
of Vienne', to the south of Lyons. Here the south-westerly spur
of the Plateau de Crémieu approaches closely the Hercynian projection of Mont Pilat. To the north of this barrier, what is now
the Plaine de Bresse was occupied by a large lake. A river flowed
southwards from western Germany through the Porte de Bourgogne
and approximately along the line of the present Doubs valley to
'lake Bresse', into which it poured vast masses of sediments. Almost
the whole of the Saône basin from where the Jurassic rocks end near
Vesoul is floored with these Pliocene deposits, except where still
newer material has been laid down over them. 'Lake Bresse'
drained southwards through a notch cut across the 'sill of Vienne'
into the gulf of the sea occupying the lower Rhône valley.

Towards the end of the Pliocene occurred the subsidence of the
floor of the Rhine rift-valley and the creation of the right-angled
bend in that river near Basel. For a time the upper Doubs probably
continued north-eastwards through the Jura to join the Rhine, until
its remarkable capture by another river, now the lower Doubs,
flowing south-westwards along the flanks of the Jura into the Plaine
de Bresse (see p. 609 and Fig. 128). The Porte de Bourgogne thus
became a major watershed in central Europe. Finally, uplift to
the south of Lyons converted the gulf of the sea into the valley of
the lower Rhône. The rivers continued to deposit vast quantities
of gravel worn from the uplifted ranges, in the form of 'stony
deltas' around the edges of the retreating Pliocene gulf.

Alpine glaciers moved westwards from the high mountains at
the maximum of the Quaternary glaciation, particularly down the
upper Rhône and Isère valleys. They covered the marginal plateaus
and coalesced to form piedmont sheets on the low ground of the
main valley. At their maximum extent glaciers crossed the Rhône
to the west of Lyons, and pushed north across the Pays de Dombes
almost as far as Bourg on the river Reyssouze (Fig. 134). Much
boulder-clay was deposited, both as distinct morainic lines and as
hummocky sheets of ground moraine, notably in the Pays de Dombes.
Still more extensive were the outwash sheets of fluvio-glacial gravels,
the ' *cailloux roulés* '. As the Quaternary glaciation waned, the main

tributaries continued to bring immense quantities of material, the heavier detritus forming cones beyond the valley-exits, the lighter sandier material washed down into the Rhône valley. The Pays de Dombes and much of Bas-Dauphiné (notably the Terres-Froides and the Plateau de Chambaran) are covered with sheets of these gravels and coarse sands.

The post-glacial Rhône and its tributaries have continued both their erosive and depositive activity. The snow-melt of early summer so much increases their volume and activity that vast quantities of material derived from the wastage of the Alps are brought down, ranging from 'rock-flour' to gravel. Even the short but torrential tributaries from the west are responsible for masses of pebbles during their winter floods. The heavier grades are deposited in the lower courses; during the low water of late summer the Isère, Drôme and Durance twist in braided channels among banks of these bleached gravels. The finer sands and clays are swept downstream to their final resting-place on the flood-plain of the lower valley or in the delta. These marshy plains of the lower Rhône, often covered with reed-swamps, contrast with the dry higher gravel terraces.

The Saône-Rhône corridor, although basically a low-lying re-entrant between two major uplands, presents therefore a varied landscape. Its margins consist of limestones of a diverse character, of Jurassic, Cretaceous and early Tertiary ages; in the north they form well-cultivated south-facing slopes, but in the south increasing aridity results in a distinctive 'garrigue' character with scrubby ever-green plants and much bare rock. The floor of the depression is filled with lacustrine, marine, glacial, fluvio-glacial and fluvial deposits in great variety, including the sands, clays and marls of Bresse, the waterlogged clays of Dombes, extensive gravel sheets, banks of fine sediments and patches of *limon*. Many have specific names, such as the '*marnes bleues de la Bresse*', the '*sables dits de Trévoux*' and the '*argiles bleues de Givors*'. The changes of base-level and course by the Rhône and its tributaries have helped to diversify the landscape by developing gorges, by leaving prominent residual hills, and by producing terraces with distinctive edges known as *côtes*.

THE RIVER SAÔNE

The Saône is formed by a group of headstreams rising on the Triassic sandstones of the Monts Faucilles and on the south-western flanks of the Vosges (Fig. 66). It flows south-westwards, with an exceptionally serpentine course, receiving a number of left-bank tributaries from the Vosges, notably the Ognon which rises on the south-western flanks of the Ballon d'Alsace. Its major tributary from the Jura, the Doubs, joins some twenty miles above Chalon (see p. 609 and Fig. 128). The Saône is not without right-bank tributaries; such streams as the Vingeanne (whose valley is utilised by the Marne-Saône Canal), the Tille and the Ouche (followed by the Burgundy Canal) flow down the steep south-eastern edge of the Plateau de Langres on to the lowlands. The Saône then swings across to the western side of the Plaine de Bresse under the steep edge of the Mâconnais, the Beaujolais and the Lyonnais. Several clearly defined terraces border the flood-plain on which the river wanders with braidings, cut-offs and shallow lakes. Its volume is increased by several left-bank tributaries, the Seille, Reyssouze and Veyle, which pick up water from springs issuing at the base of the Vignoble-Revermont ridges along the edge of the Jura. At Lyons the Saône is joined by the Rhône, enclosing within the angle thus formed the hummocky country of the Pays de Dombes.

The Saône has a more stable régime than that of the Alpine Rhône. It receives numerous large head-streams, many deriving their water from the extensive underground storage of the limestone Jura. In the Plaine de Bresse the gentle gradient of the long valley helps to even out the effects of protracted rain and late spring snow-melt, producing a steadily flowing river. As Dr. H. Ormsby so felicitously expresses it, describing the confluence of the Saône and the Rhône at Lyons, '. . . the two ill-assorted bedfellows occupy uneasily the same channel. The hurrying, often turbulent, Rhône is easily distinguished, with its milky waters, as it jostles the tranquil green flood of its companion from the north. . . .' [1]

THE LOWER RHÔNE

The Rhône between Lake Geneva and the Ain confluence crosses transversely the ridges of the Jura (see pp. 607-9 and Fig. 130), then enters the Plaine de Bresse in the neighbourhood of Lagnieu. Until recently the section between the Ain confluence and the eastern outskirts of Lyons was liable to inundation; the river wandered in large loops over a flood-plain two to three miles in width, with areas of marshland, fluctuating lakes and reed-swamps. Many disastrous floods have been experienced; the worst for several centuries was in 1840, which flooded the inter-riverine area and covered all the eastern parts of the city. Considerable regularisation has since taken place; the dyked Canal de Jonage was constructed in 1893 along the southern margin of the flood-plain, with a large reservoir-lake to draw off and hold up temporarily the flood-waters, and the Canal de Miribel follows the northern edge (Fig. 97). The former meandering course of the river, substantially reduced in volume, now lies between these two canals.

[1] H. Ormsby, *France: A Regional and Economic Geography* (1950), p. 281.

The Rhône, with its volume now greatly increased by the steady contribution of the Saône,[1] flows almost due south from Lyons for about 130 miles to Arles, where the deltaic region begins (Fig. 98).

Between Lyons and the Isère confluence near Valence the effects of the Saône's régime are still dominant, and the winter rains on the uplands of west-central Europe result in a pronounced winter maximum. The Isère, which is a tributary of such importance that it increases the volume of the Rhône by a quarter, brings down early summer melt-water from the Alpine snow-fields. Further south the drought and evaporation of the Mediterranean summer result in appreciable low-water conditions in late summer. The shorter tributaries from the Fore-Alpine hills and from the restricted catchment area of the steep margins of the Central Massif contribute little water in summer; some literally dry up. They can, however, produce sharp concentrated floods in autumn and winter, frequently spreading widely over the flood-plain; the Ardèche, descending steeply from the Cévennes, is notorious in this respect.

The Rhône follows to the south of Lyons what is really an extension of the plain of Bresse, which ends in the neighbourhood of Givors where the river cuts through the 'sill of Vienne'. To the south of this narrow section is the first of the Rhône 'basins', the little plain of Vienne, formed by the coalescence of the Gère and several other small valleys. Next comes another narrow section, again succeeded by a more open valley where some small left-bank tributaries enter from the Plateau de Chambaran, and a further narrow section between St. Vallier and the pleasant vine-growing centre of Tain-l'Hermitage. This in turn is succeeded southward by the basin of Valence, within which the Isère and the Drôme join the Rhône.

With its major headstreams, the Arc and the Drac, the Isère drains a large part of the French Alpine ranges (Figs. 132, 133). The Drôme, a much shorter river than the Isère, flows though a maze of shingle-banks in the southern part of the Valence basin. It then cuts through a northward-projecting spur of the Diois in a fine gorge five miles above its confluence with the Rhône.

To the south of the Valence basin the main valley narrows to form the Cruas gorge, steep-sided though a mile in width. At Baix, just above Cruas, the river swings against the limestone cliffs, and both road and railway are obliged to follow a series of tunnels and cuttings. Numerous islets, shingle-banks and braided sections lie within the Cruas gorge, but the main stream is now confined between training-walls and embankments for much of its length. After the river leaves Cruas it passes into the Montélimar basin, and follows the

---

[1] M. Pardé, *Le Calcul des débits du Rhône et de ses affluents* (1925), gives details of the régime of the Rhône. See also M. Pardé, *Le Régime du Rhône ; étude hydrologique* (1925).

edge of the Central Massif; the alluvium-floored basin, crossed by the Roubion and its tributary the Jabron from the Diois massif, lies almost wholly to the east of the river. Then the river enters the Donzère gorge, trenched through hard limestone for three miles. There is just room for the railways at the foot of the river-cliff, and in places they are obliged to use cuttings and tunnels. Below the Donzère gorge, the Rhône enters the plain of Pierrelatte. A large loop-canal has been completed across the eastern part of this plain from Donzère to Mondragon where it rejoins the main river (Fig. 98). To the south of the Mondragon couloir the plain of Orange opens out, next follows the Défilé de Roquemaure cut through the Tertiary rocks of the Collines de Châteauneuf-du-Pape and a narrow bar of Lower Cretaceous limestone, and then the broad triangular plain of Avignon to the north of the Chaîne des Alpilles.

The Fore-Alpine plateau country here swings away to the east, but long spurs project westward into the plains, separating the valleys of short tributaries such as the Eygues, Ouvèze and Nesque. To the west the undulating Cretaceous limestone country of the *garrigues* approaches closely the right bank of the river, except where Cévennes confluents such as the Ardèche and Cèze have eroded deep re-entrants.

A few miles below Avignon, the Rhône receives its last major tributary, the Durance, which rises far to the north-east in the Briançonnais, and drains the southern parts of the French Alps. The river emerges on to the lowland embayment between the westerly spurs of the Montagne de Luberon and the detached lime-stone Chaîne des Alpilles (Fig. 100). In Pliocene times the proto-Durance flowed to the south of the Alpilles into the Pliocene gulf, and built up an enormous delta of gravel débris, La Crau (see p. 408), but later the river abandoned this course for its present one along the northern side of the Alpilles. At Arles begins the Rhône delta.

The Saône-Rhône Navigation.[1]—The nature of the river Rhône makes it manifest that considerable difficulties are presented to navigation. Although it is officially navigable from near the Swiss frontier to the delta, that is, for about three hundred miles, the section above Lyons is in fact used little except for rafts and small pleasure craft; carrying a mere 70,000 tons of stone, gravel and sand.

The Saône has, however, been canalised as far upstream as Corre, where the southern branch of the Est Canal continues navigation over the water-parting of the Monts Faucilles into the Moselle basin (Fig. 85). About a hundred miles downstream from Corre, the Rhône-Rhine Canal leaves the Saône at St. Symphorien and

[1] M. Laferrère, 'Le projet de liaison fluviale Rhine-Rhône', in *Revue de Géog. de Lyon* (1962), vol. 37, pp. 113-29.

begins its long difficult course to Strasbourg. Other northward links include the Marne-Saône Canal from Heuilly-sur-Saône to Vitry-le-François, the Burgundy Canal (Canal de Bourgogne) from St. Jean-de-Losne to the river Yonne at Laroche, and the Centre Canal from Chalon-sur-Saône to Digoin, where it links up with the Loire navigation. This last waterway is most useful in spite of its sixty-three locks, since it serves the small but important Blanzy–Le Creusot coalfield and the industrial Nivernais.

The Saône has achieved considerable importance as a waterway, since these five canals contribute an appreciable volume of traffic. The river between Chalon and Lyons carries about 2 million tons of freight; largely because of this Saône traffic, Lyons is the ninth inland port of France (see p. 388).

Numerous attempts have been made to regularise the Rhône below Lyons by means of groynes and scouring-walls, together with dredging, under the auspices of the Government-sponsored *Compagnie Nationale du Rhône*, and to utilise it for navigation, hydro-electricity production and irrigation. During the decade preceding the war of 1939–45, there was constant discussion whether to regularise the Rhône (a scheme favoured by the city of Lyons), or to construct a separate lateral canal, as supported by Marseilles. Little had been done before the outbreak of war beyond various local and experimental works. After 1945 the concept of the multipurpose scheme was revived and the Donzère-Mondragon canal was completed (see p. 397), followed in 1958 by the Montélimar loop, and later by several others. In due course a looped lateral canal, each section supplying a head of water to a power-station, will be continuous from Arles to Lyons (Fig. 94).

At present traffic on the lower Rhône is mainly local, most of it between Pont-St. Esprit near the Ardèche confluence and Arles at the head of the delta. Powerful paddle-wheel tugs and motor-barges are used, which need to develop a speed of at least twelve knots to make much headway against the current. The downstream traffic consists of *vin ordinaire* for export, sand and gravel for construction work, and bauxite, while upstream cargoes include fertilisers, Algerian wine and petroleum.

CLIMATE

The Saône-Rhône valley forms a climatic transition between a régime in the north with continental tendencies and one in the south with distinctive 'Mediterranean' features, notably an increasingly marked summer drought. In the northern part of the Saône trough average temperatures in January are usually below freezing, although summer means may be in the neighbourhood of 66° F. Rainfall

in this area varies from 27 to 40 inches annually, according to aspect ;
thus Chalon, on the west of the valley and so to some extent in the
rain-shadow of the Côte d'Or, has an annual mean of 27·6 inches,
while Bourg on the east has as much as 38·2 inches. Throughout
the Saône valley a distinct maximum is experienced in autumn
(October), and a secondary maximum in May–June. Snow is often
widespread in winter, even on the valley-floor.

At Lyons there is still an appreciable range of temperature, with
mean figures of 35° F. in January and 69° F. in July. The mean
rainfall is 31 inches, quite well spread out through the year, but with
a winter minimum between November and March and a hint of a
drier summer between the secondary maximum in May–June and
the main October maximum.

To the south of Lyons the climate shows increasing tendencies
towards '*la transition méridionale*'. As D. Faucher puts it, in the
plain of Valence '. . . *le ciel plus clair, l'horizon plus dégagé, la tem-
pérature plus douce, tout annonce l'approche d'une province climatique
nouvelle*'. At Avignon the mean January temperature is about
40° F., the July temperature 75° F., and daily maxima of 95° F. are
frequent. The mean annual rainfall at Avignon is 25 inches, but
summer is very dry, the bare inch received on an average in June
being the result of short-lived thunderstorms. A distinct autumn
maximum is experienced, and a third of the total usually falls
between September and November, but a secondary spring maximum
is the result of unstable pressure conditions in the western Mediterranean and the passage of depressions through the Golfe du Lion.
Winds from the west and south, associated with the warm sectors of
eastwards-moving depressions, may bring some winter rain at intervals, but this season is usually much drier than is autumn. This is the
result of continental conditions, for much cold dry air moves from the
Central Massif down the Rhône 'funnel', in its extreme form known
as the *mistral*. This may originate as an air-stream behind a depression moving eastwards through the Mediterranean, with all the
characteristics of a cold front (turbulence, towering cumulo-nimbus
clouds, and squally showers of rain or hail), and then the air-flow
becomes established as a strong, bitterly cold and extremely dry
wind. The true *mistral* exceeds twenty knots, but considerably
higher forces, occasionally as much as seventy knots, have been
recorded ; its effects are most marked in winter and spring. Trees
are sometimes damaged and even uprooted, houses deroofed, tele-
graph poles snapped off at the ground and motor-cars overturned.
Even without the destructive gale-force results, the wind can do much
harm in spring to fruit-trees, vines and flower-gardens, both by direct
physical damage and by its desiccating effects. The landscape of the
lower Rhône valley is diversified by long wind-breaks of poplars,

dense cypress hedges and hurdle fences, erected in an effort to mitigate the worst effects of this unpleasant wind.[1]

Regional Divisions.—The Saône-Rhône valley can be divided into a
number of sub-regions. In the north is the upper Saône valley,
including both the actual *Val de Saône* and the lowland flanking it
to the north-west, the plain of Burgundy. The south-facing slopes
overlooking this valley also comprise a distinct sub-region, for
although they are the edges of the Jurassic uplands and of the Central
Massif, they clearly belong to the Saône region, forming the *rebord
viticole* which has made the name 'Burgundy' world-famous. To
the south succeeds the main valley between the Mâconnais and the
Jura, known as the Plaine de Bresse. Further south again in the
angle of the Saône-Rhône junction lies the *Pays de Dombes* or *la
plaine dombiste*, with its flanking terraces (*cotières*) along the Rhône,
Ain and Saône, and then follows the Lyons district. Below the
junction, the Rhône valley may be divided into three—the middle
section between Lyons and Donzère, together with the flanking hill-
country of Bas-Dauphiné, the lower section between Donzère and
Arles, and the delta (see pp. 403-11).

THE UPPER SAÔNE VALLEY

This sub-region includes the valley of the Saône as far downstream
as Chalon, together with the portions of the valleys of its almost
parallel headstreams, the Ognon and the Doubs, below the point
where they leave the Jurassic country of the Porte de Bourgogne.[2]
This 'gateway', the scene of a remarkable major reversal of drainage
towards the end of the Pliocene (see p. 370), lies at a height of about
1,150 feet. The Jurassic rocks which floor most of this gap have been
faulted and feebly folded, '*pincés entre la retombée méridionale des
Vosges et les plissements du Jura*' (E. Juillard), and now form low
limestone plateaus with occasional higher ridges, and with the
surface diversified in places by Tertiary rocks and by patches of
sands and gravels of recent deposition. Although the gap is one of
the major European watersheds, the divide is really very indeterminate; the Largue and its many small confluents drain north-eastwards across the Sundgau (see p. 295) to the Ill, while the Doubs
receives the Rapine, the Savoureuse (on which stands Belfort) and
the Luzine from the southern slopes of the Ballon d'Alsace in the

---

[1] D. Barsch, 'Les Arbres et le vent dans la vallée méridionale du Rhône', in
Revue de Géographie de Lyon (1965), vol. 40, pp. 35-45.
[2] A. Journaux, *Les Plaines de la Saône et leurs bordures montagneuses:
Beaujolais, Mâconnais, Côte d'Or, Plateaux de la Haute-Saône, Jura occidental:
étude morphologique* (1956); this is a monumental work of 526 pages.

Vosges, and the Allaine from the flanks of the Jura. To the west of the Porte de Bourgogne the Jurassic limestone country forms undulating country crossed by the Doubs, Ognon and Saône itself, known generally as the *plateaux de la Haute-Saône*.

The land slopes gently to the west and south-west to the valley proper of the upper Saône, known as *le Pays-bas bourguignon*. Broad terrace-steps rise from the flood-plain of the river to the foothills of the Côte d'Or to the north-west. These terraces are covered with sheets of Pliocene, Pleistocene and Recent deposits, with consequent variety of soils, including coarse sands and gravels, and sandy clays which become sticky in winter but hard and cracked in summer. Some soils have local names such as the reddish sandy *rouget* and the whitish ones known as *erbue*. Some are quite fertile, especially where they are of a loamy character and have been enriched by calcareous down-wash from the *côtes*.

This plain is crossed by numerous short streams flowing from springs near the base of the *côtes* to join the Saône. On the lower terraces tiny sheets of water lie among undulating sheets of alluvium, in spite of some reclamation. The lowest terraces and the present flood-plain are covered with water-meadows, marsh and osier-thickets. Despite regularisation of the river and the building of continuous embankments, these lands are liable to winter flooding.

To the east of the Saône, the plains of the lower Ognon and Doubs (separated by the ancient rocks of the Massif de la Serre) have much the same characteristics as those to the west. The soils tend to be richer, partly because of the greater amount of limy downwash from the Jura, partly because of a *limon*-like covering on the higher terraces.

The diverse land-use of the upper Saône region is summarised by the figures for the *département* of Haute-Saône, which occupies the valley as far downstream as the Ognon confluence. About 37 per cent was under woodland in 1963, 28 per cent under pasture, and 21 per cent under arable. These proportions are broadly similar in the contiguous lowland portions of the neighbouring *départements* of Côte-d'Or, Saône-et-Loire and Jura.

This high proportion of woodland is not surprising, since considerable areas of the coarse sandy soils are forested. In the plain of Burgundy the forests of Cîteaux, Chagny, Longchamp, Tart-l'Abbaye and Izeure with some smaller ones total about 135 square miles. Further east, in the plain between the gradually converging Loue and Doubs, is the Forêt de Chaux covering eighty square miles, and much of the Serre massif is also forested. These forests are dominated by oaks, but coniferous plantations have been established, and along the rivers grow osiers, willows, poplars and alders.

The most fertile lands are found on the lower clay-covered terraces of the main river and of its tributaries the Ouche, Oucherotte and

FIG. 95.—REGIONS OF THE SAÔNE BASIN.

Tille, and on the *limon*-covered higher terraces bordering the Jura. Almost half of the arable is devoted to cereals, both wheat and maize, together with sugar- and fodder-beet, potatoes, lucerne and trefoil. Tobacco, hops and mustard are also grown, and vineyards occur on the slopes, though much less extensively than a century ago. The less fertile soils to the north-west of the Saône are also assiduously cultivated, the result of centuries of effort, often originated by clearance schemes of the Cistercian houses in the Middle Ages. In some districts a period of fallow (the bare fields are known as *sommards*) is introduced into the rotation. Some of the *étangs* are drained, cultivated for a few years, flooded and used for pisciculture for a few more years before being drained again. The most prosperous and intensively cultivated districts are the market-gardens on the lower terraces of the Saône, in the neighbourhood of such towns as Auxonne, Maillys and St. Jean-de-Losne. Here the light soils, heavily fertilised and cultivated in strip-holdings, produce early potatoes and carrots, asparagus, onions and cauliflowers, which find ready markets in Belfort, Besançon, Montbéliard and Dijon.

As nearly a third of the upper Saône valley is under pasture, dairying is of importance. Water-meadows along the rivers are irrigated during the summer by means of a network of channels filled through sluices in the river-dykes; these also help drainage during winter flooding. Temporary grassland enters into the rotation systems, and fodder-crops are grown. Many riverine meadows are owned by the communes and grazed in common by the herds of the proprietors. The quality of the animals has been improved by the gradual substitution of the good milk-yielding *tachetée* breed for the small red *Bressane* type. Much milk is sold in the industrial towns, and there is an appreciable output of both farm-house and factory-made butter and cheese.

Thus the Saône valley presents a pleasantly diverse landscape. The population in this primarily rural area is not dense, of the order of a hundred people per square mile. Numerous villages, with their clustered red roofs among the trees, are mostly situated on the terraces or on small eminences away from the flood-plain. A few larger towns stand at river crossings, for the Saône lies athwart the routeways from the north. Gray (with 8,150 inhabitants) is the bridge-town on the important *N67* between the Paris Basin and Switzerland via Langres and Besançon, and Auxonne is situated at the crossing of *N5* between Dijon and Geneva. These towns are among the market- and servicing-centres, with various food-processing industries, such as the flour-mills of Gray. Agricultural implements are manufactured at Vesoul (which with a population of 15,736 is the *chef-lieu* of the *département* of Haute-Saône) and at

Arc, an industrial suburb of Gray. Lure has some small anciently established textile-factories. Dole, once a capital of Franche-Comté, on the right bank of the lower Doubs, dominates the crossing of the river, and has a population of about 26,000. It has a useful port on the Rhône-Rhine Canal (which here utilises the channel of the regularised Doubs), and industries have developed—flour-mills, the manufacture of agricultural implements and of electrical heating apparatus, and a large chemical factory using as raw material rock-salt and brine from the Salins area (see p. 616). Other long-established industries include cooperage and wood-working generally in this region of extensive woodlands, and some small specialised metallurgical industries (as at Fraisans between Dole and Besançon and at Xoidans-le-Ferroux) are survivals of forges formerly using alluvial ores and charcoal. Fraisans also has a small glass-works. This industrial activity is on a small scale, and emphasises the essentially rural and agricultural economy of this countryside of small scattered villages and large farms.

Belfort is situated at an altitude of 1,150 feet on the banks of the Savoureuse near the northern edge of the Porte de Bourgogne. It has served as a fortress-town since the thirteenth century, but was tremendously strengthened by Vauban. Its situation in this route-way from the Rhineland into central France is responsible for this strategic importance, and the town is known as the '*ville aux trois sièges*' from the three outstanding sieges it sustained, the last during the winter of 1870–1. Today the city has about 51,000 inhabitants, but it is the capital of its own territory of 235 square miles with a population of just over a hundred thousand; this was left to France in 1872 when Germany annexed the rest of the *département* of Haut-Rhin, and on the return of Alsace it retained its administrative independence. Belfort is one of a group of towns—the others being Montbéliard, Mulhouse and Basel—which form the industrial region of the upper Rhineland. The great *Société Alsacienne* has works there, manufacturing electrical machinery, turbines and locomotives, and other activities include several large textile factories. Its position inevitably makes Belfort an important route-centre; the Calais-Basel and Arlberg-Orient expresses pass through the town, and five *routes-nationales* meet there.

THE NORTH-WESTERN CÔTES

The Saône is bounded to the north-west in succession by the slopes of the Côte d'Or, the Chalonnaise, the Mâconnais and the Beaujolais, known collectively as the *Côte Bourguignonne*. These slopes rise irregularly from 700 to 750 feet in the foothills to summits of over 2,000 feet in the Côte d'Or and to 3,320 feet (the summit of Mont-St. Rigaud) in the Beaujolais. The Côte d'Or [1] consists almost entirely of Jurassic limestone, although the ancient igneous and metamorphic rocks of the Central Massif are in evidence further south. The lower slopes are veneered with down-wash and have been under the vine since pre-Roman times.

If one drives for thirty-five miles along the foot of the Côte d'Or from Dijon through Beaune to Chagny in the Dheune valley, at a distance of some fifteen to twenty miles from the Saône, one can see rows of vines tiered on the hill-sides. From these are produced the superlative Burgundy wines,[2] though not in great quantity; the *département* of Côte-d'Or produced in 1963 only 406,000 hecto-litres of wine out of a French output of 58 millions. A third of the 9,000 acres of vineyards grow in the northern part (known as the *Côte de Nuits*) as far south as the small town of Nuits-St. Georges, and the rest further south along the *Côte de Beaune*. A list of the vineyards and the wines produced reads like a high-class wine-merchant's catalogue; some are indicated on Fig. 96. As D. Faucher expresses it, '*Les subtiles différences de terrains, les impondérables variations d'atmosphère, les procédés et le savoir-faire des hommes depuis des générations, tout s'y traduit en une gamme infinie de qualités*'. Output varies immensely from year to year, both in quantity and quality; another glance at the wine-merchant's catalogue will reveal the 'vintage years'. The names of the famous wines are sometimes derived from a neighbouring town or commune, sometimes merely from a small *château* with a few acres of carefully tended vineyards.

To the south of the Dheune valley vineyards continue along the slopes of the *Côte Chalonnaise*, and again to the south of the Grosne valley along the *Côte Mâconnaise*. Both these districts are in the *département* of Saône-et-Loire, whose vineyards yielded 736,000 hl. in 1963, of which a third was of quality wine. To the south again is Beaujolais, extending as far as the Azergues valley in the *département* of Rhône. These three districts, bordered closely by the Saône at the foot of the scarp, are included within the Burgundy district, although sometimes they are differentiated as Lower Burgundy.

The vine-growing districts of the *côtes* represent a remarkable example of monoculture. The large owners and firms, and the thousands of small growers who sell their produce to the '*caves coopératives*', depend alike on their vineyards, whether they produce the '*bourgogne ordinaire*', the more select '*bourgogne grand ordinaire*',

[1] M. Dubois, 'Les Plateaux méridionaux de la Côte d'Or de Nuits à Chagny', in *A. de G.* (1950), vol. lix, pp. 336-45, provides detailed maps of the faults (p. 338) and erosion surfaces (p. 339) of the Côte d'Or.

[2] G. Chabot, 'La Côte et le vignoble', in *La Bourgogne* (1945), pp. 88-136; and P. Marres, 'Le Vignoble bourguignon', in *La Vigne et le vin en France* (1950), pp. 91-9.

FIG. 96.—THE SAÔNE PLAIN AND THE CÔTE DE VIGNOBLE.

The edge of the *Côte* is shown diagrammatically by a heavy pecked line, while spot-heights in feet on the valley floor and on the ridges indicate the steep rise between them. The right-hand map shows the country immediately to the south of that in the left-hand map. Only a limited number of the important wine-producing communes are named.

Based on (i) *Carte de France au 200,000ᵉ*, sheets 24, 41 ; and (ii) *La France vinicole: Carte publiée sous le haut patronage de l'Institut National des Appellations d'Origine*, in *Atlas de France vinicole L. Larmat*.

or the individually renowned and highly profitable (in a good year) '*vins fins de Bourgogne*'. Many of the villages have indeed sought to introduce other fruit cultivation, black-currants for making *cassis*, raspberries, and orchards of cherry and peach, while on the lower slopes grow fields of wheat, maize, sugar-beet and even hops. The vine, however, remains dominant almost everywhere.

Along the lower slopes of the *côtes*, usually where valleys open out through the hills, are prosperous attractive villages, with what might be called an '*opulence joviale*'. The centre of the wine industry of Côte d'Or is Beaune, an old walled town of 16,000 inhabitants. Chagny is a route-junction where the Dheune valley opens into the Saône plain, with roads, a railway and the Canal du Centre leading south-westward to the industrial region of Le Creusot and Montceau-les-Mines, so into the upper Loire basin. Further south the chief towns are at Saône bridge-points, for the river swings close under the edge of the uplands. At Chalon the Canal du Centre joins the Saône, and it is a road centre through which *N6* runs southward to Lyons. With a population of 46,000 people, Chalon has developed into a prosperous town, with engineering industries, barge-building and the processing of food-products, notably sugar-refining. Further down the river is Tournus, with metallurgical industries (notably using aluminium). Mâcon (27,669 people) is the commercial centre of both the western Plaine de Bresse and the Mâconnais wine-producing region, and also is the *chef-lieu* of Saône-et-Loire; it has a range of light industries, including the manufacture of motor-cycles and motor-scooters. Villefranche, with 25,000 people, is the 'capital' of Beaujolais and the centre of its wine trade. It manufactures presses, tuns and other apparatus for the wine industry, agricultural implements, pharmaceutical chemicals, and (an indication of the influence of Lyons to the south) some silk textiles. Trévoux, once the capital of the principality of Dombes (incorporated in France as late as in 1762), has factories specialising in rich cloth of silver.

The most important town of this region is Dijon, with about 141,000 inhabitants in 1962, the *chef-lieu* of Côte-d'Or and one of the most important route-centres in France. Almost every main railway-line from south and south-east France, Switzerland and Italy converges here on its way to Paris, and moreover the transverse lines linking the Rhine valley and Lorraine with western and south-western France also pass through. Seven main roads, including the Paris–Geneva (*N5*) and the Sarreguemines–Montceau (*N74*) routes, converge on it. Finally, it has a port, a barge-repairing yard and a coal dépôt on the Burgundy Canal.

Dijon has grown rapidly during the last century as a result of its dominating position and the expansion of rail communications, for in 1866 its population was only 39,000. Many of the wine organisa-

XLI Avignon, with the Palais des Papes overlooking the Rhône

XLII Arles

XLIII The port of Marseilles

XLIV The northern part of Marseilles, the approach to the
Rove Tunnel, and the limestone hills in the hinterland

tions have their central administrative offices in the town. Modern factories have been built in the suburbs, leaving the attractive old town within quadrangular boulevards which occupy the site of the former moat and defensive works needed when the city was the fortress-capital of the Dukes of Burgundy. Its industries are diverse, including the processing of foodstuffs, for which its annual *Foire Gastronomique* is a great advertisement—confectionery, biscuits, tobacco and liqueurs (such as *cassis* made from black-currants). Particular mention must be made of its mustard, for which the town is famous. Its metallurgical industries include the production of motor-cycles, pedal-cycles, machine-tools and a wide range of aluminium articles, and other activities comprise the manufacture of cement, lime, chemicals, and boots and shoes.

THE PLAINE DE BRESSE

This part of the Saône valley lies between the Doubs in the north and the Veyle in the south. It is covered with sheets of clay, the impermeable *marnes bleues*, although in the north are also considerable areas of sand, while on the eastern slopes good loamy soils have developed on the *limon* deposits. The Saône flows along the western edge under the foot of the *côtes*, and several long tributaries (Seille, Reyssouze and Veyle, each with a number of confluents) wander leisurely across the plain from the edge of the Jura to the main river. In the north there are many small lakes, some artificially maintained behind barrages and used for carp-breeding. Marshland and *prairies humides* border the flood-plains of the rivers, their courses usually lined with willows. Small groves and copses of trees occur in places, with some oak-forests, particularly in the north.

Bresse presents a varied landscape, devoted to mixed farming, though with an emphasis on livestock. Much permanent pasture is found on the damp heavy soils, as well as fields devoted to fodder-crops including lucerne, fodder-beet and a variety of maize (*le petit maïs d'Auxonne*), grown in rotation. Dairy cattle provide milk for the urban populations and for the cheese-factories in such towns as Bourg-en-Bresse and Louhans. Pigs consume the skimmed milk and also acorns from the oak-woods, and horses and poultry are reared. The last are very important both as a side-line on the dairy or mixed farms and as a main preoccupation on large poultry farms, using modern intensive methods of production and fattening; plump Bresse capons are famous throughout France, and vast numbers are sent to Paris. On the higher terraces away from the rivers areas of vine yield *vin ordinaire*, while wheat is grown on the *limon* soils nearer the Jura edge.

This predominantly rural and agricultural region is somewhat

R.G.W.E.—O

thinly populated. Small though prosperous villages and individual farms stand on the terraces above the flood-plains, while the western part is served by the Saône towns already mentioned, notably Chalon and Mâcon. The regional centre for Bresse is Bourg on the upper Reyssouze, which is well served as a road-focus (eight main roads concentrate on the town) and as a railway junction. Bourg is the *chef-lieu* of Ain, with a population in 1962 of 35,640, and is a very busy market- and despatching-centre for agricultural produce, especially for poultry. The only other place of importance in Bresse is Louhans to the north, also a market-centre.

THE PAYS DE DOMBES

This region is enclosed within the angle of confluence of the lower Saône and the Rhône, and is bordered on the east and north by the Ain and the Veyle respectively. It consists of a gently sloping plateau between 950 and 1,000 feet above sea-level, diversified as a result of an uneven covering of glacial ground-moraine, terminal moraines, and sheets of fluvio-glacial and post-glacial sands and gravels. Hummocky eminences (*poypes*) alternate with the *leschères* or marshy hollows, many of which contain small lakes. In the eighteenth century these covered an aggregate of about 50,000 acres, but today their area has been reduced to about two-fifths as the result of drainage. Most of the *étangs* are sheets of stagnant water with no inlet or outlet, bordered by reedy marshland; some have been surrounded by ring-dykes of clay, with channels (known locally as *by*) to facilitate draining; others are inter-connected by wandering streams converging on the Chalaronne, the main drainage outlet of the *pays* which joins the Saône near Thoissey.

For centuries this was a scantily populated area, liable to flooding and somewhat malarious in summer. Fishing and wild-fowling were the main pursuits, indeed considerable '*territoires de chasse*' were maintained by wealthy citizens of Lyons. Reclamation proceeded slowly around the margins, particularly on the better-drained slopes bordering the rivers—the *Côtière d'Ain* on the east, the *Côtière de Saône* on the west and the *Côtière du Rhône* on the south. Along these edges run the lines of communication. Here have grown up numerous villages, prosperous farms, attractive parks, villas and even *châteaux*, forming a rural residential area for Lyons. Orchards, vineyards and a patchwork of market-gardens, meadows, dairy and poultry farms form a '*ceinture d'or*' around the Dombes.

As indicated by the reduced area of the *étangs*, much reclamation has been effected even in the *plaine dombiste* itself. Lonely sheets of water and dreary wastes of reeds and alder are still found, but much has been improved, and a considerable area has been forested both with deciduous trees and coniferous plantations. Here again many of the *étangs* are utilised systematically by a system of alternate *évolage* and *assec*. For two years they form *étangs pisci-coles*, during which time carp and pike are reared ; the lakes are then netted and drained, the floors cultivated for two or three years, and then reflooded and restocked with fish. This practice has declined of late, for much permanent *assèchement* has been effected to supply land for market-gardens, poultry- and especially duck-farms, and orchards. Further north larger farms possess permanent damp pasture on the heavy clay-soils, and a mixed economy with a pre-dominance of livestock has developed, yielding milk, butter and veal. Pigs are reared in large numbers, and in some parts flocks of sheep are still kept for meat rather than for wool. Arable culti-vation has likewise extended; fodder-crops, potatoes and wheat (which has replaced the former dominance of rye) occupy an apprec-iable area. The major factor in this improvement is of course the constant demand for produce in the Lyons agglomeration.

Population is nevertheless still scanty. Most towns and villages are situated marginally along the *Côtières* near the main rivers—Thoissey, Montmerle, Trévoux and Neuville along the Saône; Bressolles, Montluel and Beynost along the *Côtière du Rhône* ; and Bourg-en-Bresse (a market-town for both southern Bresse and northern Dombes), Pérouges and Meximieux in the east. The con-struction of a railway diagonally across the Dombes from Bourg to Lyons has helped to make St. Paul-de-Varax and Villars (the 'capital' of the *pays*) useful market-towns. Châtillon-sur-Chala-ronne is the centre for the north-western Dombes, by virtue of its road connection with Lyons via St. Trivier-sur-Moignans and the Saône valley. Finally, the influence of the neighbouring Lyons region is again revealed in the development of several silk-thread and textile mills at Meximieux, Miribel and Montluel.

THE LYONS DISTRICT

The Romans built *Lugdunum* on a prominent hillock (the Four-vière, rising to 968 feet) overlooking the right bank of the Saône about two miles above its confluence with the Rhône (Plate XXXIX). This remains the heart of Lyons, for the old town clusters around these hills. The strategic position of the city, more or less halfway along the Saône-Rhône corridor, made it a commercial centre from early times although it inevitably experienced many vicissitudes under the rule of Burgundy, Provence, the Holy Roman Empire and the Bourbons in turn. Much of the city was destroyed during the French Revolution as a reprisal for its support of the royal cause. But in the nineteenth century its prosperity and size increased apace. The town successively expanded on to the hilly interfluve of La Croix-Rousse, which rises some three hundred feet as a peninsula above the rivers, then in the nineteenth century to the east of the Rhône (Fig. 97); this last development has necessitated considerable measures against flooding.[1] Along the east bank of the Rhône developed the residential district of Les Brotteaux and the extensive working-class quarters of La Guillotière and La Mouche, and since 1870 the city has expanded still further east into the industrial suburbs of Montchat and Montplaisir. The commune of Ville-urbanne is now a contiguous industrial town.

Lyons is the third city of France.[2] Its population, which was about 120,000 before the French Revolution, has steadily grown to about 536,000 in 1962. This figure refers only, however, to the *ville* itself; if the eight contiguous communes be included, the total population of this *agglomération urbaine* amounted in 1962 to about 900,000, nearly 100,000 greater than that of the Marseilles agglomeration. The city has a wide range of functions, administrative, commercial and industrial; it is a centre of life and thought, of religion and education, the focus not only of the *région lyonnaise* but of much of south-eastern France. Its nodal position has made it a vital road- and rail-centre, and despite the limitations of the lower Rhône the river port is the ninth in France. The building of the Port Rambaud along the Saône and of the Port Edouard Herriot (or Port du Rhône) to the south of the city has provided a series of quays, with sidings, coal-yards, warehouses and oil-tanks. The freight handled in 1963 totalled 1·63 million tons, of which nearly 1·4 million tons was unloaded.

Lyons is a very important industrial city; its advantages include the long establishment of many of its activities, its position as a centre for obtaining raw materials and for distributing finished goods, supplies of coal from the St. Etienne field to the south-west, a vast skilled and semi-skilled labour supply, and an unlimited supply of electric power from the Rhône, Alpine and Central Massif hydro-stations. About 30,000 workers are engaged in branches of engineering, and in the metallurgical and electrical industries. One special activity is the manufacture of tin-plate and the supply of containers

[1] H. Villien, 'L'Endiguement du Rhône et de la Saône: les quais de Lyon et leur efficacité contre les inondations', in *Etudes rhodaniennes* (1937), vol. 13, pp. 5-21.
[2] A detailed account of the city and region of Lyons, with thirty-eight maps in a separate portfolio, is provided by *Lyon et sa région: analyse et enquêtes pour l'aménagement du territoire*, published by the *Comité pour l'Aménagement et l'Expansion économique de la Région lyonnaise* (1955). See also Ph. Russo and A. Audin, 'Le Site de Lyon', in *Revue de Géographie de Lyon* (1961), vol. 36, pp. 296-346; M. Laferrère, *Lyon: ville industrielle* (1960); and J. Labasse and M. Laferrère, *La Région lyonnaise* (1960), in the series *France de Demain*.

for local canneries. The production of chemicals (pharmaceutical, photographic, explosives, and dyes for the textile trade) is carried on at several factories at Villeurbanne, Montplaisir, St. Fons and Vénissieux. Other activities include the processing of leather and leather-products, the refining of vegetable oils, the manufacture of foodstuffs, glass-ware and paper. About 10 miles south of Lyons, at Feyzin, an oil-refinery, with a through-put of 2 million tons, was opened in 1964. On the Rhône below Lyons the *Pierre Bénite* derivation canal and power-station were completed in 1966.

FIG. 97.—LYONS.
The steep bluffs which bound the valley-floors are indicated by hachuring. The built-up area is shown in generalised form.
The abbreviations are as follows: **L**, *Lugdunum*; **P.R.**, Port Rambaud.
Based on *Carte de France au 50,000ᵉ*, sheets XXX/31, 32, with later information.

About half of the gainfully employed workers of Lyons are occupied in the silk industry or in the manufacture of synthetic textiles. The former was introduced into Lyons in the fifteenth century, when numerous Italian *émigrés* were encouraged to settle, and in 1450 Charles VII gave the city merchants a complete national monopoly. The white mulberry was introduced into the Rhône valley, and silkworms have since then been reared in the neighbourhood and along the valley to the south; sericulture affords a supplementary cash reward to the peasant farmers, the tedious work being done by women and children. Silk-worms are still reared on this cottage basis, but in 1961 home-produced raw silk amounted to a mere 9 tons compared with an import of 840 tons, of which half came from Japan. The manufacture of silk thread and cloth grew up as a domestic industry, though organised by wealthy merchants, and the *canuts* or hand-loom weavers established themselves in blocks of flats and workshops, particularly in La Croix-Rousse. Over a thousand individual silk-making enterprises are still active within the city, and nearly four thousand within the agglomeration and in the neighbouring districts of Bas-Dauphiné, the Monts du Lyonnais, Beaujolais, the margins of the Pays de Dombes, and even in the Jura towns, for Lyons is the administrative and organising centre for a widespread industrial region. Large modern factories are now, however, responsible for an increasing proportion of the output, particularly in Villeurbanne. In 1963 France produced 582 tons of silk thread and 35,000 tons of cloth, of which half was exported, mostly to America; the rest went to the *haute-couture* and the *lingerie* industries, and a large proportion of these finished products was also exported. The Lyons area was responsible for some eighty per cent of this French output.

Rayon, nylon and other synthetic textiles have developed greatly in France, and of twenty major units active in 1961, ten were situated in the *région lyonnaise*; five were in the city itself or the suburbs (the largest at Décines to the east of the city), and others were at Izieux, Péage and La Voulte to the south.

THE MIDDLE RHÔNE VALLEY

The course of the Rhône, flowing alternately through narrow gorges and open basins [1]—Vienne, Valence and Montélimar—is shown on Fig. 98. Smaller areas of lowland along the river with individual names include *Valloire* in the northern angle between the Rhône and the Isère, *Bayane* to the south of their confluence, and *Livron* occupying the embayment of the lower Drôme. These lowlands are covered with sheets of gravel, ancient and recent; indeed, during each early summer flood-period, the Alpine tributaries renew their contributions of rounded pebbles. These deposits, as a result of complex changes in the base-level of the main river, have been eroded into terraces (the *terrasses caillouteuses*) separated by prominent edges, the *Côtes du Rhône*. Streams flowing westwards to the Rhône have dissected the terraces, forming a most uneven margin to the flood-plain. While gravels are predominant, areas of coarse sand

[1] D. Faucher, *Plaines et bassins du Rhône moyen entre Bas-Dauphiné et Provence* (1927).

lie on the higher interfluves, and much fine alluvium is on the present flood-plain. Some of the upper terraces, notably in the plain of Valence, are *limon*-covered,[1] producing good loamy soils often with a high calcareous content due to downwash from the Fore-Alpine foothills. Thus while much of the soil covering the terraces is poor and stony, there are some better-favoured areas; centuries of effort, moreover, have done much to improve the soils for agriculture.

Some of the higher terraces and interfluves are forested with oaks or in places with pines, while the flood-plain is lined with poplars. The middle and lower terraces, the slopes between them, and the floors of the larger basins are intensively cultivated, for the most part on a garden-scale; even the fields of wheat and maize seem to consist of tiny strips. Market-gardens occur especially on the lower terraces near Lyons in the neighbourhood of Vaulx-en-Velin, and in the plain of Valence where irrigation is used, more particularly on the accessible lands lying just above the wet water-meadows. Water cannot easily be applied to the upper terraces, and they are occupied by field-crops such as winter wheat. Local specialisations include the cultivation of melons and strawberries in the plain of Valence. Flowers are grown for the cut-flower trade, large quantities being sent to Paris. Early potatoes are cultivated in the sandy soils, but other roots are not grown on any scale because of the problems of drought. Dairy cattle are reared on the water-meadows.

Orchards extend almost continuously along the terraces from south of Lyons to Montélimar, growing peaches, cherries and apricots which flourish in the stony soils and sunny climate. The most renowned peach-growing district lies along the east bank of the Rhône to the south of Vienne; St. Rambert-d'Albon is said to have the largest peach-market in France and several hundred tons are sent off by rail each season. Some hundreds of acres of dessert-pear orchards flourish along the valley between the Drôme confluence and Montélimar. Groves of mulberries provide leaves for the domestic sericulturists, and these trees line most of the roads.

Vineyards once covered a much greater extent of the Rhône terraces than at the present; the phylloxera attacks in the late sixties of last century, together with the completion of the railway from Lyons, made the development of orchards more profitable. Nevertheless vineyards still extend over much of the Côtes du Rhône[2] along each side of the river, producing both *vin ordinaire* and better qualities known generally as *ordinaires Côtes du Rhône*, though not bottled and sold under the name of any individual vineyard.

[1] Suen Tang-Yuet, *Le Læss de la vallée du Rhône* (1934), provides a detailed map (p. 24) of the distribution of *limon*.
[2] P. Marres, 'Les Côtes du Rhône', in *La Vigne et le vin en France* (1950), pp. 103-11.

FIG. 98.—THE RHÔNE VALLEY BETWEEN GIVORS AND ORANGE.

The right-hand section of the maps lies to the south of the left-hand section, with a slight overlap.

The upland area is indicated generally by stipple, which emphasizes the alternation of gorges and basins.

The derivations are shown by barbed lines, the short underground section of the Canal de Carpentras (used for irrigation) by a pecked line.

The power-stations are indicated by **P**. In the neighbourhood are several newly built *cités-ouvrières*; these are: **E**, Cité de l'Ecluse; **L**, Cité du Lauzon; **P.O.**, Cité Pierre Ollivier; and **U**, Cité de l'Usine.

Based on *Carte de France au 200,000*^e, sheets 53, 59, 66, with recent revisions.

The Rhône vineyards are fortunate in that really poor years for climatic reasons, so common in the marginal wine areas further north, are rare in this sunny climate. A certain amount of high quality wine is obtained from a few special districts. One of the most famous is along the steep right bank of the Rhône near Ampuis, a few miles downstream from Vienne. This is the *Côte Rôtie*, where the vineyards perch on tiny terraces apparently cut in the solid granite, reached by steep rock staircases ; here are produced what are considered to be the best of the Rhône red wines. Immediately south of the *Côte Rôtie* are the vineyards of Condrieu, again steeply overlooking the river ; from them come the finest Rhône white wines. No more quality vineyards are found until the granitic spur of the *Coteau de l'Hermitage* rises above the left bank of the river opposite Tournon. The two well-known villages, Tain-l'Hermitage near the river and Crozes-l'Hermitage on the hill-side further north are the centres of vineyards producing both red and white wines.

A journey from Lyons to Montélimar thus produces an impression of a rural way of life, with a succession of '*jardins d'opulence*', orchards, vineyards and red-roofed villages on the terraces above the flood-plains, with *châteaux* perched on higher spurs ; green in the winter, with magnificent blossom in spring, and a sun-drenched, rather dusty appearance in summer.

Nevertheless, a good deal of industrial activity is evident, partly the result of its ancient establishment in river-side towns, partly the influence of Lyons, partly because of the modern availability of electric power. Small specialised industries, established in the Middle Ages in the towns, contrast with modern large-scale enterprises with their neighbouring *cités-ouvrières*. Large chemical factories are at St. Fons to the south of Lyons and at Péage-de-Roussillon twelve miles south of Vienne ; at the latter is the extensive *Usine de Produits Chimiques Rhône-Poulenc*, making a wide range of pharmaceutical chemicals, situated alongside the main railway and road, and with a well laid-out housing estate. Further south, in the neighbourhood of the Cruas gorge where limestone outcrops border the river, large-scale lime and cement-works have been built on the right bank at Baix, Cruas, Le Teil and Lafarge, and on the opposite side at La Coucourde and L'Homme-d'Armes. In many towns along the river the silk industry functions as part of the Lyons activity. Small factories and domestic workshops produce raw silk, despite a large decline in the late nineteenth century as a result of Far Eastern and Levantine competition, and also the disastrous effects of disease. A certain amount of silk thread and cloth is made in such towns as Vienne and St. Vallier and in many villages.

Towns and villages succeed each other along both banks of the Rhône, carefully sited on knolls or terraces away from the

o 2

river-floods, at strategic points guarding the approaches to the gorge-sections, and where outcrops of hard rock and a narrowing of the main stream have enabled the river to be bridged. Most of these are market- and servicing-centres for the individual basins, linked by railways and roads along either side of the river. After passing through several small towns with industries due to the proximity of Lyons, one comes to Givors, at the exit of the industrialised valley of the Gier (see p. 545). The ease of obtaining coal (formerly by a now disused canal, today by rail) has led to the establishment of coke-ovens, engineering works, and glass-manufacture, particularly of wine-bottles. Vienne, the *Vienna Senatoria* of the Romans (of whom many remains survive), stands on the outer curve of a prominent meander near the confluence of the Gère. It has had a long history as the residence of the rulers of Burgundy and then of the Dauphins. Today it retains little of its former administrative importance, since it is overshadowed by Lyons to the north, but with its population of 28,163 it forms a useful servicing-centre. Vienne has long been an industrial town, famous for leather since the thirteenth century, for sword-steel in the fifteenth and sixteenth, and for woollen and silk cloths; several of these activities are still prosperous. Further south is St. Vallier, also with a variety of industries, including the manufacture of pottery, porcelain and tiles from local kaolin deposits quarried around the flanks of the granitic hills, and of silk cloth.

The twin towns of Tournon and Tain-l'Hermitage, linked by a graceful suspension bridge, have a joint population of over 10,000. Tain is a wine-exporting centre, while Tournon is a town of merchants and craftsmen with a range of interests—tanning, dyeing, the making of furniture, cardboard and straw hats. Valence, also a Roman town, stands in the centre of a broad bay to the south of the Isère junction, at a point where the north-south corridor is joined by the route from Grenoble and further east. With its suburb of Bourg-les-Valence, it now has over 66,000 inhabitants, it is the *chef-lieu* of the *département* of Drôme, and a busy commercial centre for the prosperous agriculture of the surrounding basin. Its industrial activities if small-scale are multifarious, including the manufacture of rayon, silk, cartridges and furniture (particularly from local walnut), and food-processing—flour-milling, the canning of vegetables, and confectionery. Three new canal derivations and power-stations have been completed in this section (Fig. 98): Beauchastel, Baix-Logis-Neuf (*Béthenod*), and Montélimar (*Henri Poincaré*). Montélimar stands at the convergence of the Roubion and Jabron before they enter the Rhône. This attractive fortified town is a regional market for agricultural products, and has a variety of small industries, mostly food-processing (including the manufacture of the well-known nougat). Finally Viviers, the ancient capital of Vivarais, clusters

round its Gothic cathedral on a prominent eminence guarding the
northern entrance of the Donzère gorge.

THE HILL-COUNTRY OF BAS-DAUPHINÉ [1]

This undulating hill-country, situated in the angle between the
Rhône and the Isère, rises to form the Plateau des Terres-Froides in
the north and the Plateau de Chambaran in the south, where it
culminates in summits at about 2,400 feet. The superficial deposits
are extraordinarily diverse, but clays tend to predominate. These
sediments are trenched across by valleys—the Bourbre in the north,
the Valèze, the Gère, the Dolon, the Galaure and in the south the
Isère itself. Many streams flow from shallow lakes lying on the
uneven clays, particularly in the Terres-Froides, or from marshy
peat-filled hollows; some have been drained but many remain,
including the long narrow Lac de Paladru in the east of the Terres-
Froides near Voiron. The valley of the Bourbre, crossing the northern
part of the Terres-Froides, was formerly a vast marsh. A main
drainage canal was constructed between 1809 and 1814, which with
the help of some 120 miles of minor canals converted this valley-
floor in the neighbourhood of Morestel into fertile land, most of
which is now under pasture; about 12,000 acres were thus reclaimed.

The valley-trenches divide up the hill-country into a chaos of
gently swelling eminences (*mamelons*) and more pronounced ridges,
whose slopes descend by terrace-steps to the flood-plains. Along
the lower Isère valley, for example, terraces can be distinguished at
about 1,250 feet, at 850 feet, at 750 feet and at 650 feet.

This diversity of relief, drainage and soils has resulted in a varied
land-use pattern. In the Middle Ages Bas-Dauphiné was extensively
wooded, but long-continued depredations for fuel, charcoal and
building, and to obtain oak-bark for tanning, cut deeply into the
ancient forests, while the naval wars of the eighteenth century
removed many fine oaks for shipbuilding. Grazing by flocks then
prevented natural rehabilitation. As a result, by the mid-nineteenth
century much of this woodland cover had been removed; there
was, for example, virtually no trace of the large mediaeval Forêt de
Mantaille. Some areas now form scrubby heath, providing little
more than poor grazing, and a tract to the north of the Galaure
valley near Grand-Serre has been occupied for many years by a
large military training-camp. During this century much of Bas-
Dauphiné has been forested with both deciduous and coniferous trees,
some converted into improved pasture, and some put under arable.

The naturally poor soils have been improved in places by drainage,

[1] Y. Bravard, *Le Bas-Dauphiné: recherches sur la morphologie d'un piémont
alpin* (1963), 504 pp.

liming and chemical fertilisers. The districts which have benefited most are the margins of the hill-country in the west along the Rhône valley, and along the sides of the trenches of its tributaries. The better soils, such as those developed on *limon* or on the sandy clays which veneer the terraces, are under arable, growing wheat, sugar-beet, potatoes, and fodder-crops (such as lucerne) with the help of irrigation. Specialisations include tobacco, hemp and flax in the Valloire (the broad valley between the Terres-Froides and the Chambaran), and asparagus, gherkins and other market-garden produce in the north-west where '*les Balmes viennoises*' border on the Lyons region. Vineyards, orchards (particularly of peaches and cherries), mulberries and nut-groves are carefully tended on the gravel-covered lower terraces. Walnuts are a speciality and thousands of trees grow in the neighbourhood of St. Marcellin and St. Quentin; nut-picking affords a profitable seasonal industry. Along the damp pastures and irrigated meadows of the valley-floors and in the higher depressions cattle, horses and pigs are reared.

The small towns of Bas-Dauphiné have for centuries fostered local craft industries. The growth of Lyons as a regional centre, the development of communications such as the Lyons-Grenoble railway line which crosses Bas-Dauphiné diagonally through Bour-goin, La Tour-du-Pin, Voiron and other small towns, and the wide-spread transmission of electric power, have served to bring Bas-Dauphiné within the industrial '*grande banlieue*' of Lyons. Old industries have survived in a modernised form, new ones have been introduced. The manufacture of silk is carried on at some hundreds of establishments, many producing raw silk, silk thread or cloth for working-up in Lyons, others specialising in various finished materials such as satin, cloth of gold or silver and embroidered velours; Bourgoin, Moirans, La Tour-du-Pin, Tullins, Morestel, Pont-de-Beauvoisin and Romans-sur-Isère each has a range of these activities. Linen is manufactured at Voiron and St. Jean-de-Bournay from locally grown flax, and hemp is made into cordage, ropes and netting at Voiron. The long-established but small-scale metallurg-ical industry, based on alluvial ores and charcoal, survives as the manufacture of files and rasps at St. Laurent-du-Pont and of edged tools at La Fure, while electrical machinery is made at Pont-de-Chéruy to the east of Lyons. Fine papers are produced at Renage, Apprieu-Fures and Rives, with the original advantage of a plentiful supply of pure water; the last of these makes bank-note paper for the *Banque de France*. Tanneries and leather-factories have been established in Bas-Dauphiné since Roman times, using local hides and oak-bark for tanning; boots and shoes are made in Romans-sur-Isère and at Bourg-de-Péage on the opposite side of the river. Glass is made at Grand-Serre and pottery at St. Uze.

The population is thus scattered over Bas-Dauphiné in small towns and villages of one to two thousand inhabitants, with a few larger places, notably Bourgoin with 10,000 people. Their activities are based on a variety of both agricultural and industrial pursuits. That no prominent regional centre has grown within Bas-Dauphiné is because of the powerful influence of Lyons at the north-western corner.

THE LOWER RHÔNE VALLEY

The Rhône between Donzère and the apex of the delta at Arles flows in turn through the plains of Pierrelatte, Orange and Avignon, each separated by a prominent defile. To the west rises the upland country of the limestone *garrigues*, forming the foothills of the Cévennes. To the east the marshy alluvial plain of the Rhône widens to form the *Plaines Vauclusiennes*, into which spurs project from the Lower Cretaceous Fore-Alpine plateaus.

Across the plain of Pierrelatte the Donzère-Mondragon derivation canal has been completed by the *Compagnie Nationale du Rhône* since the war of 1939–45.[1] A barrage was constructed at the southern end of the steep-walled Donzère narrows, with six sluices to control the water-level of the Rhône. A derivation canal, eighteen miles in length, takes off through a locked connection above this barrage, and follows the eastern edge of the Pierrelatte plain to rejoin the Rhône where it swings eastwards again to the south of Mondragon (Plate XL). Eleven miles along the canal at Bollène, where a mass of rock beneath the alluvial cover afforded a solid foundation, the *André-Blondel* power-station (the second biggest hydro-station in France) was built. There is a fall at this point of eighty-five feet, and a navigation lock with the world's highest ship-lift was constructed. The derivation canal is wider in fact than Suez, and it has obviated the braided rapids and steep gradient of the Rhône through the western margin of the Pierrelatte plain. Several housing estates have been built for workers at the power-station and neighbouring factories (including a plutonium plant), shown on Fig. 98.

Below Mondragon the valley-floor of the Rhône is marshy and the river braids to form backwaters and elongated reed-covered islands; one of the largest lies just above Avignon, the Ile de la Barthelasse. The flood-plain is seamed with drainage channels, which have

[1] See (i) G. Kish, 'Hydroelectric Power in France: Plans and Projects', in *G.R.* (1955), vol. 45, pp. 84-7; (ii) R. Dugrand, 'L'Aménagement du Bas-Rhône', in *A. de G.* (1953), vol. lxii, pp. 368-73, which provides details and a map of the Donzère achievement; (iii) J.-B. Suchel, 'L'Hydraulique agricole dans le couloir rhodanien entre Vienne et Bollène, projets et réalisations', in *Revue de Géographie de Lyon* (1957), vol. 32, pp. 201-26.

improved the state of the higher terraces, but along the river itself there are still marshes liable to inundation, known locally as *paluds*.

The edge of the flood-plain is indicated approximately by the 350-foot contour, beyond which rise distinct erosion surfaces at about 500, 650 and 900 feet, worn in the Tertiary sediments. These are much dissected by gravel-floored valleys of the various rivers flowing down from the higher Fore-Alpine plateaus. The upper terraces are dry and rather bare, covered in places with scrubby woods of oak and box, and like the southern Fore-Alps they have suffered deforestation for firewood, charcoal and tanning bark, though some deliberate planting of pines has been carried out in recent years. Limestone spurs and knolls rise from the Tertiary alluvium—the Dôme de Donzère, the Massif d'Uchaux to the north of Orange, the Colline de la Montagnette to the south-west of Avignon, and the long rugged Chaîne des Alpilles rising to over 1,600 feet and projecting within two miles of the Rhône near Tarascon. These limestone outcrops afford valuable sites for settlement clear of the flood-plain ; the nucleus of Avignon (the cathedral and the Palais des Papes within the fortifications), is built on the Rocher des Doms overlooking the divided channels of the Rhône which enclose the Ile de la Barthelasse (Plate XLI).

Despite the disadvantages of too much water on the low-lying parts of the plain and too little on the higher areas, together with the poor stony soils, the lower Rhône valley has been an agricultural region for centuries. The basis of life was cultivation of the Mediterranean triad—wheat, vines and olives, the first of these as a winter crop using long periods of fallow. From the fifteenth century the breeding of silk-worms led to the planting of some millions of mulberry trees. Tobacco was later introduced and grown profitably until the eighteenth century. Madder-root was another valuable cash-crop introduced in the eighteenth century ; this flourished until its cultivation was killed by the discovery in 1869 of a method of extracting substitutes from coal-tar. Almost simultaneously the phylloxera scourge made its appearance. These agricultural disasters, succeeding one another, brought the region to near poverty.

Since the latter part of the nineteenth century a diverse agricultural economy has developed, capitalising the long hours of sunshine, and helped by efficient rail communications with distant markets and by the development of irrigation. The last is no recent introduction, however ; there are records of canals constructed as early as the eleventh century. In the seventeenth and eighteenth centuries several new distributaries were built, including the northern branch of the Canal des Alpilles from the river Durance to Orgon, completed in 1783 and extended to Châteaurenard in 1849. After the unfortunate vicissitudes of the '60s and '70s, the irrigation system was extended. The Canal de Carpentras was constructed from Mérindol on the Durance along the 100-metre contour northward to the Eygues at Travaillan. It picks up water from many rivers and springs, including the Fontaine de Vaucluse (which has given its name to the *Vauclusian* type of resurgence), and with many miles of distributaries running westward into the plains it serves the districts around Carpentras and Cavaillon. To the south of the Durance the Canal de Craponne has been constructed, with branches running west to Arles and south to the Etang de Berre. The Canal des Alpilles and its branches now supply the Tarascon and Château-renard districts, and the Canal de Vaucluse and the Canal de l'Isle provide for the Avignon area. The total area irrigated, both by gravity from these feeder-canals and by artesian and sub-artesian wells, is 130 square miles (Fig. 100).

Much of the cultivation of these plains is in the form of market-gardens; tiny plots of land are exploited assiduously by hand, protected by shelters (see p. 376) from the biting blast of the *mistral*, an enemy second only to drought. The most important market-garden-ing area is a triangle enclosed by Avignon, St. Rémy and Cavaillon[1] (Fig. 100), including the collecting centre of Châteaurenard. The constant succession of produce includes cauliflowers and lettuce during the winter, new potatoes as early as March, artichokes from March to June, early peas, spinach, onions and carrots throughout the spring and early summer. Tomatoes occupy a considerable area. In some districts specialisation is practised; thus Cavaillon is renowned for melons and Carpentras for strawberries, and flowers are grown for seed in the neighbourhood of St. Rémy on the northern flanks of the Alpilles. But more usually the *patron-propriétaire*, the *cultivateur jardinier*, grows a variety of items to spread his risks and to provide some continuity of output. His holding, small though it may be in aggregate, is normally divided into a number of scattered 'parcels'.

Not all the crops of the lower Rhône are irrigated. In Vaucluse the lavender grows in long rows on the dry gravel surface. Olive-groves straggle up the limestone slopes, almond, peach, apricot, cherry and quince orchards on the terraces, and walnuts and chestnuts along the sides of fields. The most extensive orchards are on the slopes to the east and south of Carpentras and along the southern flanks of the Durance valley between Châteaurenard and Cavaillon.

Although phylloxera dealt a damaging blow in 1865, vineyards have been re-established with near-immune American grafts. Their extent is only about 7 per cent of what it was (the actual area in 1963 in Vaucluse was 89,000 acres), yet the *département* produced over 1·5 million hectolitres of wine in 1963. Most of this was *vin*

[1] R. Pélissier, 'La Production maraîchère et fruitière et le marché de Cavaillon', in *Méditerranée* (1964), vol. 5, pp. 279-97.

ordinaire, but a group of vineyards on the hill-slopes overlooking Châteauneuf-du-Pape, near the left bank of the Rhône above Avignon, yield a quality wine. More than two hundred individual firms produce wines, red, white and *rosé*, which are entitled to the *appellation* of *Châteauneuf-du-Pape*. Eight miles to the north-west of Avignon the vineyards of Tavel produce a wine usually regarded as the best of the French *rosés*. It is a reflection on the decline of these Vauclusian vineyards that the little town of Roquemaure was once a busy port, shipping wine in bulk to many European countries. Table-grapes are also cultivated, particularly the high quality *chasselas dorées* and *clairettes*; hundreds of tons are sold at the markets of Cavaillon, Châteaurenard and Tarascon and despatched, carefully packaged, to Lyons, Paris and indeed to Britain.

Villages and small towns are widely dispersed among these areas of cultivation. One line of towns extends along each bank of the Rhône at suitable points for bridging, defence and flood-protection ; such are Bourg-St. Andéol, Pont-St. Esprit, Roquemaure, Avignon itself, and the towns of Beaucaire and Tarascon linked by a long suspension bridge. Others are situated within the plain on the lower slopes of hills above flood-level, such as Mondragon, Orange, Bédarrides, Châteaurenard and St. Rémy. A third string of settlements stands at the foot of the uplands on the eastern edge of the plain, including Carpentras and Cavaillon. Most of these are market-towns from which agricultural produce is shipped by road and rail, and many preserve rich legacies of their historic past.

The only town of any size is Avignon, the *chef-lieu* of Vaucluse, with over 75,000 people in 1962 ;[1] its site has already been mentioned. Today Avignon is the regional and commercial centre for the lower Rhône valley, its silk industry has been revived and a large rayon factory built, several factories manufacture packaging for market-garden produce, there are canneries for fruit and vegetables, and cement works. The first French nuclear plant was opened in 1953 at Marcoule near Avignon, mainly used for the production of plutonium.

[1] E. Delaruelle, 'Avignon capitale', in *R.G.P.S.-O.* (1952), vol. xxiii, pp. 233-64.

CHAPTER 15

THE MEDITERRANEAN COASTLANDS:
(1) PROVENCE

The coastline of southern France between the Spanish and Italian frontiers is bordered by a region often known simply as the *Midi*. From the point of view of structure and relief it exhibits great diversity. There are coasts bordered with lagoons and sand-dunes, others with lofty cliffs and deeply cut bays from which the land rises steeply inland. A great expanse of sand and mud forms the ever-growing delta of the Rhône, while by contrast ancient crystalline massifs abut on to the coast in the east. Widespread outcrops of limestone, mostly of Mesozoic or early Tertiary age, form blunt headlands, prominent ridges and deeply dissected plateaus. Huge sheets of gravel vary in age from the Pliocene to those brought down by the floods of last autumn. The region has had a complex geomorphological history. Much of the western and central Midi suffered marine transgression in early Pliocene times, forming gulfs in which sedimentation took place. Considerable oscillations of level have since taken place, and periods of high sea level in which deposition was active have alternated with low sea-level stages when the rivers cut down into these sediments, forming a series of terraces.

Upon this area of physiographical diversity the climate has imposed a unifying stamp reflected in both the landscape and the way of life.[1] The summer drought, emphasised by the widespread occurrence of limestone and of highly permeable gravels, has resulted in a vegetation cover with xerophytic characters. Holm-oak and cork-oak forests once covered large areas, but the region has been occupied by man since early times, and the gradual inevitable clearance of these forests exposed the terrain to the rains of autumn and the heat of summer; much soil was removed by erosion, and in places vegetation deteriorated into scrubby aromatic *garrigue*. For millennia the economy was based on the typical Mediterranean crops—wheat, vine and olive, utilising both the terraces of better soil and the alluvial plains where irrigation water was available. Early settlements grew into cities, for the accessible coastlands have attracted seafarers since the days of the Phoenicians. For over six centuries the Romans impressed their cultural mark, as many

[1] J. Sion, *La France méditerranéenne* (1934); and P. Carrère and R. Dugrand, *La Région méditerranéenne* (1960), in the series *France de Demain*.

of the cities testify. Although interrupted by the vicissitudes of more than a millennium of troubled history, an important agricultural, industrial, commercial and urban life has developed. In modern times the advent of the railway has encouraged a profitable agricultural economy, capitalising the sunshine, the mild winter temperatures and the early springs, and the same factors have allowed the development of a highly organised tourist industry in the eastern coastlands.

But even with these unifying features, there are some remarkable land-use contrasts.[1] The *garrigues* and the dusty gravels, offering sustenance only to goats, contrast with the luxuriance of intense cultivation in the vineyards, orchards and market-gardens, and with the groves of holm- or cork-oak. The lonely, now virtually landlocked, ports of mediaeval times contrast with the activity of Marseilles. The ancient Provençal cities contrast with the new *cités-ouvrières* near the huge oil-refineries and modern factories around the Etang de Berre. The desolate salt-marshes, *étangs* and dunes of the western and central coastlands contrast with the *plages*, promenades, villas and hotels of the fashionably thronged Côte d'Azur in the east. Yet all these form ingredients in the cultural landscape of '*le Midi méditerranéen*'.

Regional Divisions.—Two main divisions may be made to assist regional description (Fig. 99), divisions recognised by many centuries of some degree of provincial autonomy (see p. 1). In the east lies Provence, in the west Languedoc (Chapter 16).

In its broadest sense, Provence includes the land to the north of the Mediterranean between the Rhône on the west and the crestline of the High Alps in the east. Its northern margin is more difficult of definition; politically it is demarcated by the northern boundary of Vaucluse and Basses-Alpes, yet geographically there is no clear-cut limit, rather a zone of transition as the characteristics of the Mediterranean climate gradually change to those of a more continental régime. The basins of the middle Durance, the Verdon and the upper Var, together with the uplands of the limestone Fore-Alps and the ranges of the Maritime Alps, are often referred to as *Haute-Provence*. Though undeniably the Mediterranean climate exerts an influence upon this landscape, from a geomorphological point of view it is more convenient to include these parts of Haute-Provence in the French Alps (see p. 629 and Fig. 132).

Even the more limited *Basse-Provence* represents an area of extraordinarily varied structure and relief. In the west is the delta of

---

[1] A useful summary, with examples, is given by A. Perpillou, 'Types d'évolution de quelques paysages agricoles méditerranéens', in *Mélanges géographiques offerts à Ernest Bénévent* (1954), pp. 289-309. See also R. Livet, 'Les Elevages provençaux', in *Méditerranée* (1965), vol. 6, pp. 185-200.

the Rhône. Then to the east of the Etang de Berre appears a succession of ridges and plateaus of Mesozoic rocks, separated by Tertiary basins and deep river valleys floored with recent deposits; this is known generally as '*la Basse-Provence calcaire*'. Two crystalline Hercynian massifs comprise '*la Basse-Provence cristalline*', Maures between the Aille valley and the sea, and Esterel to the north-east

FIG. 99.—THE REGIONS OF THE MEDITERRANEAN COAST AND THE LOWER RHÔNE VALLEY.

The other major regions shown—the French Alps, the Central Massif, and the Basin of Aquitaine with the Pyrenees—are not sub-divided (see Figs. 132, 122 and 86 respectively).

Abbreviations used are as follows: **Av.**, Avignon; **B.**, Béziers; **C.**, Carcassonne; **D.**, Draguignan; **Est.**, Massif of Esterel; **Mo.**, Montpellier; **Na.**, Narbonne; **Nî.**, Nîmes; **Rouss.**, Roussillon.

of the Argens valley. Finally, in the extreme east, where the limestone Alps closely approach the sea, lies a narrow coastal margin known as the *Côte d'Azur*.

THE RHÔNE DELTA

The delta of the Rhône (Fig. 100) begins three miles above Arles, where the river, flowing between massive embankments, is about 170 yards in width. Here it divides to form its two chief distributaries, the Grand Rhône which flows in a south-easterly direction to the Golfe de Fos, and the Petit Rhône which wanders in circuitous meanders more to the south-west. The two mouths, twenty-five miles apart, have changed considerably in position, and the main exit has been displaced successively to the east.[1] The Petit Rhône once reached the sea much further to the west at Aigues-Mortes, a mediaeval port now only linked to the open sea at Le Grau-du-Roi by a canal four miles in length. Later the Petit Rhône entered the Golfe du Lion through a mouth further to the east, a course now followed by the Canal de Peccais. Similarly the Grand Rhône's mouth has moved successively eastward; one of its old channels, the Vieux Rhône, can be traced some miles to the west of the present one. Water reached the sea through at least six separate distributaries as late as the mid-nineteenth century. Various engineering works, notably the construction of training-walls, have helped to divert more than four-fifths of the Rhône's outfall through a single main channel, thus concentrating the deposition of much of the river's vast burden of sediment, with the result that the extreme south-eastern corner of the delta is growing outwards at an average annual rate of about forty-five yards. The present delta is known as *La Camargue*. To the east of the Grand Rhône and in the angle of the limestone hills of lower Provence extends an immense triangular plain of gravel, the Pliocene 'dry-delta' of the Durance, *La Crau*.

The Camargue.—The seaward face of the delta, nearly fifty miles in length, consists of a series of bays (the Golfes d'Aigues-Mortes, de Beauduc and de Fos), each bordered by a sweeping curve of sand-spits backed by low dunes (known as *montilles*). The westerly direction of longshore drift has developed two rounded sandy 'points', the Pointes de l'Espiguette in the west and du Sablon in the east. Behind the line of dunes lies a vast expanse of marshes (*enganes*) and shallow brackish *étangs*, connected with the open sea through shallow channels or *graus*, a term derived from the Latin *gradus* (a passage); the mouth of the Grand Rhône is known as the Grau de Pégoulier, that of the Petit Rhône as the Grau d'Orgon.

The central and southern part of the Camargue consists of marshes (*marais pré salé*), covered with sedge-reeds and stretches of *Salicornia* and *Phragmites*, and interlaced by winding channels and irregular shallow *étangs*. The largest of these, the Etang de Vaccarès, extends to sixty square miles, but is nowhere more than a yard in depth; it connects with a maze of more than twenty other named *étangs* to the

[1] An immensely detailed and well-documented piece of work is R. J. Russell, 'Geomorphology of the Rhône Delta', in *Annals of the Association of American Geographers* (1942), vol. xxxii, pp. 149-254. The author includes a bibliography of 129 references. Much of the article deals with progressive changes in the main Rhône exits, using both geomorphological and historical evidence, including some fascinating old maps.

south. Occasional clumps of tamarisk and cypress stand above the general level on long low banks of alluvium which represent silted-up and abandoned distributaries; these raised their beds above the surrounding marsh by accretion, then breached their banks at a time of flood and so occupied new channels. The dreary marshes are the haunt of bird-life and in fact a nature reserve of about 37,000 acres has been created in the Ile du Plan du Bourg in the south-east, where wild duck, herons and storks congregate and even flamingo come seasonally.

This southern part of the delta is thinly populated, although here

FIG. 100.—THE RHÔNE DELTA.

The areas of *étang* and marsh are generalised, and the vast complicated pattern of drainage channels is necessarily omitted. The stipple indicates the higher areas, approximately over 200 feet.

The abbreviations are as follows : **A-M.,** Aigues-Mortes ; **G.R.,** Le Grau-du-Roi ; **P.,** Port-St. Louis-du-Rhône ; **le S.,** Le Salins-de-Giraud.

Based on *Carte de France au 200,000ᵉ*, sheets 66, 67, 73, 74.

and there on slight eminences stand villages, whose people fish in the open sea and in the lagoons; the *étangs* are netted, and large quantities of fish are dried in the sun. The only other activity is the exploitation of salt by solar evaporation in the salt-pans or *salins*. This is done near Aigues-Mortes, at Badon to the south-east of the Etang de Vaccarès, and at Le Salins-de-Giraud; between 80,000 and 100,000 tons of common salt are produced annually from Bouches-du-Rhône, and the gleaming white pyramids in late summer stand out above the marshes. Ancillary chemical industries, including the production of magnesium and potassium chloride and of carbonate of soda, have been established at Badon, and also at Le Salins-de-Giraud where *Solvay* have a large factory. Near to these towns stand regular rows of houses in which live the *saliniers*.

For many centuries schemes of reclamation have slowly pushed into the Camargue. Progress has, however, been slow, for the disadvantages are great. Flooding has always been a menace, both from the sea breaking through the *cordon littoral* of dunes and from the rivers. The latter are especially dangerous, because their beds, built up by sedimentation, stand several feet above the surrounding land, and the Rhône with its irregular régime is liable to sudden rises of level. Numerous drainage channels (known as *drailles* and as *égouts*) intersect the land. The soil of newly reclaimed areas is impregnated with salt, difficult to remove and to maintain clear since saline solutions constantly rise to the surface by capillarity during the summers, and irrigation also tends to increase the salt-content. Other drawbacks are the scarcity of drinking-water since wells are mostly brackish, the breeding of malarial mosquitoes on the stagnant marshes, and the difficulty of access through inadequate communications.

In the mid-nineteenth century, following a disastrous decade of flooding between 1840 and 1850, ambitious plans were discussed for integrated schemes of reclamation with State financial assistance. These envisaged the construction of a number of coastal and riverine dykes, and a systematic network of canals leading to a reduced Etang de Vaccarès, which would function as an intermediate drainage-reservoir, with pumping-stations to maintain a determined water-level. Some opposition was inevitably met from fishermen, wild-fowlers and *saliniers* who feared for their livelihoods. Certain parts of this programme were, however, slowly carried out, notably the development of drainage canals in the north leading to the Etang de Vaccarès, but disputes of various kinds among interested parties and then the war of 1914–18 prevented the full implementation of the scheme.

For many centuries, the northern Camargue offered only poor pasture (known as *pâtis*) for cattle and sheep, notably for the black

Camarguais bulls bred for the Provençal rings and herded by *gardians* on horseback. Cultivation progressively spread along low ridges on which farms and then settlement clusters were gradually established, while the intervening hollows were drained to furnish rather rank pastures known as *sansouriers*.

During the last half century, the area of reclaimed land has appreciably increased. As a result, the northern Camargue, with its arable fields, vineyards, improved pastures and market-gardens, contrasts markedly with the reed-covered swamps and meres of the south. The pastures are used both for Camarguais cattle and for the more recently introduced Andalusian breed, and merino sheep have also been imported. Wheat and fodder crops are grown, and over 73,000 acres are now under rice, cultivated by modern methods;[1] it is interesting to see large combine-harvesters at work in the rice-fields. Yields of cereals are not high, admittedly; the amount of wheat produced in 1963 averaged nineteen quintals per hectare compared with thirty-seven in Nord and thirty in Aisne. Vineyards now cover about 74,000 acres, yielding large quantities of *vin ordinaire*.

Communications have gradually been improved, and so helped the progress of settlement. A single-track railway was constructed between Arles and Port-St. Louis-du-Rhône along the left bank of the Grand Rhône, and another skirts the northern edge of the western Camargue and then runs south through St. Laurent-d'Aigouze to Aigues-Mortes and Le Grau-du-Roi. Light railways link Arles with Les Stes. Maries in the south-west and with Le Salins-de-Giraud in the south-east. Roads constructed along the low ridges link up the small settlements and the individual farms, each standing within its shelter-belt of trees.

Several canals have been constructed in the delta-region. The Arles-Bouc Canal follows the left bank of the Rhône, then cuts across to Bouc on the coast near the entrance to the long channel of the Etang de Caronte; it is, however, only six feet in depth, and carries a mere 100,000 tons of freight annually. Its future is tied up with the development of the Marseilles-Rhône Canal (see p. 416) and of Rhône navigation generally. The Rhône-Sète Canal, completed in 1934, runs from Beaucaire on the Rhône south-westward to Aigues-Mortes, and then is enclosed in a dyked channel through the coastal *étangs* to the harbour of Sète. It carries only about

[1] Two interesting accounts of rice-growing in the delta of the Camargue are (i) J. Girod, 'La Culture du riz en Camargue', in *Bulletin de la Société de Géographie et d'Etudes coloniales de Marseille* (1948–50), vol. 64, pp. 55-60; and (ii) V. Prévot, 'La Culture du riz de Camargue', in *Informations géographiques* (1953), vol. 17, no. 1, pp. 13-20. In 1963 about 130,000 tons of rice were produced in Bouches-du-Rhône and the margins of the neighbouring *départements*.

300,000 tons of freight, two-thirds of which consist of petroleum and oil.

Some attractive little towns stand in the Rhône delta, but their former importance as ports has disappeared, and they survive in a peaceful yet romantic decay. Three, Aigues-Mortes, Les Stes. Maries-de-la-Mer and Port-St. Louis-du-Rhône, are situated near the mouths of past or present distributaries, while the largest, Arles, is near the apex of the delta. Aigues-Mortes, surrounded by thirteenth-century rectangular ramparts, is reached by both road and rail on causeways across the marsh. This was the port at which Crusading armies once embarked, but today, although at the junction of the Canal Maritime (leading to Le Grau-du-Roi) and the Rhône-Sète Canal, and furnished with wharves and railway sidings outside the walls, its commercial importance is negligible. There are neighbouring salt-works, and like most of these little towns it receives a considerable tourist traffic. Les Stes. Maries-de-la-Mer stands just east of the mouth of the Petit Rhône. It is reputedly the site of the landing from the Holy Land of the two Marys and their servant Sarah, whose bodies lie in the massive thirteenth-century church; to the town each May come large numbers of gypsies, for Sarah is their patron-saint. Port-St. Louis, the only harbour today actually within the Rhône delta, is linked with the Golfe de Fos by the St. Louis ship-canal, built in 1871 to by-pass the bar which obstructs the mouth of the Grand Rhône. The port is overshadowed by Marseilles, but as it has rail connection with Arles it acts in some measure as its outport, importing oil, timber, phosphates and other fertilisers, Algerian wine and wheat, and exporting some cement.

Arles itself, with a population of about 42,000, is situated on the left bank of the Grand Rhône at its lowest bridging point (Plate XLII). The town was founded on a small mass of limestone projecting above the surrounding marshlands, and it became a Roman centre, of which ample evidence survives in its magnificent amphitheatre (said to have held over 20,000 spectators) and theatre. Today it is a market-focus for both Crau and Camargue, a packing and despatching-point for the rail-shipment of their agricultural produce, and a very attractive venue for tourists.

The Crau.—The ' dry-delta ' of the Crau is composed of a pair of alluvial fans covering a gentle infilled syncline of Miocene *molasse*, which appears on the surface in the east along the margins of the Etang de Berre, rising to over 400 feet as a chain of rugged hillocks. One alluvial fan was laid down in the west by the Pleistocene Rhône, and slopes southward from about thirty feet to near sea-level. The second, larger fan was the work of the Pleistocene Durance, which at that time pursued a course much further to the south-west through a prominent gap known as the Cluse de Lamanon between the Alpilles and the Provençal uplands. This fan has its apex at a height of about 230 feet and slopes very gently south-westward towards the Grand Rhône. The Durance later abandoned this course and now flows to the Rhône below Avignon. Its varied régime is shown by the fact that its mean discharge is 12,260 cubic feet per second, as compared with a recorded minimum of 1,906 and a maximum of 326,000 cubic feet per second.[1]

The Crau consists therefore of extensive sheets of water-worn stones of all sizes,[2] from small pebbles to masses of limestone and sandstone six to nine inches and occasionally a foot in diameter, a veritable *désert de pierres*. Much of this gravel surface is loose, but in other parts it is cemented into a hard though much fissured conglomerate. It is for the most part dry because of its extreme permeability, but by contrast in some places an underlying pan has allowed the formation of saline marshes (such as the Marais des Chanoines in the west) and even a few saline lakes (the Etangs d'Entressen and de Dézeaumes). The soil cover is thin, consisting merely of a dusty layer formed by the decomposition *in situ* of lime-stone and sandstone pebbles, and of patches of coarse sandy material.

This not very attractive environment is further handicapped by the climatic régime. Scorched by the sun in summer to a bleached dusty aridity and swept by the blasts of the *mistral* in winter, as the few wind-bent trees testify, the effectiveness of its scanty winter rains is still further reduced by rapid evaporation and percolation. Much is covered by a *garrigue*-like vegetation of scrubby plants—cistus, rosemary, thyme, juniper, coarse clumps of grass, occasional patches of dwarf evergreen oak and thorny bushes. In summer the vegetation is dry and silvery-grey, but in response to autumn and winter rains an intermittent covering of coarse grass spreads between the stones, with a rather attractive though short-lived profusion of such flowering plants as asphodel.

For centuries the only importance of the Crau was to provide winter grazing for flocks of sheep which spent their summers on the Alpine pastures, moving slowly up and down through Provence on regular stock-routes. Sheep are still important, indeed the total of 297,000 in the *département* of Bouches-du-Rhône in 1963 was fifth to Aveyron, Basses-Alpes, Haute-Vienne and Hautes-Pyrénées. The breeds have been improved by crossing the Crau animals with merinos; transhumance is still carried out, but by rail transport; and the '*prairies artificielles*' have been extended both by irrigation

---

[1] R. J. Russell, *op. cit.*, p. 159.
[2] H. Baulig, 'La Crau et la glaciation würmienne', in *A. de G.* (1927), vol. xxxvi, pp. 499-508, provides a detailed account of the deposition of the gravels.

and the sowing of drought-resistant varieties of grass. Lucerne and sainfoin are grown with the help of irrigation. The sheep arrive in the Crau towards the end of November and graze on the natural pastures until mid-February, after which they spend a month or so on the cultivated meadows before returning to the foothills, the first stage of their summer journey to the alpine pastures. The flocks are carefully maintained and organised; a proportion of the lambs born in December is sold off at the Arles sales in spring.

Cultivation has gradually pushed its way into the margins of the Crau since the sixteenth century, when the first irrigation canals were constructed. Since that time the system has been extended (Fig. 100); branches of the Canal de Craponne lead westward to Arles and southward towards the Etang de Berre, the Canal de Langlade runs south-westward almost to the Grand Rhône, and the Canal d'Istres and the Canal des Martigues proceed southward along the edge of the *molasse* hills bordering the Etang de Berre. From the main derivations branches a network of minor channels, known as *béals* and *roubines*. Even so, great areas in the centre and south of the Crau are untouched by irrigation because the return would hardly merit the vast initial expense of canal construction. Moreover, the supply of water from the Durance, whence these derivations originate, is not sufficient for much extension of the irrigated area, and it is in addition fluctuating and unreliable. Water has been diverted from the Durance below the Verdon confluence into a canal which runs into the Etang de Berre, providing both for irrigation and hydro-electricity requirements.

Irrigation water is used for market-gardens, protected by fences from the mistral, and for the cultivation of hay, fodder crops such as lucerne and sainfoin, and melons. Drought-resisting varieties of winter wheat are grown without irrigation, using periods of fallow. On the edges of the Crau olives, almonds and vines appear, the first particularly on the bordering limestone slopes, and there are some large fields of lavender, which does well in the dry stony soils.

The Crau is scantily settled and thinly populated. There are isolated large farms, known in the district as *mas*, surrounded by wind-breaks of planes, elms and cypress, and noticeably without windows or doors on the north; some have formed the nuclei of small agricultural settlements, such as Mas des Platanes in the south, and Mas d'Icard and Mas de Vorgière in the west. Others, such as the Grand Mas de Pillier, are located along the railway which runs straight across from Arles to the important junction and marshalling-yards at Miramas near the north-western corner of the Etang de Berre. Most of the larger settlements are situated around the margins of the Crau, including Mouriès, Euguières and Lamanon along the southern edge of the Alpilles, and Salon-de-Provence, Miramas and

Istres in the east. Salon, with a population of about 23,000, has industries connected with local products : the refining and bottling of olive oil, the packing of olives, soap-making, fruit-preserving and the manufacture of boxes for the export of vegetable produce.

The wastes of the Crau are used for other purposes, such as the enormous sewage works serving Marseilles, a large explosives dépôt at Entressen, a motor-racing circuit at Miramas, and a military airfield at Istres. These uses, of a non-productive character, emphasise the limitations of this desolate but spacious region.

LOWER PROVENCE

The country of Lower Provence to the east of the Rhône delta is one of very considerable complexity. It consists of a series of limestone ridges, the origin of which is due to the west-east Pyrenean folding projecting westward towards the delta. The Massif de la Ste. Baume, for example, to the east of Marseilles, consists of a series of parallel folds, with the main crestline extending for about seven miles as a vertical rock-wall rising from the swathing woodlands to culminate in a prominent peak at 3,786 feet. Further north is another striking series of Jurassic ridges between the parallel valleys of the Arc and the Durance, known as the Montagne de la Ste. Victoire, with a precipitous south face. There are many more ridges and plateaus, with sharp crests, bare crags, deep gullies and flanking sheets of scree. The torrential rains form torrents which have deeply gashed this mountain country, although in summer their courses are mostly dry and boulder-strewn.

Many deeply-cut valleys and a few quite extensive basins separate these limestone uplands. Behind the port of Marseilles lies a depression floored with varied Oligocene rocks, drained by the Jarret and the Huveaune ; the western part, in the angle to the south of the Chaîne de l'Estaque, has subsided and forms the deep-water Golfe de Marseille. The most extensive basin is that of the Arc, floored for the most part with Eocene rocks. Around its margins are scarped ridges, formed by the differential denudation of the flanking Upper Cretaceous and Lower Eocene rocks.[1] The river Arc flows through the basin and then crosses an alluvial plain to enter the Etang de Berre. Other depressions drain eastward to the Argens or southward directly to the coast. Bordering the limestone country on the east is a distinct structural depression, filled with varied Permian rocks, which can be traced north-eastward from the neighbourhood of Toulon to the valley of the Argens ; the last occupies another west-

[1] R. Livet, 'Le Peuplement des cuestas du bassin d'Aix-en-Provence', in *A. de G.* (1953), vol. lxii, pp. 133-6, has a map and several photographs of these cuestas.

east structural depression of Triassic rocks between Barjols and the coast near Fréjus and St. Raphael. The railway route from Toulon via Le Luc to Fréjus indicates clearly the line of these depressions.

The coast bordering *la Basse-Provence calcaire* is very indented, since the margins of this alternation of ridge, valley and basin, submerged by the sea, form a series of bays and promontories. Some of the bays (known as *calanques*),[1] such as the Calanque de Sormiou and Calanque de Morgiou, are long deep winding inlets, between steep cliff-bound *becs* and *pointes*. This type of *calanque* seems to comprise ancient fissures enlarged by marine erosion, not just ria-like gulfs due to submergence alone. Others, such as the Baies de Cassis, de la Ciotat and de Bandol, are more open, rounded in outline and with low-lying hinterlands fronted by sandy beaches; these seem to be submerged portions of marl-floored depressions. J. Chardonnet, in fact, classifies these openings into *calanques-criques* and *calanques-estuaires* respectively.[2]

Land-Use and Agriculture.—The basis of life in much of this part of Provence[3] consists of small-scale though varied agriculture, utilising the basins and valleys where 'pockets' of more fertile clay and alluvial soils are concentrated. The limestone ridges and plateaus are *garrigue*-covered, although some poor patches of evergreen oak and Aleppo pines, occasionally of beech, are the remains of the forests cleared before the nineteenth century; much wood, for example, has gone to the shipyards of Toulon, La Ciotat and Marseilles. With the reduction in the number of sheep and goats, woodland is now increasing in area.

In the clay-floored basins and in the Permian depression, wheat is grown biennially with an intervening season of fallow, though rarely on an extensive scale. The usual holding includes a piece of irrigated land in the valley bottom near a village, growing vegetable crops. Further up the terraced slopes are patches of wheat or maize, then fruit-trees such as peaches, followed by vines and finally groves of olives and sweet chestnut. In the depression behind Marseilles this intensive polyculture supplies the local urban market. In some districts co-operation is practised in the processing and marketing of both wine (the *caves coopératives* producing *vin du Var*) and olive

[1] J. Chardonnet, 'Les Calanques provençales, origine et divers types', in *A. de G.* (1948), vol. lvii, pp. 289-97; there are several detailed maps and photographs.

[2] It should be pointed out, however, that J. Nicod, in 'Le Problème de la classification des calanques parmi les formes de côtes de submersion', in *Revue de Géomorphologie Dynamique* (1951), vol. ii, pp. 120-7, disagrees with Chardonnet's suggestion that *calanques* are due to submergence, but suggests that they are the result of karstic collapse without invoking submergence.

[3] R. Livet, *Habitat rural et structures agraires en Basse-Provence* (1962).

oil[1] (the *coopératives oléicoles*). At the southern end of the Permian depression to the east of Toulon, the clay soils and the availability of irrigation water have made the Plaine d'Hyères an '*oasis de cultures arbustives, maraîchères ou florales*', as E. Bénévent puts it. Special features are the cultivation of choice varieties of cherries, which are sent to markets in Paris, England and Belgium, and of figs. The development of the Riviera flower-industry has encouraged here also the cultivation of flowers, particularly roses. Despite the limitations of relief and soil, agriculture in this part of Provence, small-scale though it may be, exhibits a diversity and an intensity in marked contrast to the vine-covered *pays* of Bas-Languedoc.

Industry and Mining.—Industrially this part of Provence is not of any great importance, with the outstanding exception of Marseilles and its *banlieue*. There are, of course, flour-mills, olive-oil mills and wine-presses in most villages. Some of the small towns, such as Barjols and Brignoles, have tanneries; the former also has potteries and a paper-works, the latter a small silk-factory. At Aubagne, in the Huveaune valley behind Marseilles, and at Roquevaire, five miles further up the same valley, more than a dozen works make bricks and glazed tiles from local Oligocene clays. The widespread occurrence of calcareous rocks provides raw material for large-scale cement manufacture; several works are in the Marseilles area, and others are at Valdonne, near Gréasque in the Fuveau lignite-basin (which provides fuel for the kilns), and in the south near the coast between Cassis and La Bédoule, using coal from the Alès field. Nearly 2,000 Italian workers are employed in the cement-works, living in *cités-ouvrières*. At Aix, there is a variety of industries on a small scale: the manufacture of matches, agricultural implements, fertilisers, and equipment for olive-oil mills. Shipbuilding is carried on at La Ciotat, constructing mostly cargo vessels of up to about 12,000 tons, and a dry-dock is used for repair work. The varied industrial development in and around Marseilles, and the naval shipbuilding at Toulon, are described below.

A certain amount of mining and quarrying is active in this part of Provence. The deposits of the main commercial ore of aluminium, hydrated oxide of alumina (usually known as bauxite from its occurrence near the now almost deserted town of Les Baux, where it was discovered in 1821), are exploited in the valley of the upper Argens and its tributaries. Here the ore is preserved in synclinal pockets among Lower Cretaceous limestones, and is worked in shallow quarries which form red scars on the flanks of the wooded ridges at such centres as Tourves, Brignoles, Le Luc and Le Cannet.

---

[1] J. Nicod, 'Grandeur et décadence de l'oléiculture provençale', in *R.G.A.* (1956), vol. 44, pp. 247-95; this contains some detailed maps.

About 2·0 million tons of bauxite were produced in France in 1963, (a slight decrease from 2·2 in 1961), of which 94 per cent came from this *département* of Var. This represents a big increase on pre-war days, for in 1938 the output was only 680,000 tons. France is no longer the world's chief producer, however, a position which she held until the war of 1939–45, for consumption has risen so considerably that even with her greatly increased output she is behind Surinam, British Guiana and the U.S.A. The bulk of the bauxite production of Var is sent by rail to Gardanne to the east of Marseilles, where it is reduced to alumina, and this is sent by rail to the refineries of the Arc and Isère valleys where it is smelted electrolytically (see p. 657). About 206,000 tons of alumina were exported in 1963, two-thirds of it from Toulon, the rest from St. Raphaël.

Considerable deposits of lignite occur in Basse-Provence,[1] the most important being the Fuveau field in the upper part of the Arc basin. The lignite occurs in thick beds among lacustrine deposits of Cretaceous age, and forms France's only worked field; it is mined near Gardanne, Meyreuil, Gréasque, Fuveau and St. Savournin (Fig. 101). The annual production topped a million tons during the war of 1914–18, when the northern coalfields were fought over. It fell to 600,000 tons in the inter-war years, but has been stepped up again in the post-war period; 1·56 million tons were produced in 1963. Much of the lignite is used locally by a large power-station at Gardanne, and at the cement-works. The lignite mines are drained of water, which has caused much trouble, by a tunnel nearly ten miles long from near Gréasque to Gardanne, then passing under the ridge of l'Etoile to the north-eastern corner of the Golfe de Marseille at L'Estaque. The recent extension of the lignite mines has necessitated the importation of much foreign labour, since the local population can supply only about half the required personnel. Most of the foreigners are Italians, living in *cités-ouvrières* near the collieries.

Marseilles.[2]—With a population of 783,738 in 1962, Marseilles is the second largest city in France, and is the largest port; in 1964 it handled nearly a third of the total tonnage entered and cleared through the country's ports. It presents the paradox of being

[1] J. Nicod, 'L'Essor des houillères du bassin de Provence', in *Bulletin de la Société de Géographie de Marseille* (1954), vol. 65, pp. 39-50, provides some detailed maps and a number of photographs.

[2] The following articles on Marseilles are useful: (i) D. Tomkinson, 'The Marseilles Experiment', in *T.P.R.* (1953), vol. 24, pp. 193-214; (ii) F. A. Dufour, 'The Industrial Growth of Marseilles', in *Progress* (1955), vol. 44, pp. 270-6; (iii) L. Pierrein, 'Sur l'expansion économique de Marseille et de sa région', in *Bulletin de Géographie d'Aix-Marseille* (1955), vol. 66, pp. 81-90; (iv) L. Pierrein, 'Marseille et le Canal de Suez', *ibid.* (1956), vol. 67, pp. 73-94.

one of the oldest settlements in the Mediterranean while its real growth is of the nineteenth and particularly of the twentieth centuries. The town was founded at the end of the seventh century B.C. by the Phoceans, and so it became a Greek colony and port; a small rocky basin (the *Calanque de Lacydon*) was the original harbour, known today as the *Vieux-Port*, while the settlement was called *Massilia*, from which the present name is derived. It was of some importance throughout classical times, but in the great period of the Mediterranean city-states Marseilles failed to rival Pisa, Genoa or Venice. What trade used the Rhône valley went through the harbours to the west of the delta, which had more direct contact with Lyons and the Rhône valley than had Marseilles, tucked away and isolated to the south-east of the Chaîne de l'Estaque. Some development took place in the sixteenth and seventeenth centuries, including the building of new quays, but still the port was far behind Nantes and Bordeaux.

Several factors contributed to the rapid growth of Marseilles in the nineteenth century, notably increasing French interests in North Africa which followed the conquest of Algeria in 1830. The development of railways afforded vastly improved access to central and northern France, although the link with Arles and Lyons involved the construction of a difficult line from Miramas along the shores of the Etang de Berre and then the penetration of the Chaîne de l'Estaque by a tunnel. A second rail-link (the *Corniche* line) was created as a result of the development of Port-de-Bouc, running south to this from Miramas, then crossing the Etang de Caronte by a swing-bridge and viaduct, and rounding the Chaîne de l'Estaque on the west and south by a difficult route involving several cuttings and short tunnels. Perhaps the most important factor was the opening of the Suez Canal in 1869, which transformed the Mediterranean from being a *cul-de-sac* into a world highway. Marseilles has suffered competition with Genoa, especially as a result of the construction of the Alpine tunnels which drew off much Swiss traffic, but the French overseas possessions and commercial interests throughout the Mediterranean provide much commercial activity. In the last thirty years, with the immense development of the Middle East oilfields, the Mediterranean has become Europe's chief oil-route, and Marseilles with its three refineries has formed one of the main oil-terminals; in 1963 the port and its annexes handled 22·3 million tons of crude oil (slightly more than Le Havre and over a third of France's total imports), and also exported by sea 3·8 million tons of refined hydrocarbons. Most of the other imports consist of oil-seeds, wheat, sugar, timber, hides, some coal (but only 125,000 tons in 1963, compared with 1·3 million tons in 1938 and over 2 million tons in 1914), raw cotton, phosphates, oil-seeds (529,000 tons) and other 'colonial' foodstuffs and raw materials. The tonnage of exports is far less; apart from refined hydrocarbons, the chief items are cement, chemical products (especially fertilisers), flour, wines and liqueurs, and textiles and metallurgical goods for North Africa. Indeed, Marseilles mostly re-exports her imports in refined or manufactured form, since the port is not an outlet for the produce of the Rhône valley, which being perishable, non-bulky and valuable travels directly by rail.

All this development has not been achieved without considerable difficulty, for Marseilles has hardly a good natural harbour and there are considerable physical obstacles between it and the Rhône valley. Moreover, development inland to the east has been cramped by the encroaching limestone hills. The coast does, however, form a right-angle, sheltered by these hills from the north and east, with deep water offshore, virtually no tidal range, and with a complete absence of silting, unlike the delta and the Languedoc coast to the west. The tiny rock-basin of Lacydon has long been left to fishing-boats, and the modern port lies behind a breakwater-mole (Plates XLIII, XLIV) running parallel to the coast for three miles north-westward, along which basins and quays have been constructed. The basins have been gradually extended, and developments are still going on to the north in the Bassin Mirabeau and at Mourepiane. The damage caused during the war of 1939–45, involving the destruction of many port facilities and the blocking of several basins by sunken vessels, took some time to restore. No locks or dock-gates are required with the negligible tidal range, and the only impediments between the various basins are the necessary swing-bridges. A road-tunnel is under construction (1966) under the Vieux-port.

Both Lyons and Marseilles have long desired a major waterway between them, preferably of ship-canal dimensions. A canal penetrates the Chaîne de l'Estaque to the north of the port by means of the Rove Tunnel (Fig. 101), four miles in length and seventy-two feet in width. Started in 1911 and interrupted by the war of 1914–18, it was not completed until 1927. It can accommodate thousand-ton barges, and not only shortens considerably the distance from Marseilles to Bouc but also enables barges to avoid the crossing of the Golfe de Fos, which can be very stormy, particularly in winter when the mistral is blowing. The canal continues along the southern shores of the Etang de Berre to Martigues, then through the Etang de Caronte to Port-de-Bouc (Plate XLV). From here the smaller Arles-Bouc Canal runs north-west along the left bank of the Grand Rhône to Arles. This continuous waterway enables small barges to pass through from Marseilles to Arles; larger barges can move between Marseilles and the Etang de Berre; and shipping drawing twenty-six feet can use the ship-canal through the Etang de Caronte

XLV Port-de-Bouc, near the entrance to the Etang de Berre

XLVI The Lavéra refinery on the shores of the Etang de Berre

XLVII Aigues-Mortes

XLVIII The Languedoc landscape to the north of Nîmes

from Bouc to Martigues and so proceed to the tanker and other berths in the Etang de Berre.

Considerable development has taken place around the shores of the Etang de Berre, de Vaine and de Caronte, and the Golfe de Fos ; the new ports are included within the administration of Marseilles (Fig. 101). Ship-channels have been dredged from Port-de-Bouc on the shores of the Golfe de Fos to Martigues, with a depth of thirty feet, and across the Etang de Berre to its north-eastern shore. The

FIG. 101.—THE MARSEILLES AREA.
A new refinery was opened at Fos-sur-Mer in 1965.
Based on *Carte de France au 50,000ᵉ*, sheets XXIX/43, 44, XXXI/44, 45.

development of these channels, quays and tanker-terminals has progressed steadily, and several further large schemes are under construction, notably at Fos-sur-Mer and Port St. Louis-du-Rhône. The reason for this progress has been the need to cope with large-scale port industries requiring considerable space which could not be accommodated in the immediate neighbourhood of the old port and town. The areas of shallow water and marshland around the margins of the *étangs* are easy to reclaim, and afford extensive sites.

The most important of these 'new' industries is oil-refining. Four large refineries have been built in the district. On the south side of the entrance to the Etang de Caronte, opposite Port-de-Bouc, is the petroleum-basin of Port-de-Lavéra (Plate XLVI), behind which is the

R.G.W.E.—P

Lavéra refinery with an output of 3·5 million tons of refined oil in 1963, owned by the *Société Française des Pétroles B.P.* Further o the east in the Etang de Berre is an offshore tanker mooring-berth, connected by underwater pipe-line to the La Mède refinery (with an output of 5·17 million tons), owned by the *Compagnie française de Raffinage.* In the north-east of the Etang de Berre is the Berre tanker-terminal, linked by a three-mile pipe-line with the Berre-l'Etang refinery (output 3·67 million tons) owned by *Shell-Berre.* Since 1946 Port-de-Lavéra has been enlarged.[1] A dredging programme, designed to enable the entry of laden 75,000-ton tankers, was completed in 1964. A pipe-line has been built along the southern shore of the Etang de Berre to La Mède, and another one right round the eastern shores to Berre, which the large tankers cannot reach. The Lavéra terminal is now linked by a 34-inch pipe-line, 468 miles in length, with Karlsruhe in West Germany via Strasbourg (see p. 310).[2] About 25 million tons of crude oil enter the terminal annually. A new refinery was opened at Fos-sur-Mer in 1965.

The Etang de Berre district has become an industrial extension of Marseilles since the war of 1914–18, when explosives factories were built at St. Chamas in this 'safe' area. Four large petro-chemical factories have been put into operation,[3] at L'Estaque (owned by *Standard-Kuhlmann*), at Berre (*Shell-St. Gobain*), at Lavéra (*Naptha-chimie*), and at La Mède (*Cie française de Raffinage*).[4] They make a wide range of products—detergents, plastics, carbon black and many more hydrocarbon derivatives. Chemical works are in operation at Port-de-Bouc, cement works at Istres, Martigues and Fos-sur-Mer, engineering works at St. Chamas, railway workshops at Miramas and Rognac, oil-seed crushing at Croix-Sante, and by-product plants at each of the oil-refineries. Several *cités-ouvrières* have been built to house the workers, many of them foreigners. Finally, there are port- and canal-works, railway marshalling-yards, the rapidly developing Marignane airport and the Istres military air-field. In fifty years much of the desolate wastes of the *étangs* and marshes has become a region of activity.

[1] L. Pierrein, 'Le Bassin pétrolier du Port de Marseille; Marseille-Lavéra', in *Bulletin de la Société de Géographie de Marseille* (1954), vol. 65, pp. 51-9.

[2] H. Debrabant, 'Le Pipeline sud-européen : aspects techniques et économiques', in *Rev. Navig. Int. et Rhénane* (1963), pp. 377-83.

[3] The petro-chemical industries which have developed in conjunction with the oil-refineries are described, with numerous illustrations, by R. Guglielmo, 'Principaux Aspects de développement de la pétrochimie en France', in *A. de G.* (1956), vol. lxv, pp. 123-39; and B. S. Hoyle, 'The Etang de Berre', in *T.E.S.G.* (1960), vol. 51, pp. 57-65.

[4] Much of this area was demolished by the Germans during the war, and there has been considerable rebuilding in recent years.

Marseilles itself, a cosmopolitan city with a quarter of its population of foreign origin, has spread upwards on to its confining slopes. From the narrow rather furtive streets around the old port [1] to the villas among the olives and orchards on the hill-slopes, there is a bewilderment of contrasting characteristics. Quite apart from the Berre exclave, the city is an important industrial centre. Vegetable-oil refining, soap-making, the manufacture of fertilisers from North African phosphates, flour-milling, sugar-refining, the making of corks, a large ship-repairing industry and several marine engineering plants, timber industries and miscellaneous metallurgical industries have developed, as might be expected in a great port. In addition, some large cement-works use local limestone, and two outlying chemical factories are in the northern (L'Estaque) and north-eastern (Septèmes-les-Vallons) outskirts of the city. Considerable development has progressed eastward along the lower valley of the Huveaune since 1876, particularly in the fifteen years before 1939, and now extending to Aubagne. Industrial suburbs have grown along each side of the valley—La Valbarelle, St. Marcel, La Barasse and La Penne on the south, Les Caillols, Les Valentines and Les Camoins-Eoures on the north. Numerous factories making furniture, glass, pottery, chemical products, paper and cardboard, biscuits and food-stuffs generally, and miscellaneous metallurgical items have been built. Modern housing estates contrast with old villages. [2]

Toulon.—Toulon has been a Mediterranean naval base for many centuries, important since Henry IV founded the arsenal and developed the harbour-works. A west–east inner *rade* on the eastern side of the prominent peninsula of Cap du Sicié is almost enclosed by the crystalline ridges of Mourillon on the east and La Seyne on the west. Further south again, affording further protection from the south and enclosing the outer *Grande Rade*, is the peninsula of St. Mandrier, made of Permian rocks, which projects eastward to end in Cap Cépet. Three miles east of this headland is the Cap de Gard de Carqueiranne, and as a result both outer and inner road-steads are protected from strong gales, while the several hilly peninsulas provided sites for defensive shore-batteries. The limestone hills behind the town (Mont Coudon, Mont Faron and Mont Caumes), rising to over 1,500 feet within two or three miles of the port, afforded excellent sites for a perimeter of fortresses, as well as providing shelter from northerly winds. Toulon has experienced critical phases of naval history; it has been blockaded on many

[1] See footnote 4, p. 418.
[2] A detailed account, with maps and photographs, is given by M. Roncayolo, 'Evolution de la banlieue marseillaise dans la basse Vallée de l'Huveaune', in *A. de G.* (1952), vol. lxi, pp. 342-56.

occasions, notably in the French Revolutionary and Napoleonic wars, but perhaps its most tragic hour was when a large part of the French fleet was scuttled there in November 1942. Both port and town were grievously damaged during the war, and the population dropped from about 150,000 in 1938 to 125,000 in 1946. Much reconstruction has taken place, and Toulon is once again France's main Mediterranean naval-base, as well as being one of the N.A.T.O. bases, with a population of 172,586. At La Seyne, in the western angle of the inner roadsteads, are both naval and civil shipbuilding yards and repair-shops.

Toulon has a small commercial harbour, which exports bauxite from the producing centre of Brignoles, thirty miles away to the north, with which the port is connected by a circuitous railway; about 236,000 tons were shipped in 1963, rather more than in 1938. Imports included 196,000 tons of oil for the base and 30,000 tons of machinery and steel for the repair-shops, but little else. It has a weekly shipping service to Corsica in summer.

THE MAURES-ESTEREL MASSIFS

Massifs of crystalline rock reach the Mediterranean coast between Cap du Sicié, to the south of Toulon, and the Golfe de la Napoule. The massifs belong structurally to the Hercynian core of the Alps (see p. 634) and form part of a foundered continental mass. The Iles d'Hyères and western Corsica comprise similar structures, and were probably once continuous with the mainland, now separated by a fractured and sunken area forming part of the Ligurian Sea. The rocks are complex, consisting of granite, gneiss and crystalline schist, for the most part of Pre-Cambrian age.[1]

These crystalline massifs can be divided into three unit-areas. In the south-west the small Massif du Sicié rises to 1,152 feet within a mile of the coast, and is separated from the upland of Maures by the submerged southern end of the Permian depression, which forms the harbour of Toulon. The Massif des Maures is much larger, extending inland for twenty miles. These uplands are interrupted only by the broad Golfe de St. Tropez, cut in less resistant slates, and by its continuation to the south-west as a valley across which a cluster of streams converges towards the gulf. The north-eastern part of Maures, known as the Massif du Tanneron, consists in part of granitic rocks. The Permian depression swings eastward around the northern edge of Maures, reaching the sea at the broad Golfe de Fréjus. Beyond this, between the valleys of the Argens and the Siagne, is the compact Massif de l'Esterel; along the coast the rocks are again mainly granitic.

[1] Y. Masurel, *La Provence cristallin et ses enveloppes sédimentaries* (1965).

These massifs are not lofty, the highest point being only 2,550 feet, but they are rugged and gashed with steep-sided river valleys. Their impermeable rocks contrast with the limestones which form so much of Provence. The hills, while rocky, have not the near-karstic aridity of much of the limestone ; they bear woodlands of cork-oak and chestnut on their lower slopes, and coarse pasture, bracken and scrub higher up. Esterel is particularly well wooded.

The coast of Maures and Esterel is bold and massive, with prominent headlands, rocky islands, occasional broad bays and deep narrow indentations. Submergence of the margins of the crystalline rocks formed the bay of Hyères and the several outlying Iles d'Hyères.[1] One of these, Giens, has been converted into a peninsula by the formation of two parallel sand-spits from the mainland to the island, five miles long and over a mile apart, enclosing areas of salt-marsh, *étangs* and pans from which salt is extracted. The several rivers flowing into the Rade d'Hyères and into the Golfe de Fréjus have collaborated with longshore drift to build out broad coastal plains fronted with sandy beaches and low dunes, with spits across the river-mouths enclosing several *étangs* and areas of salt-marsh. Fréjus itself was a port in Roman times, but is now nearly two miles from the sea ; a small airport, serving St. Raphaël, has been developed on the alluvial flats between Fréjus and the sea. The plentiful material available for this coastal accretion is an indication of the eroding capacity of the short rivers flowing to the sea over the impermeable crystalline rocks. Further to the north-east, prominent capes of resistant igneous rocks (Caps Blanc, Nègre, Lardier and Camarat) alternate with bays worn in less resistant slates. Beyond the Golfe de Fréjus the Esterel coast is less interrupted by large bays but consists of an alternation of deep-water *calanques* and bold yet short promontories.

Apart from the towns in the Permian depression (Toulon, Hyères, Le Luc and Fréjus), few settlements are of any size. Along the coast, with its magnificent *Corniche* road and parallel railway, occur villages from which small-scale tunny-fishing is carried on. Some tourism has developed, notably at St. Raphaël, Miramar-d'Esterel and Théoule-sur-Mer, but this coast, overshadowed by the Côte d'Azur further east, tends rather to encourage individual villas and occasional hotels delightfully situated in secluded bays.

In spite of the greater surface-water supply, the agricultural economy of this part of Provence differs little from the rest. On the terraced sides of the valleys vines, olives, fruits (such as peaches) and vegetables are cultivated, and chestnut groves are widespread,

[1] A full account, with maps and photographs, is given by Y. Masurel, 'Observations sur la structure et la morphologie des Iles d'Hyères', in *A. de G.* (1953), vol. lxii, pp. 241-58.

while the higher pastures in the interior are grazed by sheep and cattle. The forests play an important part in the economy, as apart from timber and tan-bark, the cork-oak is carefully tended to provide corks for the millions of wine bottles filled every year in the Midi and elsewhere in France. This industry has however suffered considerably from competition with North Africa and Spain.

THE CÔTE D'AZUR [1]

The granitic and metamorphic rocks which compose the Massif de l'Esterel end abruptly at the Golfe de la Napoule and are replaced by rocks of Mesozoic age. From Cannes to the broad valley of the Var the coast cuts transversely across a sequence of Triassic and Jurassic rocks; a mass of resistant Middle Jurassic limestone forms the prominent Cap d'Antibes, and some Lower Jurassic fragments comprise the two offshore Iles de Lérins. Torrential streams flow southwards to the sea in narrow ravines—Brague, Loup, Valvan and Cagnes, separating steep-sided limestone *collines*. To the east of Antibes the lower ranges of the calcareous Maritime Alps trend southward towards the coast, which consists accordingly of prominent white headlands alternating with broad valleys reaching the sea as roadsteads. The largest of the rivers is the Var, whose lower valley is floored with an extensive talus of Pliocene gravels. The Paillon enters the sea in the Nice roadstead, and further east the Rade de Villefranche lies between the ridge culminating in Mont Boron and the prominent Cap Ferrat. Further east still the Cretaceous limestone hills come close to the sea, with many rocky spurs (notably Cap Martin) separating bays each with its resort. Complex movements of sea-level have occurred in geologically recent times, resulting in the features of a submerged upland coast. Much deposition results from the efforts of the sea to straighten out the coastline; in some parts fine sand-grains worn from the crystalline rocks accumulate to form the superb *plages*, as at Cannes and Juan-les-Pins, but in others (notably near the mouth of the Var) the fluvio-glacial gravels provide less attractive stretches of shingle-beach.

The Agricultural Economy.—Neither along the coast of Alpes-Maritimes nor in the interior is the terrain suitable for agriculture, except in some small clay- or marl-floored depressions among the limestone and along the lower valleys of the rivers. The *département* has in fact the lowest proportion of arable land in France; this amounted in 1963 to little more than 3 per cent of its total area, and the cultivation of fruit, vines and vegetables added only another

[1] B. Kayser, *Campagnes et villes de la Cote d'Azur* (1958).

4 per cent. Twenty-nine per cent was under permanent pasture
(much of this in the higher ranges of the Maritime Alps, the rest
consisting of scrubby limestone pasture), and about the same
proportion carried woodland, mostly thin pine-woods and rather
poor holm- and cork-oak forests. The region shares the general
summer aridity of the Midi ; both July and August have an average
of less than an inch of rainfall, frequently none at all, and what there
is comes in the form of torrential showers.

Until the mid-nineteenth century, the pattern of the economy
resembled that of the Midi generally ; on small pockets of favourable
land wheat, olives, vines, figs and other fruit were cultivated, sheep
and goats were grazed on the limestone pastures, cattle in the higher
valleys and on summer alpine pastures, and some fishing was active
along the coast. Then began the gradual development of the tourist
industry ; this revolutionised the agricultural economy. Much more
produce was required for local consumption, while conversely
better communications allowed perishable crops to be produced for
distant markets. The cultivation of flowers achieved an outstanding
place, both for the cut-flower trade and for perfume. A remarkable
ceinture fleurie developed along the coast, with concentrations at
Vallauris (between Cannes and Antibes), along the valley of the
Loup behind Cagnes-sur-Mer, in the adjoining Valvan valley at
Vence, and in the Var valley at St. Laurent. There is some specialisation, notably in mimosa at Nice, but usually a variety of flowers,
choice fruit and early vegetables, maturing in sequence, is grown by
each *propriétaire*. Competition to produce earlier crops has forced
the use of glass (cloches and greenhouses) even in this favoured
climate, especially for carnations. While the luxury resorts consume
some of this produce, three-quarters is sent away by train ; this
tendency developed during the early 'thirties of this century, when
the world depression drastically reduced the number of visitors, and
the cultivators were obliged to seek wider markets.

Some eight miles to the north-west of Cannes, in a basin drained
by a number of headstreams of the Siagne, is situated Grasse, where
since the end of the eighteenth century the cultivation of flowers for
perfume has provided a prosperous livelihood. At one time between
four and five thousand *petits-propriétaires* grew roses, jasmine,
violets, orange-blossom and other herbs and flowers to supply the
small factories in and around the town. The production of cheap
synthetic perfumes by industrial processes and the great decline of
high-price luxury markets during the world depression hit the Grasse
area badly. While today some cultivation[1] still produces the really

---

[1] O. Beniamino, 'Grasse, centre mondial des matières premières aromatiques',
in *R.G.A.* (1957), vol. 45, pp. 763-74 ; and D. Balducchi, 'La Répartition des
actionnaires de la parfumerie de Grasse', in *A. de G.* (1960), vol. 69, pp. 462-76.

expensive perfumes requiring the natural essence of flowers, much of the Grasse district has fallen into line with the Côte d'Azur generally, and is producing early vegetables, fruit (particularly peaches) and flowers. '*Après une brillante carrière, la culture des plantes à parfum, née de l'industrie, semble tuée par l'industrie.*'[1]

The Riviera Resorts.—Between the Golfe de la Napoule and the Italian frontier lies an almost continuous line of resorts catering for an enormous annual influx of visitors. The Riviera has capitalised its mild sunny climate,[2] its south-facing aspect and its protection from the *mistral* by the surrounding hills, its attractive sub-tropical vegetation of palms and mimosa, and the general charm of the coast. It can offer sunny beaches, magnificent inland scenery, and snow-covered hills in winter but a few hours away. From being merely the winter home of the wealthy, with their villas and large yachts, the Riviera has become one of the playgrounds of Europe, catering both for the fashionable and the sophisticated and increasingly also for the ordinary visitor. It is estimated that half a million people visit the Riviera between Christmas and Easter alone. The main line of the *Région-Sud* from Paris, via Dijon and Lyons, was opened to Nice in 1865, and now a heavy traffic of *rapides* leaves the Gare de Lyon every evening for this Côte d'Azur. The last section, from Fréjus round the edge of the Esterel massif to the Italian frontier, is a superb train journey, with the line following a sinuous course near the sea and using tunnels, cuttings and viaducts to negotiate the difficult terrain. The busy Nice airport on the shingle-flats to the east of the mouth of the river Var, with the end of the runway but a few yards from the sea, affords a rapid means of access from most of the cities of Europe.

There are four '*grands centres*'—Cannes, Nice, Monte Carlo and Menton,[3] and innumerable others which form coastal fringes of hotels, luxury shops, villas and casinos behind the *plages* and tiered up the hillsides. Cannes, Juan-les-Pins and Antibes comprise virtually one continuous resort from the Golfe de la Napoule, round Golfe Juan and along both sides of the Cap d'Antibes. Beyond the alluvial flats at the mouth of the river Var are Nice, Villefranche, Beaulieu-sur-Mer, Eze and Cap d'Ail. Then the famous group of Monte Carlo and La Condamine in the principality of Monaco are succeeded by Beausoleil, Roquebrune, Cap Martin, Carnolles and Menton. Thus the permanent population of Alpes-Maritimes, despite its consider-

---

[1] E. Bénévent, 'La Basse-Provence', in *La France: géographie-tourisme*, edited by D. Faucher (1951), vol. i, p. 300.

[2] L. Gorczynski, *Climat solaire de Nice et de la Côte d'Azur. Mémoire IV de l'Association des Naturalistes de Nice et des Alpes-Maritimes* (1934).

[3] L. Guéron, 'Le Tourisme à Menton', in *Méditerranée* (1966), vol. 7, pp. 51-64.

able area of rugged limestone mountains, totals half a million, three-quarters of whom live along or near the coast, a population which is doubled by the seasonal influx of visitors.

Nice.—The most famous Mediterranean resort is Nice,[1] *chef-lieu* of the *département* of Alpes-Maritimes and 'capital' of the Riviera. For long it was merely a small port and fortress, situated on a bay where the river Paillon reaches the sea to the west of the sheltering peninsula of Cap Ferrat. Its growth really started when France acquired the County of Nice in 1860, and was particularly stimulated when the coastal railway reached the town in 1865. During this century its population has increased by more than 100 per cent. As the Riviera became increasingly fashionable, Nice grew rapidly. Villas and hotels spread upwards on the south-facing hillsides and along the coast to the west in the contiguous suburbs of Ste. Hélène, St. Jean and La Californie. It so dominates the Côte d'Azur that the district is in fact sometimes referred to as '*la Côte niçoise*', and Nice is now the fifth city of France in size, with a population in 1962 of 294,976. Roads, autocar routes, the electric tramways, the railway opened in 1928 over the Col de Tende (using a series of fine spiral tunnels) to Cuneo (Coni) in north Italy,[2] and its busy airport all contribute to its becoming '*la grande métropole de la Côte d'Azur*'.

Nice has a small harbour situated to the east of the town, below the old château, with a jetty protecting an *avant-port* and three open basins. It is used by pleasure-yachts, small coasting vessels, the regular packet-steamer to Corsica, and a small amount of commercial trade, mainly the export of cement and lime from three works near the town, and the import of some coal. The port handled about four times as much trade before 1939 as at present, but there was a certain amount of war-time damage, and although reconstruction is now complete it has not recovered its pre-war position.

[1] R. Blanchard, *Le Comté de Nice. Etude géographique* (1960).
[2] Although this railway line was destroyed during the war of 1939–45, it is now once more in full operation.

CHAPTER 16

THE MEDITERRANEAN COASTLANDS:
(2) LANGUEDOC AND ROUSSILLON

The plains extending from the Rhône to the outlying masses of the Pyrenees are referred to generally as *Languedoc*[1] (see p. 1), or sometimes more specifically as *Bas-Languedoc*. Various distinctive zones can be recognised—the coastal dunes, marshes and *étangs*, the alluvium-covered lowlands and lower terraces, the upper gravel-terraces, the limestone *garrigue* country extending to the foothills of the Cévennes, and the outlying upper Aude valley or basin of Carcassonne. The small semicircular plain of Roussillon in the extreme south is sufficiently individual to be described separately.

THE COAST

The coastline of Languedoc sweeps round the Golfe du Lion as two intersecting arcs, the first from the prominent headland of Cap Leucate to Cap d'Agde (enclosing the Golfe de Narbonne), the second continuing to the western wing of the Rhône delta fronted by the Golfe d'Aigues-Mortes. In mid-Pliocene times the sea stood about 170 feet higher than at present, so that the coast was indented by several irregular-shaped shallow lagoons, extending far inland up the valleys of the Aude and the Hérault. Various masses of limestone and basalt (the capes mentioned above, together with the hills of La Clape and the Cap de Sète) stood out as islands. By the time of the Romans, sea-level had fallen more or less to its present position, but shallow lagoons still remained between these coastal hillocks. The plain in which Narbonne stands was occupied by the *Lacus Narbonensis*, the Etang de Vendres covered what is now the mouth of the Aude, and the several *étangs* to the north-east of Sète were then continuous and much more extensive.

A long process of coastal straightening by natural means has since gone on slowly but steadily. The rivers of Languedoc, often affected by violent floods in autumn and spring, bring down vast amounts of sediment; the Aude, for example, contributes an annual load estimated to be 1·8 to 2·0 million cubic metres. The

---

[1] D. Faucher, *Visage du Languedoc: géographie humaine* (1949); and R· Dugrand, *Villes et Campagnes en Bas-Languedoc* (1963), a massive monograph of 638 pp., with an immense bibliography.

rapid gain of the land has been helped also by the shallow nature of the water offshore and the gently shelving sea-floor; the ten-metre submarine contour is two to three miles away, the fifty-metre contour as much as seven miles out. Longshore drift assisted in the building of offshore bars, on which wind-blown sand has estab-lished a rampart of dunes, aligned in sweeping curves from one rocky island to the next.

Behind the bars the lagoons were slowly filled in by river sedimen-tation and by the mud-accretion of halophytic salt-marsh plants such as *Salicornia*, succeeded by reeds, rushes and salt-grasses. Slowly the *étangs* became marshes, and the marshes became pastures known as *souillères*. The work of man collaborated in the planting of sand-binding grasses on the dunes, and the building of causeways to carry railways, of dykes enclosing the Rhône-Sète and Midi Canals, and of dykes against river-flooding. The former Etang d'Ingril to the south of Montpellier has been reduced to four inter-connected *étangs*—de Pérols, d'Arnel, de Vic and d'Ingril, along the seaward edge of which runs the Rhône-Sète Canal. The river Lez has built an isthmus of its own alluvium to the sea right across a former large *étang* (through which the Lez itself is endyked to its outlet at Palavas). Parts of the *étang* now form the Marais de la Joncasse, de la Grande Palude and de la Grande Maïre, other areas in the south-west near Frontignan provide salt-pans, and parts have been drained and now grow vines. Similarly the *Lacus Narbo-nensis* is now a plain, at the southern end of which are the much reduced Etangs de Sigean[1] and de l'Ayrolle. The Etang de Vendres, into the southern end of which flows the Aude, is really no longer a lagoon of open water but a salt-marsh. The largest remaining lake is the Etang de Thau, thirteen miles in length; it lies in a dis-tinct synclinal hollow, and with a maximum sounding of eighty-two feet it is the deepest of these lagoons, most of which vary from only about six to twenty-five feet.

THE LOWLANDS OF LANGUEDOC

The term 'lowlands' is used in a general sense to denote the area between the dune-bordered coast and the edge of the limestone *garrigue* country. It is, however, a district of considerable physical variety, and several regional names emphasise this diversity: the *Costière* in the Nîmes district and elsewhere, the *Vistrenque* or alluvial plain of the Vistre between the Costière and the *garrigue*

---

[1] Ch. Caverivière, 'L'Exploitation des étangs de Sigean', in *R.G.P.S.-O.* (1950), vol. xxi, pp. 61-80, gives an account of the exploitation and partial reclamation of the *étangs*, with a detailed map of the reclamation stages, and accounts of fishing, salt-extraction, etc.

country, the alluvial plains of the *Lunelois* and those around Montpellier, the *Plaine de Montbazin* between the *garrigue* country and
the outlying ridge of Gardiole, the lower basin of the river Hérault,
the *Biterrois* to the north-west of Béziers, and the *Plaine Narbonnaise*
or the basin of the lower Aude.

This diversity is largely due to the fact that the region represents
an ancient gulf of the sea, several times covered by marine transgressions alternating with periods of emergence and denudation.
It was, moreover, affected by the earth-movements and volcanic
activity associated with the building of both the Central Massif and
the Pyrenees. Several different rocks and structures are thus
involved. Lower, Middle and Upper Jurassic limestones to the
south-west of Montpellier form the upland ridges of the Montagne
de la Mure and the Montagne de la Gardiole, separated by the
Miocene-floored plain of Montbazin; the Gardiole is a ridge
trending north-east to south-west which rises steeply to 748 feet
within a few miles of the coastal lagoons. Sète is built on and
around an Upper Jurassic limestone knoll, which culminates in a
summit 591 feet above the sea. A mass of Lower Cretaceous limestone comprises the dissected hill-country of La Clape rising to
700 feet between Narbonne and the coast. Oligocene limestones
outcrop as low hills between the Orb and Aude valleys.

One interesting contribution to the geology and relief of Bas-
Languedoc is the result of Pliocene volcanic activity characteristic
of the Central Massif. Outcrops of basalt can be traced interruptedly
southward from the Escandorgue hills on the margin of the Causse
du Larzac to the coast near Agde. To the north-west of Béziers
appears a series of these small volcanic eminences; the rounded
mass of St. Thibéry rises to 289 feet from the western side of the
valley-floor of the Hérault, and the prominent Cap d'Agde is backed
by the eminence of Mont-St. Loup (377 feet), and fronted by the
rocky island of the Roches de Brescou.

Elsewhere Tertiary and newer sediments of varying character
cover the undulating surface.[1] One feature is the presence of gravels
of Pliocene age, similar in character to La Crau to the east of the
Rhône delta. To them is given the name of *costières* or *coustières*,
after the Costière de St. Gilles to the north-west of Arles where they
are extensively developed. These gravel sheets, from 100 to 250
feet above sea-level, were laid down by the Pliocene rivers in the
form of fans. A former westerly course of the Rhône, represented
now only by the little river Vistre, was responsible for the deposition
of the gravels of the Costière de St. Gilles. Other similar *costières*
occur to the south of Montpellier, and again between the valleys of

[1] P. Demangeon, *Contribution à l'étude de la sédimentation détritique dans le
Bas-Languedoc pendant l'ère tertiaire* (1958).

the lower Hérault and Orb to the north-east of Béziers. Finally, many rivers continue to deposit fine alluvium along their lower valleys and flood-plains, while along the coast both fluvial and marine sands and clays are continually accumulating.

THE GARRIGUES COUNTRY

The country between the edge of the Cévennes and the trench of the Rhône, bounded on the north-east and south-west by the valleys of the Ardèche and the Hérault respectively, consists mainly of limestone. The greater part is of Lower Cretaceous age but much Jurassic appears in the valleys of the upper Hérault and the upper Ardèche (the latter area known as the Plateau des Gras), and to the west of Montpellier. Lower Tertiary limestones are also represented as Eocene rocks between the valleys of the middle Hérault and the Vidourle, and Oligocene further to the north-east in the valley of the middle Gard and the Alès basin.

These rocks underwent gentle folding in early and mid-Tertiary times, associated with the Pyrenean earth-movements ; the folds trend roughly south-west to north-east. Long periods of planation in late Tertiary times produced widespread erosion surfaces. While there is therefore a general fall in altitude from nearly 2,000 feet at the foot of the Cévennes to 350 feet between Nîmes and Montpellier, three dominant levels can be distinguished : a higher surface at 1,250 to 1,300 feet in the north between the rivers Gard and Ardèche, an intermediate one at 900 to 1,000 feet, and the most extensive at 600 to 700 feet. These planations cut right across the structures, and the influence of the numerous small anticlines and synclines on the present relief is therefore emphasised. The less resistant anticlines have been heavily eroded, revealing the underlying clays and marls in broad open valleys (*vaux*) and basins (*combes*), overlooked by white crags. The more resistant synclines, where the carapace of hard limestone has been preserved, form upstanding summits and crests, many of them orientated from south-west to north-east. Such a ridge, to the north-east of Vallon beyond the Ardèche valley, culminates in the Dent du Rez (2,362 feet) ; the Signal du Bouquet rises to 2,070 feet in a south-facing ridge above the valley of the Aiguillon (a tributary of the Cèze) ; and further south the Pic St. Loup (2,175 feet), a prominent landmark to the north of Montpellier, overlooks the basin of St. Martin-de-Londres.

Numerous rivers flow down from the edge of the Central Massif, both to the Rhône (Ardèche, Cèze and Gard) and directly to the Golfe du Lion (Vidourle and Hérault). Their valleys are superimposed across the different structures, and differential erosion has produced diverse relief features. The clay and marl outcrops form

basins, while the limestones are cut through in gorges reminiscent of
the Grands Causses. To the north of Uzès, between the valleys of
the Cèze and the Gard, the name *Causse* is actually used. The
Ardèche leaves the basin of Vallon (floored with Upper Cretaceous
clays) and crosses a continuous area of limestone in a cliffed gorge
nearly twenty miles in length. The most spectacular feature is the
limestone arch of the Pont-d'Arc, with an opening 194 feet in width
through which flows the river; this arch is a surviving piece of roof
of the river's former underground course. The Chassesac, the main
confluent of the Ardèche, has also eroded a magnificent gorge in
almost horizontally bedded limestone; this too was a subterranean
channel, and the top of the gorge is in places only a few yards wide.
The Cèze and the Gard flow in their middle courses across basins of
Oligocene rocks before crossing the Lower Cretaceous limestones in
winding steep-sided gorges; the former rushes down as a series of
cascades (*Les Chutes du Sautadet*) among innumerable large pot-
holes. There is much complicated underground drainage, large sink-
holes (*gouffres*), powerful resurgences and cave systems. The régimes
of the streams are variable; in late summer they diminish to trickles
among boulder-strewn beds or even vanish altogether. Numerous
dry valleys known as *cadereaux* occur, some permanently waterless
because of a lowered water-table, others sometimes swept by
torrential floods in autumn and spring.

The vegetation is characteristic of the word '*garrigue*', for this is
in fact the type-region which has given its name to xerophytic scrub
growing on limestone in a climatic régime of summer drought. The
varieties of aromatic shrubs and rock-plants include thyme, cistus,
broom, heaths, arbutus, thickets of kerm-oak, and for a few weeks
in early spring a profusion of annual flowers and bulbous plants such
as asphodel. The exotic prickly pear has spread considerably. This
vegetation cover is partly the result of man's past depredations; a
former continuous forest of evergreen oaks (ilex or holm), beech
and Aleppo pine has been removed, and its regeneration was precluded by the grazing of sheep and goats and by the frequent
disastrous fires during the dry summers. Much careful planting has
been effected, especially during the last forty years.

THE BASIN OF CARCASSONNE

The Narbonne plain narrows to the west between the foothills of
the Montagne Noire and the Massif de Mouthoumet, the northern
part of the Corbières. It leads up to the Col de Naurouze, which at
an altitude of 627 feet forms the watershed between the Bay of Biscay
and the Mediterranean. Because this broad col leads over into the
basin of Aquitaine it is sometimes given the name of *La Porte*

d'Aquitaine, but as Carcassonne dominates the approach from the east the corridor is also called the Gate of Carcassonne.

At the end of the Mesozoic era, the depression was open to the west and so formed part of the 'Gulf of Aquitaine' (see p. 313), though it was closed to the east. During Eocene times the character of the deposition varied as the transgression waxed and waned, so that deep-sea, lagoon and lacustrine deposits succeeded each other. This period of predominant transgression lasted at least until the end of the Oligocene, by which time the Pyrenean folds were being uplifted to the south. The development of the Mediterranean basin in mid-Tertiary times and the *en masse* subsidence of the Golfe du Lion wrought a profound change, for the rivers which previously flowed to the proto-Garonne were drawn into an eastward-draining system. The Aude became the master-stream; rising in the Carlitte uplands of the eastern Pyrenees, it flowed first northwards into the depression, and then turned at right angles towards the Mediterranean. To it numerous streams came from the Montagne Noire, and as the main valley was lowered by this powerful river, its left-bank tributaries (notably the Fresquel) cut back westwards, and the watershed between the Garonne and Aude systems became defined.

Denudation has been active on the eastern side of the col, and the surface rocks of the middle and upper Aude basin consist of a variety of Eocene deposits—sandy limestones, blue marls, red clays and conglomerates, for the Oligocene rocks (which cover the eastern flanks of the Basin of Aquitaine almost to the summit of the col) have here been completely removed. Subsequent denudation has produced a diverse relief of sharp ridges and deep valleys, elevated platforms and basins isolated except for gorge-like exits, and along the Aude and its tributaries at least four clearly defined terraces can be distinguished. In addition, torrential tributaries, particularly from the Montagne Noire, brought down material, forming gravel-fans along the northern edge of the Aude flood-plain and depositing fine material on the flood-plain and in the coastal lagoons.

As a result of this diversity of land-forms, within the middle and upper Aude basin several distinctive units can be distinguished. In the north along the flanks of the Montagne Noire are the ridges and valleys of *Minervois*, so called after the little town of Minerve, tucked in a steep-sided basin where the valley of the Cesse opens out between level-topped limestone plateaus. To the west of Minervois is another limestone plateau, *Cabardès*. The actual valley of the Fresquel and the Aude, the axis of the depression, contains a series of *pays*—the basins of *Castelnaudary* at the western end, of *Carcassonne* in the centre, and of *Lézignan* in the east; the last two are separated by a *cluse*-like valley at Argens, cut through one of the south-west to north-east ridges which are characteristic of these marginal areas of Pyrenean folding. To the south of the main axis are the dissected limestone *pays* of *Piège* in the west, and of *Razès* in the angle between the Fresquel and the upper Aude. The valley of the upper Aude itself, below where it leaves the Cretaceous limestones of northern Corbières, is known as *Limouxin*, after the town of Limoux situated in a basin where several tributaries join the Aude.

THE CLIMATE OF LANGUEDOC

While diversity is the keynote of the land-forms of Languedoc, the climatic régime is the unifying feature of the whole region, with a marked seasonal rhythm. As R. Plandé puts it,[1] '*Sur tous ces paysages bas-languedociens règne la même luminosité du ciel, le même rythme des saisons*'. The chief contrast is between the almost completely dry summer (save for an occasional brief thunderstorm) and the rains of autumn and spring. Rainfall totals vary from about twenty inches at Narbonne, situated away from the coast and partly in the rain-shadow of the hills of La Clape, to twenty-five inches at Nîmes and thirty inches at Montpellier. The rainiest month at the last of these is October (with a mean of four inches), but July averages less than an inch and in many years is wholly rainless. Most of this precipitation falls in a few showers of considerable intensity, causing the rivers to flow torrentially.[2] These heavy showers are associated with the onset of the *marin* (known also as the *autan* further west in the upper Aude valley), a humid wind from between south-west and south-east, which may be experienced on sixty to seventy days during the winter months. It is caused by the eastward passage of low-pressure systems through the western Mediterranean, or from the Bay of Biscay through the Gate of Carcassonne, producing a southerly inflow of humid air in the warm sector. By contrast, strong, cold and extremely dry air-streams from a northerly direction are frequent features; the wind is here known as the *cers*, which blows on an average on 140 days at Montpellier and 160 at Narbonne, mostly between November and April, but it can be experienced at any time of the year. One other characteristic wind is experienced, the humid, blustery and rather cool *grec*, blowing in spring from the east. Local sea-breezes known as the *labech* are experienced in summer along the coast, and help to modify temperatures and to freshen the atmosphere.

[1] R. Plandé, 'Le Bas-Languedoc', in *La France: géographie-tourisme* (1951), edited by D. Faucher, vol. i, p. 302.

[2] The heavy rains of late autumn and winter in Languedoc, and their resultant floods are described by M. Pardé, 'Les Crues languedociennes en décembre 1953', in *A. de G.* (1956), vol. lxv, pp. 140-2. See also G. Viallet, 'Les Crues du Lez', in *Bulletin, Société Languedocienne de Géographie* (1955), vol. xxvi, pp. 389-432; and S. Laborde, 'La Crue du Lez (nov.-déc., 1955)', *ibid.*, pp. 433-69.

The mean temperature figures for Montpellier vary between 41° F. in January and 73° F. in July, giving a quite high range of 32° F. for a near-coastal situation. On an average, frost is experienced on forty days per annum at Montpellier, again a high figure. Late frosts and cold northerly winds in spring may do much harm, especially if an exceptionally mild spell has occurred earlier in the year which has caused fruit-trees to blossom. Market-gardens are intersected with frameworks of laths over which woven mats can be drawn as a protection against night-frosts.

LAND-USE

The lowlands of Languedoc broadly correspond to the three *départements* of Gard, Hérault and Aude, and it is helpful to examine their land-use categories.

Land-Use, 1963

(Percentage of Total Area)

	Arable	Pasture	Vine-yards	Orchards	Wood-land	Agricultural Land not cultivated
Aude . .	22	21	19	—	13	16
Gard . .	14	18	15	5	27	12
Hérault . .	10	18	28	3	18	14

Source: *Ministère de l'Agriculture*, published in *Annuaire statistique de la France, 1964.*

This region, with its areas of limestone, gravel, salt-marsh and sand-dune, together with the rather arid climate liable to temperature extremes and to sudden inclement spells, is obviously subject to agricultural limitations, and the figures in the table bear this out. The low proportion of pasture is to be expected in a region of summer drought; what there is consists of salt-pasture around the *étangs*, irrigated meadows along the streams or in clay-floored basins among the limestone, and upland pasture in the foothills of the Cévennes; much of the last is fit only for sheep and goats. As a result, in the three *départements* there were a mere 39,000 cattle (Hérault with only 6,000 had fewer than any other French *département*), but 296,000 sheep and 29,000 goats. Most of these flocks are kept in the *garrigue* country and in the foothills, and many move into the Central Massif during the summer. The ewes' milk is made into cheese, much of it 'finished' in the caves of Roquefort in the Central Massif (see p. 570). Sheep rearing has, however, declined during the last century.

The percentage figures for the woodland cover are as high as they are partly because the *départements* include the rather better wooded foothills of the Central Massif, partly because much scrubby evergreen oak is included in the land-use classification, and partly because of some progress in the planting of pines behind goat-proof fences. Some areas of forest occur to the north-west of Avignon (the Forêts de Rochefort and de Malmont), the Bois de Gourdargues in the middle Cèze valley, the Bois de St. Quentin on the *garrigue* to the north of Uzès, and the woodlands within the basin of St. Martin-de-Londres. In addition scattered clumps of evergreen oaks or chestnuts surround villages and farms, isolated pines survive incredibly on limestone slopes, planes line roads and village squares, poplars and cypress form wind-breaks.

The Mediterranean triad—wheat, olive and vine—have been the staple crops for millennia, in fact this was one of the granaries of Imperial Rome. The three *départements* in 1963 had 124,000 acres under wheat, mostly 'hard' drought-resisting varieties grown in small fields (surrounded by dry stone walls or *murgers*) on the terraces and in clay-floored basins, using a period of fallow. Along the canals, where irrigation water is available, lucerne, sainfoin and vetches provide fodder. Irrigation water for the market-gardens is obtained from the rivers by means of derivation canals. A scheme was started in 1958 for a unified system of irrigation, using water brought through a Canal du Bas Rhône-Languedoc, taking off from the Rhône 2·5 miles above Arles, and running along the southern edge of the *garrigue* westward for 108 miles to the Hérault river.[1] Some 10 miles west of the Rhône take-off, water is lifted at the huge *Aristide Dumont* pumping-station, to enable the higher lands to be served by gravity flow. Farther west, water is also taken from the Orb, Hérault and other rivers. Olives are still grown but less now for their oil than for preserving and bottling, notably at Gignac and Aniane in the middle Hérault valley. They do well in the gravelly soils of the *costières* and on the limestone slopes bordering the *combes* and river valleys among the *garrigue*. Mulberries have been grown since the seventeenth century, and in spite of the calamitous silk-worm disease in the mid-nineteenth century and the vast increase in silk imports (see p. 390), occasional groves of trees and lines

[1] A discussion of the scheme, with a map giving the possible line of the canal, is given by P. George, 'Problèmes agricoles de l'aménagement hydraulique du Bas-Rhône', in *Mélanges géographiques offerts à Ernest Bénévent* (1954), pp. 223-33. See also P. Carrère and R. Dugrand, *La Région Méditerranéenne* (1960), pp. 118-19, which gives a detailed map; and N. J. Graves, 'Une Californie française. The Languedoc and lower Rhône irrigation project', in *Geography* (1965), vol. 1, pp. 71-3. See also J. Richez, 'Les Transformations des structures agraires sous l'influence de l'irrigation sur le plateau de Garons (Gard)', in *Méditerranée* (1965), vol. 6, pp. 201-18.

of them along the roads and between fields can still be seen. Table-grapes have been introduced on to some of the better lands, supplying distant markets.

Viticulture.—The dominant crop since the mid-nineteenth century has been the vine; over a quarter of Hérault is now covered with vineyards, and between a fifth and a sixth of the other two *départements*. Here is monoculture carried to its extreme.[1] The three *départements* produced in 1963 almost 19 million hectolitres of wine, or a third of the total French output. Significantly, however, only a minute proportion of this enormous yield consisted of *vin à appellation contrôlée*. The wines are mostly sold under the general name of '*vins du Midi*', although sometimes they are known under individual *crus*, as '*Corbières*', '*Biterrois*', '*Minervois*' and '*Costière*'. Some of the red wines seem harsh and sour to the unaccustomed palate, but occasional wines are of great charm.

Vines have been grown since classical times, but until a century and a half ago they were cultivated in association with other crops. Gradually the vine became dominant; from the limestone *côtes*, the little stone-walled fields among the *garrigues*, and the *costières*, the vineyards have spread downhill on to the flood-plains and the coastal plain. This is exemplified in the basin of the Aude; the former Etang de Marseillette, four miles across, lying in the valley between Lézignan and Carcassonne, has deen drained, and forms one vast vineyard with rows of vines separated by irrigation channels.

This dependence on a single crop has its dangers. From 1850-5 the Midi was swept by *oïdium* (the vine-mildew), which did much damage before the efficacy of spraying with sulphur or copper sulphate was discovered. Far worse was the phylloxera which appeared in 1863, and within twenty years had devastated much of the Midi;[2] the area under vines decreased to one-fifth. When the American *Riparia* stocks were at last introduced, the extent under vines first slowly then more rapidly increased, and gradually the coastal plain between the dunes and the *garrigues* became the major producing area. Other crises were the result of the first large-scale imports of cheaper Algerian wine, of over-production and price-slumps, of laws against distillation (as in 1903), and of some post-1950 half-hearted Government efforts at discouragement of wine-drinking in France. Nevertheless, this monoculture has persisted.

Co-operation has become the basis of production; the first *coopérative viticole* was founded in western Biterrois in 1901, and the movement increased particularly in the 'thirties after the world

---

[1] S. Agnew, 'The Vine in Bas Languedoc', in *G.R.* (1946), vol. 36, pp. 67-79. See also G. Galtier, *La Viticulture du Languedoc méditerranéen et du Roussillon* (1947).   [2] See note on p. 325.

economic depression, when the need for organisation became
critical. The 190,000 *vignerons* are grouped into a *Confédération
Générale des Vignerons* to protect their interests. The many small
proprietors (about 95 per cent of all growers) belong to one of the
five hundred co-operatives situated in the large villages and towns,
owning fleets of wine tanker-barges, lorries and rail-tankers. By
contrast, a quarter of the land under vines consists of holdings of
from a hundred to a thousand acres owned by a few proprietors,
self-contained and usually operating independently of the co-operatives.

Much work in Languedoc is afforded by occupations ancillary to
vine cultivation : in the *caves collectives*, in co-operative distilleries,
in the making of non-fermented wines known as *mistelles*, in making
barrels, bottles and corks, printing labels, and distributing fertilisers
and insecticidal sprays.

One area where there is less dependence on monoculture is the
upper Aude basin, from Lézignan up past Carcassonne to Castelnaudary. While the vine is still dominant, wheat, maize, oats and
fodder-beet are also cultivated in rotation with lucerne, clover and
vetch. There are extensive orchards of fruit trees, especially the
famous *Reine Claude* plums, and of sweet chestnuts. More livestock
is kept, not only cattle but pigs, poultry and bees. Prosperous
villages and towns are dotted about this pleasant landscape, which
contrasts in its green diversity with the sun-baked coastal plains and
the harsh *garrigue* country further east.[1]

Fishing.—The long stretch of coast, the waters of the *étangs*, and
the many little harbours and coastal villages would seem to indicate
the possibility of fishing. In point of fact, the Mediterranean littoral
is not of any great importance in the French fishing economy ; in
1963 only 14,700 tons of fish was landed here (according to the
Comité Central des Pêches Maritimes) out of a total of 385,000 tons
around the whole French coast. Of course, these figures refer only
to fish sold commercially, and much Mediterranean fishing is on a
part-time and subsistence basis. The little fishing-ports along the
coast of Languedoc—Palavas, Sète, Marseillan, Agde, Gruissan and
Leucate—do not land sufficient even to supply the towns of the
hinterland. Still, about 1,500 men are engaged full-time in fishing,
and many others fish occasionally, including Italians who come for
the summer, living in camps among the sand-dunes, before moving
on to the Midi vine-harvest. Red tunny, sardines, anchovies and
mackerel are caught in the open sea. The Etang de Thau has oyster-

---

[1] The contribution of co-operation to the agricultural economy is discussed by
B. Derousseau, 'La Coopérative agricole lauragaise', in *R.G.P.S.-O.* (1964), vol.
35, pp. 214-20.

and mussel-fisheries; almost wiped out by too thorough dragging before 1907, they are now carefully conserved. Eels, lobsters and crayfish are also caught in the lagoons.

Some of the fishing is done by curious methods. Fishermen from the villages among the lagoons work with their families, using complex nets known variously as *esturiés*, *triangles* and *trabaques*, some fixed permanently in place as fish-traps, others pulled into position to net a large area. Some fishermen even use harpoons and tridents. The Sète fishermen have a system of working their boats in pairs (*bateaux bœufs*), behind which a long net with wide wings is towed to catch sardines and anchovy. All this is on a small scale; nevertheless, along the lagoon coast the little huts of the fishermen, the boats hauled up on the sands, and fish drying in the sun are part of the Mediterranean scene. It is a coast which contrasts markedly with that of Provence in many respects, but one in particular—the almost complete absence of *plages*, of *bains*, of hotels and casinos, the non-existence of a luxury tourist industry.

POPULATION AND SETTLEMENT

In 1962 the average density of population in the three *départements* of Aude, Gard and Hérault was 111, 192 and 215 per square mile respectively; approximately 1·32 million people lived there. These average densities mean little, however; some of the *garrigue* country within a few miles of Montpellier is one of the most scantily populated parts of France, and the sand-dune *cordon-littoral* and the marshy areas around the lagoons are little better. The population is grouped in hamlets among the *combes* and basins in the *garrigue*, and in small fishing villages situated near the mouths of the *graus* or on eminences among the marshlands.

The mean densities are as high as they are because of intensive cultivation on the terraces and lowlands, forming a longitudinal belt of dense population between the coast and the *garrigues*, with a 'tongue' extending up the Aude valley into the basin of Carcassonne. This rurally-employed population lives not dispersed among the vineyards, but in large villages which have usually been nuclei of settlement for many centuries. Their sites take advantage of minor eminences, knolls and ridges rising from the formerly marshy plain, chosen both for defence and to avoid floods; [1] many have protecting ramparts surrounding a church or château. Another reason for the quite high density is the number of fair-sized towns, in common with the lower Rhône valley and Provence, for here are some of the most attractive towns in France, centres of civic life since Roman

[1] S. Agnew, 'Rural Settlement in the Coastal Plain of Bas Languedoc', in *Geography* (1946), vol. xxxi, pp. 67-77.

times, although some are indeed decayed in comparison with their past glories. From the little ports[1] the tide of commerce has receded as the accretion of mud and sand extended into the shallowing sea. Agde, with about 8,900 people, stands near the mouth of the Hérault river among the vineyards, with wharves on the Canal du Midi.

Sète is the one coastal town of any size; grievously damaged during the war of 1939–45, it has not yet regained its pre-1939 population of nearly 40,000. Compared with most towns of Languedoc, Sète is a newcomer; the port was deliberately created during the reign of Louis XIV. The limestone knoll of Mont-St. Clair rises to over 250 feet on the southern shore of the Etang de Thau, which is otherwise separated from the sea only by a long narrow beach crowned with sand-dunes. Moles were built on the south-eastern side of the hill to afford shelter from the open sea and to provide an *avant-port*. Several basins and quays have been constructed, particularly during and after the war of 1914–18. A channel is maintained by dredging across the eastern end of the *étang* to the Frontignan oil-refinery near its shores. In 1839 the railway-line between Montpellier and Sète was opened, with sidings on the northern side of the port.

The town of Sète grew up originally on the lower slopes of Mont-St. Clair but has since spread ribbon-wise eastward along the sand-spit, following the main road to Frontignan and Montpellier. During this century its industries have developed in much the same way as those of Marseilles, although on a much smaller scale. The reclaimed land along the eastern shore of the Etang de Thau has provided spacious factory sites for chemical- and cement-works, yards building canal-barges, cooperage factories and distilleries producing various spirits, including Vermouth for which the town is well known. The Frontignan oil-refinery, owned by a French associated company of *Mobil-Oil*, had an output in 1964 of 1·4 million tons. The refinery is linked by pipe-line with storage tanks along the quays of the *Bassin aux Pétroles* on the eastern side of the *avant-port*.

In 1963 Sète was the tenth port of France in terms of tonnage of shipping entered and cleared; it was used by 2,219 vessels of a net tonnage of 3·2 millions. Its chief imports were crude oil (1·6 million tons, or over five times the 1938 figure), phosphates, sulphur, Algerian wine, and smaller amounts of North African wheat, copper sulphate (for vine spray), timber, wool and coal. Its exports, only a third of the volume of imports, consisted of refined hydrocarbons (482,000 tons), cement, bauxite, liqueurs, wines and spirits, various chemical products, and live sheep and cattle to Algeria.

[1] C. Lenthéric, *Les Villes mortes du Golfe du Lion* (1876).

Sète is also an inland waterway port, for the Rhône-Sète and Midi Canals open into the Etang de Thau. The former, completed only in 1934, runs from Beaucaire on the Rhône to Aigues-Mortes (Fig. 100), then in a dyked channel through the coastal *étangs* to Sète. The Canal du Midi, completed in 1681, runs for 150 miles between the south-western end of the Etang de Thau and the city of Toulouse, crossing the Col de Naurouze by means of sixty-five locks and a tunnel. With the continuation of navigation along the Garonne Lateral Canal and the Garonne itself (Fig. 89), the canal thus negotiates the watershed between the Mediterranean and the Atlantic. In the latter part of the nineteenth century, the canal concession was bought by the Midi Railway Company in order to divert traffic from the waterway to the railway; this succeeded so well that the former ceased to be used and fell into disrepair. The Government bought it in 1898 and tried to revive navigation by freight-rate reduction, while after 1921 considerable expenditure was incurred in an effort to make it navigable to 300-ton barges. But even so only a depth of six feet can be maintained, so that the canal is still used merely by 120-ton barges. The main cargoes consist of wine moving in both directions (including Algerian wine imported via Sète), wine-casks, corks, coal, cement and petroleum.[1]

In spite of the limited use and value of the present Midi Canal, the concept of a '*Canal des Deux Mers*' is obviously attractive. The project of a ship-canal was raised several times in the nineteenth century, and in the 'twenties of this century the scheme was seriously considered. A congress held at Toulouse in 1932 produced plans for a ship-canal about 190 miles long between Bordeaux and La Nouvelle; it was to be nearly 500 feet in width, of sufficient depth to accommodate ocean-going vessels, and equipped with modern ship-lifts. But in view of the immense expenditure involved, the French Government showed little interest until February 1939; at this inauspicious time it was announced that the preliminary consent of the Government had been attained. But no further action has so far been possible.

The largest town of Languedoc is Montpellier, with a population of 123,367 in 1962. It stands on low hills (the Buttes de Montpellier and Montpellieret) rising from the coastal plain between some right-bank tributaries of the Lez. For long Montpellier has been the administrative and commercial centre of Languedoc, as it is now of Hérault. Spaciously laid out with squares and broad avenues, it was for a time a fashionable tourist-centre. It is the second wine-market of the Midi, it has light industries (food-preserving, perfumes, soap, pharmaceutical chemicals), and is an attractive intellectual

[1] R. Brunet, 'Expansion et problèmes des canaux du Midi', in *R.G.P.S.-O.* (1964), vol. 35, pp. 207-13.

and cultural centre with a celebrated university.[1]

The *chef-lieu* of Gard is Nîmes, with 105,000 people in 1962. It stands on the edge of the *garrigue* country overlooking the plain of the lower Rhône; indeed, it was on a spur of the limestone hills that the Romans built the dominating *Tour Magne* and from the foot of this ridge issued the thermal spring which supplied the famous bath systems. It became one of the finest cities of the Roman empire, of which many remarkable remains survive, including its superb arena. Today, with its nodal rail and road position, Nîmes is an important commercial centre, it has silk and wool textile and clothing industries, factories producing consumer-goods such as shoes, and metallurgical industries (including agricultural machinery and the repair of *S.N.C.F.* rolling-stock and locomotives). It is also an important market for agricultural produce.

In southern Languedoc two smaller towns, Béziers and Narbonne, have populations of about 76,000 and 36,000 respectively. The former is situated where the Orb valley opens into the coastal plain. The narrow streets of the old town ascend steeply to the summit of a prominent hill on which stands a massive fortress-like church, while the modern commercial and residential suburbs have spread out on to the plain. Béziers is the main centre of the Languedoc wine industry, and the town's growth during the last century has been closely related to the prosperity of this dominating product. In 1850 its population was only 16,000 but during the expansion in vine cultivation the total increased to 43,000 by 1866. There followed forty years of virtual stagnation while the phylloxera and other troubles which beset viticulture affected the whole economy of the district, but today the wine industry is again all important in its life; apart from processing, blending and shipping, Béziers is the main despatching centre of rail tank-wagons, and it makes barrels, bottles, corks, wine-presses and insecticides.

Narbonne too owes much of its growth during the last hundred years to the vine. For long the town strove to maintain an outlet to the sea, for it was once a port on a broad inlet, but today the Canal de la Robine (to La Nouvelle at the southern end of the residual string of *étangs*) is the sole connection and is but rarely used; it has, however, a link with the Canal du Midi. Narbonne is an important rail-junction for routes from Béziers, from Perpignan and Spain, and from Carcassonne and Toulouse, and serves as the market- and servicing-town for the lower Agde valley.

Finally, there is a series of towns up the fertile Aude valley on the route through the Porte d'Aquitaine to Toulouse, followed by

---

[1] G. Galtier, 'Les Conditions géographiques de Montpellier', in *Mélanges géographiques offerts à Ph. Arbos* (1953), pp. 237-46; published by the *Faculté des Lettres de l'Université de Clermont.*

roads, rail and the Canal du Midi. Some, such as Roquecourbe, Marseillette, Carcassonne, Bram and Castelnaudary, stand in the floor of the main valley, usually on a terrace above the Aude flood-plain. Others are situated where tributaries open out into the plain or in these valleys themselves—Olonzac, Peyriac, Conques, Saissac in the north, and Lézignan, Limoux, Montréal and Fanjeaux in the south. Neat, compact and prosperous-looking, each is the centre of a thriving agricultural life. Many have factories, specialising in textiles, shoes and leather-work, cooperage, and the processing of foodstuffs (milling, olive-preserving, liqueur-distilling). The chief town is Carcassonne, with its 44,000 people the *chef-lieu* of Aude and an important point on the Biscay-Mediterranean through-route. It stands in a basin where converge several rivers, dominated by the castle on a steep-sided plateau within a meander of the Aude. For long a vital strong-point, the castle fell into ruin, but was restored in the middle of the nineteenth century; today stands a double rampart with fifty towers surmounted by conical roofs, the old buildings within the walls and the newer town spread outside. Carcassonne is the centre of the upper Aude wine industry, and most of its occupations are ancillary to this function.

ROUSSILLON

The semi-circular *Plaine du Roussillon* is enclosed on the north by the uplands of Corbières and on the south by the Albères ridges, both of which project eastward almost to the Golfe du Lion. On the west lies the upland country of Capcir and Canigou, broadly part of the Pyrenean system. The longitudinal valleys of the Agly, the Têt and the Tech provide re-entrants of lowland far into this hill-country, known respectively by their *pays*-names of *Fenouillèdes*, *Conflent* and *Vallespir*. The three main rivers, joined by a multitude of torrential tributaries (many of which dry up in summer), flow eastwards across the plain to the sea (Fig. 102).

Roussillon was in Pliocene times a marine gulf, which has since been infilled with masses of alluvium worn by torrential streams from the bounding massifs. Much of the surface is covered with sheets of Pliocene gravels, forming plateaus on the edge of the uplands at altitudes of 300 to 750 feet, flanked on the seaward side and in the river flood-plains with newer materials—fine alluvium, sand and gravel. Recent changes of sea-level have caused the rivers to cut down their present valleys into the older gravel-sheets, forming distinct steps and terraces, and they have also resulted in marine transgressions on to the seaward margins of the plain. The material brought down by the rivers, combined with longshore drift, has created an almost complete *cordon-littoral* from the Silurian rocks of the coast near Collioure, where the Albères uplands reach the sea, to the Oligocene headland of Cap Leucate. A line of sand-dunes forms a gentle arc, interrupted only by the mouths of the three rivers and by the *graus* opening seawards from the lagoons. Many of the smaller *étangs* have been reclaimed, either naturally by accretion of

FIG. 102.—ROUSSILLON.

The edge of the uplands (at about 750 to 1000 feet) is generalised. Heights are given in feet.

Based on *Carte de France et des frontières au 200,000ᵉ*, sheet 78.

alluvium and vegetation or by man, but three remain (Fig. 102). They are surrounded by marshes, glistening white with salt encrustations, or green with stretches of *Salicornia* and other halophytes, or brown and dreary with reed-beds. Further inland, as the salt-content becomes less, poor pastures appear, green in winter but brown and arid in the dry heat of summer. The importance of *les terres salées* is shown by the common use of the salt-element in place-names now well inland from the coast, such as Salses, Rivesaltes and Saleilles.

Climate.—The climate exemplifies the Mediterranean régime in its most emphasised form in France. The summer drought is virtually complete in July and August, and the sun-baked plains shimmer in the heat. Perpignan has a mean rainfall of 21·9 inches, falling on only sixty-four days in the year. Salses, with 17·3 inches, is perhaps the driest place in France, and the mean number of days with rain is only thirty-four. Most of the rain is due to the moist *marins* and *marinades* blowing in from the Golfe du Lion, bringing short-lived but intense downpours. The tendency to dryness is emphasised both by the porous gravel-sheets and by rapid evaporation, the result of high temperatures and strong drying winds. The *tramontane roussillonnaise* occasionally blows down from the surrounding uplands as a dry chilly wind with some of the features of the *mistral*, though rarely so violent. Temperatures are higher in both winter and summer than almost anywhere else in France; Perpignan has a January mean of 44° F. and a July mean of 73° F., and indeed the maximum shade-temperature ever recorded in the country was 108° F., experienced there in 1871.

Land-Use and Agriculture.—With the exception of areas of recent alluvium along the flood-plains of the larger rivers, the plain of Roussillon is not naturally a favourable agricultural district. The scrubby tracts among the western gravel-plateaus, the stony inter-fluves between the river-valleys, the salt-marshes (known as *salobres*) flanking the inner side of the *étangs*, and the dune-belts of fine sand are all unsuited to cultivation, and the sun-baked aridity of summer can only be alleviated where irrigation is possible. Considerable areas consist of poor *garrigue*, thickets of stunted holm- or cork-oak, and poor winter pasture (utilised by the flocks brought down from Capcir and Cerdagne).[1]

Agriculture, however, flourishes wherever the physical disabilities can be overcome. The lower gravel plateaus and terraces have long been cultivated in the traditional way—hard wheat with a biennial period of fallow, olives, almonds, stone-fruits such as apricots, peaches and cherries (notably on the terraces above the Tech valley near Céret) and mulberries. Most of these flourish on the dry warm slopes, despite the stony soils. The general term *aspres* is given to these areas cultivated without irrigation. This polyculture was still more diverse in the past, when such industrial crops as hemp, saffron and madder were grown.

In the nineteenth century, however, the cultivation of the vine increased on the gravel plateaus and terraces, and such wines as

[1] This diversity of land-use is well shown by the beautifully produced Perpignan sheet of the *Carte de la végétation de la France* (*1 : 200,000*) (1950), the second of the series to be issued, compiled by H. Gaussen.

malvoisie and *maccabéo* achieved a certain fame. The area of vine-yards in Pyrénées-Orientales grew to a maximum of 200,000 acres before the phylloxera crisis, and after the inevitable resultant decline has slowly increased again. Even today, when orchards have developed at their expense, the vineyards occupy more than 158,000 acres, and in 1963 the *département* produced 2·3 million hl. of wine. While much of the yield is of *ordinaire* grade, there are several quality wines. In the neighbourhood of Thuir, to the south-west of Perpignan, alcohol-rich wines are produced from which is pre-pared the celebrated liqueur '*Byrrh*'. Many of the vineyards of the Agly valley concentrate on the production of high-quality table-grapes.

Where irrigation-water can be obtained, an intensive cultivation of vegetables on a market-garden scale has developed. Since the Middle Ages water has been taken from the rivers through deriva-tion canals to supply orchards and vegetable-gardens similar to the *huertas* of the east coast of Spain. The main difficulty is the fluc-tuating régime of the rivers; they are at a low level at the very time of year when water is most required, and they lose so much volume that even the three large ones can hardly sustain their flow to the sea. Some supplementary well-irrigation has been developed, using wind-pumps and in modern times diesel-pumps, to exploit the water from the uplands around which has sunk into the rocks of the alluvial basin. These irrigated lands are found on the lower terraces and flood-plains along the three main rivers, where villages and small towns stand among gardens and orchards. The chief districts are in the Tech valley (the *Bas-Vallespir*, with centres at Elne, Palau, Ortaffa and Céret), in the lower Têt valley (known as the *Ribéral*, especially at Perpignan, St. Estève and Ille-sur-Têt), and further north in the Agly valley (at Espira and Cases). The vine and fruits such as apricots, figs and peaches are widely grown, but the cultivation of vegetables is most important. The methods of cultivation and types of vegetables are much the same as in the lower Rhône, but the growers in Roussillon can produce salads and other *primeurs* several weeks earlier, owing to the virtual freedom from frost and strong winds; the *tramontane* does not approach either the frequency or vio-lence of the *mistral*, as is shown by the usual absence of wind-breaks, and the mild winters make cloches and glasshouses unnecessary. Marketing is organised in co-operatives, and at Perpignan station cold-stores have been built to accommodate the produce before its northward shipment by rail.

Cultivation has extended seawards on to reclaimed marshlands where the salt-content has been reduced either by years of 'flushing' by the annual floods of such rivers as the Réart and by systematic irrigation, or by cultivating salt-absorbing plants. The main areas of such improvement are known as *salanques*, the most important district being La Grande Salanque between the Agly and the Têt, hence the names St. Laurent-de-la-Salanque and Villelongue-de-la-Salanque. Here are found vineyards, often with beds of asparagus, artichokes and other vegetables on the rather sandy soils between the rows of vines, and patches of barley and of irrigated lucerne.

Settlement.—The plain of Roussillon is studded with small towns and villages, usually on the terraces well above the river-floods. The rural density of population is of the order of 210 per square mile, in some places (notably along the Ribéral) rising to over 500. Many towns were fortified, the result of their 'marchland' situation, and at some the walls and towers are still standing, as at Salses.

The sand-dune coast has few settlements beyond the huts of fishermen and *saliniers*. The few small resorts include Canet-Plage (visited by the inhabitants of Perpignan), St. Cyprien-Plage and Le Barcarès reached by a branch railway-line from Rivesaltes. Most of the larger resorts lie along the rocky coastline to the south of Roussillon between Collioure and Cerbère, known as the *Côte Vermeille*. The only port of any significance is Port-Vendres,[1] situated not on the sand-dune coast, but nine miles north of the Spanish frontier, where the ranges of the Albères reach the coast. What was little more than a creek along the rocky coast was developed by Vauban, and the main port now consists of a rectangular basin. It handles 125,000 tons of freight a year, mostly imports of cereals, wine and fruit from Algeria, but its chief importance is as a packet-port. Rail connections from the north serve this nearest port to Algeria, though since the latter attained independence the number of passengers has greatly declined.

Perpignan of course dominates the plain. The old town clusters around a low hill (*le Puig*) near the Têt, seven miles from the sea. It was for long a fortress town, guarding the land-route from Spain into Languedoc and beyond to the rest of France. The town developed industries, including the manufacture of silk cloth, and became the economic capital of this rather isolated region. This rôle was increasingly important after the railway reached the city, and with the development of intensive cultivation Perpignan became the chief administrative, marketing and despatching centre for Roussillon. In the last fifty years the town has grown considerably; with a population of 20,000 at the beginning of the nineteenth century and still of less than 30,000 at the outbreak of the war of 1914–18, the total had increased to 86,000 by 1962. At Quillan (between Perpignan and

[1] An account of Port-Vendres, in immense detail, is given by S. Laborde, 'Port-Vendres, études de géographie humaine', *Bulletin, Société Languedocienne de Géographie* (1957), vol. xxviii, pp. 3-108.

Carcassonne) a recently built plastics factory is owned by a subsidiary of *British Formica*.

About 200,000 people in Roussillon speak Catalan, the linguistic features of which are in some ways transitional between Spanish and the Provençal form of French. The French form of Catalan does differ in a number of ways from that spoken by some millions of people across the Pyrenees in north-eastern Spain.

PART II

THE HERCYNIAN UPLANDS

CHAPTER 17

ARMORICA

The term Armorica is derived from the Celtic words *Ar-Mor*, 'the country of the sea', which refer to the long indented coastline and hinterland of a triangular peninsula projecting westward into the Atlantic Ocean, the ancient province of *Bretagne*. The term is commonly applied more widely to a geographical region,[1] the basis of whose identity is structural, for it consists of a massif of Pre-Cambrian and Palaeozoic rocks, together with some large intrusive masses of granite and some smaller areas of newer rocks preserved in depressions. This geological definition is shown on Fig. 103. This larger area includes not only *Bretagne*, but also the western parts of the former provinces of *Maine*, *Anjou* and *Normandie* (Fig. 1).

GENERAL FEATURES

Structure and Relief.—Armorica has experienced a complex structural history of successive alternations of folding, peneplanation, *en bloc* uplift and renewed denudation. An early period of folding, corresponding to the Caledonian orogeny in north-western Europe, probably affected the Pre-Cambrian rocks, but it was the widespread earth-movements of Carbo-Permian times that were responsible for the basic structures. The fold-mountain ranges produced by this orogeny, known as the '*Altaides*', once extended across central Europe from south-western Ireland to southern Russia. Fragments of these ancient ranges now project as upland blocks from the surrounding sedimentary plains. The folds in the west are referred to as 'Armorican', those further east as 'Hercynian', although occasionally they are known collectively as 'Variscan'.

The trend-lines of the folding in Armorica are complex, but a central synclinorial 'furrow' can be traced eastward from the bays

---

[1] See R. Musset, *La Bretagne* (1937); M. Gautier, *La Bretagne centrale* (1947); M. le Lannou, *Géographie de la Bretagne* (1952); W. Diville and A. Guilcher, *Bretagne et Normandie* (1951); P. Flatrès, *La Région de l'Ouest* (1964); and H. Elhaï, *La Normandie occidentale* (1963), a vol. of 624 pp., many maps and an extensive bibliography.

which deeply indent the west coast through the Carboniferous-floored basins of Châteaulin in the west (now followed longitudinally by the river Aulne) and of Laval in the east (now crossed transversely by the Mayenne). Between these two basins the downfold is indicated by a narrow band of Carboniferous strata to the south of the Landes du Menez and on the northern edge of the Rennes depression. To the north and south of this synclinorium are the trend-lines of upfolds running from west-south-west to east-north-east in the Pays de Léon (hence the term 'direction de Léon'), and from north-west to south-east in Cornouaille. The latter trend is known as 'la direction de Cornouaille', but as it continues south-eastward beneath the Jurassic rocks of the Gate of Poitou to reappear in the western part of the Central Massif, the wider term 'direction armoricaine' is usually applied. The Léon anticlinorium is broken into by the roughly quadrangular Golfe de St. Malo, its fragments forming the islands of Jersey, the Minquiers and Chausey, and reappears in the southern part of the Cotentin peninsula. Further north, beyond another synclinal depression of Silurian slates in part floored with Tertiary rocks, a further broken anticlinal ridge can be traced through Guernsey and Alderney into the northern part of the Cotentin.[1] These Armorican folds become increasingly complex in the east and south-east, where they vanish under the Mesozoic and Tertiary cover. Although the original folds have been largely destroyed by denudation, their trend-lines impose a clearly defined 'grain' (Fig. 103). A large number of faults demarcate both horst-like uplands and distinct basins,[2] and account for the presence of long 'slices' of different rocks in close juxtaposition.

A long period of denudation in early Mesozoic times wore down the folded region into a peneplain cutting across the various structures. Within this general peneplanation a number of individual 'plates-formes d'érosion' at different heights can be distinguished.[3] Over this peneplain then spread the fluctuating marine transgressions which covered much of western Europe, and a widespread cover of Mesozoic and Tertiary rocks was laid down. These now form

[1] P. Morin, 'Le Golfe Normand-Breton', in A. de G. (1931), vol. xl, pp. 1-23.

[2] See, for example, a map, section and much other detail in A. Guilcher, 'Observations sur la formation du relief de la Bretagne méridionale', in A. de G. (1941), vol. l, pp. 255-65. See also maps showing the faults bounding the Basin de Rennes and those in north-eastern Brittany in A. Meynier, 'Influences tectoniques sur le relief de la Bretagne', in A. de G. (1947), vol. xlvi, pp. 170-7.

[3] The classic study is E. de Martonne, 'La Pénéplaine et les Côtes bretonnes', in A. de G. (1906), vol. xv, pp. 213-36 and 299-328. See also the detailed articles by R. Musset, 'Le Relief de la Bretagne occidentale', ibid. (1928), vol. xxxvii, pp. 209-23; and A. Darté, 'Les Abrupts asymétriques du Massif armoricain', in Norois (1966), no. 50, pp. 157-63.

the surface rocks of much of the lowlands of northern France and
Belgium, but they have vanished from Armorica except on the
eastern and southern margins and in a few depressions. One result
is the presence of ferruginous ores preserved in the shales and sandstones of the Silurian synclines, a relic of the vanished overlying

FIG. 103.—SIMPLIFIED GEOLOGICAL MAP OF ARMORICA.

Minor areas of Quaternary and Recent deposits in bays and estuaries are
omitted. N, Nantes; R, Rennes.

Based on (i) folding map in L. de Launay, *Géologie de la France* (1921); and (ii)
Carte géologique de la France, 1 : 1,000,000, published by the *Service de la Carte
géologique détaillée de la France* (1933).

Jurassic beds. These are the *Gisements d'Anjou* in the *départements* of Ille-et-Vilaine and Mayenne, extending in an interrupted
series north-westward from Angers (Fig. 72). The ore is found in
ridges of sandstone lying among the Palaeozoic slates and shales;
five mines are in operation at Segré, Soulvache and near Rouge.
Before the war just over a quarter of a million tons was mined

R.G.W.E.—Q

annually; this was raised to a record production of 788,000 tons in 1955. Other fields occur in western Normandy (see pp. 241-2).

In mid-Tertiary times the repercussions of the earth-movements associated with the Alpine orogeny further south were such that the massif suffered some uplift, with a slight tilt towards the south. This movement was not as marked as in the other Hercynian massifs, possibly because it lay more on the margins of the orogeny, but the uplift was sufficient to inaugurate a new phase of denudation. The newer cover was almost wholly removed and the ancient peneplain more or less exhumed. The resistant granites and granulites were exposed as elliptical dome-like masses, their axes also orientated

FIG. 104.—GENERAL MAP OF ARMORICA.
Q, Quimper. Land above 100 metres (328 feet) is stippled.

from west to east, for they represent the deep-seated cores of the destroyed anticlines. The crystalline schists form extensive plateaus over much of central Armorica; they are given various local names, such as the *schistes de St. Lô* and the *schistes de Rennes*, and there is considerable argument as to their exact age.

Finally, small patches of Tertiary rocks are preserved in depressions and basins. Eocene rocks occur near Mayenne in the east, areas of Oligocene and Miocene limestone and clay to the west and south-west of Rennes and in La Vendée, and scattered Pliocene outcrops survive in the south between Redon and Angers.

The rivers were superimposed across the varied rocks of the peneplain, although their courses reveal in detail an adaptation to the structure.[1] The Devonian and Lower Carboniferous slates and shales preserved in the synclinorium across the centre of the massif were worn into a long narrow depression (the basin of Châteaulin), now occupied by the river Aulne. Again, on Fig. 105 it can be seen that two streams flow due west along valleys partly the result of faulting, partly due to weak Silurian slates, in a direction almost parallel to the orientation of the Crozon peninsula, even though it is long and narrow. The same west-east trend is shown even more strikingly further south in Le Cap.[2] Where slices of resistant sandstone, quartzite and grit (often known collectively as the *grès armoricain*) alternate with clayey shales and slates, the former now form prominent though narrow ridges, the latter the intervening valleys. The Vilaine below the Rennes basin, for example, occupies several narrow valley-sections eroded across outcrops of Silurian sandstone, but between these it flows through broad basins into which come tributary strike-streams wherever shales or slates occur.

The Coast.—Perhaps the most striking feature of Brittany is its magnificent rugged coast, the edge of a rocky peninsula projecting boldly into the Atlantic. It has been calculated [3] that the total length of coastline around the Breton peninsula is no less than 2,160 miles, of which 19 per cent comprises the islands. Its characteristics are the combined result, first, of a slight marine transgression in late Quaternary times which inundated the margins of the irregularly dissected peneplain; second, of the marine denudation of rocks of varying degrees of resistance lying in close juxtaposition; and third (less marked but in places quite appreciable), the complementary processes of deposition in the sheltered bays.

The marine transgression was responsible for the drowning of the lower portions of river-valleys cut deeply into the peneplain, so forming a typical *ria* coast with long winding indentations. This is particularly marked in the west, where the trend of the coast runs transversely to the 'grain' of the structure. The Rade de Brest and the Baie de Douarnenez penetrate eastward on either side of the Crozon peninsula (Fig. 105). The first represents the drowned lower portion of the basin of Châteaulin, and the river Aulne enters the Rade through a long winding inlet. The Baie de Douarnenez

[1] Some of the complexities are discussed by R. Musset, 'La Formation du Réseau hydrographique de la Bretagne occidentale', in *A. de G.* (1934), vol. xliii, pp. 561-78.

[2] See R. Musset's study of the valley of the Loc'h and its 'fossil ria', 'Les Rias fossiles de la côte occidentale de la Bretagne', in *A. de G.*(1926), vol. xxxv, pp. 360-2.

[3] R. Musset, 'La Bretagne péninsulaire', in *La France: géographie-tourisme* (1952), vol. ii, p. 141.

represents the inundated portion of a basin worn subaerially in weak slates, into which flow a dozen short rivers instead of a single master-stream, so that the bay is more open and rounded than the usual *ria*-type of inlet. The trend of the structure-lines in the south of Brittany runs more or less parallel to the coast, but the lower courses of the larger rivers have been submerged to form long *ria*-estuaries, as in the case of the Odet below Quimper, the Ellé below Quimperlé, the Blavet and the Vilaine. By contrast, the broad island-studded inlet of Morbihan, into which flows the Auray and other small rivers, represents the submergence of a basin so shallow that large parts dry out at low tide to form mud-flats. The northern coast also lies roughly parallel to the main structural trends, but even here so many short rivers flowing northwards from the Montagnes d'Arrée and Landes du Menez have cut deep winding valleys across the various rocks that the submergence of their estuaries has resulted in some striking indentations. The estuary of the Rance, for example, runs inland for about seventeen miles from St. Malo to Dinan.

Long ridges project seaward between the various inlets (Plate XLIX), ending in cliff-fronted promontories. Their former prolongation is indicated by the patterns of the submarine contours and the strings of offshore rocky archipelagoes and submerged rock-banks (Fig. 105). Thus the granitic ridges of Cornouaille end in the Pointe du Raz, while the Ile de Sein and its surrounding islets and reefs extend seawards for over twenty miles.

A further result of submergence has been the formation of islands, the higher outliers of the irregularly dissected margins of the peneplain. Many are little more than rocky stumps or submarine shoals, others are of larger dimensions. In the right-angle of the Cotentin peninsula are the Channel Islands (*les Iles Anglo-Normandes*), the Minquiers and the Iles Chausey. Near the coast is the fascinating granitic pyramid of Mont-St. Michel, some 300 yards in diameter at the base, and rising to a height of 256 feet from its surrounding low-water sand-banks (crossed by a causeway). Further west some granitic fragments comprise the Ile Bréhat and the cluster of Les Sept Iles, and Les Héaux is made of rhyolite. Off the coast of the Pays de Léon are rocky islets which culminate in the famous Ile d'Ouessant, known to English seamen for centuries as 'Ushant'; it rises to 213 feet but is only nine square miles in area.

Along the south coast of Brittany are many more islands, several lying some distance offshore. Some are granitic fragments, such as the Iles de Glénan, Houat and Hoédic. Belle-Ile is a massive piece of schist, with a coast of alternate steep cliffs and sandy bays. Groix, lying nearer to the mainland, consists of Pre-Cambrian schists and Silurian slates, while Yeu, off the Vendéan coast, is a mass of granite rising to 115 feet, surrounded by low but steep cliffs. The isolated granitic masses of Quiberon and Le Croisic were once islands, but were converted into peninsulas by marine deposition.

The second contribution to the present Breton coastline is marine denudation, which operates unceasingly on the irregular margins of the peninsula. The resistant granites form bold steep cliffs; Pte.

FIG. 105.—THE COAST OF WESTERN BRITTANY.

The large numbers of islets and tidal rocks which cover the submarine banks west of Pte. St. Mathieu and the Pte. du Raz are not shown. The drainage pattern indicates the irregularly dissected margins of the ancient peneplain, but the west-east 'grain' is clearly noticeable, particularly in the Crozon and Le Cap peninsulas. Note the acute meanders of the Aulne, deeply incised in the slates of the Châteaulin basin. The submarine contours are in metres, but the spot-heights are in feet.

G, Goulet de Brest.

Based on (i) *Carte de France et des frontières au 200,000ᵉ*, sheet 21 ; (ii) various British Admiralty charts.

St. Cast to the west of St. Malo rises almost vertically to 160 feet, while Pte. Plouha on the western shores of the Baie de St. Brieuc is nearly twice as high. Similarly, in the south the granulitic rocks form the rugged headlands of Penmarch and Quiberon, and many of the islands have steep cliffed margins. Not only granite forms near-vertical sections of coast. Cap Fréhel and Cap d'Erquy, to the east of the Baie de St. Brieuc, are of hard Devonian sandstone, and the Crozon peninsula (Fig. 105) consists of a number of headlands of quartzites and grits, notably Cap de la Chèvre of Lower Carboniferous grit. But for the most part granitic rocks dominate along the Breton margins, and castellated cliffs, caves, arches and stacks form a most striking coastline to which the name *Côte sauvage* is justifiably applied. It is a dangerous one for shipping, as evidenced by the number of lighthouses in the west (Fig. 105). A rock platform or reef, worn by wave-abrasion, extends seaward in places for a distance exceeding half a mile; the words *'plateau'*, *'roche'*, *'banc'*, *'chaussée'* and *'chaissée'*, separated by difficult *'chenaux'*, *'passages'*, *'entrées'* and *'rades'*, scattered liberally on the charts, indicate its complexity. These platforms are partly caused by submergence, partly by wave-action; they are well developed off the northern coast near Roscoff, and again between the mainland and the Ile de Batz. Marine erosion has worn embayments from less resistant slates and shales to form *baies* and *anses*; half a dozen of these are eroded out of the shales along the Crozon peninsula, and to the west of Roscoff the bays of Plestin, Morlaix and Goulven are formed from schists. Similarly in the south-west the curving outline of the Baie d'Audierne is worn from schists between the granitic promontories of the Pte. du Raz and Pte. de Penmarch.

While submergence and erosion have combined to produce this diversified coastline, deposition seeks to smooth out the irregularities. In the more sheltered bays and gulfs accumulate first bay-head beaches of gravel and sand backed by dunes and marsh, then more extensive tidal flats of sand and mud. The attrition of the crystalline rocks produces an abundance of pebbles and ultimately of fine sand, and some fine beaches occur even on quite exposed coasts. The Baie d'Audierne, though facing south-west, is fronted by a sweeping curve of sand, and the equally exposed but smaller Baie des Trépasses between the Ptes. du Van and du Raz (Fig. 105) has a beach and a dune-cordon behind which lies a tiny *étang*. Even in the Rade de Brest dredging is constantly necessary.

A striking example of sedimentation occurs along the coast of the Baie du Mont-St. Michel, within the angle of the Cotentin peninsula where a waste of quicksands, uncovered at low tide, is crossed by creeks and channels, for the sea goes out for eight miles at spring-tides (Fig. 106). The deposits are of fine clay-sands with an admixture of finely comminuted shells, producing a slimy sand known as *tangue*. The edge of the coast now lies some miles north of its former position. Three crystalline masses project above the general level: Mont Dol (rising to 213 feet), Mont-St. Michel and Tombelaine. A marsh fronted by a sand-bar accumulated along the south side of the bay, and was for long liable to inundation during storms. To

protect this a dyke, nearly twenty miles in length, was built as long
ago as 1324 from the Pte. de Château-Richeaux eastward to the valley
of the Couesnon near Pontorson. It was soon afterwards breached
and much land was inundated until the end of the eighteenth century.
Then the dyke was rebuilt, and the Marais de Dol was drained by
a network of channels known as *biez*, administered by a syndicate of
proprietors. From 1849 to 1870 further developments reclaimed the
triangle of marsh between the eastern part of the dyke and the causeway carrying the road and railway to Mont-St. Michel. This celebrated eminence is crowned by an eleventh-century abbey-church,
and has houses and cobbled streets clustered around its steep flanks.

FIG. 106.—THE BAIE DU MONT-ST. MICHEL.
Based on *Carte de France et des frontières au 200,000ᵉ*, sheets 22, 23.

A further result of sedimentation can be seen along the south coast
where several sand-spits have been built between islands and the
adjacent mainland, particularly at Quiberon and Le Croisic. Quiberon
was a granitic island rising to 125 feet, but now it is 'tied' to the
mainland by a sand-bar four miles in length, flanked by tidal sands.
The bar is now artificially protected, and a road and railway run along
it to Quiberon. Le Croisic further to the south was also a granitic
island seven miles in length, lying parallel to the mainland at a
distance of five miles. A spit extended westward from the mainland
at Pornichet to the eastern end of the island at Le Pouliguen, thus

forming a rectangular bay, and another bar developed southward from La Turballe, although this has not quite reached the island. An extensive area of tidal marsh was thus naturally enclosed, and a considerable part has been drained by a close network of channels to form salt-pasture, leaving the tidal flats of Le Grand Trait and Le Petit Trait.

Finally, it must by remembered that weathering greatly modifies the varied rocks of a steep coast.[1]

Climate.—Brittany is a peninsula experiencing what might generally be termed 'a western oceanic type of climate', though of course differences are apparent between the coastlands and the higher interior, and again between the north and south coasts. Armorica is subject to strong onshore winds; thus Cap de la Hague and the Ile d'Ouessant have on an average 122 and 144 days in the year respectively when rough seas are experienced, and during winter it is likely to be rough on one day in two. At Brest the average number of calm days during each of the four seasons spring, summer, autumn and winter is only 3, 4, 6 and 4 respectively.[2] Gale-force winds are experienced mainly during the winter months, mostly from directions between north-west and south-west and just occasionally from the south. Along the coast of Brittany names are given to the dominant winds—the *suroît* from the south-west and the *noroît* from the north-west. Further east a distinction is drawn between the south-westerly sea-wind (the *solaire*) and the north-easterly land-wind (the *galerne*).

The Breton peninsula, exposed to moist air-masses from the ocean, is characterised by high humidity, cloudiness and much fine drizzling mist. Because of its not very considerable altitude, however, precipitation totals are by no means as high as at places much further from the sea in the Central Massif, Alps or Vosges. Even the limited range of altitude within Armorica has an effect on precipitation. Thus at the Pte. St. Mathieu station near Brest, just over 100 feet above sea-level, the mean annual total is 32 inches, a figure characteristic of most Breton coastal stations. On the exposed moorlands totals are somewhat higher; La Feuillée (in the Montagnes d'Arrée at a height of 922 feet) has 47 inches, and Edern (in the Montagnes Noires at 679 feet) receives 46 inches. As would be expected, places in the more easterly valleys and basins receive less rain; Guipry in the Vilaine valley to the south of Rennes has 27

[1] A. Guilcher, 'Formes de décomposition chimique dans la zone des embruns et des marées sur les côtes britanniques et bretonnes', in *Cinquantième Anniversaire du Laboratoire de Géographie*, 1902–52, *volume jubilaire* of the *Université de Rennes* (1952), pp. 167-81, with a useful bibliography.

[2] Figures obtained from J. Rouch, *Météorologie aéronautique* (1933), and the Admiralty *Channel Pilot.*

inches, and La Flèche on the eastern margins in the lower Loir valley only 22 inches.

This precipitation is well distributed throughout the year; at St. Mathieu the least rain experienced on an average in any one month is 1·7 inches, the highest is 3·9 inches. Summer is nevertheless appreciably drier, a season when fewer disturbances cross the peninsula and when anticyclonic conditions spreading north-eastward from the Azores tend to establish themselves. The period from May to August receives a mean total at St. Mathieu of 7 inches, compared with twice as much in the four months from October to January. At the same station twelve days with measurable rain (0·1 mm.) may be expected on an average in June, but as many as eighteen in November and nineteen in December. Finally, as an indication of the nature of the rainfall, the average amount per rain-day in January at St. Mathieu is less than half that experienced during the same month at Nice.

The other main characteristic of the Breton climate is its moderate temperatures near sea-level along the coast. The lowest range of temperature between the mean warmest and coolest months experienced in all France is about 17° F., at Roscoff; the warmest and coolest months there are not July and January, but August and February, an indication of the effects of the sea in retarding the cooling of the atmosphere in winter and its heating in summer. The most striking fact is that the mean January temperature for St. Mathieu is 45° F., only about 2° F. lower than that of Nice. The Breton coast experiences frost on about the same number of days as does the Riviera, roughly a dozen. The moorlands in the interior have naturally a more severe winter, being both further from the sea and higher, with more days of frost, a snow-cover of from fifteen to twenty days, and quite bleak conditions.

In summer mean temperatures approximate to 62° F. along the northern and western coasts, and three or four degrees higher along the southern coasts near the Loire estuary. This slight difference is nevertheless critical as far as the successful cultivation of the vine is concerned, for the northern limit runs eastward from the coast near Lorient. R. Dion has suggested that this line corresponds to the 15° C. actual isotherm for the period April to September.[1] The long summer hours of sunshine and clear bright days are one of the charms of the Breton coast, but sea-breezes modify the actual temperatures and hot days are rare. One important factor in the

---

[1] It seems, however, that the limit is in part an economic one, for the vine was grown quite widely in Brittany throughout the Middle Ages and up to 150 years ago. When communications improved so that better wines could be easily brought into Brittany, and with the spread of cider-drinking, these marginal lands ceased to grow the vine.

agricultural economy is the early spring, indeed in many years the temperature rarely falls below 43° F., and meadow-grass hardly ceases to grow.

Here then near the coast is a soft mild climate characterised by equability and humidity. On the interior uplands, however, much bleaker conditions occur—raw, wind-swept and cloudy, and with frost and snow.

Land-Use and Agriculture.—It is useful to summarise the main categories for each of the seven *départements* which comprise Armorica (excluding the three which make up La Vendée, dealt with separately below) to give some indication of the pattern of land-use.

Land-Use, 1963

(*Percentage of Total Area*)

Département	Arable	Permanent Pasture	Woodland
Côtes-du-Nord . .	53	16	12
Finistère . . .	56	13	4
Ille-et-Vilaine . .	59	17	8
Loire-Atlantique . .	46	23	5
Manche . . .	12	73	3
Mayenne . . .	41	41	6
Morbihan . . .	47	23	9

Source: *Ministére de l'Agriculture*, published in the *Annuaire statistique de la France, 1964.*

The small proportion of woodland is evident from these figures, indeed Manche has the lowest percentage of any *département* in France. These humid lands were covered with ancient forests of oak and beech, but once the woodlands had been destroyed regeneration became difficult. The humus-rich soils which had developed under deciduous woodland, thus left unprotected, were removed by denudation and gradually replaced by thin gravelly and acid soils, the product of *in situ* weathering of the granites, schists and quartzites. The solid blocks of ancient forest once provided their own shelter, but after these were removed the winds which sweep the peninsula were inimical to regeneration except in sheltered hollows and valleys. Some forests of oak and beech are carefully preserved; the Forêts d'Halouze, d'Andaine and de la Motte cover considerable areas of the plateau in the east between the headstreams of the Orne and the Mayenne. Along the ridge of the Landes de Lanvaux are coniferous plantations, and some small woodlands occur around the margins of the Rennes basin, notably the Forêts de

Paimpont and de Haute-Sève, and on the Montagnes Noires is the Forêt de Quénécan. The rest of the woodland occurs as copses around villages and farms, or along the hedgerows in the form of pollarded oaks and ash. The last, incidentally, give an impression (as in much of south-east England) of a much more wooded character than is actually the case.

Some of the higher, bleaker uplands are covered with moorland to which the ubiquitous name of *landes* is commonly applied. The impermeable acid rocks, mantled with a thin layer of either coarse gravelly soils or sticky clays, carry a vegetation of gorse, broom, patches of hawthorn and bramble scrub. On the better-drained slopes grow vast sheets of ling, with heather on south-facing aspects, and especially on the clays flourish considerable areas of bracken-fern. In spite of the general humidity, the impermeable rocks and the rapid run-off induce xerophytic characters; after a spell of drought the moorlands assume a bleached and arid appearance.

On some of the flatter moorlands and in the high depressions flourish expanses of bog-grass, sphagnum moss, reeds, bilberry and hard-fern (*Blechnum spicant*), sometimes producing an appreciable accumulation of peat. One of the largest of these upland bogs is the Marais de St. Michel, in a basin enclosed by ridges of the Montagnes d'Arrée.

Around the coast salt-marshes have developed in the angles of sheltered bays or along the margins of estuaries. Large parts of these have been reclaimed, both naturally and by man's efforts, to furnish rich pastures and arable land. In the western angle of the Cotentin the Marais de Dol lies along the coast of the Baie du Mont-St. Michel (Fig. 106), on the northern shore of the Loire estuary is the Grande Brière, and on the coastal plain of Vendée the Marais Breton and Marais Poitevin[1] (Fig. 90).

It can be seen from the table that between 70 and 80 per cent of Armorica is under either arable [2] or permanent grassland. Manche has the highest proportion of permanent pasture in France. By contrast, it is perhaps surprising to find such a low proportion of permanent pasture in the *départements* of Finistère, Côtes-du-Nord and Morbihan, but there the economy is an arable one. There is a certain amount of short-ley grass, and in addition some of the arable fields are left as fallow for a number of years (the *terres vaines*), affording some pasture.

Most of this farmland is enclosed in small fields by banks (*fossés*), crowned with a thick hedge (*haie*), often containing pollarded oaks

---

[1] A. Bouhier, 'Les Communaux de la partie orientale du Marais Poitevin', in *Norois* (1966), no. 49, pp. 5-58.

[2] A. Meynier, 'La Modernisation de l'agriculture bretonne', in *T.E.S.G.* (1957), vol. 48, pp. 37-42.

and ash, though in the west these banks are replaced by dry-stone walls. This is the *bocage* country so characteristic of north-western France, and contrasting markedly with the open hedgeless *plaines*, *campagnes* and *champagnes* of the Paris Basin. The term *bocage* is widely used; there is the *Bocage Normand* in the east, the *Bocage Manceau* of the upper Mayenne basin, the *Bocage Breton* of the west, and the *Bocage Vendéen* to the south of the Loire estuary.

The small fields, the '*champs clos du bocage*', are the basic agricultural units of Brittany, whether under arable cultivation, temporary or permanent grass, market-gardens or cider-apple orchards. The arable fields are located near the sea, and in the Châteaulin and Rennes basins. From the coast shelly sands can be obtained for sweetening the acid soils and for lightening the clays, and seaweed is used as a fertiliser. Here are the sheltered pockets of '*primeurs*' cultivation, now more profitable than cereals, capitalising the relative freedom from frost and the early springs; these meet the demands of Paris, and there is also some export to Great Britain.

Once cereals were the chief agricultural products, and grain and flour were exported by sea round to the Seine estuary and Paris. Little fields of cereals are still grown, usually oats and barley near the coast, rye and buckwheat in the interior, and wheat in the eastern districts of Maine and Anjou. Sometimes *méteil* (a mixture of wheat and rye) is grown, and also a mixture of oats and buckwheat which forms the basis of the widely eaten *pain de mêlée*. But *primeurs*, permanent pasture and fodder-crops now afford a much more lucrative use of the land. Further inland less cultivation is found on the poorer soils and under the bleaker climatic conditions, consisting merely of some patches of potatoes, cabbages, rye and buckwheat.

Armorica is one of the main dairying districts in France; in 1963 there were 3·48 million cattle in the seven *départements*, or about 17 per cent of the French total, and the most important *département* was Manche with over 649,000 head. Many of the cattle are the parti-coloured *vaches bretonnes*, small-boned as a result of the inherent shortage of phosphates and lime in the soil, although Jerseys and Jersey-crosses are increasing in number, particularly in Manche. One great advantage of the mild climate is that except during the worst weather on the uplands cattle can be left out of doors through the year. On many small farms one or two cows are kept as part of the subsistence economy; *caudelée*, a kind of curdled milk, is made and eaten by the producer or sold in the regional markets. The rearing of cattle for beef is increasing, particularly in the uplands, where the poor pasture is usually supplemented with fodder-crops. Large numbers of young bullocks are shipped from the Cotentin and the Bocage Normand to the plains of Lower Normandy, to the eastern Paris Basin and even to Belgium, and from the Bocage Vendéen to Poitou and the Charolais.

In this region of mixed agriculture, other animals afford an important contribution to the economy. About 1·93 million pigs were in the seven *départements* in 1963, or over one-fifth the French total, fattened for local slaughter and also bred for shipping away as stores; there are some famous markets, notably the '*Marché aux Porcs*' at Pont-l'Abbé. Nearly a quarter of all French horses are reared here, mainly for ploughing, indeed Finistère with 90,000 and Côtes-du-Nord with 65,000 animals were easily the two most important *départements*. Little more than a quarter of a million sheep indicates a big decline during the last century; they are kept both on the rougher pastures in the interior and on the coastal salt-marshes.[1]

Regional Divisions.—Within this general setting it is evident that a number of subdivisions can be distinguished. The coast and its immediate hinterland is *Ar-mor* itself, the '*pays de la mer*'. The upland area of the interior is often referred to as *Arcoët* (variously spelt *Argoat*, *Archoat* or *Arcoat*), which means literally 'the country of the woods', another indication of the former forest-cover, but now occupied by expanses of *bocage* interrupted by the *landes* on wind-swept eminences and in damp depressions. The three basins, Châteaulin, Rennes and Laval, merit separate treatment, as does the northward-projecting Cotentin peninsula. The lower Loire crosses on to the ancient Armorican rocks just above the Maine confluence, and its valley with the estuary forms a distinctive unit. Finally, to the south of the Loire are the rather dreary moorlands of the *Collines de Vendée*, flanked on the north by the lower plateau of *Les Mauges* and on the south by the pleasant *Bocage Vendéen*.

ARMOR

Armor comprises the coast and its hinterland from the base of Cotentin right round the peninsula to the mouth of the Loire. The north coast is higher and more rugged than the south, and consists of an alternation of sheltered bays into which lead narrow, winding and deeply incised valleys, with massive cliffed promontories where the peneplain ends abruptly. The south coast, though frequently cliffed, is generally lower, the 150-foot contour commonly lies twenty miles inland, and the estuaries and bays are broad and open. Climatically the south coast is milder and not quite so humid as the north. Yet paradoxically the north coast has a more prosperous

[1] A discussion of Brittany's engrained problems is by M. Phlipponeau, *Le Problème breton et le programme d'action régionale* (1960).

agricultural life, the result of centuries of effort.[1]

Nearly three-quarters of the population of Brittany live in Armor. Although the term '*ceinture dorée*' is sometimes used to describe the coastal zone, it indicates a peripheral continuity which does not actually exist; the alternation of valley and inlet with ridge and peninsula has resulted in the growth of small towns and villages, each with a closely settled but limited hinterland. Most of them are fishing ports, some with a small harbour exporting agricultural produce and importing coal, fertilisers and oil. Others lie at the heads of the estuaries, the '*villes fluvio-maritimes*'. On the north coast stand Dinan[2] on the Rance, St. Brieuc[3] (the biggest town in the north, with 47,000 people) on the Gouet, and Morlaix on the Rivière de Morlaix. The last although well inland has a little port with a dock. Similarly Quimper (50,670 people in 1962), placed far inland at the head of the Odet ria, is the administrative centre of Finistère and a prosperous market-town. Vannes, the *chef-lieu* of Morbihan, with a population of 34,107, is situated where a group of valleys open into the northern angle of the large Baie de Morbihan. The only concentrations of population on the Breton coast are at Brest and Lorient, mainly the result of their function as naval bases.[4]

The emphasis in Armor is on agriculture, both dairying and the production of *primeurs*, utilising 'pockets' of land around the bays and the larger areas of reclamation, as on the former marshes of Dol which provide both pasture and excellent soils for vegetables. Early potatoes, cauliflowers, onions and salad vegetables are exported, both by rail to Paris and by boat from St. Malo, Morlaix and other small ports to Great Britain.

The tourist industry is an additional source of employment, capitalising the magnificent coastal scenery, the secluded bays and picturesque harbours, in fact the general charm of the Breton landscape.

Industry is restricted, with some notable exceptions, to the processing of the produce both of the land and of the sea—the preserving of vegetables, the making of butter, the canning of sardines and tunny, and the making of cider and apple-liqueurs. A few local industries include a tobacco factory at Morlaix, a pottery at Quimper, and some small tanneries. Formerly spinning and weaving of linen and wool produced homespun clothing at a time when Brittany

[1] Y. Poupinot, 'Bretagne Nord et Bretagne Sud', in *Université de Rennes, volume jubilaire* (*op. cit.*) (1952), pp. 350-7.

[2] J. Stéphant, 'Dinan: étude de géographie urbaine', in *Chronique géographique des pays Celtes* (1948), (no vol. numb.), pp. 17-24.

[3] M. Simon, 'Les Fonctions industrielles de St. Brieuc', in *Norois* (1965), no. 48, pp. 449-58.

[4] A. Meynier, 'Villes de Bretagne', in *A. de G.* (1946), vol. lv, pp. 178-87.

was remote and of necessity largely self-sufficing.   Both flax and
hemp were grown, the latter for ropes and cordage.   Only a small
textile factory survives at St. Brieuc.   At two of the larger centres,
Brest and Lorient, shipbuilding and repair work for the French navy
are carried out, and near the latter the steel-works of Hennebont
make tin-plate for the canning industry.   The building and repairing
of boats is carried on at many of the harbours around the coast.   In
the estuary of the Rance between La Brebis and La Briantais, near
St. Malo, a 250 mW power-station operated by the tides was opened
in 1966 ; when completed it will generate 544 million kWh annually.

Fishing.—The sea may either provide the farmer with a supplementary occupation or offer full-time employment as a fisherman or
in the French navy and merchant marine.   About 20,000 people in
the six coastal *départements* are full-time fishermen, of whom half
live in Finistère.   This figure represents 40 per cent of all the personnel
in the French fishing industry, and it must also be remembered that
many of the 5,000 men employed in the trawler-fleets of Boulogne are
Bretons.

Many fishing harbours are scattered around the coast, indeed
almost every bay and inlet has a few boats ; the four most important
are :

Total Catch, 1963

(Thousand Tons)

Lorient	54·2
Concarneau . . .	45·3
Douarnenez . . .	16·0
Le Guilvinec . . .	8·0

Source : *Comité Central des Pêches Maritimes*, quoted in *Annuaire
statistique, 1964.*

It must be remembered that these figures do not include the less
important fishing harbours such as Cancale, Paimpol, St. Brieuc,
Tréguier, Lannion, Morlaix, Camaret, Brest and Audierne, which
each land a few hundred tons of fish either for local sale or to despatch via the larger centres.   The table does not include subsistence
fishing, nor the quite valuable catch of crustaceans and shell-fish.[1]

The fishing industries of north and south Brittany are markedly
different.   At many harbours in the north the men engage in coastal
fishing for herring, mackerel, skate, turbot and mullet, a scattered
and unorganised industry on a subsistence or part-time basis, where
each *patron-propriétaire* owns his boat.   Some shrimps and shell-fish

[1] The French statistical returns distinguish between *crustacés* and *coquillages*.

are gathered, mainly by women, there is sporadic fishing for crustaceans, and the cultivation of oysters at Tréguier. At Roscoff lobsters
caught off the Moroccan and Portuguese coasts are stored alive in
tanks. Once sea-going schooners operated from St. Malo, St.
Servan, Paimpol and Cancale. Indeed, as late as 1937 St. Malo was
the third fishing port of France in terms of shipping tonnage; the
terreneuviers sailed every March for the cod-fisheries off Newfoundland, where they were based on St. Pierre and Miquelon, or for
Icelandic waters, and the port handled a quarter of all cod landed in
1937 in France. Today much of this activity has passed to the steam-
trawlers of Boulogne.

One associated industry along the north coast is the collection of
seaweed, the *goémon* and *varech*, cut at low spring-tide by long-
established custom from barges or collected in carts from the wave-
worn platforms. It is used as manure, particularly on the potato
fields, or for the extraction of iodine.

On the south coast fishing is organised on a larger scale. The
waters of the Bay of Biscay are warmer than those of the English
Channel, and sardines and white tunny (*germon*) provide the main
varieties; in point of fact the total French catch of each of these
species is exceeded only by that of cod. The sardine-fishing season
starts in the Golfe de Gascogne in February, and the fleets of *bateaux
sardiniers* work gradually northwards during summer, ending for the
year off Finistère in November. The fish are caught in fine-meshed
drift-nets (*battudes*). The white tunny is fished between July and
October, using rods (*tangons*) fixed to the base of the mast.[1] Miscellaneous fish are caught by steam-trawlers based on Lorient, which
operate as far afield as the waters off south-west Ireland for hake and
skate, and drifters fish for mackerel and whiting.

Lorient is the main fishing port of the Breton coast. A modern
fish-dock was built in the years following the war of 1914–18 at
Keroman,[2] to the south of the main commercial and naval port of
Lorient, where the river Scorff enters the Blavet river. As a result,
while Lorient handled only 8,000 tons of fish in 1913, this had
increased to 33,000 tons before the war of 1939–45, a figure which
was soon attained again after a war-time decline, and in 1963 reached
over 54,000 tons, second in France only to Boulogne. The facilities
include two large basins, fish warehouses, a cold-store, an ice-making
plant, and coal- and oil-fuelling facilities for trawlers. Railway-

[1] C. Robert-Muller, 'La Pêche et la conserve du thon dans la Bretagne de
l'Atlantique', in *A. de G.* (1936), vol. xlv, pp. 375-98. See also *Pêches et pêcheurs
de la Bretagne Atlantique*, by the same author (1944).

[2] C. Robert-Muller, 'Le Nouveau Port de pêche de Lorient', in *A. de G.*
(1927), vol. xxxvi, pp. 193-212. See also M. Gautier, 'L'Evolution récente des
principaux ports de pêche bretons', in *Norois* (1966), no. 49, pp. 59-71.

sidings alongside the fish-market enable refrigerator-cars to be loaded for express despatch to Paris. Concarneau and Douarnenez are the bases of most of the sardine- and tunny-boats. Each of these has factories where the fish are canned.

Crustaceans and shell-fish provide an important item along the south coast. Lobsters are caught either in wicker-pots (*casiers*) or in heavy nets dragged along the bottom. Some vessels go for three months to the coasts of Portugal, Morocco and Mauretania, returning with their catch of live spiny-lobsters (*langoustes*), to be stored in tanks at Concarneau, Audierne and elsewhere until required for market. Oysters are cultivated at Auray, La Trinité and Carnac, but on a smaller scale than further south at Arcachon. Mussels are reared in the Vilaine estuary near Penestin, where large culture-beds (known as *bouchots*) are enclosed between long palisades.

The Ports. The port and naval base of Brest[1] is situated on the northern side of the Rade de Brest, a sheet of water nearly sixty square miles in area, reached from the open sea through the rocky channel of the Goulet de Brest, three miles long but only a little over a mile wide between the mainland and the northerly part of Crozon (Fig. 105). The town has grown up on either side of the Penfeld estuary, which is spanned by the largest lift-bridge in Europe, opened in 1954. Quays and basins line this estuary and the shores of the Rade itself, protected by moles. Most of the port is accessible at the lowest tides to vessels drawing thirty-two feet, and the only locks are for entry to the dry-dock; in places least depths exceed sixty feet. The naval port (*port militaire*) occupies the Penfeld river and the Laninon quays to the west of its mouth, where dredging enables large carriers to berth. The Port de Commerce occupies the quays and basins to the east of the Penfeld estuary.

The growth of Brest dates from the rise of France as a naval power in the seventeenth century, and Richelieu and Vauban carried out works to develop both the naval base and the arsenal, so that the heavily fortified shores of the Goulet made the base virtually impregnable from the sea. In the late nineteenth century the outer harbour in the Rade was developed, following the building of the moles. During the war of 1939–45 the port was used by the Germans as a submarine-base, and in addition the *Scharnhorst*, the *Gneisenau* and the *Prinz Eugen* lay there for many months. The installations were heavily damaged from the air, and at the date of the liberation (September 17th, 1944) the port was hardly usable; nearly 2,000 vessels were sunk in and around the waters. The work of reconstruction was badly set back in July 1947 by the explosion of a

[1] L. Chaumeil, 'Sur l'emplacement de Brest et de Lorient', in *Université de Rennes, volume jubilaire* (1952), *op. cit.*, pp. 358-64.

cargo-vessel laden with ammunition. By 1949, however, nearly 90 per cent of the quays and basins were usable, and the naval port was once again functioning.

The commercial harbour handled just under a million tons of freight in 1938, of which about one-third was coastal. Trade was of course at a standstill during and immediately after the war, but in 1946 shipments of American coal were directed through the port; in 1947 some 857,000 tons of freight, most of which consisted of coal, was handled. Traffic has increased appreciably, however, and in 1963 the freight amounted to 2·47 million tons, 40 per cent of which comprised exports. The chief imports were coal (947,000 tons) and mineral oil (224,000). Only 1,678 vessels used the port in 1963 compared with over 4,300 in 1938, and the total net tonnage was a mere 2·88 millions out of a French total of 122 millions.

Brest is very isolated for passenger traffic as compared with Cherbourg and Le Havre, the railway route from Paris is long and quite difficult, the hinterland is restricted, and the commodities produced (mainly perishables) can move more conveniently eastwards by rail or directly from Channel ports such as St. Malo. Finally, although it has a splendid harbour, the approaches are difficult, and are endangered by rocks, fogs and storms.

The shipyards situated along the Penfeld river have turned out many warships, including the *Richelieu* and the *Dunkerque*, and numerous submarines. In recent years the carriers *Clemenceau* (1957) and *Foch* (1963) have been launched. Most of the repair- and machine-shops have been rebuilt since the war, and there are ancillary engineering industries and chemical and explosive factories. As a result of these activities, together with its function as a market- and servicing-centre for western Brittany, Brest had a population of 143,000 in 1962.

Lorient has already been mentioned as the second fishing port of France, and it possesses various fish-processing and fish-preserving industries. Lorient, a creation of the Breton merchants in the seventeenth century as a base for ships trading with India, was established on a creek where the Scorff enters the Blavet estuary. The '*Compagnie commerciale des Indes orientales*' named it L'Orient, and developed it as an *entrepôt*, with large storehouses and repair-yards. Lorient declined after the virtual disappearance of the French empire in India, and when the company ceased to function the port passed to the French Government. Ship-building and -repairing yards were then created. Several cruisers were launched there in the inter-war years, although destroyers and submarines were the chief vessels handled. During the war, when it was used by the Germans as a submarine-base, the town and port were badly damaged. Its population fell from 46,000 in 1936 to 12,000 ten years later, although by 1962 it had risen to 63,294.

Lorient's importance is now almost wholly as a fishing port, for much of the arsenal has been closed and its activities transferred to Brest. The commercial port, which before the war of 1939–1945 handled annually half a million tons of freight, is now of little importance; in 1963 it imported 300,000 tons of mineral oil and 149,000 tons of coal. Hennebont, six miles further up the Blavet river, has a small steel and tinplate works, serving the fish- and vegetable-canneries along the Breton coast.

ARCOËT[1]

The Breton peninsula rises inland to two areas of upland standing above the general level, separated by the east-west valley of the Aulne. The larger mass in the north is the Montagnes d'Arrée, mostly consisting of granite and Devonian sandstone; much is above about 850 feet and the highest point, the Signal de Toussaines, reaches 1,260 feet. This upland continues eastward as the Landes du Menez, whose swelling eminences just exceed 1,100 feet, and beyond as the hills of Alençon overlooking the Sarthe valley; here the Butte des Avaloirs attains 1,368 feet, the highest point in Armorica. This elevated country in the east includes stretches of moorland, peaty swamps and woodland, but much is the typical *Bocage Normand*. While the summits are usually rounded and smooth, here and there rise tor-like masses of granite, and in some places narrow ridges of resistant sandstones have weathered to form groups of crags. This line of upland forms the main longitudinal watershed of Armorica; short streams flow directly northwards in deeply-cut valleys to the Channel (the Guer, Trieux, Gouet, Arguenon and Rance), while others drain west and south to the Aulne, directly to the Bay of Biscay, to the Vilaine system, and in the east to the Loire via the Sarthe and Mayenne.

The southern ranges of hills are much lower and less continuous than those in the north, and in places are broken through completely by such streams as the Blavet. In the Montagnes Noires, the ridge to the south of the Châteaulin depression, the highest point is 1,070 feet, but elsewhere the inconspicuous summits rarely exceed 600 feet, covered with moorland and peat-bogs, and diversified only by occasional granite tors.

The limitations of Arcoët, the result of its upland relief, its poor acid soils and the bleak climate, have already been indicated; the farms among the *bocage* country grow rather poor crops of buckwheat, rye and potatoes, and maintain some cattle and sheep. The density of population averages about 100 to 150 per square mile, only from a third to a quarter that of the coastal strip. Settlement is

[1] M. Gautier, *La Bretagne centrale, étude géographique* (1947).

widely distributed in the form of hamlets and isolated farms, usually sited on gentle slopes below exposed hill-tops but above the marshy valley-floors and depressions. Often these farms are accessible only by deeply sunk muddy lanes. This is one of the areas which has seen much emigration from the rather hard rural existence to the towns— to Rennes, Nantes, Angers and Paris.

The few towns of note are Fougères in the upper Couesnon valley in the east, Guingamp and Loudéac in Côtes-du-Nord, and Pontivy and Ploërmel in Morbihan. Most of these are market-centres, situated at road-junctions where the few north-south transverse roads make their way over the moorlands to link up with the three east-west routes: the main N12 along the northern edge of the Montagnes d'Arrée through St. Brieuc and Morlaix, a secondary road along the central depression, and a road from Nantes via Quimperlé skirting the southern margin of the Landes de Lanvaux and the Montagnes Noires. The two main railway lines follow approximately the trend of the northern and southern roads, and another single-track line runs along the central depression from Rennes to Carhaix before it cuts north-westward to Morlaix. Only two transverse lines make their way across the peninsula, a central one from St. Brieuc via Loudéac and Pontivy to Quiberon, and an eastern one from St. Malo to Rennes, from which one line continues via Redon to St. Nazaire, another directly to Nantes. The line south from St. Malo to Nantes carries through-trains to La Rochelle, Bordeaux and Bayonne (including the 'Côte d'Emeraude-Pyrénées' express). It is a reflection of the scanty population and limited resources of interior Brittany that the large area enclosed by the main lines is served only by a limited mileage of narrow-gauge light railway.

The long Nantes-Brest Canal (Fig. 89) wanders north-westward from Nantes via Redon and Pontivy (where a short branch continues to Lorient), thence to the canalised Aulne below Carhaix. The difficulty of this route between Pontivy and Carhaix is shown by the fact that 201 locks are required.

THE BASINS

Three distinct basins are contained within the uplands: *Châteaulin* (the lower Aulne valley) in the west, *Rennes* occupied by a series of rivers converging on the Vilaine, and *Laval* in the east (the valley of the middle Mayenne).

The valley of the Aulne, between the Montagnes d'Arrée and the Montagnes Noires, opens westward into the Rade de Brest. The lower Aulne itself forms a series of deeply incised meanders (Fig. 105). The basin is floored with Lower Devonian shales which have weathered to form rather wet clay-soils. In spite of its low altitude compared with the uplands to north and south, this basin is not densely populated, though a string of villages and small towns, including Châteaulin itself, lies along the main road and the Nantes-Brest Canal. It is a dairying region, and potatoes are grown.

The basin of Rennes stands out as the largest area of lowland in Brittany, where the Seiche, Vilaine, Ille, Flume, Meu and other streams converge before flowing south-westwards to the Bay of Biscay. Faulting has contributed to the formation of this basin ; the southern edge is defined by the Faille de Pontréan, which in places forms a quite distinct fault-line scarp.[1] It is floored with areas of Tertiary rocks, for the depression seems to have been occupied by a lake, certainly in mid-Tertiary times. Various Oligocene, Miocene and Pliocene deposits have accumulated, including patches of distinctive shelly sands (*faluns*). Most of these newer materials have been removed, so exposing tracts of schists, shales and sandstones, and even in some places (as to the north-east of Rennes) masses of granite. The result is that both relief and soils are diversified. Rennes itself lies near the confluence of the Ille and the Vilaine at a height of 175 feet, but the interfluves rise to 400 feet.

The surrounding uplands are mostly moorlands, although some pines have been planted, while the valleys are chequered with meadows and arable land. The lower and more sheltered basin experiences a climate appreciably drier and less windswept than the uplands to the west, and it is the scene of a prosperous mixed agriculture—dairying, stock-raising, cereal cultivation and market-gardening.

Many small towns occur in the valleys, but Rennes is pre-eminent, for with its population of 158,000 in 1962 it contained nearly a fifth of the total of Ille-et-Vilaine.[2] Its central position has been appreciated for two millennia, for it was the capital of one of the main Celtic tribes, then a Gallo-Roman town, and later the chief town first of the duchy then of the province of Brittany, where the Breton *parlement* met. It was largely destroyed by fire in 1720, and the new town was attractively laid out with spacious streets and fine squares. In the nineteenth century Rennes expanded rapidly as a communications centre ; eleven radial roads now converge and two railway lines cross here—the transverse line from St. Malo to Nantes and the longitudinal line from Paris and Le Mans to Brest. Quays line the banks of the Vilaine (which is navigable to the sea) and of the Ille-Rance Canal, which provides a minor and little used water-link

---

[1] A. Meynier, 'Influences tectoniques sur le relief de la Bretagne', in *A. de G.* (1947), vol. lvi, pp. 170-7, examines some of the geomorphological complications inherent in the formation of the Rennes basin.

[2] A. Meynier and Chr. Loscun, 'Rennes', in *A. de G.* (1956), vol. lxv, pp. 259-69, is an account of '*les fonctions urbaines*' of '*la capitale de la Bretagne*'. See also *Les Grandes Villes françaises, Rennes*, in *Notes et Etudes Documentaires, La Documentation Française* (1966), no. 3257.

across the peninsula (Fig. 89). Rennes is an industrial centre with tanneries, shoe factories, a hosiery factory, chemical works, minor metallurgical works, a large factory producing many kinds of brushes (including special types of pig-bristle), and printing works. In 1951 a *Citroën* works was opened outside the town which has grown into a large, highly automated plant. It is a commercial and servicing centre, the market for the surrounding agricultural lands, and an administrative, judicial and cultural centre; there is a famous university with a distinguished school of Celtic studies. Near Rennes at Vern-sur-Seiche a new oil-refinery has recently been completed.

Further east, on the borders of Armorica, is the basin of Laval, a depression floored mainly with Lower Devonian and Lower Carboniferous rocks, diversified on the one hand by outcrops of granite and a long narrow ridge of rhyolite, on the other by tracts of Pliocene sands and gravels. The basin is crossed transversely by the well-defined valley of the Mayenne, which, rising in the Avaloirs upland to the north, flows southwards to join the Loire below Angers. At Laval the floor of the valley lies at 150 feet above sea-level, and its clay-soils result in a varied agriculture of dairying and market-gardening. Laval, with a population of 43,196, is the market town for the middle Mayenne valley, a route-centre halfway between Le Mans and Rennes, and a small industrial district. At dairy factories in the town and in neighbouring villages the famous '*Port-Salut*' cheese is processed. On the original basis of wool from the moorland sheep and locally grown flax and hemp, Laval became a thriving textile town, and today it has factories making cotton cloth and drills of cotton-linen mixtures, together with various branches of hosiery manufacture. Attractive marbles are obtained from neighbouring quarries. Mayenne, higher up the river, shares on a smaller scale the industrial development of Laval, but has a population of only about 11,000.

COTENTIN

The Cotentin peninsula and its 'roots' consist of three distinct structural regions. In the north granite massifs and Pre-Cambrian schists form the north-western (Cap de la Hague) and north-eastern (Pte. de Barfleur) headlands of the peninsula, and the same type of rock comprises the little massif of Les Pieux projecting towards the west coast. The moorland hills rise above 600 feet, interrupted by the wide valley of the Divette worn in Silurian slates and shales, and opening into the broad north-facing bay on which stands Cherbourg. To the south of these granite hills, the Silurian and Lower Devonian rocks give rise to undulating country, with occasional summits rising to over 400 feet, dissected by little streams mainly flowing eastwards.

The central and eastern part of Cotentin consists of the lowland basin of Valognes and Carentan, drained by the rivers Douve and Taute into the broad Baie des Veys. Geologically this basin is most varied; outcrops of Triassic and Jurassic rocks in the north-east and of Permian rocks in the south are separated by lowlands covered with Pliocene deposits and recent alluvium. The flat plain of Carentan, formerly marshy along the river valleys, is still liable to flooding as a result of the convergence of so many meandering streams towards the Baie des Veys. In the centre of the peninsula, forming the heart of this lowland belt, lies a circular depression, four miles in diameter, the *Prairies marécageuses de Gorges*, partially drained by the Canal du Plessis, and to the south-east of Carentan the land is seamed with drainage channels. The main line northward through Carentan to Cherbourg is carried on an embankment because of this liability to flooding.

To the south of this central lowland the ancient rocks once more appear, rising southward to the hill-country of the Collines de Normandie and reaching heights of well over a thousand feet. These uplands form the watershed between northwards flowing rivers such as the Vire, Aure and Orne, and the Mayenne and its headstreams.

The coast of Cotentin [1] differs markedly from that of Brittany, except in the north where there are some cliffed promontories and at two places in the west where the granitic Cap de Flamanville rises steeply to over 250 feet and the Pte. du Roc projects sharply into the Baie de Mont-St. Michel. Elsewhere by contrast the coast is low and rather featureless; on the west are the sweeping curves of several *anses*, bordered with broad sandy beaches and backed by dunes, while on the east behind a similar littoral lie marshes seamed with drainage channels. Some of the dunes are fifty or sixty feet in height; at places along the west coast the sand blows inland, but most of the dunes are planted with pines to prevent any further movement.

It has already been stressed that Manche, which comprises the whole of the peninsula and its 'roots', is the most important *département* of France for dairy cattle, that almost two-thirds of its surface is under permanent pasture and a further 10 per cent under rotation grassland, in truth a '*monoculture de l'herbe*'. The cattle, gradually improved by careful maintenance of pedigree in the '*herdbook normand*', are bred both for milk and meat. Milk, butter and cheese are sent to Paris, and live bullocks and heifers are sold out of the district. Sheep are reared on both the upland grazings and on the salt-marsh pastures in the south-west along the shores of the Baie de Mont-St. Michel and in the east between Montebourg and Ste. Mère-Eglise. The distinctive types include the *Cotentin* breed in the north, the *Avranchain* variety in the south,

[1] F. Joly, 'Le Littoral du Cotentin', in *A. de G.* (1939), vol. xlviii, pp. 225-34.

and the *grévins* along the coast. Horses and poultry, particularly geese, are also reared.

Despite the dominance of livestock, some arable cultivation is found. As in the *bocage* generally, barley and oats are grown for animal feeding, root-crops such as potatoes, and vegetables, and there are pleasant orchards of cider-apples. As a result, nearly half the working population in Manche is employed in agriculture.

No *ceinture dorée* has developed along this Cotentin coast as in Brittany, and most of the rural population lives inland, spread over the countryside in villages among the *bocage*. Occasional larger towns are market-centres for agricultural produce, such as Valognes in the north, Carentan in the centre, Coutances on the west and St. Lô in the south; the last was so grievously damaged in 1944 that its population was then reduced to half its pre-war total of 12,000. The industries consist of the processing of agricultural products, such as making butter and cider.

Few settlements are found along the coast itself, since except in the west it offers small attraction to holiday-makers, and the exposed shallow anchorages are of little value as harbours. One exception is Granville (Plate L), perched on the southern side of the cliffed Pte. du Roc, from which a breakwater projects south-eastward to give some shelter to a basin and to a wet-dock. A few resorts in the west make use of the sandy beaches, such as Granville, Carteret (where the bathing is superb in the Atlantic rollers on the shelving sandy beaches) and Le Bec de Carolles. Fishing is carried on from a few ports—Barfleur, Régneville and Granville—and oyster-beds are cultivated at St. Vaast-la-Hougue in the north-east.

The port of Cherbourg stands on the northern shores of the Cotentin peninsula where a broad open re-entrant appears in the coast. As a natural harbour the site is poor, but its modern advantage lies in its virtual mid-Channel position, only eighty-three miles south of Southampton. It was a minor naval port for centuries, but its value was limited because of its exposed situation. A few years before the French Revolution the immense work began of constructing the Digue Centrale, a breakwater three miles in length running west-east and enclosing the Grande Rade within its shelter; this was not completed until 1853. Flanking moles project from either side, the eastern taking advantage of the rocky mass of the Ile Pelée. Work has progressed steadily, and several basins and docks have been excavated from the slate rocks on the western and southern sides of the harbour. In the inter-war period, the decision to make Cherbourg a transatlantic terminal and port of call was implemented by the construction of two inner moles enclosing the Petite Rade, within which a large basin, the Darse Transatlantique, was completed, with liner-berths providing least depths of forty feet. On the east of the liner-basin is the recently completed Quai de Normandie.

The port was seriously damaged in the later stages of the war, although captured speedily by the American forces. But most of the port installations and the Gare Maritime were destroyed, the two main quays were completely unusable, and the *rades* were encumbered with wrecks. However, Cherbourg was used as a supply-port for the American forces in Europe, and temporary facilities were rapidly installed. After the return of the port to the French authorities in October 1945, ambitious schemes of restoration and improvement were steadily pushed ahead, a new Gare Maritime was built, and the Darse Transatlantique was reconstructed. It has resumed its function as a liner-port; although only 464 ships docked in 1963, their total net tonnage was 4·6 millions, the seventh French port in that respect. Its importance has, however, suffered by comparison with Le Havre; the latter disembarked 50,000 passengers on the North Atlantic services in 1963, while Cherbourg's figures were only about 17,000. In point of fact, Cherbourg at present is used not by French shipping companies but by foreign lines, for French liners operate from Le Havre. A new car-ferry from Southampton opened in 1964. Imports of American coal exceeded a million tons in 1948, but this has been greatly reduced. Cherbourg has modern naval dockyards, from which in 1967 was launched the *Redoutable*, France's first nuclear submarine.

THE LOWER LOIRE VALLEY AND ESTUARY

The Loire enters its lower section at Les Ponts-de-Cé, a few miles above the confluence of the Maine; at this point the river is only forty-six feet above sea-level, yet it is still ninety miles from the sea. A sudden change occurs in the geology of the valley, for the river leaves the Upper Cretaceous area of Touraine and Anjou and crosses obliquely the ancient rocks of the southern part of the Armorican massif, which here forms a subdued peneplain. Between Les Ponts-de-Cé and the Maine confluence the flat-floored valley is trenched into Lower Palaeozoic slates, which are worked near Angers at Trélazé, France's largest quarries. Then the valley widens out across Coal Measure shales between Montrelais and Ancenis, but near Champtoceaux it is again constricted almost to a gorge through a narrow outcrop of Pre-Cambrian schists. From here to Nantes the valley widens out once more across soft shales, thickly covered with marine clays, sands and river alluvium. The flood-plain consists of marshlands extending for several miles along both sides of the river, seamed with drainage ditches and crossed by embankments. At Nantes, where the Loire is joined by the Erdre from the north-east and the Sèvre from the south-east, the river splits up to enclose several large islands. A long narrow ridge of granite, rising to about 300 feet and known as the *Sillon de Bretagne*, almost reaches the north bank of the Loire; on its south-facing bluff stands the city of Nantes. The Sillon, which rises almost to 300 feet and is covered with heath, presents a steep slope to the south-west.

From Nantes the Loire estuary extends for thirty miles to the Bay of Biscay; its mouth lies between the Pte. de St. Gildas and the Pte. de Chemoulin. The bed of the estuary as far downstream as Couëron is cut in schistose rocks upon which quantities of alluvium have been deposited; this section of the river is dyked and the shipping-channel is constantly dredged. Below Couëron, where the estuary opens out, the branches of the river flow between elongated islands and ever-changing sand-banks, despite dredging and the construction of groynes and training-walls. Before the river's final entry into the *Embouchure de la Loire* the valley once more narrows, for a low interrupted granitic ridge, trending almost parallel to the Sillon de Bretagne, forms steep rocky headlands on either side of the river. The town of St. Nazaire is built on the granite outcrop on the right bank, while the port has been developed to the east where downfaulted slates afford easier ground for dock excavation.

Both banks of the estuary are bordered with marshlands. On the north side, between the Sillon de Bretagne and the granitic ridge on which stands St. Nazaire, is the Grande Brière,[1] an ancient gulf of the sea partly filled with alluvium and still sometimes inundated in winter. Parts have been drained by the construction of the Canal de la Bouillaie in the north-east and the Canal de Trignac in the south-west, but there are still reed-covered wastes, shallow *étangs* and bogs from which peat is cut.[2] The estuary marshes on the south have been dyked and for the most part drained. Further west the marshes between Le Croisic and the mainland are covered with rectangular pans where salt is recovered by evaporation.[3]

A varied agricultural economy is found along the lower Loire valley. The area around Nantes and along the Erdre and Sèvre

[1] A.-M. Charaud, 'L'Habitat et la structure agraire de la Grande Brière et des Marais de Donges', in *A. de G.* (1948), vol. lvii, pp. 119-30.

[2] Ph. Decraene and P. Moreau, 'L'Exploitation de la tourbe en Grande Brière', in *Géographia* (1955), vol. 40, pp. 23-7.

[3] A very detailed study of the salt industry of western France from Morbihan to the Gironde, with detailed maps of pans, etc., is afforded by W. Gehlhoff, 'Die Salzgartenlandschaften an der französischen Atlantikküste', in *Petermanns geographische Mitteilungen* (1948), vol. 92, pp. 134-54.

valleys is important for market-gardening;[1] such communes as La-Chapelle-sur-Erdre, Carquefou, St. Julien-de-Concelles, Vertou and St. Herblain are each the centre of intensive vegetable cultivation, especially for the production of *petits pois* and haricot beans, to be consumed in Nantes, sent to Paris, supplied to shipping or used for preserving. Some dairying on the reclaimed meadow-lands supplies Nantes, while on the higher terraces away from the flood-plain, particularly on the south- and east-facing slopes of the Sillon de Bretagne, are orchards and vineyards.

Several towns and villages stand along the terraces of the lower Loire, minor centres of agricultural activity, occasionally of quarrying (as at Montjean, Chalonnes and Trélazé). Between Nantes and Couëron are several small subsidiary ports—La Martinière, Le Pellerin, Indret and Basse-Indre, and near the mouth of the estuary St. Nazaire, Donges and Paimbœuf; these serve the Nantes industrial region. Thus at Donges is the refinery of *Raffineries françaises de Pétrole de l'Atlantique*,[2] with a through-put in 1964 of 3·3 million tons of crude oil, and a small *B.P.* refinery. It passes various hydrocarbon by-products to the *Progil-Electrochimie* works at Pont-de-Claix. Paimbœuf imports phosphates and pyrites for nearby chemical-works, Couëron has the Port-Gibaud non-ferrous metallurgical plant (lead, copper and brass), another large chemical factory is served by Basse-Indre, and on the north bank between the last named and Couëron are the large steel-works of the *Etablissements J. J. Carnaud et Forges de Basse-Indre*. At Indret are the construction shops of the *Usine d'Etat de la Marine*.

St. Nazaire,[3] near the northern entrance to the estuary, was only a fishing village of 3,000 inhabitants a century ago. Its development began in the mid-nineteenth century, when a basin was constructed as an outport to accommodate shipping unable to negotiate the estuary to Nantes. Even though a channel is now carefully maintained for the benefit of Nantes, St. Nazaire has continued to flourish. Its basins have increased in number and size and indeed the Bassin de Penhoët, entered by a huge entrance lock, provides one of the largest docks in Europe; this lock served as a dry-dock, and was used to accommodate the *Normandie*. The strategic significance of St. Nazaire was such that the occupying Germans made considerable

[1] M. Oliviero, 'Les Cultures maraîchères de la banlieue nantaise', in *Chronique géographique des Pays Celtes* (1952), (no vol. numb.), pp. 272-83, which includes a detailed map.

[2] A.-M. Pavard-Charaud, 'Le Développement de Donges, centre pétrolier de la Basse-Loire', in *A. de G.* (1953), vol. lxii, pp. 259-70, affords a full account of the development of the *Raffineries françaises de Pétrole de l'Atlantique*, established in 1948 by the merging of two firms. The name of the company has recently been changed to *Antar P.A.*

[3] A very detailed account is provided by M. Barbance, *Saint-Nazaire* (1948).

use of it, and concrete submarine-pens were built. The port suffered severe damage as a result of the raid in April 1942, when the outer gate of the lock to the Penhoët basin was wrecked by the *Campbeltown*, and by heavy Allied air bombardment. Although many installations were ruined, the other quays and locks which the Germans had planned to destroy were saved by the capitulation. Nevertheless, it was four years before the port was restored to full service.

St. Nazaire still acts as an outport for Nantes, and coal, oil, mineral ores and other raw materials are landed. Its chief importance is, however, as an industrial centre, especially for shipbuilding, where two of the largest French firms, the *Chantiers de St. Nazaire-Penhoët* and the *Chantiers de la Loire*, merged in 1955 to form the *Chantiers de l'Atlantique* ; the *Normandie* was built in 1935 and later the 35,000-ton battleship *Jean Bart*. In 1961, the *France*, the world's longest ship, was completed. Tankers up to 100,000 d.w.t. are constructed. To the north-east of St. Nazaire, at Trignac, are the steelworks, employing over 3,500 men, of the *Usines métallurgiques de la Basse-Loire*. Other activities include ship-repairing, marine engineering, the making of ships' cables, the large plant of *Fabrique Air-Liquide* which produces liquid oxygen, a chemical factory for processing North African phosphates, a refrigeration plant, breweries and vegetable canneries. *Sud-Aviation* has a large plant on the edge of the town. The population of the town, over 40,000 in 1938, fell to less than 10,000 in 1945, but by 1962 it had reached 59,181.

Nantes.—In spite of the rise of St. Nazaire and of the other estuary harbours, Nantes is still an important port, and with a population of about 246,000 is the seventh city of France. Its situation on the southern edge of the Sillon de Bretagne has already been mentioned. The Loire flowed below the bluffs through a maze of channels, and successive schemes of reclamation have united several of these islands to the mainland to provide building land ; the Erdre is now led through a tunnel into the main river.

Nantes has long been a port at the junction of maritime and fluvial navigation. In the eighteenth century it was the leading French port, its many wealthy merchants trading with India, Madagascar and especially the West Indies. Constant work was necessary to maintain and improve the navigable channel, and the experiment was even tried between 1869 and 1892 of building a Canal Maritime along the left bank between La Martinière and La Gruaudais, but this was little used and was finally abandoned in 1911. Dyking, the construction of training-walls and dredging have steadily continued, and ships drawing about thirty-one feet can dock at any time, a substantial improvement since the war. When the German forces evacuated Nantes in August 1944, they deliberately damaged much of the port; most of the bridges were blown up, 150 wrecks lay in the river, and practically all quays were unusable. Within four years, however, the port was in virtually complete working order.

In 1963 about 3,800 vessels of a total net tonnage of 5·7 millions used Nantes, St. Nazaire and the minor Loire ports. While in 1937 about 2·7 million tons of foreign freight and 0·6 million tons of coastal freight (not including St. Nazaire) were handled, in 1945 this had sunk to under 200,000 tons. The revival of industry, the restoration of port facilities, and the increase in oil-refining capacity produced a rapid recovery. Crude-oil (3·7 million tons), coal (642,000), phosphates, wine and pyrites are the main imports, and refined oil-fuels (2·15 million) are the dominant exports.

A range of industries is based on 'colonial' imports (sugar-refining, rice-milling, tobacco-processing and oil-seed crushing), and on local market-gardening (the canning of vegetables, the manufacture of tin-plate). Consumer industries include the manufacture of furniture and wooden articles, glassware, paper, brushes, carbon-paper and typewriter ribbons.

LA VENDÉE

The region to the south of the lower Loire, comprising more or less the present *départements* of Vendée and Deux-Sèvres, was formerly known as *Bas-Poitou*.[1] The term Vendée came into use in the eighteenth century, and the individuality of the region was manifest in 1793 when the peasants rose in a counter-Revolutionary rebellion, to be later ruthlessly crushed by Napoleon. Today the term is used in a geographical sense to include also the *bocage* country of Les Mauges, now in the *département* of Maine-et-Loire but once part of the ancient province of Anjou, which (centred on Angers) straddled the lower Loire valley. Geologically Vendée clearly belongs to Armorica (Fig. 103), and its landscape too is similar, for the familiar *bocage* country is much in evidence, although lower altitude and a more southerly position induce features of land-use progressively more characteristic of southern France.[2] Maize, for example, begins to appear instead of wheat and oats.

Vendée consists of the dissected and much-faulted remnants of one of the more southerly Armorican anticlines; its 'grain' trends distinctly from north-west to south-east.[3] Four individual units can be distinguished: in the north-east is the country of Les Mauges,

[1] M. Gautier, *La Vendée (Bas-Poitou): esquisse géographique* (1949).

[2] A.-M. Charaud, 'Bocage et plaine dans l'ouest de la France', in *A. de G.* (1949), vol. lviii, pp. 113-25, analyses the agrarian structure at the meeting-place of *plaine* and *bocage* in the *départements* of Loire-Inférieure and Vendée.

[3] See a detailed map of folds and faults within the Vendéan massif, and a list of named anticlines, synclines and fault-lines, in R. Facon, 'La Formation de la Sèvre Niortaise', in *Université de Rennes, volume jubilaire* (1952), pp. 365-71.

in the centre the high upland area, the low-lying *Plaine Vendéenne*, and the coastal margins which include several tracts of marshland.[1]

Les Mauges.—This area, lying immediately to the south of the Loire valley between the Maine confluence and Nantes, is a plateau of Pre-Cambrian schists. Its general level varies from 150 to 450 feet, but it is much dissected by the winding valley of the Evre which flows northwards to the Loire, and by streams joining either the Sèvre-Nantaise on the west or the Layon on the east, both Loire tributaries. One or two gentle eminences stand above the general level, but the highest is only 575 feet. The Mauges landscape is essentially one of *bocage*.

The Central Uplands.—The uplands of central Vendée consist of a series of gentle ridges orientated along the usual north-west to south-east trend. This same trend is followed by the main drainage system, the Sèvre-Nantaise, which divides the central uplands into two parallel ridges. The eastern flanks of the uplands are drained by streams which ultimately join the Thouet and so the Loire at Saumur. The higher central ridges consist of rounded masses of granite, known as *les Hauteurs de la Gâtine* or as *les Collines de Vendée*. The highest points form gentle eminences mantled with gritty or sandy soils; the summits are usually called *puys*, such as the Puy Crapaud (the highest point, 968 feet) and the Puy Papin. They have a vegetation of ling, gorse, bramble, coarse grass and stunted trees, with many shallow lakes.[2] Occasionally tor-like masses of crags (such as the Rochers de Cheffois and the Rochers de Mouilleron) diversify the rather dreary moorlands.

The lower schist country flanks the granite on the west, and on its clay soils has developed a *bocage* landscape very similar to that of Mauges but lower in altitude. An interesting geological feature is the presence of a long narrow inlier of Carboniferous and Jurassic rocks within the schists to the east of La Roche-sur-Yon, orientated along the usual Armorican trend between Les Essarts and St. Laurs. These newer rocks form the pleasant *Plaine de Chantonnay*, with many of the *bocage* characteristics, but lower and more sheltered.

The Plaine Vendéenne.—The Pre-Cambrian schistose rocks continue westward towards the coast, though masked in places by patches of Eocene and Miocene sediments and to the south of Challans by an

---

[1] J.-M. Bourdeau, 'La Morphologie de la bordure atlantique du Massif Vendéen', in *A. de G.* (1941), vol. xl, pp. 81-93. See also M. Ters, 'Permanence et ancienneté des grandes lignes du reseau hydrographique et du relief en Vendée côtière occidentale', in *A. de G.* (1958), vol. lxvii, pp. 1-11.

[2] R. Bobin, *La Gâtine, étude de géographie* (1925).

outcrop of Upper Cretaceous clays and limestones. Granitic rocks still appear on the surface as small massifs surrounding the basin in which stands La Roche-sur-Yon, but the highest point is only 256 feet and most is' below 150 feet. It is gently undulating country, drained by a multitude of winding streams. In the north, the Boulogne flows into a shallow depression containing the Lac de Grandlieu, three or four smaller lakes, and a large extent of unreclaimed marsh, frequently flooded in winter. To the north-west of this depression the undulating country continues into the broad peninsula between the Loire estuary and the Baie de Bourgneuf, a district known as the *Pays de Retz*. Most of this *Plaine Vendéenne* differs little from the *bocage* to the west and is often known as the *Bas-bocage*; it tends, however, to be under cereals rather than permanent pasture.

The Coastal Margins.[1]—The ancient schistose rocks extend westward to and beyond the coastline, as shown by the low dark-coloured cliffs flanked by rocky wave-worn ledges and platforms;[2] near Les Sables-d'Olonnes a lighthouse is perched on a dark fang of rock about two miles offshore. Offshore are more fragments of Armorica —the granitic Ile d'Yeu and the schistose cliffs and reefs at the northern end of the Ile de Noirmoutier. Just south of Les Sables the limestone cliffs of the Pte. du Payré indicate that the Jurassic border of Armorica, curving around its southern edge, has been reached.

Most of the Armorican margin of Vendée is, however, masked with lines of dunes fronted by sandy beaches through which protrudes an occasional mass of Pre-Cambrian rock. The dunes have been planted with marram grass and conifers, notably between La Barre-de-Monts and St. Jean-de-Monts, and again in a solid block to the north of Les Sables-d'Olonnes. The low-lying Ile de Noirmoutier consists of sand-dunes and salt-marshes which have accumulated on a mass of Pre-Cambrian rocks, revealed only in the north. A causeway (*le Gois*) runs across the tidal-flats of sandy mud.

On the northern and southern flanks of the *Plaine Vendéenne* lie two large tracts of marsh, the *Marais occidental* and the *Marais méridional de la Vendée*, more commonly known as the *Marais Breton* or *Marais de Bourgneuf* and as the *Marais Poitevin* respectively (Fig. 90). Smaller areas of marsh lie between the *cordon littoral* of the dunes and the edge of the *bocage* country. The marshes are the result of the infilling of shallow embayments in the edge of the massif with both fluvial and marine sediments.

---

[1] A detailed geomorphological study is provided by M. Ters, *La Vendée littorale* (1961), of 578 pp., with numerous maps and plates.

[2] M. Gautier, 'Etude morphologique de la côte rocheuse du Pays de Retz', in *Université de Rennes, volume jubilaire* (1952), pp. 147-66.

Frequent attempts have been made to reclaim these areas,[1] the earliest probably in the twelfth century. The Marais Breton is separated from the Baie de Bourgneuf by a dyke, behind which close patterns of canals (*achenaux* and *étiers*) cover the surface, and the drainage systems are regulated by syndicates, some of them established for well over a century. Several drainage-units are called polders, such as the Polder de St. Céran in the north. About three-quarters of the reclaimed area is under pasture, the remainder forms arable land. From the general level of the marshland rise former small islets such as the Ile Bouin, now the sites of settlements.

Many rivers debouch on to the Marais Poitevin, principally the Sèvre-Niortaise, the Vendée and the Yon, and drainage was accordingly very difficult. An elaborate system of canals has been gradually constructed; the Canal de Luçon, draining the western marshes, was cut as early as the beginning of the twelfth century and subsequently several times enlarged. Later the rivers were dyked and regularised, and the Marans Canal was constructed from the Sèvre to an outlet much further south at La Rochelle. The drainage pattern thus evolved is of several main radial canals leading to the sea, fed by concentric '*ceinture*' canals draining a series of polders.[2] As a result, almost two-thirds of the total area of 250 square miles is now *marais desséché*, mostly under arable cultivation, the remainder consisting of improved pastures and *prés salés* (known locally as *misottes*).

Land-Use.—It is useful to summarise the main land-use categories of the three *départements* that comprise broadly the region of La Vendée.

Land-Use, 1963

(*Percentage of Total Area*)

	Arable	Permanent Pasture	Woodland
Vendée . . .	54	32	9
Deux-Sèvres . .	65	30	7
Maine-et-Loire . .	50	25	9

Source: *Ministère de l'Agriculture*, published in the *Annuaire statistique de la France, 1964*.

[1] *Aménagements des eaux des marais de l'Ouest*, published by the *Ligue Générale pour l'Aménagement et l'Utilisation des Eaux* (*Comité régional des Charentes et du Poitou*) (1928–29). F. Verger, *Le Marais de monts* (1946), deals with the marshland along the Vendéean coast, its physical features, reclamation, agricultural patterns, fishing and oyster cultivation.

[2] J. Huguet, 'Un Polder du marais poitevin', in *Norois* (1955), vol. 2, pp. 19-39.

XLIX The Breton coast to the north-west of Dinard

L Granville on the coast of the Cotentin

LI The Breton coast near St. Brieuc

LII The port of St. Nazaire

La Vendée resembles the rest of Armorica in the small extent of its woodlands. Oak-woods grow in the valleys and in the basins of the *bocage*, and poplars and willows flourish along the rivers, around depressions such as Grandlieu, and in the coastal marshlands. Coniferous plantations have been established on some of the granite moorlands and along the belt of coastal sand-dunes. The fields are bordered with a ditch (essential in the lower *bocage* for drainage), a bank made of the earth excavated from the ditch, and a close hedge of oak and ash, sometimes pollarded, sometimes including trees of considerable size.

Mixed farming is practised all over La Vendée, but with differing local emphasis. Large proprietors own massive château-like buildings and magnificent estates, with some of the land often rented out as smaller holdings. Some farmers have units of twenty-five to fifty acres, and there are many *petits propriétaires*, notably the market-gardeners on the reclaimed marshlands. In the lower *bocage* the emphasis is on cereals, particularly wheat; about 11 per cent of the area of each of the three *départements* is under wheat, though in the higher parts rye (grown with intervening years of fallow) is common. About 22 per cent is under fodder-crops, notably clover, turnips and kale. La Vendée is an important livestock area; in 1963 there were about 1·6 million cattle, about 446,000 pigs, and even 200,000 sheep kept both on the moorland pastures and on the salt-grazings. Some dairying is practised but the emphasis is on meat production; fat cattle appear at the markets in Chemillé, Beaupréau and Cholet and are then sent to the Paris abattoirs. Fruit is widely grown, including the vine in the valleys of Mauges and of the Sèvre-Nantaise.

La Vendée, with the exception of the moorland country of the Gâtine, presents a cheerfully pleasant and prosperous appearance, rather milder and softer than Brittany but with its same rural character. There are many individual farms and isolated hamlets, together with larger market towns at conveniently central points, such as Niort (with 39,165 people in 1962 the *chef-lieu* of Deux-Sèvres) and Cholet (36,000). Nantes, Angers and La Rochelle tend to act respectively as regional foci for the north-western, north-eastern and south-western parts of Vendée. La Roche-sur-Yon (25,456) is the *chef-lieu* of the *département* of Vendée, an almost artificial administrative centre created by Napoleon I and actually known as Napoléon-Vendée in its early days. Some of the towns have servicing industries, particularly for agricultural implements, processing industries for agricultural products, and some small rather specialised textile manufactures of cotton and linen, a legacy of a once quite considerable rural industry. Several new factories have been built in Les Mauges since the war; at St. Pierre-Montlimart in the Evre valley, for example, the *Cie. des Lampes* has opened a factory for making electronic tubes.

The marshes and sand-dunes along the coast do not encourage much settlement, providing another contrast with Brittany. A few small towns are situated on 'islands' in the marshes as centres of market-gardening, notably Bourgneuf, Bouin and Beauvoir. Some little fishing harbours and resorts are tucked in behind the dunes, such as St. Gilles-sur-Vie and Les Sables-d'Olonnes, centres of tunny- and sardine-fishing, and with fish-canning factories.

CHAPTER 18

THE ARDENNES AND THE SAMBRE-MEUSE VALLEY

The term Ardennes is applied to the western part of a group of uplands lying across the basin of the Rhine, known as the Middle Rhine Highlands or the *Schiefergebirge*. The Ardennes [1] are situated for the most part in south-eastern Belgium, although a small tract extends into France as far west as Hirson, and they also comprise the northern third of the Grand Duchy of Luxembourg. The upland areas continue eastward into Germany as the Eifel, in the angle between the Moselle and the Rhine below Koblenz.

THE STRUCTURAL EVOLUTION

The 'core' of the Ardennes consists of Lower Palaeozoic rocks, mainly Cambrian and Silurian (*Salmien*) slates and quartzites. These outcrop in the higher north-eastern parts (the Stavelot massif), again over a very small area in the centre near Serpont, and in the south-west, extending into France as the Rocroi massif. These basement rocks are exposed further north in the deeply-cut valleys of the plateaus of central Belgium (see p. 157). Otherwise the greater part of the surface of the Ardennes consists of varied Devonian rocks (Fig. 107); the lower series are mainly sandstones and quartzites, the upper limestones and shales. The Carboniferous rocks have been denuded from the higher parts and now survive only in the northern Ardennes near Dinant and in the major structural 'furrow' extending from Mons to Liège, where in addition to Lower Carboniferous rocks the Coal Measures of Upper Carboniferous age are preserved in discontinuous basins. These two areas of Carboniferous rocks are separated by a narrow outcrop of Silurian and Devonian rocks which form a plateau lying at 650 to 1,100 feet above sea-level, diversified by low parallel ridges, the most southerly of which (the Pessoux) is also the highest, dominating the Famenne depression.

The Ardennes owe their structural features to the Hercynian orogeny of late Carboniferous-Permian times. This folding was extremely complex, but certain major trend-lines (Fig. 108) can be traced; the Meuse valley, trenched across the 'grain' of the country, is most helpful in determining the location of these structures.

[1] G. Hoyois, *L'Ardenne et l'Ardennais*, vol. i (1949), vol. ii (1953), is a vast double reference volume of 983 pp., in remarkable detail.

In the south ancient rocks of the Ardennes rise prominently from beneath the Jurassic rocks of the Lorraine scarplands, a prominence emphasised by the valleys of the Sûre-Attert in Luxembourg and of the upper Semois in Belgium which lie along the margins of the upland. The most southerly structural feature is an upfold known as the anticline of Givonne in southern Belgium. This anticline is succeeded to the north by the two major thrust-faults of the Faille d'Aiglemont in France and the Faille de Herbeumont extending across Belgium into the Grand Duchy. Then again to the north appears a much contorted synclinorium, known in Belgium as the

FIG. 107.—SIMPLIFIED GEOLOGICAL MAP OF THE ARDENNES.
Based on *Atlas de Belgique*, sheet 8.

Neufchâteau, in Luxembourg as the Wiltz or sometimes as the Eifel synclinorium.

The main Ardennes anticlinorium lies next to the north, forming a series of broadly parallel major folds; its core, consisting of masses of overthrust Cambrian and Silurian rocks, has been exposed in the Stavelot, Serpont and Rocroi massifs already mentioned, because of the greater denudation of these more sharply folded and prominently uplifted areas. Part of its southern flank runs eastward across northern Luxembourg as the Bastogne anticline.

An interruption to the outcrop of Cambrian-Silurian rocks in the north of the Stavelot massif is provided by the so-called '*Fenêtre de Theux*', to the south of Verviers. It is a small massif, consisting mainly of Devonian rocks, outlined by perimeter faults, the *Failles de Theux*. It is possibly a piece of a nappe revealed through the removal of the overthrust Cambrian-Silurian rocks by denudation, hence the term '*fenêtre*'. It is associated with past volcanic activity, and some rhyolites and kindred *roches éruptives* occur in the neighbourhood of Spa; the famous mineral springs are another symptom.

To the north of the Ardennes anticlinorium is the broad synclinorium of Dinant, comprising at least a dozen minor synclines and anticlines, and involving Middle and Upper Devonian, Lower

FIG. 108.—STRUCTURAL MAP OF THE ARDENNES AND ITS MARGINS.

Based on (i) J. Halkin, *Atlas classique* (1934), plate 16; and (ii) *Atlas de Belgique*, sheet 10.

Carboniferous and some Coal Measures strata. This Dinant synclinorium narrows in the east to form the Massif de la Vesdre, lying between the Cretaceous plateau of the Pays de Herve and the *Fenêtre de Theux*. From the western end of this synclinorium, near Hirson, emerges the anticline of Artois, trending west-north-west to the English Channel.

Next to the north succeeds the narrow but intensely contorted Condroz anticline[1]. This is represented by a narrow outcrop of

[1] It must be noted that some Belgian geomorphologists do not regard this as an anticline, but as the complex '*failles de charriage de Condroz*' separating the structures of the Dinant and Namur synclinoria.

Silurian rocks (Fig. 107), flanked on the north by Middle Devonian and on the south by Lower Devonian, both, however, resting on the same basement strata of Cambrian and Silurian. The folding has been so severe that thrust-faults have developed, the best defined of which is the *Grande Faille du Midi* on the southern side of the anticline, with others, notably the *Faille de la Tombe*, on the north. As a result, the Devonian and Carboniferous rocks have been thrust northwards, partly over the Namur synclinorium. The Coal Measures are preserved in this complex downfold as a narrow 'furrow', now followed by the lower Sambre and the Meuse. The synclinorium of Namur is continued westward under a cover of Chalk and newer rocks as the Haine syncline into northern France; here is the 'concealed coalfield' of the Mons, Valenciennes and Douai basins. The Coal Measures are exposed to the east in the Namur synclinorium from west of Charleroi. The complexity and intensity of the folding and associated faulting have caused difficult mining conditions; in extreme cases Devonian, Carboniferous Limestone and Lower Coal Measure strata have been thrust over the younger coal-bearing Upper Coal Measures, and as a result deep shafts are sunk through the older rocks to reach the underlying coal. This 'coal furrow', then, may be regarded as the northern edge of the Ardennes.

The next phase was one of prolonged denudation, lasting until the Cretaceous period, that is, for approximately a hundred million years; during this long span the Hercynian mountain ranges were gradually worn down to a peneplained surface. In the Cretaceous came the extensive marine transgression of the Chalk Sea, partly caused by the *en bloc* sinking of this worn-down upland; indeed, some geomorphologists claim that marine erosion contributed appreciably to its final planation. In this sea, which covered so much of western and central Europe, was deposited the Chalk, and later still during further transgressions rocks of Tertiary age.

The third major phase was renewed uplift and resultant denudation of the peneplain, during which the newer rocks were almost completely removed, although a few small patches of Triassic and Cretaceous rocks survive, especially on the high eastern uplands. In some places residual Clay-with-Flints rest on the Devonian rocks, testifying to the now vanished Chalk cover. This sequence of uplift and denudation was by no means continuous throughout the Tertiary. During the Oligocene period a renewed marine transgression left its deposits in the Ardennes in the form of marine sandy clays lying both on Cretaceous and Palaeozoic rocks, showing that denudation was well advanced before this renewed transgression. These Oligocene deposits are found in several localities in the west, and again in the north-east, at heights exceeding 1,800 feet. Further uplift followed, probably associated with the mid-Tertiary Alpine folding to the south, and so denudation again became active. Finally, late Tertiary uplift and tilting produced the long northward slope towards the North Sea Basin (see p. 158).

The net result of these alternations of uplift and denudation is an upland area, standing prominently above the surrounding lowlands. The Palaeozoic rocks and the ancient structures have been resurrected and their 'grain' revealed. Along the axis of the Ardennes anticlinorium, where the original elevation and resultant denudation had been most pronounced, the Cambrian-Silurian rocks are exposed as gently rounded summits exceeding 2,000 feet in altitude; these High Ardennes proper are the 'roots' of the Hercynian fold-ranges.

The effects of the various periods of denudation and uplift are shown by distinct continuous surfaces at several heights; such surfaces can be distinguished both to the south and to the north of the High Ardennes, at about 1,800, 1,500 and 1,300 feet, and another at 1,000 feet on the northern side only. These surfaces are worn mainly from the Devonian formations.[1]

THE RIVERS

Many of the present features of the Ardennes landscape are the work of rivers, which usually rise in swampy depressions on the plateau surface, and then flow rapidly outwards over the impermeable rocks, becoming increasingly incised within narrow and sinuous valleys. This tendency has been emphasised by phases of rejuvenation associated with the successive uplifts. For the most part the river valleys are entrenched across the different rock formations with little regard to their boundaries, the results of the superimposition of the drainage. In detail, however, the valleys show minor features which are the result of differential denudation, particularly in the Condroz, where compact sandstones alternate with less resistant shales and limestones.

The High Ardennes form a major watershed between streams draining west and north to the Meuse, and those flowing east and south to the Moselle (Fig. 109). This watershed is, however, very indeterminate; thus only a gently swelling ridge at about 2,000 feet separates the neighbouring headwaters of the Ourthe Occidentale (a Meuse tributary) from those of the Sûre and the Wiltz flowing eastwards across Luxembourg.

---

[1] The erosion surfaces of the Ardennes are discussed in detail by P. Macar, 'L'Evolution géomorphologique de l'Ardenne', in *B.S.R. Belge G.* (1954), fasc. 3-4, pp. 9-33. See also C. Stevens, 'La Géomorphologie ardennaise', *ibid.* (1955), fasc. 1-2, pp. 7-17; and P. Macar, 'Aperçu synthétique sur l'évolution géomorphologique de l'Ardenne', in *Travaux géographiques de Liège* (1965), no 150, pp. 3-11.

The Meuse System.[1]—After crossing the Liassic clay-vale in the scarplands of the eastern Paris Basin, the Meuse continues northwards across the Ardennes into Belgium and so to its junction with the Sambre at Namur (Plate LIV). This course is transverse to the general trend of the structure, superimposed on the pre-existing cover of Cretaceous and Tertiary rocks now almost wholly removed.

FIG. 109.—GENERAL MAP OF THE ARDENNES.
Based on *Atlas de Belgique*, sheet 6.

The valley forms three distinct sections. In the south, from below Mézières to Givet, the river flows over Cambrian and Lower Devonian rocks in a tortuous gorge, 300 to 500 feet below the surface of the High Ardennes plateau. Then from Givet to just above Dinant it crosses the more low-lying Famenne of Upper Devonian rocks, receiving tributaries from both west and east along this depression. From Dinant to Namur the Meuse once more cuts transversely across the plateau, and the valley is in places spectacular, particu-

---

[1] J. Vereerstraeten, 'Contribution à l'étude hydrologique du Bassin de la Meuse en Belgique', in *B.S. Belge Et. G.* (1952), vol. xxi, pp. 269-318; this gives a very full account of the Meuse and its tributaries, their flow, seasonal variations, etc.

larly where the river cuts across bands of compact limestone, forming gorge sections which alternate with more open valleys. The river meanders considerably, forming acute loops whose necks have been sometimes cut through by the river, leaving isolated meander- cores, as at Profondeville, about eight miles south of Namur, and again at Anhée, just north of Dinant (Plate LIII).

At Namur the Meuse undergoes a marked change of direction as it enters the west-south-west to east-north-east line of the 'coal-field furrow' flanking the edge of the Ardennes. The river, in fact, follows the trend of its main tributary, the Sambre, coming in from the west (Plate LIV). This direction, at right angles to the consequent drainage lines originally established, must have been initiated after the cover of younger rocks had been removed, thus revealing the structural line of the Namur synclinorium, now followed by the lower Sambre and the Meuse. Probably a left-bank tributary of a northwards-flowing consequent river (represented now by the line of the Ourthe and the Meuse below Liège) cut back and captured the Meuse at Namur. Erosion would then be rapid in the Coal Measure shales in the floor of the furrow, particularly as this is confined on the north by the Cambrian and Silurian rocks of the Brabant massif.

The Meuse thus continues eastwards to Liège through a broad open valley, though with a distinct steep edge to the north. It receives numerous tributaries, in contrast to its isolation in the Lorraine scarplands (see p. 246). The southern Ardennes are drained by the Semois, which rises near Arlon and flows at first over the Jurassic rocks, but near Florenville like the main stream it crosses on to the Devonian rocks and incises an even more striking succession of meanders. The Semois picks up most of the southwards-flowing drainage from the High Ardennes. The other Meuse tributaries— the Lesse, the Ourthe and the Amblève—developed their courses transversely across the Palaeozoic rocks in which they too are now deeply incised. The middle sections of both the Lesse and Ourthe systems have, however, developed longitudinally in Upper Devonian shales, and the two headstreams of the Ourthe, in fact, are wholly longitudinal rivers (Fig. 109), converging near Houffalize from the south-west and the north-east respectively. In the Condroz plateau further adaptation to structure is revealed by the many minor tributaries, which have eroded shallow valleys in the less resistant limestones and shales, leaving between them rounded ridges (known as *tixhes*) of more resistant sandstone. The limestone areas, both the more extensive Devonian and the Carboniferous, reveal underground drainage features (see p. 499).

The Meuse Navigation.—After the Meuse enters Belgium, despite some difficult sections through the Ardennes it is navigable for a

R 2

distance of about 116 miles to Lanaye, near the Dutch frontier south of Maastricht. The river in this section has a variable régime, much more so than the upper French portion, as a result of receiving numerous torrential Ardennes tributaries. Below Namur, in fact, the flow may vary from 35 cu. m. per second at low water to as much as 3,000 cu. m. per second at flood. Since about 1852 the Government has carried out regularisation schemes, and has constructed twenty-one locks, sluices and stabilising barrages (Fig. 110) in an effort to maintain an adequate navigational depth; this, however, still fluctuates from seven to nine feet. A new master-barrage has been completed at Neuville-sous-Huy, nine miles above Yvoz-Ramet, which has replaced the three barrages at Amay, Ampsin and Huy (numbers 17, 16 and 15 on the Meuse).

The effective limit of downstream navigation is the Monsin barrage just below Liège, completed in 1930 near where the Albert Canal branches off. The regularised river is navigable for barges of up to 2,000 tons between Liège and Huy, and for barges of up to 1,350 tons between Huy and Namur, while the section from Namur to the French frontier can now also accommodate barges of 1,350 tons.

FIG. 110.—THE REGULARISED SAMBRE-MEUSE WATERWAYS.
Based on information received from the *Institut National de Statistique de Belgique*.
The figures indicate the official numbering of the barrages.

The Meuse is joined at Namur by the Sambre, which affords fifty-eight miles of navigable waterway in Belgium and another thirty-four miles in France as far upstream as Landrecies (Fig. 54). A navigational depth of seven feet is maintained on the river by means of thirty-one locks, of which twenty-two are in Belgium. Work is in progress to improve still further the section of the river between Namur and Charleroi.

Some indication of the navigational importance of the two rivers within Belgium is provided by the following figures:

Million Tons (1963)

	Meuse	Sambre
Tonnage carried . . .	15·83	4·94
Loadings at river-ports . .	5·78	1·95
Unloadings at river-ports .	6·08	2·11

Source: *Annuaire statistique de Belgique, 1964.*

Loadings on the Meuse in 1963 included 2·90 million tons of building-stone from Ardennes quarries and 0·23 million tons of coal, while unloadings included 3·51 million tons of coal, 1·12 million tons of mineral ores, and 1·13 million tons of building-stone. On the Sambre, too, 0·61 million tons of coal were loaded. Thus the rivers contribute notably to the industrial life of the Charleroi-Namur-Liège industrial region.

The Moselle Drainage.—The drainage of the eastern Ardennes finds its way ultimately to the Moselle and so to the Rhine. There is a remarkable convergence of drainage waters towards the south-eastern angle of Luxembourg. The river Our rises in the High Ardennes near Monderfeld and then wanders southwards, forming for much of its length the Luxembourg-German frontier, to its confluence with the Sûre. The Clervaux from the north, and the Wiltz and the Sûre from the High Ardennes to the west, converge across the Luxembourg Ardennes, their combined waters reaching a well-marked west-east depression along the southern margin of the uplands, and then flowing in a general easterly direction to join the Moselle near Wasserbillig. The gradients of these rivers are steep and their upper courses are torrential; the Sûre, for example, rises at an altitude of 1,801 feet to the south-west of Bastogne and leaves the Ardennes near Ettelbruck at 640 feet, a fall of nearly 1,200 feet in only about forty miles. Still more strikingly, the Blees, a tributary of the Sûre, descends from its source at 1,640 feet to 600 feet in little more than twelve miles. These eastern Ardennes rivers are deeply incised, flowing several hundred feet below the plateau surface in deep winding valleys, hemmed in by steep forested slopes or by rock cliffs. Prominent spurs are sometimes only a few hundred yards across at their necks, round which the river swings in a tight loop.

In 1964 the canalisation of the Moselle, to take 1500-ton barges, was completed by means of fourteen locked barrages, of which three are on the Luxembourg section of the river. A modern river-port and a hydro-station have been constructed at Grevenmacher.[1]

The Ardennes may be divided into a number of sub-regions (Fig. 111), which will be described in turn.

FIG. 111.—THE REGIONS OF THE ARDENNES AND ITS MARGINS.

[1] A. A. Michel, 'The canalization of the Moselle and West European integration', in *G.R.* (1962), vol. 52, pp. 475-91; and F. Chanrion, *Une Victoire européenne : la Moselle* (1964).

THE HIGH ARDENNES

The upland of the High Ardennes is more or less defined by the thousand-foot contour both on the north and south. In the north-east the plateau continues over the German frontier as the Eifel, while in the south-east the general level falls gradually to the Luxembourg Ardennes. Almost the whole of the High Ardennes consists of Devonian rocks, except where the Cambrian and Silurian rocks outcrop. The main summits are marked on Fig. 109; the highest point is actually the Botrange (2,277 feet), but it is of no great prominence. The broad line of highest elevation trends southwestward, interrupted by the valleys of the Amblève, Ourthe and Lesse, and gradually diminishing in altitude. Thus the highest point of the Plateau des Tailles (between the Amblève and the Ourthe) is the Baraque de Fraiture (2,140 feet), while the Forêt de St. Hubert between the Ourthe and the Lesse attains 1,933 feet. Further west the Croix Scaille near the French frontier rises to 1,657 feet. Most of these plateau areas form rounded summits separated by shallow depressions, often containing peat-bogs or wet moorland known as *moeras*, notably the Plateau des Hautes-Fagnes in the north-east which is continued into Germany as the Hohe Venn. The drier eminences are often heath-covered, but there is also much woodland (Fig. 112) covering about half of the total area, and occurring both in the deeply-cut valleys and also on the plateau surface. The southern portion along the French frontier is heavily wooded; from the Meuse valley the dark forest-wall can be seen in the distance, meriting the regional name of the *Forêt des Ardennes*. In the valleys are some attractive oak-birch and beech forests, but the plateau surface also bears plantations of spruce and Scots pine. The Belgian province of Luxembourg, in which much of the High Ardennes lies, contains officially 754 square miles of woodland, or almost exactly 33 per cent of the total wooded area in the country. Some of the best-maintained forests are in the Eupen-Malmédy districts, acquired from Germany in 1919.

Physical conditions are somewhat adverse for agriculture. The thin, acid soils developed on the slates, quartzites and sandstones are for the most part infertile, and waterlogging is common on the plateau surface, especially in the depressions. Precipitation is heavy: Baraque Michel has a mean annual precipitation of 47·7 inches, and Chiny, in the Semois valley to the south-west, has 49·6 inches (officially the wettest place in Belgium). Some of this precipitation is in the form of snow, which lies above 2,000 feet during an average year for over fifty days, and at an altitude of about 1,000 feet for about thirty days. The final German offensive in the

Ardennes in January 1945 drove westwards over snow-covered country. Low cloud, frequent hill fogs, and a frost occurrence on an average of about 120 days all combine to make the Ardennes uplands distinctly bleak.

In the official agricultural census of 1961 only 2 per cent of the arable land of Belgium was recorded within the *région agricole* of the *Haute-Ardenne*. Within this region 89 per cent of the small area classified as farmland was under permanent grassland. Beef-cattle are bred on the uplands to be sent to lowland areas for fattening and some dairy-farming is practised, mainly for butter and cheese-

FIG. 112.—THE ARDENNES FORESTS.
Based on *Atlas de Belgique*, sheet 29.

making as a result of the limited market for liquid milk in the scantily populated district. Arable farming, mainly the cultivation of oats, rye, trefoil and potatoes, is carried on in the valleys and basins, particularly in the lower south-western parts. The area around Bastogne, though at an altitude of nearly 1,600 feet, has more arable land than any other part of the Ardennes, for it lies to the east of the massif and has a lower rainfall and a south-eastern aspect. The deeply-cut, sheltered Semois valley in the south has a specialised production of tobacco, the chief cash-crop of the farmers. Small-holdings devoted to it are found on little alluvial flats below the steep sides of the valley between Bouillon and Bohan, each with its drying shed or *séchoir*. The crop is grown intensively year after year on the same land with heavy fertilisation.

The density of population is well below a hundred per square mile and much is quite unpopulated. A few small towns stand on the plateau, mainly along the five railway lines which cross it—Butgenbach and Bullange in the extreme north-east, St. Vith, Bovigny, Bastogne and Libramont. St. Vith was almost completely destroyed during the Ardennes offensive of 1945 and has been attractively rebuilt.

Several railway lines negotiate this barrier between central Belgium and the Rhineland; one important international line (Brussels-Namur-Arlon-Luxembourg) crosses the watershed at Libramont at a height of 1,608 feet. Bastogne is particularly important as a route-centre, lying in the upper valley of the Wiltz, for seven roads converge on it; it was as a result the focal point of the German offensive in 1944–5. These small towns are minor market-centres for the higher plateau areas. Others in the valleys include Stavelot in the Amblève valley, Houffalize in the valley of the Ourthe-Orientale, and La Roche-en-Ardenne in the main Ourthe valley. Some are tourist centres capitalising the attractive wooded valleys and pleasant walking country. The most famous resort is Spa, once called 'the café of Europe'; situated on the northern edge of the Hautes-Fagnes, at a height of 800 to 1,000 feet in a wooded valley, its mineral springs have made it a health-resort since the sixteenth century, and in the eighteenth it was at the height of European fashion.

Industry is of no great importance in the High Ardennes. Some woollen factories survive in the villages on the northern side of the Hautes-Fagnes within the orbit of Verviers. The leather industry is carried on in valley-towns such as Malmédy and Stavelot, using tan-bark from the local oak forests and the hides of cattle bred in the uplands. This industry has been long established in the Ardennes, indeed Roman tanning-pits have been identified. Quarrying, particularly of quartzite for road-metal, is widespread; fifty quarries were in operation in 1964, four in the neighbourhood of Bastogne.

The High Ardennes then consists of bleak monotonous uplands, covered with heath, peat-bog or pine-forest, with a scanty agriculture, small isolated market-towns, and the lowest density of population of any part of Belgium.

THE ROCROI UPLAND

A small part of the High Ardennes plateau extends west of the Meuse valley between Mézières and Givet, forming the triangular massif of Rocroi (Fig. 113), with its apex projecting towards Hirson. The core of this massif consists of Cambrian rocks along the axis of the Ardennes anticlinorium, while the northern part is composed of Lower Devonian rocks. A few surviving patches of newer rocks rest on the Palaeozoic base—some Eocene sands near Signy-le-Petit and Oligocene clays to the west of Rocroi.

The plateau is demarcated approximately by the 1,000-foot contour; the highest point, a few miles west of Monthermé, attains 1,355 feet. It is exceptionally cut up by river valleys, forming in effect a radial drainage pattern, as Fig. 113 shows. The Oise itself, so definitely a French river and one of the great Seine 'family', flows for its initial ten miles within the Belgian portion of this upland.

FIG. 113.—THE ROCROI MASSIF.

The approximate edge of the massif is shown by a pecked line. Heights are given in feet.

Based on (i) *Carte de France au 200,000ᵉ*, sheet 10; and (ii) *Carte géologique de la France*, 1:1,000,000, published by the *Service de la Carte géologique détaillée de la France* (1933).

The plateau presents the usual Ardennes appearance—monotonous, with a few unobtrusive summits separated by shallow depressions, poor acid soils weathered from the shales and slates, peat-moors and bogs in the waterlogged depressions, and sombre woodlands. Some cultivation takes place on the gentle outside slopes of the meanders and on small alluvial terraces. The only other activity is the quarrying of Palaeozoic slates at Monthermé, Fumay and Haybes in the Meuse valley, and at Rimogne and Harcy in the Sormonne valley. These quarries were flooded and their surface installations destroyed during the war of 1914–18, but were reopened and re-equipped in the following years. At Chooz near the Belgian border an underground atomic energy plant is under construction (1966–7) jointly by France and Belgium as part of the *Euratom* programme.

The plateau is thinly populated and few roads ascend on to its higher parts. Some small towns are market-centres for agricultural districts. Rocroi stands at a height of almost 1,300 feet, on the open plateau at the very centre of the drainage dispersal, not in a valley. From miles away one can see its church-tower rising above the sky-line, an indication of the even nature of the plateau surface.

THE LUXEMBOURG ARDENNES

The section of the Ardennes which extends into Luxembourg (sometimes called the *Oesling*) is broadly similar in character to the uplands in Belgium. Quartzites and slates predominate rather than sandstones, however, and a remarkable series of these strata appears in parallel zones trending more or less from south-west to north-east. These include the coarse Bas-Bellain Slates, the darker Trois-Vierges and Kautenbach Slates, the Heinerscheid and Schuttbourg Quartzites and Gritstones, the beautifully coloured Red Slates of Clervaux, the dark Wiltz Slates, and the Berlé Quartzite.

The Luxembourg Ardennes are situated on the eastern margins of the whole massif and are markedly lower in elevation than in Belgium. The highest points, although insignificant and inconspicuous as summits, reach 1,835 feet in the Burgplats near Huldange in the extreme north, and 1,788 feet in the Napoléonsgaard in the west near Rindschleiden. The plateau varies in height from about 1,300 to 1,650 feet, but it is deeply dissected by rivers, forming four distinct upland blocks separated by narrow valleys. There are considerable tracts of high *Calluna* moorland, poor *Nardus* grassland, and some areas of peat-bog. Scattered beech-woods and some solid coniferous plantations occur on the plateau, with thickly wooded valley slopes.

The climate is neither so bleak nor so wet as that in the Belgian Ardennes, since it is considerably lower and also to some degree lies in the rain-shadow of the higher plateau to the west; Clervaux in the north, for example, has a mean rainfall of about 32 inches. Few meteorological stations are situated on the plateau, but mean figures do not apparently attain 40 inches. Nevertheless, the elevation and exposure of the uplands, while less than in Belgium, result in bleakness, cloudiness and a snow-cover of twenty to thirty days.

The Luxembourg Ardennes, therefore, is not a favourable agricultural area. Potatoes and oats are grown on the plateau as subsistence crops and rye is still cultivated. One result of the harsh climate is that seed potatoes are grown for export to the milder south of the Grand Duchy. The rearing of livestock has recently become more important, particularly cattle (the characteristic *pie-rouge*) and pigs, and even today draught-oxen can be seen. Since 1927 developments in co-operative livestock breeding and dairying have been effected in an effort to improve the standard of animal farming. *Syndicats d'élevage* have been created by voluntary associations of farmers, and co-operative dairies have been organised which send cream to the main butter factory for northern Luxembourg at Hosingen, or to another at Ettelbruck on the southern edge of the Ardennes. The main agency, *le Syndicat de Vente des Laiteries de Luxembourg*, operates a fleet of lorries to collect cream and despatch butter to retailers. In the last few decades the plateau-pastures have been improved, the result of ploughing and seeding with better grasses and the use of lime and fertilisers on the sour soils. The valleys are of little value for arable agriculture because of their steep walls and winding narrow floors, although some of the alluvial flats produce hay crops; in places these flats are intersected with irrigation channels, producing two crops of hay during the summer.

Despite these activities, the average density of population is low, the result of large unpopulated areas of moorland, woodland and pasture, and people live in isolated villages and hamlets. In the three Ardennes cantons of Clervaux, Wiltz and Vianden, the average density of population per square mile in 1960, the date of the last available census, was 120, 117 and 128 per square mile respectively, compared with 295 per square mile over the Grand Duchy as a whole. The Ardennes support only 15 per cent of the total population of the Grand Duchy, although the upland occupies 32 per cent of the area. Furthermore, the population of some of the rural cantons of the Ardennes is declining; Clervaux had a population in 1871 of 13,706 but in 1960 of 10,425, and Wiltz had 16,203 in 1871 but only 10,888 in 1960. The attractions of better-paid employment in the industrial area of the south have caused many to leave the more rigorous uplands.

The only town of any size in the Luxembourg Ardennes is Wiltz, with a population of merely 3,904 in 1960. The old town (*Oberwiltz*) grew up around a castle on a meander-spur, then spread over the river to the valley-floor on the other side (*Niederwiltz*). It is situated on the railway line running westward to Bastogne in Belgium and is the focus of a number of roads, so that the town acts as a market-centre for the eastern Ardennes and is also a pleasant little tourist resort. Vianden (1,605 inhabitants in 1960) is a tourist centre in the Our valley near the German frontier, and Clervaux (1,459) grew up around a castle in the wooded valley of the river of the same name, a tributary of the Wiltz. A few other large villages are situated along these valleys, and others such as Bourscheid (1,026 inhabitants in 1960), Heiderscheid (1,023) and

Putscheid (1,034), are on the plateau itself.

In 1964 the world's largest pumped storage hydro-station, with a 900 mW capacity, was completed, with a dam across the river Our at Vianden.

THE FAMENNE DEPRESSION

A broad depression, parallel to the main structural trend of the Ardennes, runs from the neighbourhood of Chimay in a north-easterly direction towards Liège; the section lying west of the Meuse is sometimes known as *La Fagne*.[1] Most of the Famenne lies below 600 feet, and it forms a distinct trough eroded in the Upper Devonian shales and schists, less resistant than the sandstones and quartzites to the north and south. As the original consequent streams developed their northward courses, subsequents cut back along these Upper Devonian rocks. In the west the Viroin with its two headstreams, the Eau Noire and the Eau Blanche, flow to the Meuse itself in broad valleys (Fig. 113). The section east of the Meuse is occupied by the Lesse and its confluents, the Lhomme and the Wamme. These each have the usual northward course until they reach the less resistant rocks of the depression, whereupon they abruptly change direction and flow westwards to the Meuse master-stream. A distinct divide, attaining about 1,000 feet to the north-east of Han, separates the western part of the Famenne from the valley of the lower Ourthe, which turns abruptly eastwards along the eastern section of the Famenne near Noiseux. The Famenne is followed throughout its length by a railway from Chimay through Dinant, Rochefort and Marche to Liège, the only line across the Ardennes region which runs parallel to the structure.

The Famenne is mostly an area of gently undulating relief, interrupted by limestone hills rising more prominently to 700 or 800 feet, while the valley-floors are in places as low as 300 feet. The hills are often wooded, and forest covers nearly two-fifths of the total area. In many parts occur outcrops of Upper Devonian limestone, with underground stream-courses, grottoes and resur-gences.[2] A tract of limestone appears in the neighbourhood of Rochefort, where there are numerous caverns. One of the best known series of caverns is the Grottes de Han, including the Salle du Sabbat, 295 feet high. The Lesse formerly occupied a large loop to the north-east of Han, the abandoned valley of which is

[1] A. Gamblin, 'Quelques aspects de la morphologie de la Fagne de Chimay', in *Bull. de l'Assoc. de Géographes français* (1954), nos. 241-2, pp. 68-78.

[2] Much detail about the caves and underground streams is given in E. van den Broeck, E.-A. Martel and E. Rahir, *Etudes hydro-spéléologiques sur le calcaire dévonien du bassin de Dinant* (two volumes, 1910); it includes many maps and plans. See also J. Corbel, 'Les Karsts de Belgique', in *Les Karsts du Nord-Ouest de l'Europe* (1957), pp. 381-429.

clearly visible, but the river now disappears as a cascade into the Perte de la Lesse, to reappear a mile away at the Trou de Han after a complex subterranean passage. The grottoes consist of inter-connected caverns representing a former underground course of the river at a still higher level, now abandoned except during extreme floods. Further to the south-west are the stalactite caves of Revogne near the village of Pendrôme.

The Famenne is rather more densely populated than the higher country to north and south, for it is lower and milder, with consider-able areas of calcareous loams and heavy clays. A particularly prosperous district lies in La Fagne to the east of Chimay, where oats, fodder crops and vegetables are grown. This is the 'calcareous corridor', where a band of Devonian limestone, only three miles wide, has weathered to form loamy soils of considerable fertility, and as a result the prosperous, well-populated agricultural country contrasts markedly with the forested sandstones to north and south. In the agricultural census of 1961, 70 per cent of the Famenne's farm-land was under permanent pasture, a proportion rising to 90 per cent in the Fagne, and it forms a dairying region with some pro-duction of beef-cattle. Most of the hills and the steep valley-sides are, however, wooded.

Many of the little towns are route-centres where the trans-Ardennes routes cross the diagonal line of the Famenne, and the attractive landscape has a certain tourist interest. Marche, in the centre of the Famenne on the watershed between the Lesse and the Ourthe, Rochefort on the Lhomme, and Durbuy on the Ourthe, are the main resorts and market-towns, each with about 4,000 people.

THE CONDROZ

The plateau contained to the south-east of the Meuse right-angle is known as the Condroz, where the complexity of the 'graining' of the Lower Palaeozoic rocks is well shown. The plateau here has a general elevation of between 600 and 1,000 feet, but it rises towards the southern edge overlooking the Famenne to 1,122 feet near Durbuy. There are many parallel ridges, formed mainly of sand-stone, some quite steep and prominent, others with rounded crests. Between them long parallel valleys are developed in the less resistant Carboniferous and Upper Devonian shales and limestones. The most prominent (although not the highest) ridge is in the extreme north, where outcrops a narrow belt of Lower Devonian and Silurian rocks. Numerous streams have developed longitudinal courses, such as the Bocq draining westwards from near Ciney, but the deeply-cut Meuse valley to the north has caused many north-wards flowing streams (notably the Samson and the Hoyoux) to break through to the main river across the 'grain' in steep-sided transverse valleys.

The sandstone ridges are mostly wooded, while the valley-floors are used for mixed farming, although the soils are not particularly good, and farms tend to be large. They usually possess arable land under oats, winter barley, rye, potatoes, trefoil and even a little wheat, but the proportion of permanent pasture has increased rapidly during this century. Dairying to provide milk for the industrial towns of the Meuse valley, and cattle-rearing for beef, are the main farming occupations, though horse-rearing is still important.

The population is nucleated in large often isolated villages, situated at intervals along the roads which exhibit the same parallelism to the 'grain' of the country, for naturally they follow the valleys. Where the occasional transverse road, climbing over the plateau from the Meuse valley to the Famenne, crosses these longitudinal routes, there is usually a village, and settlements follow the line of the Namur-Arlon railway-line. Such is Ciney, a town of 7,187 inhabitants, a railway junction and the focus of eight roads; it is a market town, with a small factory making stoves. The chief town is, however, Dinant (6,790 people in 1964), which owes its importance to its position in the Meuse valley, the chief transverse corridor through the Ardennes, where the important longitudinal highway from Valenciennes via Maubeuge and Philippeville to Liège crosses the river. It was for long a fortress town, with its citadel perched on steep limestone cliffs overlooking the river. Once also it was an industrial town, renowned for its chased copper- and brass-ware, but today it functions as a centre for the tourist industry of the Meuse valley; a *téléferique* takes one swiftly from the river-side to the citadel, steamers make river-excursions, and coach tours radiate through the wooded hills and valleys.

ENTRE-SAMBRE-ET-MEUSE

To the west of the river Meuse, the structural features revealed in the Condroz are continued in the district of Entre-Sambre-et-Meuse;[1] the eastern part of this is given the *pays*-name of *Marlagne*. As far west as Philippeville the alternating ridge and valley structure can still be seen, although it is more interrupted by transverse valleys than is the Condroz. The land gradually decreases in altitude to the west of the frontier, forming a region known in France as the *Plateaux préardennais*.

This is a thinly populated area, contrasting markedly with the numerous small towns along the Sambre valley to the north. Much

[1] P. Bourguignon, 'Contribution à la géographie régionale de l'Entre-Sambre-et-Meuse condrusien', in *B.S. Belge Ét. G.* (1953), vol. xxii, pp. 223-59.

of the country is wooded, particularly the ridges, though some farming is practised in the valleys, mainly the rearing of cattle and horses, and the cultivation of fodder crops such as oats. Industries are few and related to local needs, including the long-established manufacture of tubs, wine-casks and clogs at Philippeville from local timber.

The valley of the Sambre-Meuse extends parallel to the structure-lines along the northern edge of the Ardennes. In this belt, more than a hundred miles in length but only three to ten miles wide, live approximately a quarter of the people of Belgium. This is the 'industrial crescent' based on the southern coalfield or *Bassin Sud*. There is a series of large towns—Liège, Namur and Charleroi, with Mons situated in the western part of the 'coal-furrow' though not on the Sambre, which enters the industrial area a few miles above Charleroi. These towns are surrounded by large sprawling satellite villages, and here is situated the greater part of Belgium's heavy industry—iron and steel, chemicals, glass and non-ferrous metal-lurgical industries, for which the coalfield provided the initial momentum, and it still helps to sustain them. The importance of the waterways is emphasised by the fact that in 1963 976,000 tons of coal were loaded at points along them, and 3·5 million tons were unloaded. Most of the latter came from the Kempenland or from the Netherlands and West Germany, consisting of coking coal, while much of the former went to Brussels, to the Flanders plain, and to France, or made short journeys to industrial units within the area.

The Southern Coalfield (Fig. 114).—The southern Belgian coalfield forms part of an elongated series of Coal Measures which extend from the *départements* of Pas-de-Calais and Nord across the French frontier. The structural complexities make this field extremely difficult to work, for faulting and overthrusting interrupt the con-tinuity of the seams (there is a classic example near Mons where a single shaft 1,115 feet in depth passes through the same seam six times), some seams dip at a high angle particularly on the southern side of the fields, and minor anticlines divide the districts into individual basins. Thus in the Liège district there are three distinct basins (Seraing in the south-west, Liège itself in the north, and Herve in the south-east) where mining is concentrated, separated by less productive or even barren ground. Sometimes the coal is so shattered that it has to be briquetted, or used in thermal gene-rators, or burnt *in situ* for underground gasification. The fractured seams hinder mechanisation, and fire-damp is prevalent, contri-buting to a very high accident rate. Further disadvantages are that the exploited seams are thin, though numerous; in the Mons district few of the 157 seams are thicker than a yard, and at Charleroi there are about fifty, the thickest of which is four feet.   Many of the mines are deep, particularly those in the west where the productive Coal Measures are covered by Cretaceous and Triassic rocks;

FIG. 114.—THE COALFIELD OF SOUTHERN BELGIUM.

For the location of collieries on the French side of the frontier, see Fig. 44. Since this map was drawn, a large number of collieries has been closed; only 28 are still active in the whole southern field (including the Liège section).

Based on *Atlas de Belgique*, sheet 37 (*Charbonnages* I), with revisions from official information.

near Mons the mines exceed 3,300 feet and are among the deepest in the world.

With these adverse physical factors it is not surprising that the southern field is difficult and expensive to exploit, emphasised by the fact that the mining region is now 'old'. This is literally the case, since the Liège portion of the field vies with South Limburg in its claim to possess the first mine worked in continental Europe. Long before the Industrial Revolution, vertical shafts were sunk to provide coal for the smiths and metal-workers of Liège, while the deeply-cut valleys of the Meuse and its tributaries enabled horizontal adits easily to be driven for drainage. The nineteenth century saw the removal of the most accessible coal—output reached 23·5 million tons in 1900—and many parts of the field have now either been worked out or abandoned as uneconomic. The number of enterprises has declined from a maximum of 175 in 1875 to only 77 in 1939, and still further to 28 in 1964, and the number of active pits has fallen from 271 to 53. One section of the field, the Namur basin, is wholly exhausted.

The southern coalfield is divided into five districts; the most easterly is the Liège area, the second most productive, geologically separated by barren strata from the exhausted basin around Namur, while the Charleroi district, the Centre district (with its focus La Louvière), and the rapidly declining Couchant de Mons or Borinage[1] district extend westward to the French frontier.

Coal Output in the Southern Field

(Million Tons)

				1938	1952	1956	1964
Couchant de Mons (Borinage)	.	.	.	4·90	4·80	3·99	2·84
Centre	.	.	.	4·26	3·71	3·60	
Charleroi	.	.	.	7·98	7·21	6·97	5·25
Namur	.	.	.	0·39	—	—	—
Liège	.	.	.	5·52	4·96	4·53	3·08
	Total	.	.	23·05	20·68	19·09	11·17

Source: *Annuaire statistique de la Belgique, 1964*, and *Institut National de Statistique* by correspondence.

The nature and quality of the coal vary greatly from place to place; in general the volatile content of the seams is higher in the upper strata and on the southern side of the field. The long-flame

[1] R. C. Riley, 'Recent developments in the Belgian Borinage', in *Geography* (1965), vol. l, pp. 261-73.

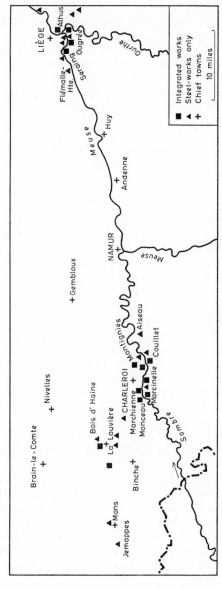

FIG. 115.—THE MAJOR IRON- AND STEEL-WORKS IN SOUTHERN BELGIUM.

Only the major establishments are shown. The chief concerns are the *Cockerill-Ougrée* plants at Seraing, Ougrée, Grivegnée and Tilleur; *Hainaut-Sambre* at Couillet and Montignies; *Forges de la Providence* at Marchienne; *Espérance-Longdoz* at Seraing, Chertal, Jemeppe and Genk (Kempen); and *Gustave Boël* at La Louvière. Based on *Carte du bassin houiller belge et des voies navigables* (n.d.), with details of industrial establishments revised to 1965.

coals, with over 25 per cent volatile matter, are found mainly in the extreme west in the upper strata of the concealed part of the field near Mons; such coals, used for gasification, are known as *Flénu*, after the colliery of that name which closed down just before the war of 1939–45. The other categories are the bituminous coals (*gras*) used domestically, in gas-works, and for steam raising; the semi-bituminous coals (*demi-gras*) burnt in coke-ovens to produce hard metallurgical coke; and short-flame semi-anthracites (*maigre*) of low volatile content. The bulk of the Liège district's production is *maigre*, a regrettable fact from the point of view of the iron-masters, who are obliged to use Kempen, Limburg or Ruhr coking-coal; the best southern coking-coals are in fact worked in the Centre and Charleroi fields. Yet, notwithstanding the limitations of this coalfield, it forms the basis of the industrialisation of southern Belgium.

The Iron and Steel Industry.—In 1965 the country produced 8·36 million tons of pig-iron and ferro-alloys, 9·17 million tons of crude steel, and 6·0 million tons of finished steel; more than 90 per cent came from this southern industrial region (Fig. 115).

Liège had been an industrial centre of European pre-eminence long before the Industrial Revolution had developed. In 1817 John Cockerill, son of an English mechanic who migrated to Belgium at the end of the eighteenth century, established workshops at Seraing, a few miles upstream of Liège within a northerly loop of the Meuse. Supplies of pig-iron were at first used from the charcoal-fired furnaces of the Condroz and the Famenne to the south. But Cockerill from the beginning was attracted by the possibility of smelting his own pig-iron and so establishing on a single site a large-scale self-contained metallurgical unit, and his first coke-fired blast-furnace was built in 1823. On his death in 1840 his industrial empire was reorganised as the *Société Anonyme John Cockerill*, in which the Belgian government held 50 per cent of the shares. The name of Cockerill has been pre-eminent in Belgian industry for a century and a half, and the vast Seraing works still stand on the original though greatly enlarged site. The western part of the Sambre-Meuse coal-field also rapidly developed during the first half of the nineteenth century, and although the Charleroi district did not possess the industrial antecedents of Liège, the metallurgical industry grew following the erection of the first coke-burning blast-furnace at Hauchies near Charleroi soon after that at Seraing. Later still furnaces were installed at La Louvière, using the good coking coals of the Mons-Centre basins.

Today most of Belgian steel is produced by a few large integrated concerns situated (with the notable exceptions of *S.A. d'Angleur-*

Athus near the French-Luxembourg frontiers and of the works at Clabecq fifteen miles south of Brussels) in the southern industrial region. For many years two of the largest companies, both in the Liège area, have been the *S.A. John Cockerill* already mentioned and the *S.A. d'Ougrée-Marihaye* also on the banks of the Meuse; in 1955 these two companies were merged to form one of the largest metallurgical combines in Europe, producing about 5 per cent of the E.C.S.C. steel output. The *S.A. Métallurgique d'Espérance-Longdoz* also operates steel-works in eastern Liège; their new plant at Chertal, 7 miles north of Liège between the Meuse and the Albert Canal, was completed in 1963, and other works are at Seraing,

FIG. 116.—THE LIÈGE INDUSTRIAL REGION.

See note to Fig. 114 (p. 503).

Based on (i) *Atlas de Belgique*, sheet 38 (*Charbonnages* II); (ii) T. H. Elkins, 'Liège and the Problems of southern Belgium', in *Geography* (1956), vol. xli, p. 91; and (iii) J. A. Sporck, *L'Activité industrielle dans la région liégeoise* (1957).

Liège and Jemeppe. The Charleroi district (Fig. 117) contains several large-scale combines, situated along the banks of the Sambre.

The heavy engineering industries are also located on the southern coalfield, and particularly near these sources of steel; in fact, many of these industries are integrated with the iron- and steel-producing units, frequently on the same or an adjacent site. The output includes boilers, girders, bridges, diesel engines, electrical apparatus, locomotives and rolling-stock; the first Belgian locomotive was built at Seraing by *S.A. John Cockerill* in 1835, and was used on the Brussels-Mechelen railway, the first European line to be operated with steam locomotives. They are still constructed at Seraing, and also at Couillet, Tubize and Haine-St. Pierre. Most of the big towns already mentioned along the Sambre-Meuse valley have heavy engineering works.

Numerous establishments concerned with light industry are located on the southern coalfield, many with age-old traditions.

FIG. 117.—THE CHARLEROI INDUSTRIAL DISTRICT.

The names of the communes in the Charleroi conurbation are shown.

The main iron and steel works are as follows, indicated on the map by initials: (1) *S.A. Laminoirs, Hauts Fourneaux, Forges, Fonderies et Usines de la Providence* (**P**), at Marchienne-au-Pont (M.-au-P.) and Fontaine-l'Evêque; (2) *S.A. Société Métallurgique Hainaut-Sambre* (formerly *S.A. Sambre-et-Moselle* (**S.M.**) and *S.A. Métallurgique du Hainaut* (**H**) at Couillet; (3) *S.A. Hauts Fourneaux, Forges et Aciéries de Thy-le-Château et Marcinelle* (**M**), at Marcinelle; (4) *S.A. Aciéries et Minières de la Sambre* (**S**), at Marchienne-au-Pont; (5) *S.A. Fabrique de Fer de Charleroi* (**F**), at Marchienne-au-Pont; (6) *S.A. Laminoirs et Boulonneries du Ruay* (**R**), at Monceau-sur-Sambre; (7) *S.A. Usines et Aciéries Allard* (**A**), at Mont-sur-Marchienne.

There are many other factories in the Charleroi neighbourhood. They include the *Ateliers de Constructions Electriques de Charleroi* (**A.C.E.C.**) at Marcinelle, the *Solvay* chemical works at Couillet, and two large glass-works at Courcelles (*Glaces de Courcelles* and *Glaver*). The Bois du Cazier colliery at Marcinelle, the scene of the disaster in August 1956, is named. Since this map was drawn, a number of collieries has been closed (see p. 503).

Based on *Plan de Charleroi et de la grande banlieue* (1 : 15,000), *Carte No. 61* of the *Editions R. de Rouck* (Bruxelles).

Liège and its satellite towns are of major importance (Fig. 116); in the Herstal region to the north of the conurbation are many medium-sized and small firms engaged in the production of hardware, motor-cycle, bicycle and aircraft parts (including jet engines), electrical goods and small-arms. Liège has had an international reputation for weapons since the fourteenth century, and until recent years small-arms were made by highly skilled craftsmen in workshops on virtually a domestic scale. A number of separate firms are grouped within the *Union des Fabricants d'Armes de Liège*, with a specialised production of sporting weapons of jealously guarded reputation. But the dominant producer is the *S.A. Fabrique nationale d'Armes de Guerre*, which makes the *F.N.* rifle now adopted by the armies of the N.A.T.O. countries. Wire, nails and screws are produced in the Charleroi area at Fontaine-l'Evêque and Anderlues, and machine tools, electrical apparatus, nuts and bolts.

Settlement.—It is obvious that much of the southern coalfield is an 'old' industrial area from its appearance. Derelict collieries, overgrown spoil-banks, a chaos of pit-shafts, blast-furnaces and steel-works, chemical factories, long rows of small, drab, gardenless dwellings built in irregular rows—all these are typical of the crowded and haphazard industrial development of the nineteenth century. However, not all the southern coalfield is like this; new housing estates, and (particularly in the western part of the field) more open industrial villages, small-holdings and farmland intermingle in a manner characteristic of so many parts of Belgium. To the north of Mons, away from the cramping bounds of the Meuse valley, extend the fertile *limon*-covered arable lands of the Hainaut plateau. But elsewhere the very concentration of industrial activity along the narrow line of the Sambre-Meuse valley leaves little space for planned development.

Liège (Fig. 116) is the fourth city of Belgium,[1] with a commune population in 1964 of 154,561; with the adjacent communes of Herstal, Ougrée, Angleur, Grivegnée and Bressoux, the total population of the official agglomeration exceeded 450,000. The city stands in the deep alluvium-floored trench of the Meuse at the point where the trend of the valley markedly changes, and near the junction of the Ourthe, with its tributaries the Vesdre and the Amblève, which have cut their valleys transversely across the Ardennes. The Ourthe valley provides one of the few route-ways from the Meuse valley into the Famenne and the southern Ardennes. Liège therefore stands at the point of contact between the Hesbaye in the north, the Pays de Herve in the east, and the Condroz to the south, and it has long been a centre

---

[1] For a full description of Liège, see (i) T. H. Elkins, 'Liège and the problems of southern Belgium' in *Geography* (1956), vol. xli, pp. 83-98; (ii) J. A. Sporck, *L'Activité industrielle dans la région liègeoise : étude de géographie économique* (1957), which provides much statistical material, plates and maps; (iii) L. E. Davin, L. Degeer and J. Paelinck, *Dynamique économique de la région liègeoise* (1959); and (iv) *L'Economie de la Région liègeoise* (1962), published by the *Conseil Economique Wallon.*

of communications in western Europe. The Sambre and the Meuse upstream of the city are useful waterways, although they have required much regulation (Fig. 110). Some miles below the city the Meuse becomes an international river, for it is followed by the Dutch-Belgian frontier, though virtually unnavigable; it was not until 1940 that the long-desired major waterway link between Liège and Antwerp was established with the completion of the Albert Canal (see pp. 126-9 and Fig. 38). The city has been a road-centre since the early Middle Ages; routes converged from the Flemish ports in the west, from Paris in the south-west, from Lorraine and Burgundy to the south, and from the Rhineland in the east. The modern road-system shares this focus-character, which will be further emphasised when the Belgian contributions to the European *auto-strade* network are completed, for six arterial roads will converge upon the city. As a railway centre it has its difficulties; the main line from Brussels is obliged to negotiate the Ans bank over the edge of the northern plateau (see p. 157), and routes southward through the Ardennes are difficult. Nevertheless Liège is crossed by several international routes (Paris-Charleroi-Köln following the Meuse valley, Amsterdam-Luxembourg-Basle and Ostend-Brussels-Leuven-Köln), and it is the focus of five other lines.

It is not surprising therefore that the city should have long nurtured a flourishing commercial life. Its industrial activities, based at first on local iron-ore, charcoal from the Ardennes forests, and water-power from the many streams, have long been of major importance, and the coalfield has been worked since the twelfth century at least. Since the Industrial Revolution the development of the Liège mining and metallurgical industries has been on a very considerable scale, as described above. In addition to these basic industries, it is one of the largest producers of refined zinc in the world, and it has a range of other non-ferrous refining and consuming industries. Many factories produce heavy chemicals, glass-ware (notably at the long-established *Val-St. Lambert* works at Seraing), rubber tyres made by *Englebert et Cie.*, leather, pottery, and the lighter consumer goods.

Namur is a much smaller town (32,345 people in 1964), although with the neighbouring communes of Jambes and St. Servais the population of the agglomeration was just over 50,000. It has an important position at the junction of the Meuse and the Sambre, 'the gateway to the Ardennes'. As a result, it has been a fortress-town for centuries, and has suffered many sieges, right down to 1914 when the Germans finally captured it after destroying its ring of outer forts. It has developed a flourishing tourist industry under its progressive *Syndicat d'Initiative*. Although Namur's economically exploitable deposits of coal are now exhausted, its heavy industries are well established, using coal brought in by the waterways. In addition to its steel-using industries, ranging from cranes and boilers to cutlery, it has many miscellaneous manufactures—cement, glass, paper, leather, glue, soap, tobacco and even pianos. It is also an important market town and the centre of considerable areas of market-gardens (known locally as *cotlages*) on the *limon*-covered area within the south-eastern angle of the Meuse.

· Charleroi forms the heart of a considerable urban agglomeration (Fig. 117). The population of the commune itself in 1964 was only 25,662, but with the satellite towns of Jumet, Gilly, Montignies, Marcinelle and Marchienne-au-Pont the total within the conurbation was over 300,000. Moreover, with the additional small towns and villages around there is a continuous agglomeration, officially created for administrative purposes in 1942, now with a population of a quarter of a million. Charleroi is the centre of one important basin of the southern coalfield, and it has metallurgical industries and two of Belgium's largest glass-factories.

Mons, with a population of 27,144 in 1964, is the centre of the most westerly part of the southern coalfield, known generally as the Borinage. Numerous mining villages and collieries spread beyond the town to the south-west, but coal-mining is a rapidly declining industry; by mid-1963 only five collieries remained in activity. Unlike the large towns already described, the Mons district has few heavy industries except for coke-ovens, briquetting plant and chemical by-products. Other new factories, opened recently to help combat industrial unemployment, make chemicals, electrical equipment, aluminium ware, and pottery and refractory ware. There are also soap-works, textile mills manufacturing cotton and rayon (for it is not far from the Flanders textile region), tobacco factories, breweries, a rope-works and a cement-works. Several large sugar-refineries process beet grown on the *limon*-covered plateau of Hainaut to the north.

Thus Belgium's chief industrial area, producing two-thirds of her coal and much of her steel, lies as a long narrow zone along the northern margin of the Ardennes, the country's least productive and most thinly populated region. In fact large numbers of work-people live in the small towns and villages of the Condroz and Entre-Sambre-et-Meuse and travel in daily to their work in the industrial crescent.[1]

[1] For a full analysis of this situation in Belgium and the Netherlands generally, see R. E. Dickinson, 'The Geography of Commuting: The Netherlands and Belgium; in *G.R.* (1957), vol. 47, pp. 521-38.

CHAPTER 19

THE VOSGES

The Vosges form an upland area rising impressively along the western side of the broad rift-valley of the Rhine, then falling away more gradually towards the scarplands of Lorraine. The uplands are at their widest in the south, becoming narrower and lower in the vicinity of the 'Saverne Gap', and continuing northward to the German frontier (Fig. 66). The term 'Vosges' was used originally in a general way to denote forested lands. In this sense it survives as a *pays*-name, *La Vôge*, which refers to a small wooded district of the upper Saône basin; probably the name was first given to this, and later transferred to the whole of the uplands to the east.

Various regional subdivisions may be defined. Because the *département* boundary (which was actually the Franco-German frontier in 1871–1918 and again in 1940–44) between Vosges and Moselle on the west and Haut- and Bas-Rhin on the east closely follows the crest-line, the western and eastern sections are sometimes known as the *Vosges lorraines* and *Vosges alsaciennes* respectively. Again, a fundamental difference in structure is recognised in the terms *Vosges cristallines* applied to the southern part and *Vosges gréseuses* to the hills in the north. From the point of view of altitude, there are the southern *Hautes-Vosges* (Plate LV) and the more northerly *Basses-* or *Petites-Vosges*.

STRUCTURE AND RELIEF

The core of these uplands consists of ancient crystalline gneiss, schist and granite (Fig. 67). The gneiss appears to be of Pre-Cambrian age, and occurs as three distinct massifs; one lies to the east of the Col du Bonhomme in the neighbourhood of Ste. Marie-aux-Mines, another to the north of Gérardmer, the third to the north-west of Remiremont. Associated with these gneissic rocks are varied schists about whose age there is some doubt, although they are commonly ascribed to the Cambrian. The main mass of the Vosges comprises intrusions of early Palaeozoic granitic rocks of varying composition. In the south-east and south appear several extruded masses of trachytes and andesites.

These rocks, together with some Lower Carboniferous slates, were involved in the Hercynian orogeny and were very complexly folded; the structural trends can be traced from north-east to south

LIII The Meuse at Monthermé, with the steep valley-sides
rising to the Ardennes plateau

LIV The confluence of the Sambre and the Meuse at Namur

LV The Vosges near Gérardmer

LVI The Zorn valley, followed by the river, the Marne-Rhine Canal, and the railway between Strasbourg and Nancy west. Several distinct fault-lines form trough-like depressions, parallel to the structural 'grain', in which newer rocks are sometimes preserved. The Vosges share the tectonic character of the Black Forest to the east, in fact until late Tertiary times the two were probably a structural unit.

The Hercynian orogeny was succeeded by a long period of denudation which reduced these mountains to a gently undulating peneplain. This denudation seems to have continued into Permian times, but it was in turn followed by a long-sustained period of deposition. Some Permian rocks still survive on the surface, preserved in the downfaulted St. Dié basin.

During extensive submergence by the inland Triassic sea, really widespread deposition took place, and over great areas of what is now Alsace and Lorraine, as well as in the Haardt and the Pfälzer Wald of western Germany, Lower Triassic sandstones were laid down to a thickness of approximately 1,600 feet. These comprise fine-grained sandstones, clays and limestones (known collectively as the *grès bigarré*) of Lower Bunter age, followed by much more extensive coarse-grained Upper Bunter Sandstones (known as *grès-vosgien*, or sometimes where their colour is particularly vivid as *grès-rouge*). Then follows the mid-Triassic *Muschelkalk* or Shelly Limestone (*calcaire coquillier*), a hard yellow fossiliferous limestone which now appears as an interrupted outcrop five to ten miles wide along the western edge of the sandstone uplands, in places forming a quite distinct escarpment, notably to the east of the Sarre valley and to the west of Epinal. Elsewhere the Muschelkalk rises little above the general level, but forms a strip of rather dry but often well-cultivated country, differing markedly from both the forested sandstone to the east and the clay-lands of Lorraine to the west. Sedimentation continued throughout Triassic and Jurassic times.

Towards the end of the Jurassic, the Vosges–Black Forest massif was bodily uplifted, and it must then have stood above the waters of the widespread marine transgressions to the north and west, in which were deposited Cretaceous and Lower Tertiary rocks. The next phase developed during mid-Tertiary times, when the massif formed part of the Hercynian foreland of the central European orogenic zone and so contributed to the alignment of the Alpine arcs. On the other hand, the effects of the orogeny were experienced by the massif itself, so that it was bodily uplifted and at the same time strongly faulted. Some of these fault-lines are associated with mineral springs, as at Bussang and Luxeuil-les-Bains.

The most drastic modification of the unit-massif was caused by the formation of the Rhine rift-valley, outlined by two broadly parallel lines of stepped-faults now reflected in the terrace-like descent to the floor of the rift-valley. The faults involved the crystal-

R.G.W.E.—S

line basement rocks, the overlying Triassic sandstones, and even in places surviving Jurassic limestones; indeed, some of these rocks now outcrop in places on the actual floor of the rift-valley (see p. 293). It may be that the formation of this rift-valley began as early as Eocene times, and continued through the Tertiary period; certainly Oligocene strata are preserved on its floor. However, it is probable that the actual fracturing of the uplifted block took place in the late Tertiary. Although these rift-valley fault-lines are the most clearly defined, there are others to the west with a roughly parallel trend but with a smaller throw, so that the westward slope is also broken into broad terraces separated by low but distinct steps. Some associated volcanic activity produced minor results, including the formation of the Kaiserstuhl, a mass of basalt protruding from the rift-valley floor in Germany to the north-west of Freiburg. In the Vosges, however, only a few small basalt flows are to be seen to the north of the High Vosges in the valley of the Bruche.

As a result of this parallel fracturing, the former massif was separated into two. The highest summits in both the Vosges and the Black Forest occur near their steep inner edges overlooking the rift-valley, from which the land descends more gently westward into the Lorraine scarplands and eastward into the Swabian scarplands respectively. Thus from Epinal in the upper Moselle valley at 1,070 feet the land rises to the summit crest 3,000 feet higher in a distance of over thirty miles, but from the top of the Ballon de Guebwiller eastward to the town of Guebwiller 4,000 feet lower is less than six miles.

Perhaps during the period of renewed late Tertiary uplift which tilted the Ardennes (see p. 487), further movements elevated the southern part of the Vosges. This was responsible for the greater eminence of the High Vosges, outlined by a number of well-defined faults along the southern margins overlooking the Belfort depression. The final result forms what was called by a French geologist [1] '. . . *une sorte de grand dôme à noyau hercynien*'.

Since mid-Tertiary times denudation has proceeded relentlessly, and the Triassic and newer rocks have been completely removed from the central parts of the High Vosges, revealing the core of granite and gneiss and in the extreme south-east some Lower Carboniferous slates. The newer rocks form a frame—a broad rim to the west covering most of Lorraine, a narrow one in the east where outcrops of Triassic and in places Jurassic rocks are preserved between the stepped-faults, the *zone sous-vosgienne*. In the north the Jurassic limestones have completely vanished, but the Triassic sandstones survive over the Low Vosges as far north as the Saar Basin. Here then are the basic differences between the High and Low Vosges—altitude and structure.

[1] L. Bertrand, *Les Grandes Régions géologiques du sol français* (1934), p. 146.

THE HIGH VOSGES

The surface of the High Vosges has an average altitude of about 3,000 feet, rising in places to individual summits known as *ballons* [1] (or in German *Belchen*). The highest point is actually the Ballon de Guebwiller (4,679 feet), with the Hohneck (4,482 feet) further north (Fig. 118), and the Ballon d'Alsace (4,101 feet) stands prominently on the southern edge of the massif overlooking the Porte de Bourgogne. A motor-road passable for nearly half the year actually leads to the summit of the last-named. In the northern part of the High Vosges the uplands are of sandstone, with prominent tabular summits flanked by steep slopes; the forest-covered Mont Donon (3,307 feet), for example, is a mass of sandstone rising from its exposed granitic base. Further north still the sandstone cover is uninterrupted, even in deeply-cut valleys.

The summits of the granite peaks have been worn by denudation into massive rounded humps (hence the name *ballon*). Occasional tors diversify the plateau surface, rising from broad spreads of granite boulders and pebbles surrounded by a gritty clay, the product of *in situ* decomposition of the granite.

The numerous Moselle headstreams (Meurthe, Mortagne, Moselotte and the Moselle itself) drain lengthily north-westwards across Lorraine, while the shorter eastern tributaries (Thur, Lauch, Fecht, Scheer and many more) are soon picked up by the Ill a few miles to the east. There is in effect a pattern of radial drainage from the main mass of the High Vosges culminating in the Hohneck, as shown on Fig. 118.

These torrential headstreams, fed by rapid runoff over the granite surface, are powerful eroding agents, and deep valleys have been worn. Several of the *ballons* reveal steep rock-slopes falling away sharply from their rounded summits, especially on the east where gradients are steep, and gorge-like valleys open out into the *région sous-vosgienne* and the rift-valley. To the west the Moselle system has worn a form of 'scarp-and-vale' structure in the westerly dipping rocks. East-facing escarpments can be distinguished, each paralleled by a river which in due course breaks through the ridge in a *cluse*-like valley. Thus on Fig. 118 the Collines de Vologne lie to the west of the Moselotte, and parallel to it but still further west are the valley of the Chajoux and its bordering Collines de Chajoux. Thus although the general trend of drainage on the western side of the High Vosges is to the west and north-west, the rivers have alternate sections flowing parallel to the ridges and short transverse sections.

[1] This is sometimes spelt *bâlon*, but *ballon* is used on the *Carte de France au 50,000ᵉ* and on other recent maps.

During Quaternary times the higher parts of the Vosges were covered with small ice-caps from which glaciers moved outwards along the pre-glacial river valleys. The impress of ice on the physical landscape is revealed by the profiles of over-deepened valleys, sometimes containing moraine-dammed 'ribbon-lakes'. The Vologne, for example, rises on the north-western flanks of the Hohneck, flows torrentially down to the small Lac de Retournemer, and then descends into the steep-sided flat-floored valley in which lies Lac de Longemer at an altitude of 2,349 feet (Fig. 118). Further west is Lac de

FIG. 118.—THE HIGH VOSGES.

The relief is so complex that this map is largely diagrammatic. The main crest-line (the former Franco-German frontier) runs across the east-centre of the map (Les Hautes Chaumes, Le Hohneck, Kastelberg), marked by a heavy pecked line. The steep eastern slopes, notably where cirques have been cut back into them, are indicated by hachuring. The minor crest-lines indicate the complexity of river erosion in this dissected crystalline massif.

Based on *Carte de France au 50,000ᵉ*, sheets XXXVI/18, 19.

Gérardmer, which drains into the Vologne; this lake actually stands on a col with a low watershed half a mile to the west. It seems that the Vologne once flowed directly westwards through the lake, but it was captured by a more active stream which had cut a deep gorge into which the upper Vologne was diverted, so that it now flows down through this gorge to Bruyères and hence to the Moselle at Jarmenil. As a result, the Lac de Gérardmer now drains north-eastwards to the Vologne, a complete reversal of direction.

Glaciation also accounts for a series of fine cirques and cirque-lakes below the central crest-line (Fig. 118). Seven cirque-lakes lie in deep hollows along the eastern side of the Chaumes-Hohneck ridge, as well as swampy hollows which were once obviously lake-filled. Two of the most striking are Lac Blanc at an altitude of 3,450 feet and Lac Noire at 3,140 feet; both have been artificially deepened with small dams, but they are true rock-basin lakes, lying in steep craggy-walled hollows and separated from each other by an impressive granite arête. Lac Blanc is in fact a double basin, with depths of 190 and 157 feet separated by a submerged rock-bar, and Lac Noire is 118 feet deep. Further to the south are Lac Vert (so called because of the prolific growth of green weed in summer), where depths of over 200 feet have been sounded, and the Lac des Truites, enclosed on its eastern side by a small but distinctive moraine. This hollow was once quite dry, the result of the stream cutting down its outlet, but it was artificially dammed in the late nineteenth century, allowed to fill, and then stocked with fish. These cirque-lakes are more common on the steeper eastern side of the ridge, but the Lacs de Blanchemer, des Corbeaux, de la Cuve and du Drumont lie on the western side of the main ridge in similar cirques.

In post-glacial times river erosion was resumed, and sands and gravels were deposited both on terraces along the edge of the Rhine-Ill plain in the east, and as sheets over the valley-floors of the Moselle and its family.

Land-Use and Agriculture.—The altitude of the High Vosges has an important effect on their climate, and the hills carry a snow-cover for about fifty days during the winter at elevations above 1,500 feet, though on summits exceeding 4,000 feet it usually lies for as long as five months. Most of the roads over the High Vosges are closed intermittently, except for the Col du Bonhomme (3,084 feet), crossed by the road from Colmar to St. Dié, which is kept open by snow-ploughs.

The High Vosges present an example of the effects of aspect, and the crest-line forms a striking climatic divide, shown both in pre-cipitation (Epinal with a mean annual rainfall of 37 inches contrasts markedly with Colmar which has only 19 inches) and also in tem-perature. In the western valleys snow lies longer, spring comes later and the summers are less sunny than on the eastern slopes. The difference is illustrated by the fact that vineyards are rare in the west, but widespread on the south-east Alsatian slopes; in 1963 the *département* of Vosges on the west yielded a mere 28,000 hecto-litres of *vin ordinaire*, while Haut-Rhin on the east produced 638,000 hectolitres of quality wine.

The granite summits of the High Vosges are covered with moorland, with occasional peat-bogs (*faignes*) in the depressions, and with nearly level stretches of granite rubble among which grow scrubby plants. Considerable areas consist of rough pastures known as *chaumes*, in fact the long ridge-line running northward from the Hohneck is called Les Hautes Chaumes (Fig. 118). These are dotted with stunted shrubs and are rather bleak, although in places they have been improved for summer grazing. The summit plateaus bear few trees, except where plantations of conifers have been deliberately established. Possibly these bleak uplands were naturally devoid of tree-cover owing to exposure, for the more sheltered valley slopes are commonly covered with beech and spruce and on the eastern side of the uplands with chestnuts. It is more probable that a former forest-cover, once destroyed, could not naturally regenerate because of the thin gravelly soil and also because of the destructive grazing of sheep and goats.

It is possible to give some indication of the land-use in the High Vosges. The figures are on a *département* basis, and Vosges includes land well to the west while Haut-Rhin includes the western side of the Rhine valley-floor, but the two *départements* do include the High Vosges, and their figures are indicative.

Land-Use, 1963

(Percentage of Total Area)

	Pasture	Woodland	Arable Land
Haut-Rhin. .	22	37	29
Vosges . .	30	43	17

Source: *Ministère de l'Agriculture*, published in *Annuaire statistique de la France, 1964*.

The limitations of the summits are obvious, but agriculture is surprisingly important in the valley margins, and arable crops such as rye and barley are grown as high as 2,750 feet on the Alsatian side. The upland villages and isolated farms on both sides of the range concentrate on dairy farming, the arable crops being used mainly for supplementary stock-feed. The high pastures graze dairy cattle during the summer months, and patterns of transhumance between them and the valley villages are long established. In 1963 174,000 dairy cattle were in the *départements* of Vosges and Haut-Rhin. The milk is used mainly for cheese production, either at the farmhouses or at small co-operative dairies (*marquairies*); the *marcaires* (literally 'milkers') spend summer at the high pastures and make cheese at the *marquairies*. Several distinctively named cheeses are produced, the most renowned being *Gérômé-Munster* (known popularly as *geromés*) which rather resembles *Camembert*. Sheep and goats are not kept in their former numbers, but in 1963 23,000 and 9,000 of these animals were in Vosges and Haut-Rhin respectively.

Further down the slopes on either side of the ridges farming assumes a more mixed character. In the east dairying is associated with the cultivation of patches óf cereals and vegetables, and there are orchards of chestnuts, walnuts, cherries and even peaches. In the west, where rather coarse hungry soils are developed on the sandstones, less farmland and much more woodland is found. Some varied cultivation appears around Epinal, and areas of orchards are maintained, notably of cherries from which is distilled the *Kirsch* liqueur for which the town is famed.

On the foothills of the High Vosges grow some 25,000 acres of vineyards; [1] although these extend northward along the flanks of the Low Vosges and across the German frontier into the Palatinate, the most important area is in the south, with Colmar as its centre. The output of wine is small, totalling in 1963 for the *départements* of Hair- and Bas-Rhin only 1,136,000 hectolitres (less than 2 per cent of the French total). The vineyards too are small, owned by a large number of *vignerons* who sell their wine to merchants for blending, bottling and marketing. The grapes are grown on pockets of calcareous down-wash soils from the Jurassic outcrops, usually on south-facing slopes of valleys, such as the Thur, Fecht and Weiss. The most popular varieties of grape are *Riesling, Sylvaner* and *Traminer*, from which are produced light white wines generally marketed under the name of the grape rather than that of the locality. There are a few estate-bottled wines, such as *Clos du Maquisard*, which is produced from a vineyard near Riquewihr. Many delightful villages, picturesquely situated in the foothills, are centres of these vineyards, notably Riquewihr (to the north-west of Colmar), Ribeauville, Turckheim and Hunawihr (which was completely destroyed in the latter stages of the 1939–45 war but has been attractively rebuilt).

Industry and Settlement.—The villages and small towns in the High Vosges valleys have an air of quiet prosperity, partly the result of their function as market towns, and partly because of the tourist industry, for the High Vosges are extremely popular, with their delightful scenery of hill, forest and stream, and afford magnificent walking country. Gérardmer is said to receive 100,000 visitors each year. In addition, the Vosges has for long been an important industrial area, so affording alternative and supplementary sources of livelihood to agriculture. Admittedly it is not always easy to

[1] P. Marres, 'Le Vignoble alsacien', in *La Vigne et le vin en France* (1950), pp. 85-9.

distinguish between these categories, since many agricultural labourers are employed in the factories in winter while some industrial workers go to the land for the harvest and the *vendange*; some factories close down at these times.

While textile manufacturing, the most important branch of industry in Alsace, is now concentrated at Mulhouse, Colmar and Epinal, many small factories in the towns and villages in both the Alsace and the Lorraine sections of the Vosges still contribute to the output. Such towns as Thann, Ste. Marie-aux-Mines, Ste. Croix-aux-Mines (the *mines* refer to long-exhausted deposits of silver ore), St. Amarin and Guebwiller in Alsace, and St. Dié, Gérardmer and Remiremont in Lorraine, possess many factories, both within the towns and along neighbouring valleys. The industry began in mediaeval times on a domestic scale with the advantages of local wool, pure soft water from the granitic uplands, and fast-flowing streams for power; the long winters and the need for supplementary employment were additional incentives. In the eighteenth century small-scale calico and muslin weaving and printing works were established, then a little later the spinning of cotton was introduced as a cottage industry. As the nineteenth century brought the steam-power of the Industrial Revolution, the textile industry began to concentrate in Mulhouse and Colmar, but many small factories and domestic producers continued to function, either supplying part-finished material or undertaking contract piece-work for the large centres. Today the distribution of electric power through the French grid has helped the survival of these small producing units.

With the exception of St. Dié, most of the industry, both domestic and factory, was situated in Alsace until after the Franco-Prussian War, when workers migrated across the new frontier into the western Vosges valleys. Epinal on the Moselle owes its considerable increase in population (from 8,000 in 1870 to 28,000 in 1900) to this migration and resultant industrialisation. This increase has not been sustained; in fact, the population of Epinal reached 30,000 by 1911, had declined to 29,000 in 1954, though it has since reached 34,086 in 1962. These western textile factories are widely dispersed, but the majority are located along the railway from St. Dié to Epinal, and down the Moselle valley towards Nancy in Lorraine. As one looks from a ridge towards a little town clustering in a valley, a characteristic sight is the tall chimney of a single small mill. Local specialisations are often of long establishment: Gérardmer still produces fine linens, Soultz spins silk thread, and Barr is a hosiery centre.

Minor industrial occupations include forestry; numerous saw-mills and pulp-mills are directly powered by fast-flowing streams, others by electricity from the grid. In some forests wooden runways (known as *schlittwege*) are used, down which timber is conveyed on sledges. Pit-props and constructional timber are extracted from the carefully preserved forests, and many wood-using domestic and small factory industries produce barrels for the Alsatian wine industry, furniture, toys, *sabots*, and tourist *bric-à-brac*. Even charcoal-burning still survives in places. Several paper-mills near Epinal use local pulp and pure water from the Moselle.

The High Vosges is then a region of remarkable contrasts—of bleak moorlands and dark forests, of snow-covered uplands and sun-bathed valley slopes, of rich dairy herds and productive vine-yards, of prosperous farms and active textile-mills. There are many small villages, and a few rather larger towns situated in Lorraine well back from the ridge-line, such as Epinal and Remiremont. In Alsace they are much closer, both high up in the steep valleys and lower down where these open into the rift-valley (Munster, Kaysers-berg, Turckheim, Guebwiller and Thann).[1]

These towns and villages are quite well served by roads, many of which were built for strategic purposes when the crest-line was a vital frontier, and maintained today largely for the tourist industry. The famous *Route des Crêtes*, for example, runs along what was the frontier-ridge, reaching a maximum altitude of 4,450 feet; though snow-blocked from November to the end of May, it is a popular summer road with magnificent prospects. Another tourist road ascends to the top of the Ballon d'Alsace. A few roads cross the High Vosges—the Col du Bonhomme from Colmar to St. Dié, the Col de la Schlucht (3,737 feet) between Gérardmer and Colmar, and the Col de Bramont (3,173 feet) between Gérardmer and Thann in the Thur valley; these are blocked by snow, continuously or inter-mittently, for much of the winter, except for the Col du Bonhomme. Two railway lines cross the uplands, both built since the war of 1914–18 to tie Alsace more closely into the rest of France. Formerly the line from Epinal terminated at St. Dié, but it was extended up the Fave valley to Saales, then by means of tunnels through the Vosges watershed into the Bruche valley and so to Strasbourg; this affords a useful through-route for express trains between Dijon and Strasbourg. In 1937 a second line was completed, also from St. Dié; it tunnels due east, emerging in the Lieporette valley near St. Marie-aux-Mines, and continues down the valley to Sélestat on the edge of the Rhine valley.

THE LOW VOSGES

The High Vosges really end at the 'Saverne Gap' to the north-west of Strasbourg, where a prominent embayment in the side of the

[1] J. Dion, 'Etude des peuplements forestiers : quelques vallées alsaciennes des Vosges', in *Rev. G. de l'Est* (1965), vol. 5, pp. 141-55.

rift-valley (Fig. 81), together with a narrowing and decrease of elevation of the Bunter Sandstone, forms a gap affording a line of
communication between the Rhineland and Lorraine. The lowest
part of the gap, dominated by the old fortress town of Phalsbourg
standing on a steep Muschelkalk ridge, is crossed by the Strasbourg-
Nancy road. The main Paris–Strasbourg railway and the Marne-
Rhine Canal both prefer a route further south along the narrow
Zorn valley (Fig. 119). Both require tunnels to negotiate the watershed, known as the *Zaberner Senke*, which is actually the narrowest

FIG. 119.—THE SAVERNE GAP.

Relief is shown in a generalised way by means of hachures and spot-heights
in feet. In the east is the edge of the Vosges, fronting the Rhine rift-valley.

The main road from Strasbourg to Sarrebourg zig-zags up the edge of the Côte
de Saverne on to the plateau surface at about 1,300 feet, some 200-300 feet lower
than the hills to north and south; the fortress-town of Phalsbourg stands in this
shallow gap. Minor roads are omitted.

Based on *Carte de France au 50,000ᵉ*, sheets XXXVI/15, XXXVII/15.

part of the Vosges, and the canal ascends from Strasbourg by means
of fifty-two locks (Plate LVI).

The Upper Bunter Sandstone extends northward beyond the
Saverne Gap, though only the southern part comprises the Low
Vosges, for beyond the German frontier the uplands are continued
as the Haardt and the Pfälzer Wald. The sandstone cover is still
complete, despite erosion by the west-flowing headstreams of the
Sarre and by short Rhine tributaries such as the Moder and the
Sauer. The valleys are winding and deeply cut, separating irregular
tabular sandstone summits and sharp ridges, the highest of which is
the Wintersberg (1,906 feet) near the German frontier; in many
places these summits are weathered into fantastic crags and pinnacles.
The average altitude of the upland surface varies from only 1,300 to

about 1,600 feet, but its dissected nature makes it difficult to negotiate.

The Low Vosges are extensively forested and only in the valley-floors is the forest cover interrupted by strips of pastureland; the *département* of Bas-Rhin, which includes much of the Low Vosges, had 34 per cent of its total area under forest in 1963. Far less population and settlement is found here than in the High Vosges, despite the appreciably lower altitude. There are a few small towns—Bitche, Rohrbach and others—and the railway line from Strasbourg to Sarreguemines crosses the hills, utilising the upper part of the Moder valley. Some of these towns once had iron-works and a few outposts of the textile industry survive, but the chief occupations are now dairying, forestry and the manufacture of wood products. The Low Vosges stand out prominently as an area of scanty population, for some communes have a density of less than fifty per square mile.

Chapter 20

THE CENTRAL MASSIF

The Central Massif [1] is an upland area, more or less bounded by the thousand-foot contour, and composed of varied rocks among which ancient crystalline rocks are dominant. It covers about 33,000 square miles, or a sixth of the total area of France. Although its average height is about 3,000 feet, the maximum altitude is only 6,188 feet, attained in the Puy de Sancy in Auvergne. In places there are deep gorges and rugged pinnacles, it is true, but much of the Massif consists, in the words of Ph. Arbos, of '. . . *ondulations lentes ou . . . surfaces planes*'. Its geomorphological history has been one of great complexity, the details of which are by no means wholly unravelled.

GENERAL FEATURES

The foundations of the Massif consist of a crystalline *socle* of granite, gneiss, schist and mica-schist. [2] Some of these rocks are of Pre-Cambrian age, others consist of highly metamorphosed sediments (described on the official *Carte Géologique de la France* as '*cristallophylliens d'âge indéterminé*'), and some of the granites may be Carbo-Permian intrusions since they cut across the schists and gneisses. Areas of indisputable Palaeozoic rocks are small in extent, but Silurian rocks occur in the extreme south-west, others of Devonian age also in the south-west and again in the Morvan, and Lower Carboniferous rocks near Lyons and in small patches further west.

The whole area may have been peneplaned before the end of Carboniferous times (the so-called 'pre-Hercynian Peneplain'), but the evidence for this is decidedly scanty, and the first major event in the geological evolution of the Central Massif was the Carbo-Permian (Hercynian) orogeny. Two main trend-lines of folding can be distinguished, the Armorican orientated from north-west to south-east, the Variscan from north-east to south-west; there must have been a complex structural apex where these met in the south-centre of the Massif. This orogeny has not left such clear results on the ultimate 'grain' of the Massif as in some of the other Hercynian uplands, mainly because of the uniform resistance to subsequent denudation of the granites, gneisses and mica-schists.

[1] S. Derruau-Boniol and A. Fel, *Le Massif Central* (1963); and R. Joly and P. Estienne, *La Région du Centre* (1961), both in the series *France de Demain*.

[2] R. Calalp, 'Connaissances sur le socle cristallin du Massif Central français', in *A. de G.* (1965), vol. lxxiv, pp. 68-72.

However, the trend of the north-east to south-west folding can be seen in the eastern uplands of Lyonnais and Vivarais, where different crystalline rocks appear in succession in broadly parallel bands.

More striking is the pattern of Coal Measure synclines and Permian inliers (Fig. 120). The little coal-basin of Ahun in north-eastern Limousin lies on the line of a north-west to south-east fault, and the Permian basin of Brive with several tiny coalfields is orientated similarly. The Autun-Epinac and Blanzy basins enclose between them the crystalline upland of Autunois; the St. Etienne 'furrow' (traced by the Furens-Gier valleys) separates Lyonnais and Vivarais; the smaller fields of Prades and Alès on the south-eastern flanks reveal the same trend. The outstanding Hercynian line is the *sillon houiller* or 'coal-furrow', which can be traced diagonally for a distance of 180 miles. In the extreme south-west, between Villefranche-de-Rouergue and Najac, it forms the structural boundary of the Massif and is followed closely by the river Aveyron. This 'coal-furrow' represents a distinct line of infolding associated with down-faulting, hence the preservation of several long coal-basins, never more than about nine miles in width.

This orogenic period was long continued, not one of violent folding and sudden cessation, for both the surviving Upper Carboniferous and Permian rocks show evidence of folding. Then followed a long period of planation, which produced the first of the traceable major erosion surfaces. This probably started well before the end of the Carboniferous, since in places the Permian rocks lie unconformably on a surface already worn in Upper Carboniferous rocks. The result was an extensive peneplain which can still be traced in the higher parts of the Cévennes and Limousin, and around the margins of the Massif. This planation may be in part marine, slowly worn as the Mesozoic seas gradually transgressed, but other evidence is suggestive of subaerial weathering under semi-arid tropical conditions.

Deposition, mainly of limestones, went on slowly during the Triassic and Jurassic periods, though these deposits formed for the most part only a thin layer over the crystalline *socle* and indeed were soon to be removed, with one notable exception. In the south a synclinal depression or local 'deep' in the Jurassic sea projected northward between the crystalline promontories of the Montagne Noire–Ségalas uplands and the Cévennes; here deposition went on to a thickness of at least 4,500 feet as downwarping continued. When later denudation removed the limestones from most of the Massif (though remaining an important element on its flanks), they survived in this depression as the Grands Causses. It is not known how much of the Central Massif was covered by this Mesozoic transgression, since so little of the rocks survive, but it probably

FIG. 120.—THE COAL BASINS OF THE CENTRAL MASSIF.

The approximate edge of the Central Massif is shown.

Based on the *Carte géologique de la France*, 1 : 1,000,000, published by the *Service de la Carte Géologique détaillée de la France* (1933).

did not cover Limousin, then the highest part of the Massif. By the end of the Jurassic the whole of the region had emerged, and the Cretaceous sea merely 'lapped' it around; a glance at a geological map shows the widespread Cretaceous deposits on the margins.

Denudation probably began to remove the Jurassic deposits during Cretaceous times, but the main period of activity was Eocene and Oligocene, and this produced another distinctive surface, called by French geomorphologists the *Eogène*. This can be traced widely within the Central Massif, especially in Limousin, and on the borders it cuts across both the Mesozoic and the ancient crystalline rocks. This surface is characterised in places by a veneer of residual deposits known as the *dépôts sidérolithiques*.[1] These vary in character, sometimes consisting of Clay-with-Flints, at other times of bedded sands and gravels, or of reddish clays (the *argiles rouges*), which according to H. Baulig are indicative of erosion under renewed semi-arid conditions.

During Middle and Upper Oligocene times, deposition was once more widespread. Rocks of this age, deposited under fresh-water or brackish lacustrine conditions, are preserved in the south on the flanks of Margeride, in the northern Ségalas, on the margins of Cantal near Aurillac (where they are part-covered with lava-flows), and much more extensively in the basins along the valleys of the Loire, Allier and Cher. In Limagne they accumulated to an appreciable thickness, indicating that the Eogene planation, which provided the detritus, was long-continued.

In mid-Tertiary times the Central Massif was greatly affected by the Alpine orogeny. In point of fact, the south-western parts had experienced faulting since the Jurassic, and this had increased in severity during early Tertiary times in association with the Pyrenean folding movements. The rigid structure of the crystalline block resisted these movements, and indeed it acted as one of the stable bastions which directed the alignment of the folding of the geosynclinal sediments to the south. The Massif however was affected both by associated *en masse* uplift and by faulting. It may be that the Pyrenean movements in effect 'revived' some of the Armorican trend-lines in the south, and that the Alpine movements 'revived' some of the Variscan lines in the east and south-east. The net result was an uplift which inclined the massif both from east to west and from south to north, so that the main watershed now lies on its south-eastern margins. The faulting was mostly experienced in the south (where the lines run from west to east), on the east (where multiple stepped-faults form the edge overlooking the Rhône valley), and in the centre where the rift-valleys of Limagne, Forez, Roanne

---

[1] The origin and character of these deposits are discussed in detail by P. Fénelon, *Le Périgord* (1951), pp. 131-6.

and several others were created. Thus the broad outline of the Central Massif was defined.

There were two other major contributions, however, to the pattern of things; one was vulcanicity, the other further stages of denudation. Most of the volcanic activity can be attributed to the Pliocene, although some flows in Velay and Vivarais are clearly Miocene and the trachytes and andesites of Cantal and Mont Dore are Pleistocene. In some districts, notably the last two mentioned at least three phases of volcanic accumulation can be discerned. One effect was to move the point of maximum altitude; from its position in Limousin in the Jurassic it shifted to the Cévennes as a result of the mid-Tertiary orogeny, and now although the highest foundation rocks are in the tilted south-east, the superimposition of volcanic rocks has located the highest individual eminences in Auvergne. The effects of vulcanicity are seen most markedly along a north–south line through Auvergne. Further east they appear in both Limagne and Forez, in the lava tablelands of Aubrac and the Le Puy basin, and in Vivarais where high peaks rise from the ridge-line and lava flows extend down the marginal slopes almost to the Rhône near Montélimar. The effects are seen also in the southern part of the Grands Causses, extending as an interrupted line of basalt buttes to the Mediterranean coast near Agde (see p. 428). Almost the only part of the Central Massif unaffected by vulcanicity is Limousin, another indication of its prolonged stability.

The uplift and tilting of mid-Tertiary times began a new cycle of erosion. An individual Mio-Pliocene surface has been determined in Ségalas at about 1,000 to 1,050 feet by A. Meynier,[1] and again in Limousin at about 920 feet by A. Perpillou.[2] According to H. Baulig's views,[3] the Central Massif consists not merely of a single warped peneplain, but of several surfaces intersecting each other at low angles; in other words, there has been a series of cycles or partial cycles, producing in fact a polycyclic relief. Some are ancient surfaces, subsequently covered with newer deposits and later still resurrected, while others belong to the period subsequent to the late Pliocene, and he attributes their origin to eustatic changes of sea-level during which the land-mass remained stable. The main erosion surfaces distinguished by Baulig in the south-east of the Massif are at 590, 920 and 1,250 feet, with others less clearly defined at 490 and 820 feet.

Rivers were markedly rejuvenated as a result of these changes in

[1] A. Meynier, *Ségalas, Levézou, Châtaigneraie* (1931).
[2] A. Perpillou, *Le Limousin: étude de géographie physique régionale* (1940).
[3] H. Baulig, *Le Plateau central de la France et sa bordure méditerranéenne: étude morphologique* (1928), especially pp. 432-50, 'Les Grandes Surfaces d'aplanissement cyclique'.

base-level. The remains of the erosion surfaces are preserved as lofty gently sloping plateau-interfluves, contrasting with the steep-sided valleys with their fragmentary benches. These valleys are most clearly developed in the south where the mid-Tertiary uplift was greatest, so that the long rivers flowing west and north have formed gorge-like valleys. In the north-west the gorge sections occur more on the margins, beyond the plateau surfaces where the rivers still flow in their shallow old-age courses.

The general drainage pattern of the Central Massif has developed as a result of the mid-Tertiary uplift. The main north-flowing arteries are the Loire and the Allier, originating near the south-eastern edge and following elongated tectonic basins to the margins of the Massif. The western and south-western rivers, notably the Dordogne, Lot and Tarn, were superimposed on the Eogene pene-plain; the Tarn, for example, rises on the crystalline rocks and passes on to the limestones and marls of the Grands Causses, crosses the crystalline rocks again in the south of Ségalas, and then flows over Cambrian limestones and slates into the Basin of Aquitaine (Fig. 121).

In detail, however, some of the Tertiary structures are expressed in the courses of the rivers; the Aveyron, for example, turns abruptly south-west for twenty-five miles at Villefranche - de - Rouergue along one of the major marginal faults. In the south the Thoré and the Jaur, though flowing in directly opposite directions, follow the Pyrenean fault-trend between the Lacaune and Montagne Noire massifs. The Tertiary uplift and tilt were responsible for the many short streams, furrowed in the steep upland edge, which flow south-eastwards to the Rhône or directly to the Mediterranean. The Gard rises on the ancient mica-schists on the flanks of Mont Aigoual, crosses an outcrop of granite on to the mica-schists once more, and descends over Lias marls and in turn over Jurassic, Cretaceous and Oligocene limestones to the Rhône flood-plain. These steep and powerful streams have by headward erosion pushed back the main watershed to the north-west; the Chassesac for example has captured streams that once flowed either to the Lot or to the Allier. Further north the Doux, Gier, Brevenne, Grosne and Dheune follow the south-west to north-east Variscan trend.

Volcanic activity has also induced a number of drainage modifica-tions. The huge cones of Cantal and Mont Dore became centres of radial drainage, and down their flanks torrents flowed both to the Dordogne and the Allier. The Truyère possibly once flowed north-westwards, continuing the direction of its present headstream between Margeride and Aubrac to the river Alagnon, hence to the Loire. Lava-flows issuing south-eastwards from Cantal blocked its course and forced it to turn at right-angles towards the south-west, so cutting a deep gorge-like valley to the Lot. The lava plateau of Aubrac thus became a centre of radial drainage; the headstreams of the Truyère and the Lot rise on the slopes of Margeride only a few miles apart, flow parallel to each other towards the west, and then diverge at right angles in diametrically opposite directions around Aubrac (Fig. 121), to unite at Entraygues.

River erosion has continued during Quaternary and Recent times, accentuated by rejuvenation. Resultant deposition has taken place

Fig. 121.—The Drainage Dispersal of the Southern Central Massif.

Only the names of the more extensive *Grands Causses* are given; further details can be obtained from Fig. 126.

The outcrops of Jurassic rocks are stippled.

Some towns are indicated by abbreviations, as follows: **A**, Aurillac; **B**, Brive-la-Gaillarde; **C**, Cahors; **C.F.**, Clermont-Ferrand; **F**, Florac; **L**, Limoges; **Mi**, Millau; **Mo**, Montauban; **N**, Nîmes; **P**, Le Puy; **St. E.**, St. Etienne.

Based on (i) *Atlas de France*, sheets 4, 5; (ii) *Carte géologique internationale de l'Europe*, 1 : 1,500,000, sheet 30.

in the bordering basins of Aquitaine and Paris, in the form of sheets and cones of débris on the western flanks of the Rhône valley, and in the basins of Limagne, Forez and Roanne.

One more element, if on a relatively minor scale, enters into the pattern, the effects of glaciation. The volcanic cones and the higher parts of the crystalline uplands nurtured small snow-fields from which glaciers moved outwards, and as a result cirques, U-shaped valleys and terminal moraines were formed. The increased flood-waters of the rivers towards the close of the Quaternary glaciation also exercised pronounced effects, trenching radially the major volcanic cones. Nivation processes were effective on the crystalline massifs, particularly in Margeride and Limousin. Mass movements of decomposed granites and coarse sands charged with water from the melting snows bared the upper slopes, filled broad depressions and sometimes obliterated breaks of slope. The more severe periglacial conditions formed block-spreads on these uplands.

The net results of this complex geomorphological history involve four distinct structural elements. There is (i) the Hercynian *socle* or crystalline basement; (ii) a covering of Mesozoic rocks, mostly removed from the Massif except in the Grands Causses, but contributing an essential element on the marginal plateaus and edges; (iii) the Eocene and particularly Oligocene deposits that accumulated under lacustrine conditions in the down-faulted basins of the Loire and Allier; and (iv) the volcanic rocks, including both large cones and extensive basalt flows.

Superimposed on this diverse structure and relief is an equally varied climate. The lofty upland is characterised by bleakness, by winter cold both on the higher parts and often as a result of inversion in the deep valleys and depressions also, and by a precipitation which in places exceeds eighty inches but exhibits great variability. The winter cold is emphasised by the facts that over 3,000 feet only about three months are frost-free, and the snow cover may lie for three or four months, even for six months in Cantal and on the Mézenc.[1] No permanent snow-fields exist, although after a snowy winter some of the high cirques in Cantal may contain a snow patch sufficiently large to survive the following summer. Some seasons are much worse than others; during the winter of 1951 there were exceptionally heavy falls, and the streets of high villages had drifts eighteen to twenty feet deep, while the road up to the Puy Mary in Cantal was blocked until June 23rd.

Within the Massif appear considerable climatic variations, both in a general way because it lies intermediately between Atlantic, Mediterranean and continental influences, and in detail because of altitude and aspect. South-facing slopes in the south of the upland grow olives, mulberries, figs and even pomegranates; maize appears in the south-west in place of the rye and buckwheat of Limousin. Some areas in the west and north are too damp and bleak for anything but

[1] P. Estienne, 'La Neige dans le Massif Central', in *Mélanges géographiques offerts à Ph. Arbos* (1953), vol. i, pp. 197-200.

moorland, conversely others in the south and east are too dry and too sun-scorched in summer for anything but *maquis* or *garrigue*.[1] While drainage is necessary in some places, paradoxically irrigation is required in others.

Soils too are very diverse. Those derived from the granitic and schistose rocks are base-poor, coarse and infertile, while the warm soils developed on limestones can if adequately watered support excellent crops. The surfaces of the newer basalt flows are rocky and arid, while by contrast the older ones have decomposed to form dark base-rich soils. Some of the Tertiary and Quaternary sediments consist of coarse sands and gravels, such as the *varennes* of Limagne, others yield clay-soils of good texture and rich in calcium salts. Areas of deficient or impeded drainage occur both on the uplands where shallow depressions are underlain by impermeable rocks and also in lowland basins where clays or sands are underlain by a hard-pan. The multitude of rivulets on the crystalline uplands (the term '*Millevaches*' means a thousand springs, not a thousand cows), the springs bursting out among the basalts, and the wandering streams of Limagne and Forez, contrast with the near-karstic aridity of the surface of the Grands Causses.

As a whole, then, the Central Massif affords a limited *milieu*, though by no means a negative one, for human use. Population is thinly spread except in a few favoured localities, and the emphasis is on a stock-rearing economy which can utilise the upland pastures. In the centre and north cattle are dominant, while in the south (and particularly in the Grands Causses) sheep are important, although not on the scale of a century ago. Well-defined seasonal movements of stock still take place; sheep from Languedoc move up to Aigoual and Lozère or from the Causses to Aubrac, and cattle from the lower pastures of Limousin transfer to the uplands of Millevaches. A steady supply of calves and mature beasts leaves the Central Massif for the lowland pastures or moves directly to the markets of Paris and Lyons. Despite factors of remoteness and difficult communications, dairying is widely carried on, and results in such products as the *fromages bleus* of Auvergne. The arable economy is necessarily subsidiary to livestock, growing fodder-crops and short-ley pasture, but cereals and potatoes are cultivated widely.

A further contribution is provided by the forests. The former woodlands which swathed all the Massif but for the highest uplands

[1] A. Fel, 'Le Climat agricole et les limites altitudinales de l'occupation du sol dans le Massif Central', in *A. de G.* (1955), vol. lxiv, pp. 401-12, considers the relationship, *inter alia*, between the index of aridity and the yield of rye, and hence the possibility of settlement. He includes a map (p. 405) which distinguishes between '*montagnes humides*' and '*montagnes sèches*'. See also A. Fel, *Les Hautes Terres du Massif Central* (1962), a detailed study of the agricultural economy.

(these carry in fact a sub-Alpine flora) have been largely removed by centuries of cutting for fuel (including charcoal-burning) and for construction, and by burning and clearance to increase the area of pasture. Vestiges of former oak and beech woods remain, and chestnut groves occur widely on the south-western and south-eastern margins, contributing to their economy. During the last seventy-five years the area under forest has once again increased in the form of beech woods and of pine, spruce and fir plantations. This is largely due to official encouragement in the direction both of the creation of State forests (as in the Cévennes) and of subsidising private planting of small wood-lots (as in Millevaches).

One would hardly call the Central Massif an industrial region, yet there are some industrial centres of importance. Advantages are indeed few; they include the tiny coal-basins, some small-scale deposits of metals (still mined sporadically) and of kaolin, other local materials such as timber, skins and hides, available labour which seeks to supplement agricultural production, and water power. The last, used to work mill-wheels for centuries, has been capitalised since 1920 in the Dordogne, Truyère and Lot valleys, where barrages pond up reservoirs to supply power-stations linked into the grid.[1] Although the rivers experience low water in summer, their winter maximum is complementary to the minimum of those in the Alps and Pyrenees which suffer from freezing.

For centuries various craft manufactures have been carried on at the small towns, including enamels, leather, textiles, lace, paper and wooden articles of all kinds. With the help of hydro-electric power, many of these activities still flourish, and some specialisations survive in a modernised form. Numerous centres of iron and steel production are found within the Central Massif, usually associated with the coalfields (Fig. 120). They grew up near small ore deposits, now exhausted or economically unworkable. In 1876 the forty-two blast furnaces in operation produced over 400,000 tons of pig-iron, a quarter of France's total. They survived through sheer inertia, through the development of specialised industries based on steel, through the utilisation of the coalfields for steam-raising and some coke production, through the labour supply available in the isolated upland valleys and basins, and more recently through the development of hydro-electric schemes which afford current for electric furnaces. They have concentrated on the production of highly fabricated articles, mostly importing pig-iron from Lorraine to make the special grades of steel required. Before the war of 1914–18, the obvious

[1] (i) G. Veyret-Verner, 'L'Evolution de l'équipement hydro-électrique du Massif Central', in *Mélanges géographiques offerts à Ph. Arbos* (1953), vol. i, pp. 211-17; and (ii) G. Kish, 'Hydroelectric Power in France: Plans and Projects', in *G.R.* (1955), vol. 45, pp. 88-91.

vulnerability of the north and north-east of France stimulated the armament industry in the centre, and the later military devastation of the frontier areas caused a boom.

Three towns have become the centres of considerable modern industrial agglomerations, and as a result are included among the thirty-two French towns with populations of over 100,000. These are St. Etienne, Clermont-Ferrand and Limoges. Other industrial towns, smaller but still of importance, include Le Creusot and Montceau-les-Mines in the north-east, Alès in the south-east, Decazeville and Rodez in the south-west, and Montluçon and Moulins on the northern margins. The varied attractions of tourism are expressed in the growth of Vichy as a fashionable spa, of Le Puy in the upper Loire basin, and of Millau as a centre for the Grands Causses.

By contrast, however, to these centres with specially favourable circumstances, much of the Central Massif is an area of low and in places decreasing density of population. This has been emphasised since 1870 by a rural exodus from the hard and unrewarding labour of the uplands for the attractions of the towns. More people migrate from Lozère, Cantal, Ardèche and Corrèze than from any other *département* in France; they go to Paris, Lyons and the towns of Bas-Languedoc. The age-structure of the population is changing as a result of this exodus of many young people, of a resultant declining birth-rate, and of the losses of manpower in two wars. In the four *départements* there were only 10,608 births in 1963, compared with 10,090 deaths. If the few larger towns are excluded, the total population of these *départements* is less now than a century ago. In individual communes in the uplands the number of people has halved, as indicated by the many deserted farms and hamlets.

It seems most practicable to distinguish seven individual areas (Fig. 122). In the north-east projects the distinct block of the Morvan. Then along the eastern edge of the Massif for a distance of nearly 250 miles are the high marginal uplands, from Autunois in the north to the Cévennes in the south-east. The heart of the Massif, though consisting of both crystalline basement rocks and of volcanic outpourings, constitutes a third sub-region, flanked on the south by the limestone plateaus and valleys of the Grands Causses. The crystalline uplands of the Montagne Noire, Lacaune and Ségalas form the south-western margins, and the plateau of Limousin the north-western. Finally, it is convenient to group together the low-lying basins of the Loire and Allier valleys and the margina lands of Bourbonnais into whic hthese valleys gradually merge.

THE MORVAN

This upland of ancient crystalline rocks projects boldly from the north-eastern corner of the Central Massif into the Mesozoic rocks

FIG. 122.—THE REGIONS OF THE CENTRAL MASSIF.

The Roman numerals (**I** to **VII**) correspond to the main sections of the text, as follows : **I**, The Morvan ; **II**, The Eastern Margins ; **III**, The Central Uplands ; **IV**, The Grands Causses ; **V**, The South-western Uplands ; **VI**, Limousin ; **VII**, The Northern Basins and Margins.

which cover the southern part of the Paris Basin, and forms, in J. Beaujeu-Garnier's apt phrase, '*un môle de terres crystallines au milieu des terrains sédimentaires*'. The Morvan is defined by a series of clear-cut faults on both its western and eastern margins.[1] On the west sometimes occurs a single fault, as near Bazoches where the crystalline rocks lie directly against the Mid-Lias marls, sometimes by two or more broadly parallel faults, while the eastern faults are much more confused and less continuous. On the south the upland is separated from *Autunois* by a down-faulted depression trending from south-west to north-east; this *cuvette autunienne* is occupied mainly by Permian rocks and the narrow Autun-Epinac coalfield (Fig. 120), and drains south-westwards by the river Arroux to the Loire.

Around the western, northern and eastern margins of the crystalline rocks lies a band of Mid-Lias marls, continuous except in the north-west where the faulted edge of the Archaean rocks lies directly against Middle Jurassic limestones. Elsewhere the marls have been worn down to form a distinct *dépression périphérique*, to which is given several *pays*-names (see p. 226). Beyond this depression a prominent limestone scarp faces inwards towards the Morvan, its continuity interrupted only by the valleys of streams draining northwards to the Yonne and the Armançon.

Geologically the Morvan massif is one of great complexity. Most of its rocks are crystalline, of Pre-Cambrian age, but areas of Devonian and Lower Carboniferous slates also appear in the south. In the extreme north within the long syncline of Sincey-les-Rouvray lies a narrow exposure of much metamorphosed Upper Carboniferous rocks where anthracite has been worked in the past. Structurally too there are many complex features; J. Beaujeu-Garnier traces seven distinct anticlinal axes and four synclinal axes of Hercynian age,[2] and faulting has introduced further structural problems. Peneplanation has cut right across these various rocks and structures. The post-Hercynian surface, which is still apparent in the north and north-east, has been subjected to a series of *aplanissements*, the relics of which are fragmentary. The net result is a gently undulating surface sloping from 850 feet in the north (*Bas-Morvan*) to over 2,500 feet in the south (*Haut-Morvan*). The highest summits, the rounded culminating points of two granitic bosses, are the Bois du Roi (2,959 feet) and Mont Beuvray (2,658 feet). The massive homogeneous rocks, especially the granites and gneiss, for the most part weather into gentle surfaces, although occasionally differential erosion does produce more striking features,

---

[1] J. Beaujeu-Garnier, *Le Morvan et sa bordure: étude morphologique* (1951), has several large-scale maps on which these faults are traced.

[2] J. Beaujeu-Garnier, *op. cit.*, particularly the map facing p. 160.

such as the granulitic crags of the Roche du Chien in the valley of the Cure to the west of St. Brisson, and the porphyry cone of Mont Genièvre (2,093 feet) in the south-west.

The drainage of the Morvan is radial, and from the impermeable gently sloping rocks a myriad of rivulets flow outwards, their upper valleys but slightly incised. In the more deeply-cut main valleys, terraces at approximately 50, 100 and 230 feet above the present flood-plain can be distinguished, related by Beaujeu-Garnier to the various erosion surfaces. The streams on the north find their way to the Serein, the Cousin and the Cure (themselves tributaries of the Yonne) or to the Yonne itself which rises on the north-western slopes of the Bois du Roi. Another group from the south-western margins of the Bois du Roi and Mont Beuvray work their way to the Aron, a right-bank tributary of the Loire, and others from the south and south-east of the massif flow down into the Autun depression to the river Arroux, another Loire tributary.

The impermeability of the rocks, the gentle gradients and the superficial depressions have resulted in the formation of a multitude of shallow *étangs*, known in the Morvan as *mortes-eaux*. Some have been transformed by the accumulation of sphagnum peat into upland bogs (the *tourbières morvandelles*), some have been artificially drained, others have been dammed and deepened for water supply or for pisciculture. The largest sheet of water is the Etang des Settons, which covers an area of 800 acres in the upper valley of the Cure. Another large reservoir has been created by damming the Yonne above Montreuillon; the water now fills the main valley for five miles upstream, extending also into tributary valleys.

Land-Use and Agriculture.—Much of the surface of the Morvan is wooded, although not as continuously as in the past because of agricultural colonisation schemes on the one hand and of exploitation for timber on the other. About a third of the *département* of Nièvre is under woodland, and some fine forests still exist, such as the Forêt d'Anost in the heart of the uplands to the south of the Etang des Settons, and the Forêt de St. Prix which swathes the Bois du Roi and the other summits of the Haut-Morvan. The beech is the dominant tree over the uplands, with oaks on the northern margins and chestnuts on the lower slopes, while the area under plantations of conifers has greatly increased during the last thirty years.

For many centuries the Morvan's woodlands have been exploited for fuel and constructional timber, much of it being sent to Paris. Until just before the war of 1939-45, the timber was mostly rafted down the headstreams; it was stacked at certain points to await the deliberate releasing of flood-waters from *étangs* dammed higher up the valleys for that purpose.[1] It was floated downstream to collecting points such as Clamecy and Coulanges on the Yonne or Vermenton on the Cure, and then sent by barge along the Nivernais Canal and the canalised Yonne to Paris. Today much of the timber travels by lorry, although pit-props are still transported by canal. Saw-mills, timber-yards and pulp-mills are in operation at such towns as Clamecy and Prémency.

About 10 per cent of the surface of the Morvan is covered with moorland and upland bog, generally known as *landes*. This area of waste is less than in the past, partly because of afforestation, partly because the area under permanent grassland has increased. Some cultivation is practised, mainly of wheat (which has largely replaced rye and buckwheat) and potatoes, helped by heavy liming and fertilising of the coarse acid soils. Farming activity is, however, mainly concerned with livestock; the rather poor *race morvandelle* has been supplanted by Charolais cattle, young stores being grazed on the hill pastures and then sent down to the lowlands for fattening. Pigs are reared and allowed to pannage in the beech woods.

Population and Settlement.—Inevitably this upland area has suffered depopulation, as shown by ruined farms and even some abandoned hamlets. The attractions of employment in the towns around in the Loire and Saône valleys, in the Le Creusot industrial district, and in Paris have drawn off much of the younger population. Château-Chinon in the south-west and Saulieu in the north-east are the only places of any size within the Morvan, and (unusually) they are situated high on the upland rather than in valleys; Château-Chinon rises in tiers up the slopes of a hillside, culminating in the church at a height of exactly 2,000 feet. A single-track line, the only railway to penetrate the Morvan, climbs circuitously from the Yonne valley line at Tamnay-en-Bazois to its terminus at Château-Chinon. Most of the other Morvan settlements are however in the valleys; thus Cussy-en-Morvan stands on the eastern side of the Selle valley, while Chissey-en-Morvan is a bridge town on the Vernin. The chief market towns for the region are in the marginal depression, such as Avallon on the north, Semur-en-Auxois on the north-east, and Autun on the south.

Some hamlets and small villages are found surprisingly high among the uplands, usually in a depression where surrounding hills afford protection from the winds. But the forest-covered heart of Haut-Morvan, from the Forêt d'Anost to the Bois du Roi, is virtually unpopulated, except for a few hamlets along the winding

---

[1] An interesting account of these operations is given by J. Levainville, *Le Morvan: étude de géographie humaine* (1909), pp. 99-128, including a map (p. 102) of saw-mills.

road between Château-Chinon and Autun, the only main road to cross the upland.

The eastern edge of the Central Massif overlooks the lowlands of the Saône-Rhône valley and of Languedoc for a distance of nearly 250 miles. The main rivers—Loire, Allier, Lot and Tarn—rise near this edge and trench their valleys across the whole Massif. With the exception of the volcanic peaks of Auvergne and the Mézenc, the highest points in the Central Massif are on this south-eastern margin, notably Mont Lozère (5,584 feet) and Mont Aigoual (5,128 feet). The height of this rim decreases northward; to the west of Lyons it just attains 3,000 feet, and in the Mâconnais and Charolais overlooking the Plaine de Bresse it is 1,750 feet or less.

While it is broadly true to say that this eastern margin represents a fault-line scarp, the dislocations are multiple and complex. Some of the faults are associated with the original Hercynian structures, thus trending from north-east to south-west. In several downfaulted depressions Permian and Carboniferous rocks have been preserved among the crystalline rocks, including workable Coal Measures (Fig. 120). This faulting has caused diverse rocks to lie in close juxtaposition, so affording full scope for differential denudation. Some of the rivers have developed their valleys in downfaulted areas of less resistant rock, so forming distinct north-east to south-west depressions; one such is occupied by the Dheune flowing to the Saône and the Bourbince flowing in the opposite direction to the Loire. Similarly the valleys of the Grosne, Brevenne, Gier, Doux and other minor streams follow the trends of faults.

Autunois and its Margins.—The small massif of Autunois consists of a block of granite in the west and of more complex granulites and schists in the east, partly covered with Triassic and Liassic sandstones and marls. It is of no great altitude, the highest point being only 2,244 feet and the greater part under 2,000 feet. The river Arroux, draining the depression containing the Autun-Epinac coalfield, cuts across the western part of the granite in a broad valley to join the Bourbince just above its confluence with the Loire. Like the Morvan to the north, much of Autunois is forested (notably the large woodlands of the Forêt de Planoise and the Bois de Grosne to the south-east and east of Autun); the rest is under moorland, rough grazing and some arable. Many of the shallow lakes are artificial, and are used to maintain the level of the Centre Canal.

Paradoxically, the main significance of the Autunois massif lies in the depressions which flank it to north and south. The former is floored with Permian and Upper Carboniferous rocks, and the

Autun-Epinac field produces annually about a quarter of a million tons of *gras* coal, consumed in a thermal station at Epinac. Bituminous shales are also mined, totalling about 15,000 tons a year; oil is distilled from these at Autun. This depression forms a routeway between the Loire and Saône valleys, avoiding a lengthy détour around the forested uplands of the Morvan. The Romans appreciated this fact, and sited Autun (*Augustodunum*) on a prominent hillock near the south bank of the Arroux. This is a busy town of over 17,000 people, with several fairs and markets, hotels catering for a useful tourist activity, and a number of manufacturing industries, notably of furniture and other wooden articles from the timber of the Morvan and Autunois. It is a route-focus, and nine major roads converge on it.

More important is the southern depression, which forms a quite densely populated industrial re-entrant, lying diagonally across the uplands, between the Autunois and the Charolais. This contains the Blanzy coalfield, which produced 2·3 million tons of coal in 1963, with the busy mining towns of Blanzy, Montchanin and Montceau-les-Mines, and the iron- and steel-works of Le Creusot, Gueugnon, Breuil, and Montchanin (Fig. 123). The chief concerns are the *Schneider* works (the *Forges et Aciéries du Creusot*) and the *Forges de Gueugnon* at Gueugnon to the south-west of Le Creusot. There is a variety of metallurgical products, notably armaments and locomotives. Other industries have developed along the banks of the Centre Canal, which utilises this depression, including the making of bricks, tiles, earthenware pipes and sanitary ware. Montceau-les-Mines (29,364) and Le Creusot (33,779)[1] now form agglomerations of steel-works, factories, nineteenth-century housing and modern *cités-ouvrières*.

Charolais.[2]—The Monts du Charolais form an upland mass between the Blanzy depression and the broadly parallel Grosne, which joins the Saône below Chalon. The Grosne valley is sometimes known as the Val de Cluny, from the main town situated there. Structurally Charolais and Mâconnais to the south-east are part of a single ancient Hercynian anticline, and the valleys of the Grosne on the north-east and of the Sornin on the south-west represent its axis, denuded at an early date and infilled with Mesozoic rocks.

Charolais can therefore be divided into two. There is *Charolais cristallin*, the uplands of granite and gneiss, rising to such eminences

---

[1] The development of industry in Le Creusot before the last war is given by M. Perrin, 'Le Creusot', in *A. de G.* (1934), vol. xliii, pp. 255-74.

[2] This district is sometimes referred to as *Charollais*, after the town of Charolles. French practice is to use the term *Pays de Charolles* for the area around Charolles, but to use *Charolais* for the wider upland region.

FIG. 123.—THE ST. ETIENNE AND LE CREUSOT COALFIELDS.

St. E., St. Etienne.

Based on *Carte de France et des frontières au 200,000ᵉ*, sheets 41, 47, 53, with areas of the coalfield taken from the *Carte géologique de la France*, 1 : 1,000,000, published by the *Service de la Carte géologique détaillée de la France* (1933).

as the Roche de Montmélard (2,533 feet) in the extreme south and Mont-St. Vincent (1,978 feet) further north.   Much of it once was forested, but now this has been largely replaced by pastures, heavily limed and fertilised to make good the deficiencies of the thin acid soils.   In contrast *Charolais sédimentaire*, sometimes called the '*bon pays*', is an area of varied Jurassic rocks—Lias clays and marls and Middle Jurassic limestones, lying on the western flanks of the crystalline rocks in the valley of the Sornin, a district known as the *Pays de Charolles* after the town of that name.   The Mesozoic rocks occur too on the east in the Grosne valley, further diversified with patches of Triassic sandstone and Pliocene sands (the *Sables de Chagny*).   These sedimentary rocks form a gentle country of limestone hills and clay-floored vales.

Charolais is famed for its large white beef-cattle ; there were over 496,000 cattle in Saône-et-Loire in 1963.   About 40 per cent of this *département* consists of permanent pasture, both on the Jurassic limestones and Lias marls, and on the crystalline uplands.   Another 10 per cent is under fodder-crops—trefoil, lucerne, mixed grains and legumes, and roots.   Animals are bred mainly for meat ; mature animals are despatched directly to the abattoirs of Paris and Lyons and young stores are sent to other districts of France for fattening— for example, to the Paris Basin where they are fed on fodder-beet and on sugar-beet pulp.   Stock-fairs are held at Charolles, Cluny, St. Christophe-en-Brionnais, Paray-le-Monial and several other places, attended by buyers from a considerable distance.   While this emphasis is on beef-cattle, most of *Charolais sédimentaire* forms a prosperous mixed farming area ; horses, pigs and poultry are also reared, wheat and potatoes are grown on the arable land, and vine-yards (see p. 382) cover the limestone slopes overlooking the Saône valley.

Mâconnais.—The upland of the Mâconnais projects in a north-north-easterly direction into the Plaine de Bresse.   The Saône flows closely along its eastern margins, and in fact makes a right-angle bend near Chalon around its northern extremity.   A narrow 'slice' of granite overlooks the Grosne valley to the north-west ; this rises for much of its length to over 1,500 feet, with one summit (la Mère-Boîtier) reaching 2,408 feet.   A few other granite outposts appear to the north-west of Mâcon, but the rest of Mâconnais consists of Jurassic limestone and Lias marls.   These rocks are banded in a direction parallel to the granitic 'slice', the result of profound faulting.   There are even narrow exposures of Eocene clays and sands down-faulted among the limestones.

These varied rocks suffered the usual phases of peneplanation, but subsequent erosion has had full play.   Several sharp-edged limestone scarps overlook the Saône valley, each dropping as a step to the next marl terrace; the Roche de Solutré, for example, not far from Mâcon, culminates in a vertical cliff. Some parts of the limestone country form rather bare plateaus, with solution hollows, caves and disappearing streams. By contrast, the marl- and clay-filled depressions are damp and usually under grass, while the rounded granitic ridges to the west are forested.

The chief feature of the economy is the vine, grown on the *côtes* overlooking the Saône valley (see p. 382). The proximity of these uplands to Charolais has also induced a considerable development of cattle-rearing on the hill pastures.

Beaujolais.—A much higher group of uplands, the Monts du Beaujolais, extends southward from the high valleys of the Grosne headstreams as far as a distinct west-east structural depression, known as the Seuil de Tarare. This southern limit is emphasised by the river Reins draining westwards to the Loire and the Tardine eastwards to the Azergues, with between them a col through which passes the main road (*N7*) and (in a tunnel) the railway between Roanne and Lyons. The higher parts of Beaujolais, culminating in the rounded summit of Mont-St. Rigaud (3,321 feet), consists of porphyries and granulites, while outcrops of Lower Carboniferous limestones and shales are preserved within down-faulted zones which extend westward across the Loire valley to the south of Roanne. As in the case of the northern massifs, Jurassic and Tertiary rocks appear on the eastern flanks, a feature particularly evident on the slopes rising from the Saône valley near Villefranche.

Beaujolais is much dissected by a well-developed pattern of valleys; the upper sections of many of these run north-south, following the fault-lines, and leaving between them smooth-topped ridges orientated in the same direction. The long valley of the Azergues, for example, forms a broad gently sloping re-entrant into the heart of the uplands. Other streams drain more directly eastwards to the Saône or westwards to the Loire. This radial pattern leaves a substantial upland area, the Plateau de Poule, in the heart of Beaujolais.

A marked contrast is presented by the granite uplands (*La Montagne*), the Jurassic slopes descending in steps to the Saône (*La Côte*) and the broad valleys. The uplands, covered with thin soils, carry rough grazing, considerable tracts of gorse-scrub, and pine plantations. The *Côte* on the east has long been devoted to the production of the celebrated red Beaujolais wines (see p. 384), although this has been less of a monoculture since the phylloxera ravages. Orchards, fodder-crops and even small fields of cereals diversify the agricultural landscape.

The main valleys are quite densely inhabited; large farms and hamlets can be seen far up their heads to about 2,500 feet, and Chènelette, for example, is situated almost at the head of the Azergues valley. Vaux-en-Beaujolais is situated to the north-west of Ville-franche, on the slopes overlooking the valley of the Vauxonne at a height of 1,750 feet; wooded or pasture-covered slopes rise to rounded ridges, while the sheltered village is surrounded by orchards, vineyards, little fields of arable and patches of meadow-land. One reason for this relative density of population is the surprising indus-trial activity. For centuries textiles have been made on a domestic basis, first wool, then silk and cotton. Today many small towns have factories, usually subsidiary to the big concerns in Lyons, as at Tarare, Thizy and Amplepuis. Special cotton fabrics are made, and numerous local specialisations are evident.

Lyonnais.—The Monts du Lyonnais extend southward from the Seuil de Tarare to the well-defined coal-basin of St. Etienne. This is perhaps the most massive of the marginal uplands, for it consists solidly of mica-schists, gneiss and granite. On the west the faulted edge ends abruptly at the Tertiary-floored Plaine du Forez, in the east it terminates even more abruptly, so that just to the north of Lyons the Saône actually cuts into the crystalline rocks. The flanking Jurassic rocks are here absent, with the exception (to the north-west of Lyons) of the little outlying mass of Mont d'Or culminating in the 2,051-ft. summit of Mont Verdun, a limestone plateau resting on a foundation of crystalline rocks; these limestones have long been quarried to provide stone for the buildings of Lyons.

Much of the plateau of Lyonnais exceeds 2,000 feet, the highest point reaching 3,294 feet near St. Héand in the west. The gently swelling and rather bare ridges alternate with shallow depressions, sometimes marshy and peat-filled, though other parts are wooded, the higher areas with pine and beech, the lower slopes on the east with oak and chestnut. Agricultural activity is evident on the east-facing slopes and valleys, largely owing to demands of the Lyons markets. Cattle are reared for both milk and meat; vines and orchards (particularly of peaches) grow on the terraced slopes; and lower down near the main valley-floor heavy fertilising has helped to create productive market-gardens.

As in the case of Beaujolais, the proximity of Lyons has influenced the development of a considerable textile industry, mostly connected with silk, at such towns as Arbresle and Chazelles. Moreover, work-people from the eastern Lyonnais villages travel daily considerable distances into Lyons. Two other industrial activities are the result of fortuitous geological circumstances. In the heart of the crystalline massif, a narrow strip of Upper Carboniferous coal-bearing rocks is preserved in the syncline of Ste. Foy-l'Argentière, yielding from

20,000 to 50,000 tons of coal a year. Near St. Bel some deposits of pyrites are mined to supply chemical works in Lyons.

The St. Etienne Region.—Lyonnais is bounded on the south by a depression through which the Furens flows westwards to join the Loire, and the Gier follows one of the characteristic structural lines in a north-easterly direction to the Rhône at Givors; their head-streams are separated by a watershed at a height of about 1,500 feet. The St. Etienne field (Fig. 123) lies mainly in the Furens valley and is worked near St. Etienne itself and at Roche-la-Molière, but it is also exploited over the watershed to the east near Terre Noire, St. Chamond and Rive-de-Gier, and again to the south-west near Le Chambon and Firminy in the valley of another Loire tributary, the Ondaine. The coal seams are much disturbed by faulting and are difficult to work, but the mines were vigorously exploited during the war of 1914–18. St. Etienne is linked with Lyons by a railway following the Gier valley, and about a quarter of the coal is consumed in the Lyons industrial district. About 452,000 tons of metallurgical coke were produced in 1963 in pit-head cokeries. The rest of the coal output (which totalled 2·1 million tons in 1963) was used for steam-raising in the St. Etienne industrial district, for gas-making, for thermal-electric generators (notably the huge Centrale le Bec) to supplement the hydro-stations, for the railways (which took 400,000 tons in 1961), and for domestic consumption.

The iron and steel manufacturing region[1] extends from Firminy over the watershed into the Gier valley. At Givors itself the *Etablissements Prénat* have blast furnaces, further up the valley at Rive-de-Gier the *Etablissements Marrel* operate a large steel-plant, modernised in 1952, and numerous steel-works are at St. Etienne itself, St. Chamond, Assailly and Firminy. Compared with Lorraine, the actual output of steel is small (of the order of 200,000 tons per annum), but there is an important production of special alloy-steels for armaments, tools, parts of cars, cycles and aircraft, nuts and bolts, textile machinery, and a range of other metal articles.

An application of the post-war principle of 'readaptation' has taken place in the St. Etienne district. Under-investment, the restrictive independence of small producers, and war-time stagnation had resulted in this area becoming in the post-1945 years what M. Monnet had called 'a backward pocket' when in 1946 he urged a merger of the four major steel-plants in order to effect modernisation and reconstruction. This was then turned down, but after the formation of the E.C.S.C. action was taken; the four plants were

---

[1] A survey of the industrial development of St. Etienne and its neighbourhood before the last war is given by M. Perrin, *Saint-Etienne et sa région économique* (1937).

R.G.W.E.—T

merged into the *Compagnie des Ateliers et Forges de la Loire*, and modernisation, conversion and concentration have been effected.

There are many specialised textile manufactures, mainly of silk and man-made fibres; St. Chamond makes ribbons, laces, hosiery and elasticated cloth, and St. Etienne, St. Chamond and Izieux have rayon factories. Glass-works have been long established at St. Etienne and Rive-de-Gier, and pottery is made at these two towns and at Lorette and La Grand-Croix. Chemical works are associated with the coke-ovens, producing tar, benzine, methanol, sulphate of ammonia and dyes. A considerable industry of textile dyeing was based originally on the availability of pure water from the rivers.

The district has been helped by its communications, although St. Etienne is situated at a height of 1,600 feet. The railway between the city and Andrézieux, nine miles to the north-west in the Loire valley, was actually the first line to be opened in France (in 1828). Lines run down the Gier valley to Givors and Lyons, northward to the Loire valley and Roanne, and south-westward to Le Puy.

St. Etienne is an important industrial centre and the economic capital of the eastern margins of the Central Massif. It is a market- and shopping-focus for a widespread rural district, for it is situated in one of the main route-ways by which the eastern rim of the Massif can be negotiated. As an educational centre it is especially famed for its *Ecole Nationale des Mines*, founded in 1816. The population, which totalled 45,000 in 1830, by 1962 had reached 203,633.

Three other groups of industrial towns occur in this district. On the west of the watershed lie L'Ondaine, La Ricamarie, Chambon-Feugerolles, Firminy (the largest of these with 26,000 people) and Unieux; in the Gier valley are St. Chamond, Izieux, St. Julien and L'Horme; and lower down is a separate group of Rive-de-Gier, Lorette and La Grand-Croix. With a total population of over 300,000 people, this industrial 'belt' lying diagonally across the eastern rim of the Central Massif affords a marked contrast with the uplands to north and south.

Vivarais.—The name Vivarais[1] is applied somewhat widely to the uplands along the east margin of the Central Massif from the St. Etienne depression to the Cévennes. It is difficult to define the boundary between Vivarais and the Cévennes, and in point of fact the name *Cévennes vivaroises* is bestowed upon that part of Vivarais overlooking the upper Ardèche valley. It is convenient, if a little arbitrary, to take the line of the Chassesac–lower Ardèche valleys, as the boundary between Vivarais and the '*Cévennes propre-ment dites*'. A distinction must also be drawn between the crystal-

[1] E. Reynier, *Le pays de Vivarais* (1947); and P. Rozon, *La Vie rurale en Vivarais. Etude géographique* (1961).

line upland (*la Montagne vivaroise*), and the lower plateau region (*le piémont vivarois*), lying between the high edge and the Rhône. The *piémont* is commonly known as the Plateau d'Annonay, and is much dissected by many short streams (Cance, Ay, Doux) which flow down between projecting spurs. These distinctions are mainly the result of altitude, for Vivarais as a whole is made up of solid masses of granite and gneiss which continue westward into Velay. The watershed between the headwaters of the Loire and Allier and those of the Ardèche really forms the division between Vivarais and Velay.

The plateau surface is smooth and uniform, mostly between 3,000 and 4,000 feet in height, with occasional swelling summits rising to 5,000 feet. By contrast their eastward slopes are gashed with ravines worn by the torrential streams making their way to the Rhône. Between them project ridges, at first broad and uniform, but narrowing eastward as the ravines widen into valleys; these are the *serres*, which become still more prominent further south in the Cévennes.

Another group of features is due to the effects of volcanicity. The remains of basaltic lava-flows form the highest summits of the Mézenc (5,754 feet) and the Gerbier de Jonc (5,088 feet), a neat little peak on the southern slopes of which rises the Loire. Small craggy cappings of basalt survive here and there to form prominent summits, such as the Suc de Banzon and the Vestide du Pal, contrasting with the smooth granitic slopes.

Finally, two quite individual uplands project prominently towards the Rhône, the Massif du Pilat in the north and the Coiron in the south. The former comprises a spur of gneiss and granulite surrounded on three sides by the Gier valley and the Rhône, culminating in the massive rounded summit of the Crest de la Perdrix (4,705 feet), and the more craggy ridge of the aptly named Crest des Trois-Dents. The Coiron is by contrast a much dissected spur of Upper Jurassic limestone capped with an escarpment of phonolitic lavas of Pliocene age, forming a narrow tableland running for fifteen miles in a direction south of east almost to the banks of the Rhône. Its sides are deeply scalloped by the valleys of torrential streams flowing to the Lovenzon on the north, to the Ardèche and Frayol on the south. Fantastically eroded piles of dark basalt often form ragged cornices overhanging the valleys.

A distinct zoning of vegetation and land-use is apparent from the ridges to the Rhône valley. The higher summits are covered with rough pasture, moorland and in places plantations of pine, larch and fir, with the remains of more continuous beech woods, and lower down chestnut. The greater part of Vivarais falls within the *département* of Ardèche; just under one-quarter of its total area was under woodland in 1963, and exactly one-third was under permanent pasture, utilised mainly by cattle in the north and by herds of sheep in the south, many of which are brought up in summer from the limestone country of the Rhône valley. But more than a third was waste, and only a tenth was returned as arable, most of which occurs on the lower terraced slopes just above the floor of the Rhône valley and in valley-depressions. On the lower terraces fruits are grown (notably peaches, cherries, plums and in favoured localities figs), vines and mulberries, although the last are now much less important than in the past. Irrigation is commonly used, and water is led from rivulets in channels along the terraces. Small fields of wheat, potatoes, fodder-crops and vegetables of various kinds are grown, and even quite high up under the crest of the uplands are patches of rye and potatoes.

Vivarais is not an area of dense population, and parts of the high uplands are virtually uninhabited. Nevertheless, over the whole of Ardèche the density averaged about 117 per square mile in 1963, a figure achieved without any major urban centre to swell the total, for the largest town is Annonay with 19,000 inhabitants and the *chef-lieu* is the little town of Privas with only 9,200. Most of the population of Vivarais live in small towns and villages in the valleys, many of them situated where the slope of its valley becomes markedly gentler and the walls recede. A line of these settlements can be traced from north to south—Bourg-Argental, Annonay, Lamastre, Le Cheylard and Privas. On the southern margins are Prades (the centre of a little coal-basin), Aubenas, Largentière and Ruoms, strung out along the valley of the middle Ardèche. A few small villages, often consisting of high-storeyed stone buildings clustered on the terraced slopes, are found far up the valleys, some as high as 4,000 feet. Even on the ridge-plateau are such small settlements as Devesset and Mézilhac.

Little industrial activity is found in Vivarais. Annonay, centrally situated in the valley of the Cance, is a market town, and has tanneries, glove-making works and a paper-mill. Around the flanks of Mont Pilat are villages (such as Bourg-Argental and Pélussin) which come within the Lyons industrial orbit and possess small silk-mills. Vals-les-Bains on the southern flanks of the Coiron has utilised the numerous mineral-springs which burst out of the sides of the valley to become a pleasant little spa.

The Cévennes.—On a clear day one can see from viewpoints in Nîmes or Montpellier a dark blue line of hills thirty miles away to the north-west. Here the edge of the Central Massif is defined most clearly by a fault-line scarp trending from north-east to south-west; one of the most important faults which define this scarp is the *grande faille méridienne de Villeforte*. The ridge-line consists of a broad upland of crystalline rocks, the *montagne cévenole*, more or less continuous with Margeride to the north and flanked by the Grands Causses on the west and south. It forms a rolling tableland at a height of between 4,000 and 4,500 feet, gently incised on the north-west by streams that find their way westwards to the Lot and the Tarn. Above this general level, rounded summits rise merely a hundred feet or so, described by E.-A. Martel as '*croupes mamelonnées*' and '*gibbosités de granit*'. A northern group culminates in the mass of Lozère (5,584 feet), the highest point on the whole eastern margin of the Central Massif, and a more southerly group of summits has its highest point in Mont Aigoual (5,128 feet), crowned with a meteorological observatory. In places occur great piles of rectangular granite blocks, with sometimes curious pinnacles (such as the Monolithe de Pourcarès on the western slopes of Aigoual). Elsewhere the slopes are covered thinly with coarse granitic gravels, so smooth that in winter they form pleasant ski-fields. Much of the upland consists of less resistant metamorphosed slates (mostly phyllites), which also weather to form gentle slopes; Mont Lozère is so called from the *lozes* or plaques of slate which occur commonly on its flanks. The ridge is at its narrowest to the north-east of Mont Aigoual, where it is actually trending from west to east; the lowest point is the col of the Barre des Cévennes, at only 3,051 feet, while a little to the north-east another gap, the Col de Jalcreste (3,140 feet) is crossed by the motor-road between Florac and Alès via the little town of Anduze, sometimes known as '*la Porte des Cévennes*'.

Numerous depressions occur on the uplands where Mesozoic rocks (mostly Lias clays) have been down-faulted along lines running from west to east. Even occasional patches of Upper Triassic sandstone survive, as in the depression between the Montagne de la Lozère and the Montagne du Bougés to the south. Generally speaking, therefore, the ridge-line and the western slopes and valleys of the Cévennes, planed by the various cycles of erosion, are gentle and mature in appearance, as A. Meynier describes them, '*très réguliers, très étendus, très monotones*'.[1]

The eastern slopes of the Cévennes present a very different appearance. Deep steep-sided ravines (*cams*) run up to the edge of the ridge-line, separated by narrow crumbling rocky ridges known as *serres*. These valleys, again in the words of Meynier, are '*profondes et escarpées*', by comparison with their westerly neighbours which are '*douces et évasées*'. The tilting of the Central Massif left a steep edge facing the Mediterranean; from the summit of Mont Aigoual the land falls 4,000 feet in a direct distance of only four miles. The major part of the steep face is eroded into the crystalline rocks themselves; both the beds of the ravines and the rocky sides of the *serres*

[1] A. Meynier, *Géographie du Massif Central* (1935), p. 144.

show this quite clearly. The slates tend to form wider and less rugged valleys than do the granitic rocks.

A series of nearly parallel torrential streams flows south-eastwards to join the Cèze, the Gard and the Hérault. Their sources are working back rapidly through headward erosion, the result of rapid runoff and steep gradients. The rain tends to fall in concentrated downpours; the most notable record in this area was the 39 inches received in forty-eight hours at Valleraugue in September 1900, which gashed and scoured the landscape.[1] In the words of Ph. Arbos, '*Le relief . . . manifeste la violence de l'érosion méditerranéenne*'. These easterly headstreams (known as *gardons*) interlock with the more gentle rivulets which form the Tarn and the Lot (Fig. 121); indeed, in several places the Hérault source-streams have captured former headstreams of the Dourbie in the depression between Mont Aigoual and Mont Lingas. The Hérault is a particularly active river, for the main stream rises on the southern slopes of the Aigoual well to the west of the actual summit, and flows southwards first over the crystalline rocks, then crosses a south-easterly extension of the limestone Causses; one of its headstreams, the Vis, in fact drains the eastern margins of the Causse du Larzac. The gorges of the Hérault (in places 1,300 feet deep), the Vis, and its left-bank tributary the Lamalou, are on a dramatic scale; the lower Lamalou gorge, known as the Ravin des Arc, with its water-worn cliffs, pot-holes, arches and cascades, surpasses anything in the Grands Causses to the north. The Grotte des Demoiselles, in the valley of the upper Hérault below Ganges, contains some fantastic calcite formations.

These contrasts between the relief of the crest-line and western slopes of the Cévennes on the one hand and of the steep eastern flanks on the other is reflected in the land-use and the economy. On the uplands a pastoral way of life has been dominant for many centuries. The hill-slopes carry pasture of variable quality, in places improved by liming and fertilising, elsewhere either so overgrazed or conversely so neglected that it has degenerated into rough grazing or still further into heath, covered with ling, broom and coarse grasses.[2] Along the valleys of some of the west-flowing rivulets appears better meadow-land, in places improved by the trenching of irrigation channels over the surface. Patches of arable land near the occasional settlements grow rye, buckwheat, oats and potatoes, and vegetables are cultivated in carefully tended gardens (often protected

---

[1] A. Meynier, *op. cit.*, p. 145.
[2] J. W. House, 'A Comparative Study of the Landscapes of the Plateau de Millevaches and the Western Cévennes', in *Transactions and Papers of the Institute of British Geographers* (1954), no. 20, pp. 159-80, gives some interesting land-use statistics for sample communes, and emphasises changes that are taking place.

from winds by high stone walls) for local needs. But the area of arable is small, usually less than 5 per cent of any commune, and moreover half of that in any one year is under fallow.

The animals reared are chiefly sheep, and cattle are rarely seen. Some flocks live permanently in the Cévennes, moving from hamlets in the valleys to the upper slopes, but most sheep come up from Bas-Languedoc, following an age-old pattern of transhumance. The route-ways or *drailles* winding up from the plains of Languedoc can be seen from far away as white ribbons on the hillsides; they are potent causes of soil erosion, since their worn-down surfaces become runnels which readily develop into ravine-gashes. During the last fifty years sheep-rearing has markedly decreased, together with transhumance. It is difficult to give exact figures, since only parts of three *départements* fall within the Cévennes region, but to use Lozère as an indication, there were 300,000 sheep in 1890 and only 200,000 in 1963. This decline is due to the deterioration of upland pastures, to the increase in woodland, to the tendency towards rural depopulation with resultant shortage of workers, and to the generally unprofitable character of upland farming.[1]

A long struggle has taken place on these uplands between the pasture and the woodland. Except perhaps for the highest summits of Aigoual and Lozère, where relics of a sub-Alpine flora can be discerned (the tree-line lying at about 5,000 feet), thick beech woods with some ash probably covered most of the slopes; in the local *patois* the term 'Cebenno' indicates a wooded slope. Rainfall is everywhere adequate, indeed plentiful, for tree-growth; at the Aigoual observatory the mean annual total is 92 inches. But people of the upland villages have cut gradually into the woodland cover for fuel or building material or to increase the extent of pasture, and uncontrolled burning and close grazing by sheep and goats for long prevented any natural forest regeneration. In the third quarter of the nineteenth century a counter-offensive began, carried on both by individuals with financial assistance from the State and by the State itself. Though rainfall is adequate, the chief climatic disadvantages are the wind, for the *mistral* blows over the exposed ridges towards the Mediterranean with icy force, and the summer drought, which together make the early years of plantation establishment difficult. In addition summer fire-hazards are grave. However, both State forests and privately owned plantations now cover most of the available land, and post-war planting has made good the inevitable heavy inroads of 1939–45. Large compact blocks of beech and spruce, together with the native pine, some Douglas and silver fir, and larch on the lower slopes, have been planted. Most of the high communes now have a quarter of their land under forests, some more

[1] J. W. House, *op. cit.*, pp. 170-1, clearly emphasises this point.

than half. The State forests are carefully managed and a system of gradual thinning and progressive planting rather than complete felling is employed. In some communes the widespread progress of rural depopulation has been checked by forestry employment; some men are whole-time forestry workers, others work on a part-time basis, providing a useful supplement to the limited income derived from a small farm. Even so, the shortage of labour is such that it is necessary to bring in labour-gangs for felling and removal, to supplement the labour of permanent employees.

Population is scanty and settlements few. Some small villages lie in the high valleys and depressions well above 3,000 feet; one of the most elevated hamlets in the whole Central Massif must be Salarials, on the southern flanks of Lozère at a height of 4,632 feet. A few other settlements are situated in the high valleys of the Lot and the Tarn, some with hotels, notably Bagnols-les-Bains with its thermal springs. Others have been centres of a sporadic mining activity, including Bleymard in the Lot valley with its mines of calamine and argentiferous galena, Villefort and Cubières also with lead mines, and Masseguin with hematite mines. But except for a line of villages along the main road down the Lot valley, other settlements are few and widely separated.

The south-eastern slopes of the Cévennes present a very different aspect. On a diverse terrain of steep rugged ridges, deeply-cut valleys, and, lower down, gently inclined but stepped slopes, are imprinted many of the characteristics of a Mediterranean climatic régime and an intensive polyculture. On the lower south-facing terraces are mulberries (now much less important than they were) and olives, long rows of vines, patches of wheat in narrow fields enclosed by dry stone walls, orchards of peaches, apricots, cherries and higher up apples, market-gardens commonly irrigated by rivulets led along the terraces, and huddled villages of tall stone houses among the cypresses. On the rugged slopes of the ridges between the terraced valleys flourishes the *garrigue* in all its variety, with scrub-oaks among the aromatic shrubs.

Still higher, from about 1,350 feet to 2,500 feet, appears a zone of carefully tended chestnut groves, degenerating among the rocky slopes into scrubby semi-wild trees. Villages and large farms are located on the floors of the valleys, their occupants depending on this mixed agricultural economy, though for long the basis of subsistence has been chestnut porridge and goats' or ewes' milk cheese. Some of the high basins contain meadows of good quality, often irrigated, and here cattle have increased in numbers, supplying milk for the towns of Languedoc. On this Mediterranean side of the Cévennes there is again evidence of rural depopulation in the part-ruined hamlets and abandoned farms, with the chestnuts and fruit trees degenerating into the *garrigue* that has spread around them. Roads push their way, sometimes by incredible loops and zig-zags, up through these valleys. A few motor-roads cross the ridge, improved for the ubiquitous autobus services which link remote hamlets with civilisation, for the timber- and produce-lorries, and for the cars of tourists. Rail communications are difficult and limited. One remarkable main line (the chief longitudinal rail-route in the Central Massif) works its way north from Nîmes and Alès via Villefort, crossing transversely the ridges and ravines by means of innumerable viaducts and tunnels to penetrate the uplands to the Allier valley, hence to Clermont-Ferrand. A branch from this line at La Bastide runs westward to Mende and Millau, thus affording a complete crossing of the Cévennes. Two other lines lead westward to rail-heads, one up the valley of the Gardon d'Anduze, the other via St. Hippolyte across to the Hérault valley to a terminus at Le Vigan.

Many villages and hamlets are situated along these railways and roads, others are reached only by tracks into *cul-de-sac* valleys. Little towns at the mouths of each valley form servicing- and market-centres, with their periodic fairs. Some contain small specialised silk industries, notably Le Vigan which has made silk hosiery for centuries, St. Jean-du-Gard and Anduze.

Along the margins of the Cévennes occurs a series of depressions in the Lias marls, forming an area of prosperous agriculture; the many streams down the slopes are used for irrigation. A string of towns—Alès, La Grand Combe, Salindres, Ambroix and Bessèges—form a linear '*paysage minier jusque dans la châtaigneraie*' (Ph. Arbos). The basis of their industrial activity is the Alès coalfield, which produced about 2·2 million tons in 1963. Its output is varied, including some anthracite, and about half is made into patent fuels. A small-scale iron and steel industry, originally using local ores, now produces a small amount of high-grade steel, and a variety of specialised engineering and metallurgical industries has developed. Other activities include the manufacture of chemicals at Salindres and of silk at several towns. Mulberries are widely grown, and silk-worms are reared domestically.

THE CENTRAL UPLANDS

The term Auvergne, derived from a Gaulish tribal name *Arverni*, is often applied, if rather loosely, to the central uplands as a whole.[1] Some geographers restrict the term to the line of volcanic uplands

---

[1] The standard monograph on this part of France is Ph. Arbos, *L'Auvergne* (1932, with several subsequent editions). See also L. Gachon, *L'Auvergne et le Velay* (1949). A detailed account of the volcanic features is by A. Rudel, *Les Volcans d'Auvergne* (1962, new edition 1963), a monograph of 166 pp.

T 2

lying west of the Allier valley from the Puy de Dôme to Aubrac. Others include the western part of the Allier valley, centred on Clermont-Ferrand, as *la grande Limagne auvergnate*. The granitic uplands to the south-east are sometimes described as *la Margeride auvergnate* in distinction to the more outlying *Margeride du Gé-vaudan*. On the northern margins are the crystalline uplands of the *Combraille d'Auvergne*. In this section, however, the usage of the term Auvergne is restricted to the line of volcanic hills, one major ingredient in these central uplands.

The central uplands may be divided into two main groups (Fig. 122): the crystalline massifs of Margeride, Livradois, Forez and Madeleine, and the volcanic hills of Auvergne proper and of the

FIG. 124.—GEOLOGICAL SECTION ACROSS THE CENTRAL MASSIF.
The length of the section is about 125 miles.
Based on A. Cholley *et al.*, *La France* (n.d.), p. 240.

Plateau du Velay. The last of these is complicated by the fact that it includes the Bassin du Puy, the most southerly of the basins through which the Loire pursues its northward course; it is, how-ever, so much part of the volcanic uplands, with its lava flows and plugs and much of it above 2,000 feet, that it is desirable to include it in this region of central uplands.

Margeride.—Delimited by the headstreams of the Truyère and the Lot in the west and by the long line of the Allier in the east, lies the massive upland of Margeride (Fig. 121). In general outline it consists of broad planated plateau-surfaces, 4,000 to 4,500 feet in altitude, with rounded '*sommets mamelonnés*' rising barely three or four hundred feet above this level and cols sinking only a couple of hundred feet below. The highest point, in fact, the Truc de Randon in the south, only attains 5,098 feet. In the southern *Margeride du Gévaudan* the rock consists predominantly of well-jointed granite, which has weathered to form a surface diversified with large rectan-gular blocks, culminating at intervals in tor-like mounds, columns and obelisks known as *trucs*. Sometimes these granitic masses project irregularly from a coarse vegetation cover, elsewhere from bare granite pavements. In the northerly *Margeride auvergnate* the rock is predominantly gneiss and mica-schist, and the relief is smoother and more monotonous; its higher surfaces are only gently furrowed by many rivulets flowing in a north-easterly direction to the Allier, and south-westerly to the Truyère and the Lot.

The surface of Margeride is one of the most desolate in the whole Central Massif, with vast extents of poor upland grazing, ling-covered heathland, bilberry moors and peat-bogs, snow-covered and bleak in winter. In the words of Ph. Arbos, '*une atmosphère de mélancolie, de tristesse même, baigne cette montagne, une des régions les plus désertes de l'Auvergne*'.[1]

Livradois, Forez and Madeleine.—This group projects boldly northward between the downfaulted Limagne on the west and the series of Loire basins on the east. It forms, in fact, the middle 'prong' of hills for those who visualise the uplands of the Central Massif as a trident, providing a remarkably continuous line of high-level uplands; it is possible to walk northwards, if one is so disposed, for a distance of over ninety miles without ever descending below 3,000 feet.

Livradois is separated from the Monts du Forez by the downfaulted valley of the Dore. Both consist of granites and granulites, with some masses of gneiss and of micaschist in the south-west. Their relief is even more subdued than that of Margeride. The highest point in *Haut-Livradois* in the south-east is Notre-Dame-de-Mons, a rounded eminence attaining 3,970 feet. *Bas-Livradois*, sloping gently towards Limagne, represents the surface of an early Tertiary peneplain, diversified only by a few tiny down-faulted depressions (such as that of St. Dier) containing Oligocene sediments.

The Monts du Forez consist largely of the surface of a peneplain at about 3,000 feet, from which swell the rounded vestiges of higher levels rising to nearly 5,000 feet.[2] The highest point, Pierre-sur-Haute, attains 5,381 feet, formed by a chaotic pile of weathered rectangular boulders similar to the *trucs* of Margeride. Some features on the eastern slopes of Forez are the result of volcanic activity, especially to the west of Montbrison; these include basalt-flows, culminating in Mont Semiol (3,025 feet), and small cones. The flanks of the Forez are diversified with striking boulder-strewn gorges. In the higher southern parts distinct U-shaped valleys,

---

[1] Ph. Arbos, 'La Margeride', in *Mélanges géographiques offerts à Ph. Arbos* (1953), vol. i, p. 66.

[2] B. du Rosselle, 'Les Monts du Forez: recherches morphologiques', in *A. de G.* (1950), vol. lix, pp. 241-58, plots on a map (p. 243) four distinct surfaces, together with major fault-lines and the extent of the Quaternary glaciation.

cirques (notably that of Valcivières), and terminal moraines afford traces of the former glaciers. Most of the plateau is covered with coarse pasture or with a heath vegetation of myrtle and bilberry, though large areas are wooded, mostly by pines with some beech.

The Monts du Forez end in the north at the Col de Noirétable, which falls to 2,500 feet between the headstreams of the Durotte and the Auzon. Beyond this col, separated by the deep valley of the northward-flowing Besbre, are the uplands of the Bois-Noirs (4,262 feet) and the Madeleine (3,822 feet), beyond which the crystalline rocks vanish steeply below the Tertiary sediments of Bourbonnais. As the name of Bois-Noirs would imply, they are thickly wooded.

The Puys.—In contrast with the monotonous crystalline uplands, the volcanic landscapes present a variety of physical forms, ranging from peaks and extensive lava flows to minute cones and residual plugs. In the north is the remarkable landscape of the *Chaîne des Puys*, sometimes referred to as *les Monts Dôme*. From a uniform plateau-surface varying in height from about 2,700 to 3,250 feet, worn both from the crystalline basement and the products of ancient periods of vulcanicity, about seventy little cones, mostly of Pleistocene age, rise for a further few hundred feet. The majority are ash- and cinder-cones, with a thin vegetation cover in places, but much of the surface is covered with rough black cinders. Other cones consist of solidified siliceous lavas. The cones are strung out in chains from north-north-east to south-south-west, '. . . *une véritable galerie des divers types de cônes*'; indeed their forms are so varied that they form in truth '*un musée de reliefs éruptifs*' (Ph. Arbos). The Puy de Jumes and the Puy de la Coquille have regular craters with circular rims; the Puy de Pariou has a cone with a crater 200 yards in diameter within an outer partly destroyed crater-ring; the Puy de Louchadière forms a miniature caldera; the Puy de Côme has a double crater with a cone on the outer rim. Some circular depressions are the result of explosive activity without any extrusion of lava, notably the Gour de Tazenat. Some of the volcanoes are of the 'Peléean-dome' type, in which the siliceous lavas were so highly viscous that they formed a craterless extrusive dome. The best example of these, and the largest of the individual volcanic peaks, is the Puy de Dôme itself, '*une gigantesque pustule*' (A. Meynier) which attains a height of 4,806 feet. It was long thought to be either a small granite boss or a laccolith revealed by denudation, but it is clear that it was built up by slowly extruded trachytic lava (known as *domite*). Other examples of these *puys domitiques* are the Sarcoui, the Chaudron, the Clierzou and the Petit-Suchet. An interesting *puy* of a different character is the Chopine (3,874 feet), about whose origin there has been much discussion; it consists of a mass of granite, a fragment of the *socle cristallin* which probably stuck in the 'throat' of the volcano and was subsequently exposed by the removal of the surrounding cone.

A striking feature of the landscape is the number of basalt-lava flows (*coulées*), which have penetrated neighbouring valleys.[1] They are exceedingly numerous, both in space and time; on the flanks of the Puy de Dôme, for example, seven different lava flows are superimposed. The newest flows, known as *cheïres*, are of fissured lavas, and form desolate rocky regions with an irregular wrinkled surface. Some of these flows have blocked valleys; the lava from the twin Puys de la Vache and Lassolas moved down towards the narrow Veyre valley, and blocked the mouths of several valleys, so creating a number of lakes. Some, such as the former Lac Randamme, are now peat-filled, others, notably Lac d'Aydat, still form sheets of water.

Mont Dore.—To the south of the *puy* country occurs the complex volcanic structure of *Mont Dore*. Its present height is 6,188 feet, but at the time of its maximum activity it probably exceeded 8,000 feet, and it is about seventeen miles in basal diameter, considerably bigger than Vesuvius. The original cone has been so much dissected by fluvial and glacial action that the crater has disappeared and the inner structure of the volcano is revealed. Volcanic activity probably began in the Miocene, associated with the dislocations responsible for the downfaulting of Limagne, and continued until the late Pliocene. A variety of trachytes, andesites and basalts was poured out, probably from several different vents, forming both vertical plugs and gently inclined flows. Radial drainage was succeeded by the Quaternary glaciation; the Dordogne actually rises in a large cirque on the north-western side of the massif. The resistant trachytes and andesites now form sharply pinnacled residual peaks, notably the Puy de Sancy which forms the highest point, the Aiguiller, and a number of other peaks, while a massive basalt-flow in the north-west comprises the plateau-summit of the Banne d'Ordanche.

Cantal.—Further south still is the huge cone of Cantal, noteworthy both for its regularity and its size. About fifty miles in diameter, its base covers an area of just over a thousand square miles, approximately the same extent as Mount Etna, resting on a basement of both crystalline and Oligocene rocks; the latter are visible in the southwest and also in deeply trenched valleys in the north-east. Its origin is still a matter of conjecture; some authorities attribute its vast size to two major vents, others to three, though one theory postulates a much denuded gigantic single caldera. Whatever the origin may be,

---

[1] L. Gachon, 'L'Evolution morphologique des coulées volcaniques en Auvergne', in *A. de G.* (1945), vol. liii, pp. 254-73.

the result is a mass of volcanic rocks of Miocene and later age, mainly andesitic breccias and conglomerates, with also masses of scoriae, metamorphosed mud-flows, and layers of fine ash. The forces of denudation have had full play on such heterogeneous materials, and

FIG. 125.—THE MAJOR VOLCANIC AREAS OF THE CENTRAL MASSIF.

The three main volcanic peaks are shown by initials as follows: **M.D.**, Mont Dore; **P**, Puy de Dôme; and **P.C.**, Plomb du Cantal.

The towns shown are A, Aubusson; C.F., Clermont-Ferrand; and S.F., St. Flour.

Based on *Atlas de France*, plate 7 (1939).

a pre-glacial radial drainage system developed which trenched the slopes. Probably the huge broken-rimmed crater nurtured a Quaternary *névé*, from which glaciers flowed outwards, enlarging the valleys, forming cirque-basins and depositing moraine. Many of the valleys have a distinct U-section, and numerous lateral hanging-valleys or *gouttières* can be seen. Several small lakes (the Lacs de Guéry, de la Crégut and des Bondes) occupy some of these glacial hollows, others are now filled with peat, forming some *tourbières circulaires.*

Post-glacial river action has continued the work of destruction; headstreams of the Truyère flow down the southern slopes, the Cère, Jordanne, Doire and Maronne down the western slopes to the Dordogne, and the Rhue on the north also to the Dordogne. Between these gashed valleys inclined plateaus (*planèzes*) narrow upwards into rocky peaks. The largest of these spreads out towards the east as the Planèze de St. Flour, forming an extensive level lava-plateau, while others radiate towards the north-west (the Planèze de Mauriac), the north-east (Limon), and south-east (Carladès).[1]

The result of these several processes is a magnificent irregular pyramid with four curvilinear faces culminating in three major and numerous minor summits. These main peaks are quite different in character; the Puy Mary (5,863 feet) in the west is an ice-rounded dome of andesite, the Plomb du Cantal (6,096 feet) on the east consists of a rather unimpressive rounded mass of basalt where several *planèzes* converge, and, most striking of all, the Puy Griou (5,558 feet) is a pinnacle of phonolitic trachyte which projects steeply for about 200 feet. The last may represent a near-vertical dyke exposed by denudation. Some subsidiary cones occur on the flanks, notably Puy Violent in the west.

The surfaces of the lava flows are extraordinarily weathered, on the lower slopes providing rich black soil, higher up forming a rough surface of bare rock. Some of the basalts are so permeable that water penetrates them, forming sink-holes, subterranean drainage systems and copious springs at the margins.

Aubrac and Cézallier.—Less striking than the volcanic peaks, but making a considerable contribution to the relief, are the basalt plateaus of Aubrac (to the south of Cantal) and Cézallier (between Cantal and Mont Dore). Aubrac is composed of lava flows varying in age from late Miocene to Pliocene, with the basal ones resting on the Eogene peneplain cut across the granitic and schistose rocks. The result is a plateau twenty-five miles in length from north-west to south-east and eighty miles broad. The surface is remarkably uniform at about 4,250 feet; the highest point, Mailhebiau (4,826 feet) is a rounded mass of basalt.[2]

Cézallier is an equally monotonous area, with a general height of 3,500 to 3,900 feet, rising to 5,101 feet in the Signal du Luguet. It represents a relatively thin accumulation of basalt on a gneissic

[1] The *Carte de France et des frontières au 200,000ᵉ*, sheet 58 (Aurillac), shows these features admirably by means of contours and hill-shading.

[2] M. Ayral, 'Le Plateau d'Aubrac', in *A. de G.* (1928), vol. xxxvii, pp. 224-37.

basement. At the base of the basalts, lying on the gneiss, various much-altered lignites and diatom clays of possibly Miocene age have been discovered. The basalt flows are probably of Pliocene age, the topmost ones consisting of large tabular masses.

The surface of these lava plateaus is uniformly smooth, '*une désolation émouvante et grandiose*', except near the margins, where the rivers flowing radially from Aubrac to the Lot and the Truyère, and from Cézallier to the Alagnon and the Allier, have cut steep-sided valleys. The surface of the basalts here too has weathered to yield a good soil, largely pasture-covered except where there are beech-forests.

The Plateau du Velay.—An area of volcanic rocks, separated from Auvergne by the granitic massif of Margeride, lies across the head-stream region of the Loire.[1] In the west is the plateau-like ridge of the *Chaîne du Devès*, in the centre the shallow Tertiary *Bassin du Puy*, the floor of which has been modified by volcanic activity, and in the east the Mézenc-Mégal-Gerbier de Jonc group of peaks. The last, however, belong to Vivarais, forming part of the south-eastern marginal rim of the Central Massif.

The Chaîne du Devès, nearly forty miles in length and culminating in the Montagne du Devès (4,800 feet), forms a distinct range sep-arating the Allier and the Loire. This upland is the product of a series of Pliocene fissure-eruptions, and comprises for the most part a basalt plateau, slightly inclined towards the margins, with a central line of low volcanic hills. These are geologically older than the *puys* of Auvergne, and have suffered more denudation, but they survive as gentle cones, some with quite distinct craters; one explosion-crater contains the almost circular Lac du Bouchet. The surface of the lava has been much weathered to form a thick black soil, and the plateau is covered with quite good upland pasture, together with beech- and pine-woods.

In the centre of the Plateau du Velay the granite basement has been downfaulted to form a shallow basin, sometimes referred to as the *Creux du Puy*. The Loire enters this basin from the south by way of a valley deeply cut through the granitic plateau, and leaves it in the north through a series of fine gorges (notably that of Peyre-deyre) across another granite horst. Three diverse elements enter into the composition of the basin of Le Puy: the underlying granitic floor, an incomplete veneer of Tertiary sediments, and volcanic accumulations overlying both granitic and Tertiary rocks. The

[1] An interesting account of the volcanic elements in the relief of Velay is given by P. Bout, 'L'Erosion des reliefs phonolitiques et basaltiques de la Haute-Loire depuis le dernier Glaciaire', in *Mélanges géographiques offerts à Ph. Arbos* (1953), vol. i, pp. 91-102.

granite floor is exposed as a low ridge extending diagonally across the basin from north-west to south-east, and also as several isolated masses. The incomplete Tertiary cover consists of Oligocene limestone, marls, clay and gypsum, and of Pliocene sands. The volcanic contribution includes Miocene basalt flows in the south and east, Pliocene flows in the west, and many small cones. All these have been much dissected by the Loire and its numerous tributaries converging towards the centre of the basin in deeply trenched valleys. The clays and marls form small basins and depressions, the limestones in places stand out as low hills.

Many of the basalt flows have been eroded into steep-sided tablelands, with some fantastic columnar or 'organ-pipe' structures (*orgues*) around their margins. The more resistant basalt forms a horizontal cap-rock so that a vertical cornice falls away from the summit, succeeded by an abrupt change of slope where the less resistant underlying Tertiaries appear. Sometimes the lava flows are quite thick; the plateau of Polignac, for example, forms a small flat-topped eminence, a '*rectangle isolé*', rising sheer from the floor of the basin. The most striking relief features occur near Le Puy itself, where several isolated rock pinnacles diversify the landscape. The Rocher d'Aiguilhe rises sheerly for 279 feet, crowned by the church of St. Michel reached by a winding rock staircase. The town of Le Puy stands on the lower slopes of Mont Anis, culminating in the craggy mass of the Rocher Corneille surmounted by a large statue of Notre Dame de France. These and other rock pinnacles may be erosional survivals of dissected basalt flows, or they may be resistant plugs that have remained after the surrounding cones have been removed (Plate LVII). In the east and south of the basin numerous small cones (*sucs*) of phonolite sometimes reveal well-developed craters; the highest, the Suc de Rauzon, rises to 4,396 feet. The Lac d'Issarlès provides another example of a crater-lake, and has no outflowing stream.

Land-Use and Agriculture.—It is not easy to describe in general terms the features of the economy of such a varied upland region, although its limitations are obvious. The three *départements* of Puy-de-Dôme, Cantal and Haute-Loire cover a considerable part of the region, and afford some indication of the pattern of land-use.

The woodland areas are found chiefly on the northern crystalline uplands of the Madeleine and the Bois-Noirs, on the slopes of the Forez, in the valleys which dissect the volcanic district of Auvergne, on the flanks of the volcanic hills of the Devès, in Livradois where there are several State forests,[1] and on the eminences within the basin of Le Puy. The natural woodland was probably beech, and this is still the most common tree, although pines have been planted. Sweet chestnut grows well on the crystalline slopes. The chief areas of forest occur between about 2,000 and 2,750 feet; although the upper tree-line on sheltered slopes is as high as 4,000 feet, most of the bleak wind-swept plateau surfaces are devoid of trees and form dreary moorlands, peat-bogs and areas of rough grazing.

Land-Use, 1963

(Percentages of Total Area)

	Arable	Permanent Pasture	Woodland	Waste and Non-cultivated Land
Cantal . .	17	54	15	10
Haute-Loire .	23	32	23	14
Puy-de-Dôme .	26	39	21	15

Source: *Ministère de l'Agriculture*, published in *Annuaire statistique* (*1964*).

The area of arable land is surprisingly high in this upland region. Haute-Loire of course contains the upland basin of Le Puy with its areas of quite fertile calcareous loams enriched with volcanic débris, while the figures for Puy-de-Dôme include the *terres noires* of Limagne (see p. 590). But agriculture pushes its way far into the uplands, making use both of the deep valleys that dissect the edge of the volcanic region of Auvergne and of the surfaces of the *planèzes*, where the fields are enclosed by black dry-stone walls made of basalt blocks. Arable farming occupies great areas of the basaltic plateau-surface of Devès, and is even found in sheltered depressions high up on the crystalline uplands, as evidenced by the little village of Estables near the source of the Loire at a height of 4,430 feet, with its tiny walled fields. Rye, once universally grown, is still found, but it has been largely replaced by wheat (grown as high as 4,000 feet on the volcanic plateaus of Velay), barley, oats, potatoes and increasingly fodder-crops. Favoured slopes in Auvergne and Velay are covered with vineyards and orchards.

Considerable areas of permanent or temporary pasture and of fodder crops are used for stock-rearing; these include the poor moorland pastures of the crystalline massifs (the *montagnes*) and the better pastures of the well-watered volcanic soils (*montagne à graisse*). They are, however, snow-covered for several months, and so seasonal movement of animals necessarily takes place. The

---

[1] L. Gachon, 'Géographie de la végétation arbustive et arborescente dans le Massif du Livradois', in *Mélanges géographiques offerts à Ph. Arbos* (1953), vol. i, pp. 113-29.

chief element in the economy is cattle, and 845,000 animals were in the three *départements* in 1963, of which over half a million were dairy beasts; the *Salers*, *Aubrac* and *Mézenc* breeds are all kept. The animals move seasonally between villages and farms in th valleys and depressions up to the high *montagnes*. Stall-fed in the winter on fodder-crops (which now occupy about a third of the arable), they spend a month or two in spring on the irrigated water-meadows, and then move on to the high pastures. The emphasis is on milk production, although calves for veal are sent away in early summer to the markets of Paris and Lyons. Cheese is produced in large quantities; the '*fromages bleus*' of Auvergne are made at centres such as Thiézac in Cantal and Laqueille near Mont Dore, and several well-known varieties (*Cantal*, *Bleu St. Nectaire*, *Laguiole* and *Fourme*) are produced. Sheep have declined in numbers, but in 1963 there were still 458,000 in the three *départements*. Many of them come up from Bas-Languedoc for the summer months, or move across from the Grands Causses on to the high pastures of Aubrac and Margeride when the summer aridity becomes pronounced. Much ewes' milk is turned into cheese which is finally processed in Roquefort.

Population and Settlement.—Population is dispersed widely though somewhat thinly over much of this region, and villages and hamlets are found at high altitudes in sheltered valleys and depressions. The summits of the crystalline uplands are largely deserted, except for shepherds' huts; Margeride must be one of the most extensive unpopulated areas in all France.

There are obviously few large towns, and the regional foci are actually situated on the margins. Thus Clermont-Ferrand (see p. 593) is the regional centre for the uplands of northern Auvergne, Thiers on the eastern edge of Limagne for the Madeleine, Ambert and Montbrison on either side of the Forez. In Cantal several market-towns are situated in the radiating valleys, notably Aurillac in the valley of the Jordanne to the west, Murat in the Alagnon valley to the north-east, and St. Flour in the upper Truyère valley to the south-east. Similarly Marvejols on the upper Colagne is the centre for southern Aubrac, and Mende is the focus for three distinct regions—Margeride, Lozère and the north-eastern Causses. Le Puy, an attractive town of 28,000 people, is the *chef-lieu* of Haute-Loire, and an administrative, commercial and tourist centre. This town has been famous for its lace for centuries, and once employed over 100,000 women, but the industry has sadly declined, although some quality lace is still sent to the Paris fashion-houses. Other small industries include paper-making and the distillation of liqueurs.

THE GRANDS CAUSSES

The geological map of the southern part of the Central Massif shows an extensive area of Jurassic limestone, a curious Z-shape enclosed between Ségalas and the massifs of Lozère and Aigoual. This region is known as the *Grands Causses*,[1] or as the *Causses Majeurs*. Structurally this limestone region is the result of the accumulation of sediments in a basin within the crystalline rocks, trending approximately north to south, as described above (p. 525). Most of these deposits consist of limestones of Middle and Upper Jurassic age, the latter appearing on the surface in the extreme east. The limestones rest on and largely cover the Upper Lias marls, which now occur on the surface only around the margins.

The Causses region underwent planation in early Tertiary times, then it was uplifted, tilted and fractured in mid-Tertiary times; vast faults can be discerned in the strata forming the walls of some of the gorges, with throws of hundreds of feet.[2] Most of the faults which affected the Causses trend from west to east. Two major fault-lines in this direction, to the south of the Lot and Aveyron valleys, enclose a rift-valley containing Jurassic rocks which form a westerly prolongation of the limestone plateaus, the Causses de Rodez and Séverac. This, incidentally, is a structural feature of great age; it probably represents a gulf of the sea in late Palaeozoic times, for it contains several small coalfields (Fig. 120) and deposits of Permian shales and sandstones, over part of which lie the Jurassic rocks. Other fault-lines, penetrating the most southerly Causse de Larzac, are followed by the valleys of the Cernon and the Sorgues, forming broad re-entrants in which the Lias marls are exposed.

The cycles of erosion inaugurated by the mid-Tertiary uplift and tilting have cut across the varied structures, and a series of surfaces at various levels from 3,900 feet down to 2,000 feet has been recognised by P. Marres.[3]

The rivers which rise on the crystalline rocks near the high south-eastern rim of the Central Massif flow westwards over the limestone and then again on to the crystalline rocks before escaping into the Basin of Aquitaine (Fig. 121). Their valleys have divided the pene-plained surfaces of the Causses into a number of individual blocks (Fig. 126); the valleys and the plateaus therefore form two main relief elements. Differential erosion has resulted in a third; the

---

[1] E. Coulet, 'Morphologie des Grands Causses', in *Bul. Soc. Languedoc Géog.* (1962), *fasc.* 1, 2, pp. 3-62.

[2] Nine distinct major fault-lines have been distinguished by P. Marres, and are shown and named on a folding-map in *Les Grands Causses* (1935), vol. i (frontispiece).

[3] P. Marres, *op. cit.*, vol. i, pp. 24-42.

less resistant Lias clays now form a series of '*dépressions péri-phériques*', known as *vallons*, around the margins of the Causses between the limestones and the crystalline rocks.

The Valleys.—The northern margin of the Causses is roughly defined by the valley of the Lot; only a few small outliers of lime-stone appear to the north of it. The main river of the Causses is the Tarn, with its two tributaries the Jonte and the Dourbie; it rises on the granitic uplands of Mont Lozère at a height of about 5,000 feet, but descends nearly 1,500 feet down the western slopes in less than ten miles. At Florac the river enters a deep gorge, and for nearly fifty miles between Florac and Millau the valley-sides rise for heights of 1,500 to 2,000 feet above the river-bed. In places these precipitous cliffs fall sheer to the water's edge, elsewhere the walls recede and leave shingle-banks and a strip of meadow. Thus in 'the Narrow' (*Le Détroit*) near La Malène the walls approach closely, to widen out into the broad vale of the steeply walled Cirque des Baumes a few miles downstream, below which a north-western spur of the Causse Méjan (the *Eperon*) projects boldly to form an over-hanging beaked promontory, narrowing the valley once again. For the most part the Tarn valley maintains the nature of what has been called a '*couloir farouche*'.

Even more striking is the valley of the Jonte, where vertical walls of resistant limestone are separated by sloping terraces or ledges worn in the narrow bands of shale or marl, producing a steep stepped effect. This river flows intermittently underground for a consider-able distance from below Meyrueis to its final resurgence at Les Douzes. The Bonheur, one of the headstreams of the Dourbie, which rises on the western slopes of the Aigoual, plunges down the Perte du Bonheur into a labyrinthine underground course seven miles long, part of which has been exposed as a gorge by the collapse of the roof. The water finally issues from a vertical rift in a lime-stone cliff as a fine waterfall, the Abîme de Bramabiau. The deep valley of the Dourbie further to the south-west divides the Causse Noir from the Causse de Larzac.[1]

The régime of these rivers is most variable. Heavy rains on the crystalline uplands to the east supply their headstreams with a run-off which contrasts with the waterless character of the limestone plateaus through which they flow. The main streams receive much underground water by way of resurgences, the most prominent of which are plotted on Fig. 126.[2] The Tarn receives no surface

---

[1] A detailed account, with many maps, diagrams and photographs of the caves and other phenomena of the Grands Causses is given by E.-A. Martel, *Les Causses majeurs* (1936).

[2] P. Marres (*op. cit.*) has a map (p. 93) on which the resurgences are named.

tributaries between Florac and the confluence of the Jonte, but its flow is maintained by five major and about twenty-five minor underground affluents; just below Le Détroit, for example, a powerful torrent bursts from a cave on the right wall of the valley. During autumn and winter the concentrated rains can produce sudden flooding. It is recorded that during the floods of 1876 the water-level of the Tarn rose in 'the Narrow' sixty-five feet in a mere eight hours; immense destruction was wrought in riparian towns as far downstream as Montauban. By contrast, in summer the volume of the rivers is much reduced; shallow but still fast-flowing, the playground of canoeists, the numerous branches of the current flow between shingle-banks.

The Plateaus.—These valleys divide the limestone into individual blocks which are named on Fig. 126. The plateaus form an extensive area of limestone karst; when one stands on a slight prominence the wide nature of the erosion surfaces is abundantly evident. The general level does, however, swell to a number of gentle eminences, as Ph. Arbos expresses it, '*un moutonnement de mamelons*'. The highest point of the Causses in fact attains 4,193 feet in the east of Méjan.

The surface, despite its general planation, is far from uniform in detail, for it bears the marks of former fluvial erosion in the shape of complex patterns of dry valleys (*combes*). Many of these contain pockets of granitic alluvium and pebbles brought down by now vanished streams once flowing from Lozère and Aigoual. The *combes* are flanked by steep even overhanging cliffs, known as *corniches* or *valats* in the Causse Méjan and the Causse Noir, where they are particularly well developed. Larger depressions of a *polje*-like quality are also numerous. In fact P. Marres uses the term '*les poljes caussenards*' to describe the elongated hollow of Carnac in the north-west of the Causse Méjan, and also that of St. Maurice-la-Clastre and St. Pierre-de-la-Fage which extends diagonally across the Causse de Larzac from north-east to south-west. The second of these, five miles in length, has a lowest depth in the centre of the basin of 1,969 feet, with walls rising to 2,070 and 2,100 feet. Patches of quartz gravels can be seen on its floor, although mostly it is covered with *terra rossa*. The original line of the depressions was initiated by now vanished Tertiary rivers, and they have been deepened by processes of solution.

The Causses well reveal the minor karstic features of limestone solution. Rock pavements are seamed with crevices, and shallow circular solution hollows are common, known as *cros* when they are small in size and as *sotchs* (or locally as *sots*) when they are more than 100 or 150 feet in diameter. Their floors are covered with the residue of limestone solution, *terra rossa* clay, sometimes in

FIG. 126.—THE GRANDS CAUSSES.

The abbreviations represent towns, as follows: **F**, Florac; **L**, Lodève; **la M**, La Malène; **M**, Mende; **Me**, Meyrueis; **Mi**, Millau; **St. G**, St. Geniez.

The main *Causses* are outlined by hachuring; Aubrac in the north, although flanked by a prominent edge, is, of course, a lava plateau. The higher granitic and crystalline uplands to the east of the *Grands Causses* are named. A number of spot-heights (in feet) is given to emphasise the general altitudes. The Causse de Rodez lies to the west of Séverac.

The relations of the *Grands Causses* to the wider dispersal of Central Massif drainage, together with the position of the lower *Causse Aquitain*, are shown on a smaller scale on Fig. 121.

Based on: (i) *Carte de France au 200,000ᵉ*, sheets 58, 65; (ii) E.-A. Martel, *Les Causses majeurs* (1936), folding map; and (iii) P. Marres, *Les Grands Causses: étude de géographie physique et humaine* (1935), Tome I, planche XXX, 'Carte hydrographique des Grands Causses', p. 93.

sufficient thickness to form an impermeable covering and so allow a small lake (*lavogne*) to accumulate. The deeper holes (*avens*) lead down to underground caves and grottoes, a veritable *monde souterrain* well known to speleologists, some systems containing underground rivers and lakes. The most famous 'pot-hole' is the Aven Armand in the Causse Méjan, explored by Martel in 1897; at the bottom of this, 650 feet below the surface, was discovered a magnificent series of caves with stalagmite columns known as the 'Forêt Vierge'. The celebrated Grottes de Dargilan, discovered by a shepherd in 1880 on the flanks of the Causse Noir, consist of a series of magnificent caves, including the superb 'Salle des Lacs' where stalactites and calcite 'curtains' are present in profusion.

Differential weathering helps to diversify the surface, for in addition to the compact limestones, layers of weak shales and marls occur, and also masses of hard but much fissured dolomite. The last form some fantastic pinnacles and castellated rocks, notably in the Cirque des Rouquettes near Montpellier-le-Vieux on the southern edge of the Causse Noir, overlooking the Dourbie valley near La Roque. As Ph. Arbos puts it, there is '*une forêt de piliers et d'aiguilles dolomitiques*'. The '*rocs ruiniformes*' defy description;[1] in fact, Martel describes these weathering remnants as '*les plus remarquables du monde*'.

The Vallons.—On the margins of the Causses are the *dépressions marneuses* of less resistant Liassic marls. On the east their outcrop is narrow, but the depression can be traced southward from near Mende in the Lot valley through the Valdonnez. Then it is followed to the south of Florac by a left-bank tributary of the Lot, the Tarnon; this latter section is sometimes referred to as the Sillon de Florac. Further south again, on the western flanks of Aigoual, is the depression of Meyrueis, occupied by the headstreams of the Jonte. On the north of the Causses the Lias outcrop is followed closely by the Lot valley between Mende and Rodez, and on the south headstreams of the Hérault occupy the basins of Bédarieux and Lodève.

The Lias outcrop is at its most extensive in the west, where the basins of Millau and St. Affrique form broad fertile lowlands lying between the Causses and the crystalline uplands. These marginal lands, with their lower elevation and good marly soils, are favoured for agriculture and settlement compared with neighbouring districts.

Land-Use and Agriculture.[2]—The Grands Causses and their margins

---

[1] E.-A. Martel (*op. cit.*), p. 243 has a map showing fifty-three named rocks, with grandiose but descriptive names.

[2] Volume ii of P. Marres' work (*op. cit.*) entitled *Le Labeur humain*, provides a detailed analysis of the features of agriculture, industry and settlement.

occupy the greater part of the two *départements* of Aveyron and Lozère.

Land-Use, 1963

(*Percentages of Total Area*)

	Arable Land	Permanent Pasture	Woodland	Waste and Non-cultivated Agricultural Land
Aveyron . .	35	34	11	19
Lozère . .	11	44	16	17

Source: *Ministère de l'Agriculture*, published in *Annuaire statistique, 1964*.

It is probable that the area of woodland was formerly very much greater, but as in other uplands once clearance had started natural regeneration and maintenance proved to be virtually impossible. The protective cover of vegetation was removed, soil was then washed away revealing much naked limestone, and even where young trees could start to grow, grazing soon destroyed them. In favoured areas, such as the floors of the depressions and some of the sloping valley-sides, appear groves of evergreen oak and beech, and clumps of *Pinus sylvestris*; the western part of the Causse de Sauveterre is particularly well wooded. Between the wars many plantations, mainly of Austrian pine, were established, notably in the Cavalerie district of the Causse de Larzac. Considerable areas are covered with a patchy scrub of box, juniper, dwarf oak, lavender, blackthorn and small lime-loving plants growing in crevices among the bare limestone pavements.[1]

The areas of arable are confined mainly to depressions on the plateau surface floored with *terra rossa*, to small tracts in the river valleys, and to the Lias clay districts of the *vallons*. More than half the arable in Lozère, usually enclosed by dry-stone walls (*clapas*), is under cereals, either wheat or oats, though in Aveyron the proportion drops to a third, while a quarter of Lozère and two-fifths of Aveyron were devoted to fodder-crops of various kinds. Orchards and vineyards cling to south-facing slopes (the *adret*) on natural or man-made terraces; the shelter, the quite high summer temperatures, and the sunshine which seems doubly bright reflected from the limestone cliffs behind, combine to create a remarkable impression of subtropical luxuriance. In many places water is led from springs in channels along one terrace, then on to a lower one. As a result apricots, peaches and plums all flourish, and even figs, almonds and

[1] P. Marres, *op. cit.*, vol. i, pp. 148-98, 'La Végétation des Grands Causses', goes into considerable detail, with long lists of species found in various localities.

pomegranates do well. Vegetable-gardens and patches of maize and tobacco are also patiently cultivated.

A large part of the Grands Causses and their margins is covered with permanent pasture. The limestone plateau carries much sweet though scanty grass, forming '*les vastes pacages*', and the Lias marls grow a rich pasture. For many centuries sheep have been grazed in large herds; in 1963 Aveyron had 675,000 sheep, Lozère 200,000 (between them over 8 per cent of the French total), while other flocks come up from the Mediterranean coast during the summer months. The sheep are kept principally for their milk, from which *Roquefort* cheese is made, so called after the town which clings to the sides of the valley of the Soulzon on the western edge of the Causse de Larzac, with cliffs towering above the highest houses. The famous caves, part natural, part artificially hollowed out and supported with columns, maintain a temperature and humidity constantly favourable for the maturing of the cheeses, with the beneficial aid of *penicillium glaucum*. The development and commercialisation of cheese production have been helped by the development of co-operation. The first co-operative dairy was opened in 1887, and now over 500 individual firms are grouped within the *Société Anonyme des Caves Réunies de Roquefort*, others within the *Société Agricole de Roquefort*. Ewes' milk is processed not only from the Grands Causses, but also from the surrounding crystalline uplands, from the Pyrenees and even from Corsica.

Cattle are not as important as sheep, but the extension of fodder-crops, of improved temporary pastures on the Lias marls, and of irrigated water-meadows on the valley-floors, has contributed to the fact that there are now some 361,000 cattle in the two *départements*, of which nearly half are dairy animals.

Population and Settlement.—The Grands Causses are among the most sparsely populated parts of France. The population of Lozère in 1962 was 81,868, the lowest total of any *département* in France, and with a density of only forty-one per square mile it had the second lowest average after that of Basses-Alpes. In places, notably in the west along the Lias clay margins, the average per square mile goes up to about eighty, but some parts of the limestone plateau are virtually uninhabited except for shepherds during the summer living in their scattered stone cottages. Occasional large but isolated farms stand in sheltered depressions surrounded by trees, with small arable fields of *terra rossa* enclosed by stone walls and from a thousand to fifteen hundred acres of rough grazing. Apart from these, few settlements are found on the surface of the Causses, and most of the villages occur along the valleys, clinging to a terrace at the foot of a steep cliff. Between Florac and Millau, for example, are Ispagnac,

Ste. Enimie, La Caze, La Malène in 'the Narrow', Les Vignes, Peyreleau, Bogne and Aguessac, linked by a road which follows the north bank of the river, sometimes along a terrace blasted out of the limestone cliffs or tunnelled through projecting spurs of rock.

The larger towns are all in the flanking *vallons*; they are peripheral market towns and route-centres for both the Causses and the neighbouring districts. The largest town is Rodez (24,352 people), the *chef-lieu* of Aveyron but lying to the west of the Grands Causses proper, and serving as a market town both for the Causse de Rodez and for a large part of Ségalas (see p. 572). It is the focus of a number of roads and of a well-developed autobus service, and holds numerous markets and fairs.[1] The chief town of the *Causses* region proper is Millau (22,000 people), situated in a broad basin surrounded by gentle slopes culminating in limestone scarps. Here converge the Tarn and Dourbie, while below the town the Tarn valley leads westward to Albi and ultimately to the Gironde. It is a pleasant town, set among orchards and gardens, a gateway to the Tarn valley for tourists, and with small-scale industries such as glove-making from the skins of local sheep. St. Affrique (8,023 people) in the south-west is the market town for neighbouring areas of the Causses, and for parts of Ségalas and the Montagnes de Lacaune. Séverac-le-Château in the Lot valley serves as a centre both for the northern Causses and for Aubrac. Mende, with only 10,061 people, the *chef-lieu* of Lozère, is situated on the banks of the Lot in the north-east of the Causses on the borders of Margeride. Behind the town rise gentle slopes of pasture, steepening and becoming forest-covered, to the dissected limestone crags under the edge of the Causse de Mende. It has some small textile industries. Florac, on the banks of the Tarnon just before it joins the Tarn, is a tourist resort. Roquefort, as already mentioned, is primarily concerned with cheese-processing and -exporting. In all, these little towns indicate that this is one of the least urbanised parts of France.

Communication links are difficult; indeed no railway crosses the area from west to east, though one line, using tunnels, spirals and viaducts, runs southward from Montluçon through Auvergne by way of St. Flour, Marvejols and Séverac-le-Château to Millau (up which steep section the trains are double-headed) and then on via Bédarieux to Béziers. The road system is well-engineered despite physical difficulties, and has been developed largely for the tourist industry, though many parts are roadless and served by little more than mule-tracks.

[1] Y. Pomarède, 'L'Essor d'un petit centre régional: Rodez', in *R.G.P.S.-O.* (1954), vol. xxv, pp. 243-59; and *ibid.*, pp. 271-3, 'Le Rôle de la route dans les vicissitudes d'un petit centre régional: Rodez'.

THE SOUTH-WESTERN UPLANDS

The south-western uplands include first the plateau of the *Ségalas*, so-called from the former dominance of rye (the *pays de seigle*), lying between the Dordogne and the Tarn, and second the Pre-Cambrian massifs of the Lacaune and the Montagne Noire, flanked to north and south by considerable outcrops of Cambrian schists and limestones and on the east by a varied series of minor uplands and depressions in the neighbourhood of Lodève. These south-western uplands are characterised by a number of major fault-lines, which in the north trend in the characteristic Armorican way from north-west to south-east, forming a clear-cut boundary between the crystalline massifs and the Jurassic rocks of the Causses du Quercy. Further south another longitudinal fault (but with an orientation more from north-north-east to south-south-west) separates Ségalas proper from the Causse de Limogne; the Aveyron below Ville-franche-de-Rouergue flows along the line of this fault for twenty miles. Most of the other faults in this region trend from west to east. Several parallel fault-lines enclose a long down-faulted depres-sion enclosing the Causse de Rodez, the Permian basin of Marcillac, and the coal-basin of Campagnac-Aubin-Decazeville (Fig. 120). Other faults trending more or less from west to east define the southern margins of Ségalas and both edges of the Montagne Noire.

Ségalas. This name, applied originally to the upland projecting westward between the Aveyron and the Tarn, now signifies the wider *pays siliceux*. In a broad way there is a certain uniformity; distinct erosion surfaces (notably the Eogene) cut right across the slates, mica-schists, gneisses and the occasional granite intrusions.[1] The land slopes gently from 2,250 feet in the north-east to 1,300 feet on the margins of Albigeois and Lauraguais. In detail, however, much more diversification is apparent. Bordering the Millau Liassic depression on the north-west are gneissic rocks which culminate in the broad ridges of Lévezou and Palanges, forming swelling summits (the highest point, the Montagne de la Tousque, reaches 3,806 feet), separated by deeply notched cols. Further north the peneplain is interrupted by butte-like eminences known locally as *peuchs*, the residuals of a former erosion cycle. Further north still, between the Cère and Cèle valleys, the land rises to the bleak summit of La Falzinde.

Conversely, many parts of Ségalas sink below this general level. The river valleys are prominently incised across the crystalline rocks,

---

[1] These various surfaces are discussed by A. Meynier, *Ségalas, Lévezou, Châtaigneraie* (1931).

especially the Lot and the Truyère, which, with their main confluents (mostly rushing torrents with numerous cascades), dissect
the plateau into a number of independent fragments, some of which
form the most isolated and remote districts in the whole Central
Massif. The middle Tarn crosses the Permian rocks which lie to
the west of the Grands Causses, forming a broad depression floored
with red Permian soils (*rougiers*) which flanks Ségalas on the south.

The diversity in the physical landscape of Ségalas is reflected
in the number of individual *pays*-names: the *Ségala du Quercy*
which borders the Jurassic lands of Quercy in the north between the
Cère and Cèle valleys; the *Châtaigneraie* to the south of Aurillac;
the *Veinazes* bordering the northern side of the Lot valley below its
confluence with the Truyère; the *Viadène* in the extreme east on the
edge of Aubrac; the *Ségala rouergat* to the south of Rodez; and
the *Ségala tarnais*[1] to the north of the Tarn valley.

The bleak uplands of Ségalas are covered with tracts of heath
(known as *brossiers*) and gorse-covered scrub (*cams*), while much
consists of poor scrubby pasture. The thin acid soils weathered
from the siliceous rocks are not very fertile, and much of Ségalas
was for centuries a poor agricultural region, with an economy
based on rye, chestnuts and sheep. An area of heath was burnt off
(a process known as *issartage*), cropped with rye for four or five
years, and then allowed to revert; a privately owned grove of
chestnuts, or communal rights in one, provided nuts for porridge
meal; and sheep were reared on the scanty pasture. That was the
basis of life, perhaps supplemented by charcoal-burning, tanning,
and the domestic spinning and weaving of cloth. Some parts of
Ségalas are still poor areas with a scanty population; the upland of
the Ségala de Quercy grows much rye, and the Châtaigneraie is so
limited that to neighbouring districts the name is synonymous with
poverty—'*ce pauvre pays de Châtaignes*'. But over much of Ségalas,
particularly in the south, the agricultural economy has been transformed as a result of improvement of the soils by lime and fertilisers.
Lime became available when kilns were built in 1820 at Carmaux,
fired by coal from local collieries, and later better road and rail communications enabled fertilisers to be brought in. Several west–east
railway lines now cross the region, and an important longitudinal line
works its way northward from Toulouse via Gaillac, Villefranche
and Figeac to Aurillac. These enable produce to be exported from
the region. As a result, rye has almost disappeared from many
parts, replaced by wheat, potatoes and fodder-crops and in the south
by maize. Some of the basins have become important for fruit
(peaches, apricots, cherries, pears), almonds, and even near Marcillac

---

[1] G. Bertrand, 'Société rurale et réaménagement agricole dans le Ségala tarnais', in *R.G.P.S.-O.* (1962), vol. 33, pp. 163-82.

and Camarès for figs. The number of cattle has increased greatly, bred both for veal and dairy produce,[1] and pigs also. Much of the lower Ségalas landscape now has a *bocage* appearance, with small fields of permanent pasture or arable surrounded by hedges from which rise occasional oaks. Some small woods of oak and beech still survive, mainly on private estates, and there has been afforestation with conifers, mostly in Lévezou.

On these well-watered uplands, the population is widely dispersed in individual farms and small hamlets. Many are remarkably isolated, especially those in the north away from the railways; some indeed are reached only by rough tracks seven or eight miles from the nearest autobus route. By contrast large villages and small towns are located in the valleys (many of them with the rectilinear street-plan of the mediaeval *bastide*) which have served as commercial centres for centuries. The railway which curves across Ségalas from Figeac via Rodez to Carmaux links dozens of these little towns, each '. . . *une petite agglomération commerciale, entrepôt, lieux d'expéditions, siège de magasins coopératifs ou particuliers* . . .' (A. Meynier). Some of the towns on the little coalfields have associated metallurgical and textile industries. At Viviez, a few miles west of Decazeville, the Belgian firm *S.A. des Mines et Fonderies de Zinc de la Vieille-Montagne* built a refinery to smelt local zinc ores. A modern refinery, using electric power from the grid, now smelts a quarter of France's output of zinc metal, and also refines cadmium.

On the borders of Ségalas stand two more important towns. Villefranche-de-Rouergue is situated on the Aveyron, on the margins of the Causse Limogne and Ségalas; of *bastide*-pattern, it has long been a market-centre, and at one time had a variety of metallurgical industries based on local iron- and lead-mines, and some flourishing textile manufactures. Its population in 1801 was about 11,000, but with the decline of its industrial importance this was in 1962 only 10,461. Rodez, the *chef-lieu* of Aveyron, is another marginal town lying between Ségalas and the Grands Causses.

Lacaune.—This crystalline upland projects boldly westward to the south of the Tarn valley, separated from the Montagne Noire to the south by a remarkable through-valley drained westwards by the Thoré, eastwards by the Jaur, each flowing along a clear-cut fault-line and separated by an indeterminate watershed. The more active erosion of the steeper torrential Jaur and its tributary torrents are pushing the watershed westward at the expense of the Thoré.

The Monts de Lacaune form the highest point (4,154 feet) of a gneissic plateau flanked with Cambrian slates; as the river Agout

---

[1] J. Vayron, 'L'Elevage dans le Ségala du Quercy', in *R.G.P.S.-O.* (1962), vol. 33, pp. 163-82.

forms a deep re-entrant far into the upland, it is sometimes known as the Massif de l'Agout. It consists of rounded bosses swelling inconspicuously from damp depressions, covered with poor pasture and some forests of oak and beech. In the depressions and valleys a limited amount of arable land produces rather meagre crops of rye, buckwheat and potatoes. Both sheep and cattle are reared, but not in large numbers.

More striking is the south-western part of the massif, a small oval boss of granite between the Agout and Thoré valleys, known as the *Sidobre*. The well-jointed rock forms in places a chaos of huge blocks known as *compayrés*; individual monoliths and tor-like masses project from the gravelly soil, sometimes balanced precariously on each other, such as the famous '*Pierre Clavetée*'. Some granite is quarried, but otherwise the economy is limited; in the words of Ph. Arbos, these are '. . . *pays rude . . . d'agriculture archaïque . . .*'.

The Lacaune massif is defined on the south-east by a clear-cut fault-line, where the gneissic rocks are down-faulted to considerable depths, so bringing less resistant Cambrian, Devonian and Lower Carboniferous slates and shales against the crystalline rocks. Differential erosion by the Jaur and the Orb has worn a deep valley bounded by the steep fault-line scarp of the *Espinouse*; its sides are fantastically eroded. Some cultivation is practised on the terraced slopes, and the grazing of animals, but the main features are rugged gorges, steep slopes of bare rock and scree, and scrubby woodland of oak and beech.

A few towns and villages are situated in the lower valleys on the flanks of the massif and along the Agout valley. The regional centre for Lacaune is Castres, situated on its margins where the Agout leaves the uplands for Lauraguais. On the north-eastern flanks lies the small down-faulted Carboniferous basin of Graissesac, where some coal is mined (Fig. 120). A number of small but long-established industries (glass-works, brick-works and textiles) thrive at the town of Lodève.

The Montagne Noire.—This prominent massif of Pre-Cambrian rocks (mostly gneiss and mica-schist, with several oval bosses of granite along its structural axis) forms the south-western culmination of the Central Massif. It has suffered the usual vicissitudes of peneplanation, and of uplift and tilting associated with the past orogenies. The surface of the plateau forms a monotonous upland, from which rounded summits project but slightly; the highest point is the Pic de Nore (3,970 feet). Its flanks are more accidented; short streams flowing north to the Thoré have cut steep-sided gorges, while the longer rivers descend the southern margins towards the Aude, crossing flanking limestones (varying in age from Cambrian to

Eocene) and producing a rather confused relief of ridges and valleys known in the east as *Minervois*.

The higher parts of the Montagne Noire consist mainly of poorly drained moorlands, diversified by plantations of conifers. A remarkable contrast is apparent between the northern and southern flanks, for apart from the obvious difference in aspect the upland forms a climatic boundary between Atlantic and Mediterranean influences. The northern and north-western slopes are wooded with chestnut, oaks and beech, and some plantations (including State forests) of pine, spruce and occasionally evergreen oak; seen from the Thoré valley, these forested slopes present a distinctly sombre aspect, hence the name bestowed on the massif. The main features of the economy consist of cattle-rearing (which has increased in importance of late at the expense of sheep), and the cultivation of wheat, rye and potatoes on the lower slopes and in the valleys. In favoured places irrigation is used for the improvement of the valley-meadows.

On the southern and south-eastern slopes rainfall is appreciably less and the summer aridity more pronounced. As a result, the poor pasture is scorched brown in summer and there are considerable areas of *maquis*-like scrub and bare limestone, relieved only by occasional woodlands of evergreen oak and chestnut. The economy has a Mediterranean character; terraces enclosed by dry-stone walls grow vines, olives and fruit trees, irrigation is used for vegetable gardens, and sheep and goats increase in number at the expense of cattle.

The character of the settlement changes too. While in the north isolated farms and small hamlets are found, in the south occur the typical Mediterranean agglomerations of high-storeyed houses clustering around a church on a hillside, sun-baked and drowsy. The southern flanks belong to the basin of the Aude and to the Mediterranean; its regional centres are Carcassonne and Castelnaudary, and indeed in the south-east Béziers. The only town of importance in the north is Mazamet in the Thoré valley, which carries on a long-established industry of separating wool from sheep-skins by special techniques. Based originally on local sheep, the factories in the Thoré and Arnette valleys now import skins from the southern hemisphere; both the rough and washed wool is sent to the textile-manufacturing areas of France, Switzerland, Belgium, and even to Great Britain and America. Some wool is used locally in the textile and clothing factories of Mazamet itself, Labastide-Rouairoux, Labruguière and St. Amans-Soult, and leather working (including footwear) is active at Mazamet.

Finally, mention must be made of some sporadic mining activity on the southern slopes of the Montagne Noire, producing copper, arsenic, gold, silver, bismuth and pyrites in small quantities. A small refinery is in operation at Lastours.

LVII Le Puy, with the Rocher de l'Aiguille (279 feet high), crowned with the church of St. Michel

LVIII The Plateau de Leucamp, in the Central Massif

LIX Ridges and valleys in the Jura

LX The valley of the Arve near Cluses

The Eastern Margins.—Between Lacaune and the Montagne Noire to the west and the prolongation of the Causse du Larzac in the east lies the rather complex region of *Escandorgue, Bédarieux* and *Lodève*. Geologically this comprises a *mélange* of outcrops ranging from Cambrian to late Tertiary, resulting in a most varied relief, including karstic limestone uplands (the Monts du Pardailhan), and basaltic butte-like hills, the product of Pliocene volcanic activity. Several depressions, notably that of Bédarieux (drained by the river Orb), are floored with Permian and Triassic marls and sandstones, and the larger Lodève depression is covered with fertile red Permian marls, known locally as *ruffes*.

The countryside has a Mediterranean character—terraces with olives, vines and fruit trees, patches of hard wheat in fields enclosed by walls, irrigated gardens, groves of evergreen oaks and chestnuts, irrigated meadows, and extensive poor upland pasture grazed by sheep whose milk is mostly destined for Roquefort. In the larger depressions agriculture is likewise on a larger scale.

There are many nucleated villages, and a few larger towns with old-established industries now using Graissesac coal or electricity from the grid, such as textile manufacturing at Bédarieux and Lodève. Lamalou-les-Bains has exploited its waters to become a small spa-town.

The Development of Hydro-Electric Power.—One of the most important contributions of the Central Massif in general and of Ségalas and its margins in particular to the French economy is the generation of hydro-electricity. The installed capacity of Central Massif generators at the beginning of 1964 was 3·09 million kw, just over a fifth of the French total, and in 1963 they produced 9,284 million kwh, nearly a quarter of the total output. Most of the large stations are situated in the valleys of the Dordogne, Cère and Truyère, with a few outlying ones on the Lot and the Tarn. These rivers, rising in the centre and east of the Central Massif where rainfall exceeds fifty inches, with a host of headstreams and gorge-like valleys cut in impermeable rocks, offered obvious sites for the construction of power-stations. Their disadvantages are the rapid torrential runoff over the crystalline rocks, and the frequent periods of summer drought and thus uneven flow; at Bort-les-Orgues on the Dordogne the ratio between minimum and maximum rates of flow is of the proportion of 1 to 780.[1]

The solution has been the creation of huge barrages at carefully selected points to impound reservoirs far back up the valleys.[2] The

[1] G. Kish, 'Hydroelectric Power in France: Plans and Projects', in *G.R.* (1955), vol. 45, p. 90.

[2] G. Veyret-Verner, 'L'Evolution de l'équipement hydro-électrique du Massif Central', in *Mélanges géographiques offerts à Ph. Arbos* (1953), vol. i, pp. 211-17.

R.G.W.E.—U

first major scheme was completed between 1932 and 1934, when the
Sarrans and Bromme barrages were built across the Truyère to
supply the Sarrans and the underground Brommat power-stations.[1]
Later the Couesque and Lardit stations were constructed, supplied

FIG. 127.—HYDRO-ELECTRIC INSTALLATIONS IN THE WESTERN VALLEYS
OF THE CENTRAL MASSIF.

Only major stations are shown, marked by an open triangle.

Based on *Atlas de France* (1952), sheet 46, '*Energie*', with additions.

with water from the rivers Selves and Selvet. This group has a total
output of 1,100 million kwh. The Marèges dam and power-station
on the Dordogne were completed in 1935. Since the war a great

[1] Brommat, the sixth largest hydro-station in France, produced 950 million
kwh, and Sarrans 349 million kwh.

concerted scheme has been worked out (Fig. 127), and in all a series of fifteen high-head barrages has been built on the Dordogne and its tributaries.[1] The largest, at Bort-les-Orgues, is 394 feet high, ponding up between the walls of the gorge (on which columnar basalts—*orgues*—are exposed) a reservoir fifteen miles long and from two to four miles in width. To supplement this, a left-bank tributary, the Rhue, is dammed at Coindre, and water from the reservoir thus impounded flows through a nine-mile tunnel to Bort. Similar dams and tunnels utilise the water of two right-bank tributaries, the Luzège and the Doustre. The total head of water between the highest and lowest of the Dordogne dams is 1,800 feet. The Coindre, Bort-les-Orgues, Val-Beneyte, Neuvic-d'Ussel, Aigle and Marcille stations have been built along the Dordogne. The Aigle station, supplied with water from a reservoir behind a beautiful curving dam (in which the station is incorporated), was completed in 1947. Other major stations include St. Geniés on the Maronne; St. Etienne-Cantalès, Lamativie and Laval-de-Cère on the Cère; Castelnau on the Lot; and Pinet on the Tarn.

The name Limousin refers in a broad sense to the plateaus which form the north-western part of the Central Massif. This geographical region includes not only the ancient province of that name, but also Marche bordering it on the north (Fig. 1). Here more clearly than anywhere in the Central Massif can be seen the dominating crystalline basement rocks, little disturbed by complex faulting and with an almost complete absence of down-faulted depressions and associated volcanic activity. The greater part of the surface of both the crystalline and flanking Mesozoic rocks is formed by the Eogene peneplain; the post-Hercynian surface can be detected only in small areas near the margins where it has been protected by recently removed sedimentary rocks. A. Perpillou also attributes much of the lower Plateau de Limoges to the Mio-Pliocene surface.[2] *En masse* movements have uplifted and tilted the peneplained massif, but have caused little in the way of striking dislocations. The only really important structural line in this part of the Central Massif, the 'coal-furrow' (Fig. 120), in fact defines Limousin on the east; there is also the small coal-basin of Ahun. Some fault-lines, it is true, can be traced within the uplands, such as that separating the granites and granulites of the centre and east from the mica-schists of the west, and marginal faults in the west bring the crystalline rocks abruptly against the Jurassic rocks of Périgord and Charente. But these

[1] V. Prévot, 'Les Aménagements hydroélectriques en France. I. Le Bassin de la Dordogne', in *Acta Geographica* (1952), pp. 68-97.

[2] A. Perpillou, *Le Limousin: étude de géographie physique régionale* (1940).

structural lines in no way resemble the violent riftings of Auvergne, the Loire and Allier valleys, and the south-eastern uplands.

A broad distinction can be drawn between the higher uplands in the east-centre above 2,000 feet, referred to as *La Montagne*, and the *plateaux inférieurs* on the flanks, sometimes known collectively as *Besse*. The latter is much dissected by diverging river valleys, for Limousin is the centre of a remarkable radial drainage system, the result of its heavy rainfall (mostly over 40 inches per annum), impermeable rocks and rapid runoff.

La Montagne.—The term *La Montagne* is bestowed by the people of Limousin on all the uplands in a general sort of way, and this is reflected in many place-names (such as St. Léger-de-la-Montagne, St. Yrieix-la-Montagne and St. Martial-de-Mont); it refers in fact to what might conveniently be termed *Haut-Limousin*, as on Fig. 122. The greater part is usually known as the Plateau de Millevaches, flanked on the north by the Plateau de Gentioux, on the south by Les Monédières, and on the south-west by the Plateau d'Ussel. La Montagne forms in fact a rough quadrilateral, sixty miles from west to east, thirty miles from north to south.

La Montagne culminates in rounded summits, the remnant of a peneplained surface, presenting the familiar '*croupes mamelonnées*' and '*larges bombements*', the '*lignes molles*' and the '*contours arrondis*', the highest of which attains 3,209 feet. They are covered with heath and rough grassland, the *landes de bruyères*. Between these hillocks are shallow depressions filled with the gritty residue of granitic decomposition, from which project tor-like masses of granite given such fanciful names as '*Rochers du Diable*' and '*Pierres du Crapaud*'. The granitic residue overlying the impermeable bed-rock is usually saturated with water, sometimes forming shallow *étangs* and peat-bogs (*mouillards*), from whose edges ooze rivulets to form the headwaters of several large rivers. The fact that much of the surface of the high plateau is so damp may explain the derivation of the place-name Limousin from the Latin word *limosus*, meaning marshy. It is dreary country, covered with snow in winter and bleak even in summer, but with a certain charm for the walker. In the classic words of A. Demangeon, '*ces étendues infinies contemplées le soir du haut d'un sommet laissent dans l'âme une sensation inoubliable de grandeur et de tristesse*'.

The diverging rivers (Indre, Creuse, Vienne, Vézère, Corrèze and on the southern margins the Dordogne) flow placidly in open valleys across the plateau, separating broad interfluves. For the most part they ignore structural differences, being superimposed across the Hercynian structure-lines, although occasionally they adapt themselves to lines of weakness; the Creuse below Aubusson, for example, flows north-west along the down-faulted Ahun coal-basin.

The Marginal Plateaus and Valleys.—The *plateaux inférieurs* surround La Montagne on the north, west and south, and here again many regional names are apparent: the *Plateau de la Marche* on the north, the *Plateau de Limoges* on the west (sometimes called *Bas-Limousin* or *Limousin Occidental*), the *Plateau d'Uzerche* on the south-west and the *Plateau de Xaintrie* on the south. The dwellers on the plain of Aquitaine refer generally to these lower plateaus as '*La Montagne*', though the inhabitants of Millevaches describe them as '*Les Pays-Bas*'.

These lower plateaus present a more diversified landscape than La Montagne because the streams, flowing from high depressions through shallow, hardly noticeable valleys, lower down dissect the several erosion surfaces. Some distinct breaks of slope can be distinguished, and numerous impressive gorges and incised meanders occur, notably on the Corrèze and the Vézère. These rivers and their many affluents have so strongly dissected the edges of the Limousin plateau that where the valleys widen out towards Berry, Poitou or Charente, residual '*petits monts*' stand up prominently. Their summits sometimes partake of the character of La Montagne, with heath-covered surfaces. In the north, between the Cher and Creuse valleys, fragments of the Plateau de la Marche form the Buttes de Royères and the Pierres Jaumâtres. To the west of the Creuse rise the granite hummocks of Guéret, and to the north-west of Limoges the isolated Monts de Blond and Monts d'Ambazac, the latter culminating in the 3,000-foot summit of the Puy de Sauvagnac. To the south-west of Limoges is another much dissected outlying fragment, the Monts de Châlus, wooded and gently undulating, and culminating in the summit of the Forêt de Vieillecour (1,850 feet). These more varied margins of Limousin do in fact emphasise the essential monotony of relief of the region.

Land-Use and Agriculture.—Limousin is covered conveniently by three *départements*, Haute-Vienne, Creuse and Corrèze. Each, however, contains part of La Montagne, of the lower plateaus and river valleys, and of the surrounding marginal lands, although the bulk of the Plateau de Millevaches lies in Corrèze and southern Creuse.

An appreciable distinction is apparent between the agricultural economy of La Montagne and of the lower plateaus. On the uplands a rainfall exceeding forty inches, strong winds and a long-lying snow-cover combine with thin acid soils and poor drainage to limit the agricultural possibilities. Much consists of heath and

Land-Use, 1963

(Percentage of Total Area)

	Arable Land	Permanent Pasture	Woodland	Waste and Uncultivated
Corrèze . .	24	30	24	8
Creuse . .	40	30	14	9
Haute-Vienne .	39	32	16	9

Source: *Ministère de l'Agriculture*, published in *Annuaire statistique, 1964*.

rough grazing; the distinction between the two is not always clear. Heath certainly occupies more than half the area of most of the upland communes; in the case of three sample communes studied by J. W. House,[1] the percentage in 1951 was 65, 63 and 73 respectively. What is more, these proportions indicate an appreciable increase since 1830, in the case of the commune of Peyrelevade from 50 to 63 per cent. This is caused by the unprofitability of a hill-farming existence, the consequent migration of rural workers, the decline in the number of sheep, both of permanent and transhumant flocks (in the three communes studied by House the numbers fell from 5,104 in 1830 to 2,248 in 1951), which enables the heath to creep forward, and the unchecked leaching of the soil. Farms and hamlets are found on the flanks of valleys and depressions, away from the marshes but with some degree of shelter, and increase in number with diminishing altitude. Patches of land improved by liming and fertilising surround each farmstead, growing subsistence crops of rye (which still occupies more than half the arable), buckwheat, potatoes and vegetables in small strips. Once again J. W. House's selected communes show a marked decline in the area of arable (from 19 to 7 per cent, from 19 to 3 per cent, and from 12 to 1 per cent of the total area of the three units studied). The basis of the economy is sheep, though reduced in number, and hill-cattle. Animals from the lower plateaus are brought up to graze during summer, and then sold off at fairs held in autumn at Lonzac, Bourganeuf, Eymoutiers and Meymac, on the flanks of La Montagne.

Another possibility of some economic return from these uplands is afforded by afforestation. Conditions are far from favourable, owing to exposure to wind, heavy snow-fall which can break branches, and long periods of frost. Since 1870 planting has made progress (helped by the completion of the railway across the plateau from

[1] J. W. House, 'A Comparative Study of the Landscapes of the Plateau de Millevaches and the Western Cévennes', in *Transactions and Papers, 1954, of the Institute of British Geographers*, no. 20, pp. 159-80.

Montluçon to Brive in 1881), mostly by private individuals and communes with State assistance, rather than the extensive State forests common in some parts of the Central Massif. Many farms and holdings have wood-lots, and the area of *pré-bois*, that is, scattered copses among meadow-land, has also increased. Larger patches are found on better drained hill-crests and more sheltered south-eastern slopes. The trees most commonly used are pine, spruce and Douglas fir.

Conditions are more favourable on the marginal plateaus to the north and the west. The climate is less severe, soils are superior owing to the accumulation of downwash, and drainage is better. While areas of heathland still survive, much of the land presents a *bocage*-like aspect of fields of arable land and improved pasture, surrounded by thick hedges, with occasional copses of oak, chestnut and birch. In some of the communes of Corrèze woodland occupies as much as a sixth of the total area. Exploitation both of mature timber and of coppice contributes to the economy, and provides firewood, constructional timber, and wood for barrel-making, vine- and hop-poles, and trellis-work. Oak-bark is used in the tanneries of St. Yrieix, Saillat and Cornil, pigs feed on acorns and beech-mast, and chestnuts form a supplement to the economy. Arable land has not increased much in extent, though with the use of lime from the kilns of Berry and Charente and of fertilisers there has been a distinct improvement in quality. Rye and buckwheat on the higher lands, wheat and barley lower down, even maize in the south-western plateaus, are grown. Oats has increased in importance as a fodder-crop, and potatoes are grown and shipped to the Paris markets. In the neighbourhood of Limoges and other towns are extensive market-gardens.

The main progress in the economy of Limousin has been in the direction of cattle-rearing. The three *départements* had in 1963 a total of 710,000 cattle, and not only did permanent pasture occupy more than a quarter of their total area, but temporary pasture and fodder-crops comprised nearly a half of the arable; much of the former fallow is now utilised profitably in these ways. A striking development has been effected in irrigation practice; two local sayings, '*Le Limousin ne pourra périr de sécheresse*' and '*C'est l'eau qui fait l'herbe*', illustrate the outlook. A network of irrigation channels (known as *levades*) seams the broad valley-floors, usually leading from a storage-reservoir (*lacassou*). The water is used both for water-meadows, enabling two crops of hay to be taken each summer, and for crops of trefoil and sainfoin. Even in the more deeply-worn valleys near the plateau-margins, water-meadows occupy much of the valley-floors and meander-flats.

The Limousin cattle are one of the outstanding French breeds, and the markets in Limoges and elsewhere attract buyers from far afield. Though an ancient breed, only a century ago it was not a particularly good type of animal; since 1850, and especially since 1886, when the Limousin herd-book was established, careful breeding has produced great improvements, as evidenced by the export of bulls to many parts of the world. Their primary value is for beef and veal, although they are also used for draught purposes, but they are not particularly good milkers. Another contribution to the agricultural economy is the rearing of pigs, and large numbers are sold off at the fairs at St. Yrieix, Tulle and Masseret.[1]

Towns and Industries.—La Montagne is scantily populated; small farms and isolated hamlets are situated in sheltered positions, but considerable areas are quite uninhabited. Some of the large communes contain a dozen or twenty hamlets, each a mile or so from the next, the centre of the commune being marked merely by one larger hamlet containing the church and *mairie*. A few larger villages stand high up in the river-valleys—Peyrelevade near the source of the Vienne, Millevaches on the valley side overlooking a right-angled bend of the upper Vézère, and Sornac near the source of a Dordogne tributary.

Small market-towns are situated in valleys on the flanks of the central upland, forming minor route-centres—Aubusson in the Creuse valley with about 6,000 people, Ussel on the opposite (southern) side of Millevaches in the valley of the Diège, and Eymoutiers in the valley of the Vienne. On the lower plateau small towns are more frequent—Meymac, Treignac, Bourganeuf, Eygurande, Guéret, St. Léonard and Tulle. An outer ring of towns stands on the margins of Limousin, serving parts of that region and its borders—Argenton on the borders of Berry, Montmorillon of Poitou, Confolens of Charente, Thiviers of Périgord, Brive[2] of Quercy, Bort-les-Orgues of Auvergne and Chambon of Bourbonnais. The function of these towns is primarily commercial, and most hold fairs and markets for their rural districts. Some are on the two main railway lines that cross Limousin (Montluçon to Aurillac, and Clermont-Ferrand to Limoges), on the north-western peripheral line (Montluçon-Guéret-Limoges), or on minor lines that ascend the valleys (Ahun-Aubusson-Ussel and Limoges-Eymoutiers-Meymac). Most towns are served by autobus routes. Some have small-scale industries, such as paper-mills (at St. Léonard and St. Junien).

[1] An interesting account of the rural economy of part of Limousin, and of changes which have taken place in the last century, is given by G. Beis, 'Transformation de l'économie rurale dans les plateaux limousins du Sud-Est', in *A. de G.* (1946), vol. lv, pp. 164-77.

[2] A. Meynier, 'Les Activités urbaines du bassin de Brive', in *R.G.P.S.-O.* (1962), vol. 33, pp. 49-71.

Considerable developments of hydro-electricity have taken place along the valley of the Vienne and of its tributaries the Creuse, Taurion and Maulde. A small station was built at Bussy as early as 1910, and in 1920 the *Société des Forces Motrices de la Vienne* was set up to construct barrages and stations, the most important of which is Eguzon on the Creuse, completed as early as 1926; this forms one of the main nodal points on the French grid, with a transformer station from which radiate power-lines. Nine barrages and eighteen stations are now in operation in the Vienne basin, with three more on the Maulde under construction; the most important, apart from Eguzon, are Roche-aue-Moxines and Roche-bat-l'Aigle on the Creuse, Peyrat-le-Château on the Maulde, and Roche-Talamine on the Taurion.[1]

The largest city of Limousin is Limoges, which contained 103,000 people in 1962. The ancient *cité* with its thirteenth-century cathedral stands on a bluff at a height of about 950 feet on the right bank of the Vienne. Limoges has been a route-centre since Gallo-Roman times. A ford is said to have crossed the river; today there are five bridges, and nine roads and four railway lines converge there. The Vienne valley is narrow and steep-sided and no main road follows it, so that the town is essentially a focus of roads radiating across the plateau. The old town developed a most interesting duality; the *cité* was under the bishop's jurisdiction, the *ville* under that of the Counts of Limoges, each unit enclosed by walls. Today these two nuclei, though surrounded by the newer industrial and residential districts, are still distinguishable, with boulevards occupying the sites of the walls.

Limoges has been an industrial centre for more than a thousand years, in spite of stormy vicissitudes during the Hundred Years War and at other times. Its mediaeval craftsmen were famed for their metal-work, especially of gold, enamel, cloth (notably flannel) and leather-work. The kaolin deposits near St. Yrieix to the south of Limoges were first exploited in 1755, and have nurtured an industry which has made the name of Limoges synonymous with fine porcelain. The first factory began operation in 1774, and in the nineteenth century progress was rapid as numerous establishments and workshops were opened. By 1898 the industry employed about 10,000 workers, and the manufacture of pottery, tiles and bricks about the same number. The population growth in the nineteenth century as a result of these activities was rapid; from 25,000 inhabitants at the time of the French Revolution it increased to 46,500 in 1856 and to 92,000 in 1911. The pottery industry has had its setbacks—the war of 1914–18, the competition of such new countries as Czechoslovakia, the world economic depression which reduced the demand for high-

[1] P. Garenc, 'Les Aménagements hydroélectriques du bassin de la Vienne', in *A. de G.* (1952), vol. lxi, pp. 106-22.

class luxury products (only 2,000 workers could find employment in 1934), and the war of 1939–45. Since then the industry has contributed to France's export drive, though the proportion of ordinary to high-class products has increased. In addition it has developed ancillary trades such as the manufacture of electrical porcelain. Other industries are tanning and shoe-making (another legacy of the past developed on modern lines), the making of coach-work for cars (hence the origin of the word *limousine*) and accessories for motor-cycles, the processing of tobacco, and specialised textile industries (cloth for uniforms and flannel). It still indeed maintains its rôle as one of France's major regional centres.

THE NORTHERN BASINS AND MARGINS

The upper Loire and its major headstream the Allier flow from south to north through lines of down-faulted basins more or less parallel to the eastern edge of the Central Massif. The general tilt of the uplands ensures that the drainage of most of the northern and eastern parts of the Massif must find its way northwards or north-westwards to the lower Loire by way of the Allier, Cher (occupying in part a similar though smaller down-faulted basin), Indre, Creuse and Vienne. The upper valley of the Loire belongs to the central uplands, below which the river enters first the Plaine du Forez and then the Bassin du Roannais. Further to the west, beyond the granite uplands of the Forez and Livradois, the Allier leaves its steep upper valley, cut through the crystalline rocks, and traverses first the small basins of Brioude and Issoire and then the more extensive Limagne. The two rivers converge beyond the northern margins of the crystalline rocks in Bourbonnais.

The Plaine du Forez.—The Plaine du Forez forms an oval of low-land about twelve miles from east to west and twenty-five miles from south to north, lying between the Monts du Forez and the Monts du Lyonnais, its margins sharply defined by faults, especially on the east. The basin itself slopes gently northward from about 1,300 to 1,100 feet. It has been filled in both by Oligocene sediments laid down under lacustrine conditions, and by deposits of more recent alluvium brought down by the Loire and its torrential tributaries, which gully the uplands on either flank. Into these deposits the Loire has trenched itself, forming a series of terraces. Some masses of Pliocene basalt project through the Oligocene sediments and form prominent little summits such as Mont d'Uzore (1,768 feet) and the mass on which stands the town of Montbrison.

The sedimentary infilling yields soils of no particular fertility, since they are derived from the flanking granite uplands. The compact clays which cover much of the surface are known locally as *chaninas* or *chaninats*, heavy, cold and frequently waterlogged, with shallow *étangs* lying on their uneven surface. Since the middle of the nineteenth century several *syndicats de dessèchement* have drained and reclaimed about a third of their former total area of 7,500 acres. Some, however, are periodically flooded, and used for breeding carp and tench. In contrast to these clay soils are the light siliceous sands, the *varennes*, formerly of little use other than for pine woods. The best soils, of limited extent, are the loamy *chambons*, developed on the recent alluvium along the flood-plain of the Loire.

Improvements during the last century have appreciably modified the economy. Mixed farming is practised, with an emphasis on stock-rearing, especially of Salers and Charolais cattle, pigs and fowls, and the former unproductive system of rye alternating with fallow has been replaced by a rotation of wheat, potatoes, fodder-beet, lucerne and legumes. The construction of the Canal du Forez and about 120 miles of *rigoles émissaires* since 1865 has facilitated the cultivation of lucerne, trefoil and meadow-grass under irrigation. Although the district was badly hit by phylloxera, some vines are grown on the slopes.

As a result of these improvements, the population has increased by 50 per cent during the last century and the density now averages about 155 per square mile. Several small towns are situated around the margins of the basin—Montbrison and Boën on the west, Feurs (the Roman town of *Forum Segusiavorum* from which the Forez derives its name), Meylieu and St. Galmier on the east. In the south a small group (St. Rambert, St. Just, Andrézieux and Sury-le-Comtal) is situated on either side of the Loire. The influence of the St. Etienne region to the south-east is felt, for people from these southern towns travel to work in the factories, and moreover some manufactures have spread to the Forez—the making of cycles at Sury, textiles at Montrond, lace at Montbrison, and glass at André-zieux, St. Romain and St. Just. St. Galmier, Montrond-les-Bains, Sail-sous-Couzan and one or two other little towns have a certain tourist activity, due to the thermal springs; St. Galmier even exports bottles of mineral water. The largest town is Montbrison, but has less than 10,000 inhabitants, so that the rural way of life is clearly dominant.

Roannais.—The Loire on leaving the northern end of the Forez basin cuts through a rather confused upland area of Lower Carboni-ferous slates and associated ancient igneous rocks, known as the Plateau or '*seuil*' de Neulise, to the Plaine de Roanne.[1] The

---

[1] A very full account of Roanne and the *Pays Roannais* is given by J. Labasse, 'Quelques Aspects de la vie d'échanges en Pays Roannais', in *A. de G.* (1954), vol. lxiii, pp. 193-218.

gradient is steeper than in the Forez basin, and the river, enclosed in a steep-sided valley, forms the picturesque cataracts of the Saut-de-Pinay and Saut-du-Perron.

Roannais is bounded on the west by the granitic Montagnes de la Madeleine, the edge of which is defined by one of the most continuous faults within the Central Massif, trending from north-north-west to south-south-east for thirty miles. An abrupt change occurs between the steep granite slopes and the Oligocene sediments of the basin-floor, partly covered with Pleistocene and Recent gravels and alluvium. The eastern margin of Roannais is less clearly defined, for stepped-faults have allowed the preservation of Triassic and Jurassic sandstones, marls and limestones from which small masses of granite protrude. A much more gradual ascent leads from the floor of the basin to the uplands of Beaujolais and Charolais than on the west.

The basin slopes gently northward from about 900 to 650 feet. Like Forez, it has been infilled with lacustrine and alluvial deposits, but there is less clay and more gravel and sands, notably the *sables du Bourbonnais*. The basin is not 'dammed' at its northern end (as is Forez by the Seuil de Neulise), so that there is a steady downfall through a deeply trenched valley. As a result, the surface of Roannais is much better drained and has few *étangs* and areas of marshland.

Its landscape and economy are, however, much the same as that of Forez, although being lower, better drained and with more fertile soils the agriculture is more prosperous. Between the hedges and rows of poplars are fields of arable and permanent pasture, with orchards and vineyards on the slopes, for the keynote is mixed farming with an emphasis on livestock. Some of the areas of sand and the outlying granitic hills are thickly wooded.

Small towns and villages are aligned along the foot of the Madeleine (Le Donjon, Lenaix, Changy), and more dispersedly in the broader valleys of such tributaries as the Arconce and the Sornin on the east. Some are market-towns with large fairs (such as La Pacaudière and Renaison), and there are some spa-towns (notably Sail-les-Bains). Individual farms and prosperous little villages are widely dispersed. By contrast, the town of Roanne in the south is the centre of a prosperous industrial region; for some centuries textile industries, based on local wool, flax and hemp, have flourished. In the late eighteenth century cotton manufactures developed, especially the production of dyed cloth and yarn introduced by the merchants of Lyons. The industry received a boost in 1871 when the Treaty of Frankfurt removed Mulhouse and the Alsatian cotton industry from France. New mills were built and installed with mechanical looms, and the textile industry spread from Roanne up the neighbouring valleys of the Trambouse and the Reins to such little towns as Cours, Thizy, Bourg-de-Thizy, St. Victor-sur-Reins and Regny. A variety of cotton goods is produced, also cotton-silk mixtures, and there is a small rayon factory. Other industries include hosiery and millinery, wrapping-paper, tanning and leather goods, and tiles and drain-pipes made from local clay. This varied industrial activity has resulted in the rapid growth of Roanne during the last seventy years. It had long been a centre on which routes converged from the Paris Basin up the Loire, from the upper Saône by way of the Bourbince-Dheune depression, and from Lyons by the Seuil de Tarare between Beaujolais and Lyonnais. The opening in 1838 of the Roanne-Digoin Canal (a lateral canal along the left bank of the Loire) resulted in the growth of a busy little port at Roanne, handling coal from Montceau-les-Mines for local industries. The construction of a main-line railway over the Col des Sauvages has improved links with Lyons, while direct rail communication to the south with St. Etienne is a further advantage. The population of Roanne, which was under 7,000 at the beginning of the nineteenth century, had increased to 40,500 in 1931 ; there has been a less rapid growth since that date, the 1962 figure being about 53,000, but if the contiguous communes of Riorges and Coteau are included the agglomeration totals over 60,000. It forms therefore a considerable urbanised area in the middle of the *paysage rural* of the middle Loire basin.

Limagne.[1]—Several small Tertiary basins are aligned along the course of the upper Allier, forming indeed '*un chapelet de dépressions*' (A. Meynier), known generally as the *Petites Limagnes*. They are bounded by crystalline rocks, their margins defined by fault-lines complicated by small volcanic masses and outlying granitic hillocks, and their floors for the most part are infilled with Oligocene lacustrine sediments. The first of these depressions (excluding the Bassin du Puy) is Langeac, though this is not one of the *fossés tertiaires* but a rift of Hercynian age, floored with Upper Coal Measures which, however, have yielded but little coal. After another steep valley-section through the crystalline rocks, the Allier enters the larger basin of Brioude, floored with Oligocene limestones and a veneer of alluvium, continued again to the north by the basin of Brassac where another small coalfield has been preserved (Fig. 120). Then follows the basin of Issoire, diversified by basaltic masses rising above the Oligocene limestones and marls, and by a mass of granite trenched across by the Allier.

[1] M. Derruau, *La Grande Limagne* (1949), pp. 8-9, has an interesting discussion on the origin of the name. It is related etymologically to *limon*, and it is regarded by Derruau as '*synonyme de terre grasse*'. The name is used for the adjacent parts of Bourbonnais to the north, as the *Limagne bourbonnaise*.

This group of small basins, together with several others along the tributary valley, affords a striking contrast in land-use and economy with the bleak uplands which surround them. Their milder climate, earlier springs and lower rainfall, their quite fertile alluvial soils and gentle slopes, allow a prosperous agriculture—wheat, malting barley, fodder-crops for the cattle, market-garden produce, fruit and vines on the slopes. The small towns, each of about 5,000 inhabitants, situated on the higher margins of the basins away from flood-dangers (which are very real because of the rapid runoff from the surrounding uplands), are market-centres, though several have industries; Brassac and Ste. Florine are the centres of small-scale coal-mining and some metallurgical activities. Brioude manufactures furniture, an occupation based on local walnut, and other wooden articles. Brassac possesses specialised textile industries, such as embroidery and ribbons.

The *Grande Limagne* occupies the largest of the Tertiary depressions, known sometimes as the Bassin de Clermont-Gannat, and extending from south to north for sixty miles. Though narrowed in the south by a prolongation of Livradois, the Limagne basin opens out further north to a width of about twenty-five miles. A long curving fault on the west marks the edge of the high uplands of Auvergne, although to the west of Gannat other faults define the Horst de Jenzat which projects boldly eastward into Limagne, partially enclosing to its north-west the little Bassin d'Ebreuil. Another series of faults on the east defines the margins of the Monts du Forez. The basin is enlarged by the fact that into it opens the broad valley of the Dore in the south-east. This river flows through an Oligocene-floored down-faulted depression (in which stand the towns of Marsac and Ambert) between the mountains of Livradois and Forez, and its lower course (the basin of Courpière) is likewise enclosed by faults.

The sedimentary infilling consists of Oligocene limestones and marls, with a veneer in places of coarse granitic and basaltic débris, elsewhere of clays. The *grandes nappes alluviales* of this superficial material, including also clay-sands derived from disintegration of the surrounding granite, cover much of the basin to the east of the Allier, and are referred to collectively as the *varennes*. The darkish clays (known as *terres noires* and in the north as *forterre*) are found mainly in the south-west and also to the north-east of Vichy as the Sologne bourbonnaise is approached. A variety of gravels and alluvial deposits occurs along the terraces of both the Allier and the Dore.

The plain of the Grande Limagne exhibits considerable diversity in its relief features. In the west low limestone ridges and buttes, orientated more or less from south to north, and sometimes defined by scarp-faces known as *tureaux*, rise above the intervening marl-floored depressions, in places marshy. The name *Pays des Buttes* is usually applied to this western zone. In the centre of the basin, between the Pays des Buttes and the Allier, is the clay-floored and rather damp *plaine marneuse*, which once consisted of marshlands (the *Pays de Marais*), though parts are now drained.

Volcanic activity of both Pliocene and Pleistocene age contributes diversification to parts of the basin lying west and south of a line from Riom to Billom. On the north-western margins of Livradois, protruding into the southern Limagne, a continuous volcanic cover forms the Plateau de la Comté, where the remnants of at least fifty individual cones and lava-flows can be traced, orientated in three lines from north-east to south-west; '. . . *le relief est morcelé en minuscules coulées et en pointements isolés*' (M. Derruau). Lava flows project eastward from the Chaîne des Puys, crossing the fault-scarp and overlying the Oligocene limestones and clays. Some basalt masses have been eroded into steep-sided 'tables', such as the Corent, the Butte de Gergovie, the Côtes de Clermont and de Châteaugay, so contributing a distinct element to the Payes des Buttes. The Montagne de la Serre comprises a ridge projecting several miles into the Limagne plain. The dark-coloured andesitic lavas are quarried; much of Clermont-Ferrand (including the cathedral) is built of this stone from the quarries at Volvic, which have been worked for eight centuries. There are also numerous little cones and hillocks, some of them are probably small laccoliths; the Puy de Mur, Puy de Crouelles and Puy de St. Romain project prominently from the floor of the basin.

The net result is that the Grande Limagne can be divided into three distinctive regions—the *paysages de buttes volcaniques ou sédimentaires* in the south and west, *la plaine marneuse* in the west-centre (the Allier to the north of Pont-du-Château swings well to the east), and the *varennes*.[1]

The soils of Limagne are thus variable, ranging from near-sterile sands underlain by a hard-pan (here known as *mâchefer*) and gravels to calcareous marls frequently enriched by the products of basalt disintegration. Some of the poorer soils are forested, notably in the Forêts de Randan and Montpensier in the north-east and the volcanic plateau of Comté in the south-east, to which in fact is given the name of *Pays au Bois*. Many of the volcanic *puys* have a fringe of woodland around their upper slopes, and pollarded willows, poplars and aspens stand in lines among the marshes.

---

[1] These divisions form in fact the basis of M. Derruau's detailed study, *La Grande Limagne* (1949). Of considerable interest is a detailed study by the same author, 'L'Occupation humaine dans la Varenne de Lezoux (Limagne)', in *A. de G.* (1947), vol. lvi, pp. 178-91.

By considerable effort Limagne has been made into a productive agricultural region. Climatically there are difficulties, for much of the basin receives only about 20 to 24 inches of rainfall, and its winters are cold. Parts (the sands) suffer from an inadequacy of water, paradoxically others (the marshlands) have an excess of it, and so both drainage and irrigation have their place; indeed, the same channels (*rases*) frequently serve each function at a different season. Much of the better soil is under wheat, the *blé dur* similar to that grown along the Mediterranean coastlands, which is made into various *pâtes* in the factories of Clermont-Ferrand. Rye, formerly grown on the poorer soils, has virtually disappeared, but malting-barley, oats, sugar-beet (the second most important crop to wheat) and fodder-beet have increased in acreage during the last fifty years. Market-gardens and orchards appear near towns such as Clermont-Ferrand, Vichy and Riom, and form tongues of intensive cultivation projecting into the western Limagne from the basalt hills.

Limagne is pre-eminently an arable region, but the number of livestock (cattle, pigs and poultry) has increased during this century, and the area both of permanent and temporary pasture and of fodder-crops has likewise expanded. In 1890 the vine covered about 110,000 acres and in places formed a profitable monoculture, but although phylloxera arrived later than in many parts, it wrought great destruction between 1895 and 1899, and in the first decade of this century mildew caused further havoc. Now the cultivation of the vine is restricted to the southern slopes of the ridges, along some of the higher Allier terraces (as near Pont-du-Château), and on the western terraces overlooking the Sioule valley in the extreme north, where a pleasant white wine is made at St. Pourçain.[1] Most of the *vignerons* are now employed only part-time in their vineyards, and usually own livestock or a plot of arable land.

One feature of the agricultural economy of Limagne is the extraordinary degree to which '*parcellement*' has been carried out among a large number of small proprietors. As P. Coutin expresses it,[2] '*une parcelle de propriété est parfois divisée en plusieurs parcelles de culture; d'autres fois, plusieurs parcelles de propriété ne forment qu'une seule parcelle de culture*'. A certain amount of grouping and consolidation of holdings has been effected, however, during the last twenty years, partly as a result of war-time legislation.

In this predominantly agricultural area small towns are dispersed as market-centres. A few stand on the banks of the Allier, such as Pont-du-Château, Puy-Guillaume, Maringues and Vichy. The last

---

[1] M. Derruau, *op. cit.*, pp. 207-35, has a full account of the problems of viticulture in Limagne, including a detailed map.

[2] P. Coutin, 'La Remembrement des terres en Limagne', in *Mélanges géographiques offerts à Ph. Arbos* (1953), vol. i, pp. 149-56.

is a spa of considerable repute, the result of its alkaline springs; others are found near by at St. Yorre and Cusset. Though known since ancient times, it was not until the reign of Napoleon III that Vichy became really famous; now it is a town of 31,000 permanent inhabitants, '*la reine des villes d'eaux*', and with its parks, hotels and shopping streets supplementing the therapeutic qualities of its waters, it attracts many visitors. Certain associated industries have developed —the bottling of Vichy water, and the making of pharmaceutical chemicals and toilet articles. Royat and Châtel-Guyon have similar thermal establishments on the western fault-line of Limagne. Other small market-towns of 5,000 to 7,000 people are situated at intervals over the plain—Thiers in the Dore valley, Randan, Lezoux and Billom to the east of the Allier in the *varennes* country; Gannat is a nodal point of road and rail in the north-west on the edge of the *pays de buttes* and *la plaine marneuse*. Riom was once the capital of the Dukes of Berry, and is encircled by boulevards occupying the site of the former fortifications; situated at the edge of a basalt spur, its position was naturally strong. Many of these towns have industries, sometimes long established. As centres of prosperous agricultural regions, some possess canning and preserving factories. Local heavy clays supply raw material for the brick- and tile-works of Varennes-sur-Allier, St. Amand-Tallende has paper-mills, Martres-de-Veyre has a large printing-works, Courpière, Billom and Lezoux have pottery and earthenware-works, Riom processes tobacco and has a large modern factory making electrical apparatus. Thiers is the Sheffield of France, with an ancient cutlery industry originally based on water-power.

Clermont-Ferrand.—While there is this widespread diversity of small-scale industry over a pre-eminently rural region, most of the urban and industrial activity is concentrated at Clermont-Ferrand, which dominates the economic life of at least the western Limagne. It stands on the slopes of one of the volcanic buttes at a height of 1,350 feet, overlooking the valley of the Tiretaine. It is at the crossing-point of the north-south (Paris-Nîmes) route through the Allier valley with an east-west (Lyons-La Rochelle and Bordeaux) route crossing the Monts du Forez via Thiers and the Col de Noirétable and the Chaîne des Puys by the Col de la Moréno. The town is a commercial- and marketing-centre, and for centuries has possessed minor industries such as the tanning of leather, the making of paper, flour-milling and the processing of other local agricultural products, and wool-weaving.[1] But it was not until the nineteenth century that

[1] A most interesting account of the industrial development of Clermont-Ferrand is given by Philippe Arbos himself, in *Mélanges géographiques offerts à Ph. Arbos* (1953), vol. i, pp. 28-44.

the real industrial expansion took place. In 1832 a small factory for making rubber was established, but little development occurred until the invention of the pneumatic tyre and the growth of the cycle and automobile industry; after 1890 progress was immense, associated with the name of *Michelin*. The rubber industry, which employed 320 people in 1863, had 3,620 in 1911, and today about 18,000. The three *Michelin* factories, the biggest of which is the Usine des Carmes, cover a great expanse of land to the north-east of the city; badly damaged by aerial bombardment in March 1944, they have been rebuilt and re-equipped, and in fact have gained by this compulsory modernisation. Another rubber factory, that of the *Bergougnan* company, stands in the north of the town. Other modern industries include the making of sulphuric acid by the *Teisset-Kessler* company of Lorraine, the construction of railcars, mining equipment and of engineering machinery generally, textiles (notably ready-made clothing), footwear, and confectionery (particularly chocolate, jams and preserves). The town still has a wide sphere of influence, both in Limagne as a market- and servicing-centre and in central France generally.[1]

Thus Clermont-Ferrand has become second only to St. Etienne in the Central Massif. In 1872 its population was 37,000, by 1911 it was 63,000 and by 1962 it had reached 134,263. The city includes the ancient town of Montferrand, a mile to the north-east, a mediaeval *bastide* of 7,000 people which has changed little for centuries; in the apt words of Ph. Arbos, it forms '*un fossile médiéval incrusté au milieu de l'alluvion urbaine du XXe siècle*'. Montferrand was joined administratively to Clermont in 1731. Today the agglomeration includes the contiguous towns of Royat (with its mineral springs), Aubière, Beaumont and Chamalières, and has a total population of 167,000. Large blocks of *cités-ouvrières* have been built to house the industrial population, and the cathedral and the old town on the 'Plateau Central', bounded by boulevards, are now surrounded by several square miles of built-up area.

Bourbonnais.—As Limagne widens to the north, the river Allier flows in a broad valley, bordered by a distinctive series of terraces, parallel to the Loire, before the two rivers converge near Nevers. Further to the west the much-faulted crystalline rocks of northern Auvergne gradually give way to newer rocks as the land sinks towards the *Champagne berrichonne*. In spite of this diversity, it is logical to regard this as a unit-area on the northern margins of the

---

[1] A. Meynier, *op. cit.* (1935), has an interesting map (p. 220) showing its spheres of influence. See also Ph. Arbos *et al.*, 'Clermont-Ferrand et sa région', *Association française pour l'Avancement des Sciences*, 68th Congress (1949).

Central Massif. The name *Bourbonnais* is justified in that it formed one of the provinces (Fig. 1) and *gouvernements militaires* of the *ancien régime* before 1789, with its capital at Moulins on the banks of the Allier. Today it coincides quite well with the *département* of Allier, and Moulins is its *chef-lieu*. For convenience, however, the region may be subdivided into three: the *Sologne bourbonnaise* in the east, the *Bourbonnais occidental*, and the small down-faulted basin of the upper Cher known as the *région montluçonnaise*.

The *Sologne bourbonnaise* forms a gently undulating plateau, sloping northward from 1,000 to 600 feet between the converging Loire and Allier. The greater part is covered, like the Sologne proper to the north, with a sheet of Miocene sands (the *sables du Bourbonnais*), diversified with layers of quartz gravel and sheets of clay, and frequently underlain by a hard-pan. The rivers have cut down through these deposits, exposing in places the Oligocene lime-stones, and their terraces and flood-plains are covered with Pleisto-cene and Recent gravels, sand and fine alluvium. The low gradients, the sheets of clay and the underlying hard-pan do not make for adequate natural drainage, and until the nineteenth century it was a poor area of *étangs* and marshes, alternating with heathland on the sands known as *brandes*. A considerable amount of reclamation and improvement has been accomplished—the drainage of marshes, the fertilising of impoverished sands, the planting of trees, and the improvement of roads and rural housing, but there remain many *étangs* (some used for pisciculture) and much heathland.

The pattern of the geology and the relief is more complex in *Bourbonnais occidental*. The southern part consists of gneiss and granite, dominated in the south by the well-named Signal de la Bosse (2,539 feet). The crystalline rocks are cut through by the north-eastern part of the 'coal furrow' (Fig. 120), containing the small Noyant field, while half a dozen others, including that of Com-mentry, lie on the northern flanks. In succession northward appear an area of Permian rocks, a band of Trias, and then Jurassic marls and limestones as the lowland of Berry is approached. The whole region is much faulted and several outlying masses of granite and gneiss project through the newer rocks. In all, this part of the Bourbonnais forms '... *sur la carte géologique un bariolage qui témoigne de sa diversité de nature*' (Ph. Arbos). The many streams flowing to the Allier and the Cher trench boldly through these rocks, often forming gorges, as in the valley of the Aumance near Hérisson, where the striking relief due to differential erosion gives rise to the somewhat affected appellation of '*la petite Suisse*'. Else-where the peneplained surfaces form a series of monotonous plateaus descending to the north.

The Cher rises to the south on the granite plateau of Combrailles, and flows northwards into the down-faulted basin of Montluçon. It is bordered by clean-cut faults, and floored as it is by Oligocene marls in the south and Miocene sands in the north, it partakes of the general character of the other Tertiary basins of the Central Massif.

It is not easy to summarise the character of this variegated region ; an impression is given by the fact that in 1963 just under half of the *département* of Allier was under arable, about 30 per cent under permanent pasture, and 12 per cent under woodland. The woodland (much formerly preserved in domainial forests) has been somewhat reduced from a quarter of a million acres in 1840 to a little under 200,000 acres, but some fine forests of oak and beech still exist.

Much of the country has a rather *bocage*-like character (in fact the term *bocage bourbonnais* is sometimes used), the result of the patchwork of fields surrounded by hedgerows and the extent of permanent pasture, especially in the *Sologne bourbonnaise*. Though many holdings are small, farmed by individual proprietors, some large estates still survive, created through the colonising activity of the nineteenth century, some growing wheat, others divided into smaller units and farmed by *métayers*. This method of sharetenancy has declined, although as late as 1932 more than half the land was farmed on this system, a distinction shared in France only by the *département* of Landes. Wheat occupies more than half the total arable area, but fodder-crops have increased during the last half-century. Curiously, this is the most important part of France for the cultivation of artichokes. Livestock are important, and 424,000 cattle were present in the *département* in 1963, including both dairy animals (about half) and the Charolais breed for meat, and nearly a quarter of a million pigs.

Bourbonnais is pre-eminently a rural region with an agricultural economy, and individual farms and hamlets are widely peppered over the landscape. The density of population is about 132 per square mile, or more than double that of a century ago. The little market-towns are usually situated on a river and serve one of the valley re-entrants into the upland—Lapalisse, Cosne-d'Allier, Bourbon-l'Archambault and Néris-les-Bains. A few towns are concerned with coal-mining, such as Noyant, St. Hilaire and Commentry. Three larger towns are Montluçon in the Cher valley, Commentry in the valley of the Œil (a Cher tributary) and Moulins on the Allier. The last is primarily an administrative town and has not grown much during the last century ; its population in 1840 was 15,000, in 1962 only 26,000. It has a few small industries of leather-tanning, hosiery and furniture-making, but it can hardly be called an industrial town. It is a notable railway junction where north-south and west-east lines cross; it is said that one can get direct trains to more cities from Moulins than from any other town in France except Paris and Lyons, a measure of its centrality. Commentry, though with less than 10,000 people, is a busy industrial town, with collieries and steel-works.

Montluçon has become the major industrial centre of this rural area. Situated on the margin of the Paris Basin and the Central Massif, it has long stood at a cross-roads; today it is a focus of four railways and the terminus of the Berry Canal by which raw materials such as Lorraine pig-iron are brought. The neighbouring coalfields are small, but they helped the industrial development of the town in the nineteenth century; blast-furnaces and glass-works were set up in the 1840's, and thereafter progress was rapid. Steel-works are operated by the *Cie des Forges de Châtillon, Commentry et Neuves-Maisons*, including electric furnaces built under the post-1945 modernisation plan. Armaments, motor-car parts, and special tools are manufactured, and there is a long-established industry of iron pipes and, more recently, steel tubes. Rubber manufacturing, introduced in 1920, is carried on at the *Dunlop* works. Glass, pottery, chemical fertilisers and commercial waxes are made, leather is processed, and a large rayon factory was built between the wars. In all, its flourishing industrial development is shown by the fact that its population, only 4,500 in 1840, increased tenfold in a century, and today is nearly 60,000.

PART III

THE FOLD MOUNTAINS

CHAPTER 21

THE JURA

The Jura form a crescent-shaped mass of uplands extending for 150 miles from the southern end of the Rhine rift-valley to the middle Rhône near Lyons.[1] The maximum width is thirty miles between the valley of the Saône to the west and the Swiss Plateau to the east, but tapering to six or seven miles at each extremity. The frontier between France and Switzerland crosses the upland area obliquely from Basel to Geneva, leaving all the south-western Jura in France and the greater part of the north-eastern Jura in Switzerland. The name Jura is derived from a Celtic word meaning forest, probably akin to the Slavonic word *gora*. The term *Jurassic* has passed into geological usage from the excellent development of limestones and associated mid-Mesozoic rocks in this type-region.

STRUCTURE AND RELIEF

The basement rocks consist of biotite-gneisses similar to those appearing on the surface in the Vosges; though these crystalline rocks never actually outcrop in the Jura, their presence is known through deep borings. After the peneplanation which succeeded the Hercynian orogeny, a long period followed of extensive though intermittent marine transgressions which covered most of central Europe. Permian conglomerates and sandstones were laid down on the crystalline basement rocks, and were succeeded by a considerable thickness of the Trias, comprising the Bunter Sandstone, the Muschel-kalk and the Keuper Marls. The last are overlain by Rhaetic marls and limestones, which indicate a renewed marine transgression following a regression during the Keuper. These Triassic rocks appear on the surface only on the flanks of the Jura—in the extreme north-east in Switzerland, along the northern margins near Mont-béliard, again near Besançon, and as a narrow outcrop between Poligny and Lons-le-Saunier. In the Muschelkalk occur salt-beds

---

[1] E. de Margerie, *Le Jura* (1922), is one of the classic French regional monographs.

which have long been exploited, as the names Salins and Lons-le-Saunier would indicate.

These rocks were succeeded by great thicknesses of Jurassic strata deposited during another prolonged period of marine transgression. At the base are Liassic marls and shales, varying in thickness from 100 to 300 feet, and invariably resting on the Triassic formations. The Middle Jurassic deposits, 500 to 1,300 feet thick, consist of oolitic and marly limestones; these form the surface rocks extensively in the west and stand out as long ridges in the east. The Upper Jurassics, varying in thickness from 300 to over 3,000 feet, comprise coralline and dolomitic limestones and some marls. Almost all these are of marine origin, although at the end of the period freshwater beds (the Purbeck Limestones) indicate a temporary regression of the sea.

The Jurassic rocks make up the great mass of the Jura, but some deposits of younger rocks survive in places. Lower Cretaceous marls, chalky limestones and glauconitic sandstones once probably covered the whole area, but have been preserved only in the downfolds. Particularly in the north-east appear outcrops of Eocene ironstones, Oligocene limestones, gypsum, clays, fresh-water and marine Molasse sandstones, and Pliocene pebbles and sands. These Tertiary rocks are represented only to a very small extent in France.

The formation of the Jura was associated with the earth-movements responsible for the Alps. The Hercynian horsts exercised less controlling effect in the central Jura, where the folds were able to splay out, hence the folding is less strongly developed, but further to the east pressure was concentrated against the southern edge of the Black Forest and the folding is more intense. The long arc of folds lying along the north-western margin of the Swiss Plateau is given the name Folded Jura (the *Jura plissé*), but only its western and south-western portion lies in France.

The term Jura is not restricted to this folded zone, for to the west lies a distinctive area of Jurassic rocks known as the Plateau Jura (*Jura tabulaire*), which forms the greater part of the French Jura. The result of tangential pressure from the south has been the formation of a series of fault-lines which divide the plateau into a number of blocks. Along the outer (north-western) margins of the plateau further folding combined with faulting has formed a boundary-flexure, so producing a prominent sharp edge.

A long period of denudation succeeded the Alpine folding, and it is estimated that the Jura are now less than half as high as they once were. The Tertiary and Cretaceous sediments were removed except in some of the synclines in the east. The extent of the denudation has of course varied; in parts of the plateau where the Upper Jurassic is still the surface rock, probably as little as 300 feet of sedimentary rocks have gone, while in the extreme north-east, where

Triassic rocks now appear on the surface, more than 3,000 feet must have been stripped from the former folds.

It is possible, as some French geographers have done, to divide the whole upland area latitudinally into *le Jura septentrionale* or *le Jura du Doubs*, *le Jura central*, and *le Jura méridional*. Undoubted differences in landscape and economy are apparent between north and south, mainly the result of distinct variations in climate, but this division cuts across the obvious longitudinal structural lines. It is preferable to distinguish (i) the Folded Jura proper (*le Jura plissé*), otherwise known as *les hautes Chaînes du Jura central*; (ii) the *Jura méridional*, the extreme southern wing where the Rhône cuts across the packed folds, forming the distinctive regions of Haut- and Bas-Bugey and Crémieu; and (iii) the Plateau Jura, known as *le Jura tabulaire* or *les Plateaux jurassiens*. There remains a small unit-area, (iv) the Pays de Gex, tucked in a corner to the west of Lake Geneva between the high easternmost Crêt de la Neige and the Swiss frontier (Fig. 128).

(i) **The Folded Jura.**—The folding of the Jura affected only rocks younger than the Bunter Sandstone, and is of a literally superficial character. It seems that the newer rocks were pushed forward over the salt-beds of the Middle Muschelkalk, which in effect acted as a plane of lubrication, while the gneissic basement, the Permian and the Bunter Sandstone, all lying beneath this plane, were virtually unaffected. A large number of individual anticlines was formed; some estimates put the total in the central region as about 160, but it is difficult to calculate this since so many anticlines pitch-out and are succeeded by others appearing from a neighbouring syncline; this pitching-out is a further indication of the superficial nature of the folding. The most pronounced folding is found along the inner (Swiss) edge of the Jura, especially in the north-east where the fold-zone is at its narrowest and most compressed.

The majority of the anticlines are more or less symmetrical in character. Nevertheless, in places more complicated fold-forms can be found; thus the main arch of an anticline may contain two or more secondary anticlines, or pressure may have been intensified locally to form steep-limbed 'trunk anticlines', asymmetrical anticlines, and even occasionally fan-folds and over-folds. It seems from the evidence of railway-tunnels that even clean-cut thrusts are present. In fact, these not only occur in the heart of the folded zone, but the outer anticlines have been thrust on to the Plateau Jura to the north-west, and some outlying portions have been isolated by denudation to form *Klippen*, prominent hillocks rising from the plateau surface three or four miles beyond the outer ranges of the Folded Jura.

In most cases the anticlines still correspond to the upstanding ridges (known as *monts*) and the synclines form the valleys (the *vaux*, singular *val*). The latter are usually floored with sandstones and clays of the Molasse and Cretaceous, and are followed by longi-

FIG. 128.—THE UPPER RHÔNE-SAÔNE BASIN AND THE JURA.

The abbreviations are as follows: **A**, Lake Annecy; **Ch**, Champagnole; **G**, Geneva; **L**, Lons-le-Saunier; **M**, Martigny; **N**, Nantua; **P**, Poligny; **Pt**, Pontarlier; **St. Cl**, St. Claude.

The numbers **I** to **IV** refer to the four physical units of the Jura, described in the text.

tudinal sections of rivers. Nevertheless, as long periods of denudation have worn away part of the original upfolds, the form of these valleys and ridges is far from simple or regular. Torrents (*ruzes*), flowing down the sides of the anticlines, furrow deeply into the limestone, and erode headwards into the less resistant underlying clays and marls. Sometimes a torrent may cut right back into an anti-cline and so form a high-lying depression (*combe*) along its crest

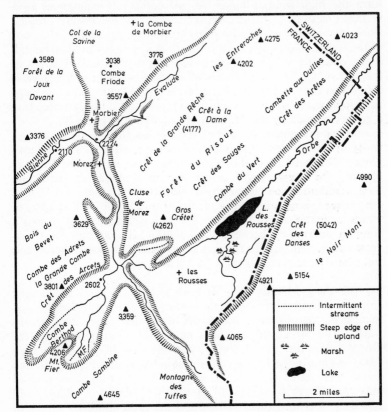

FIG. 129.—*Crêts* AND *Combes* IN THE FOLDED JURA.

The edge of the upland is shown by hachures in generalised form, in order to bring out the broad pattern of ridges and valleys. Heights are given in feet.

Some of the headstreams of the Bienne rise in a group of *combes*, Berthod and Mont Fier (M.F.), with sharp infacing *crêts*, notably on the north (the Crêt des Arcets). The Bienne then cuts northwards through the Cluse de Morez, and makes a right-angled bend, before following a rocky steep-sided valley to the south-west. The Lac des Rousses lies in a broad *val* trending north-eastward, drained by the Orbe. The Risoux ridge, cut through by the Cluse de Morez, has been dissected into a series of long narrow *combes* separated by *crêts*.

Based on *Carte de France au 50,000ᵉ*, sheet XXXIII-XXXIV/27.

(Fig. 129). These *combes* are usually both short and narrow, but occasionally denudation has proceeded so far that a basin-like depression of appreciable size has been created. This process has rarely gone on so far in the Jura, however, as to produce synclinal ridges, a complete reversal of the relief.

The *combes* are walled with infacing escarpments (*crêts*), which form the high summit-lines. A *crêt* commonly culminates in a vertical limestone cliff (the *corniche calcaire*), below which a gradual slope, covered with scree and in parts wooded, descends to the floor of the *combe*. Although most of the folded zone lies in Switzerland, by an odd trick of the frontier (which approaches Lake Geneva to the east of the Col de la Faucille) the highest point of the Jura is actually in France, the Crêt de la Neige (5,653 feet). This fine ridge runs southward to culminate in the Grand Crêt d'Eau, overlooking a gorge occupied by the Rhône above Bellegarde (Fig. 130).

Another prominent feature of the Folded Jura is the transverse valley or *cluse* which cuts across an anticline, often as a precipitous gorge. The existence of these *cluses* involves an antecedent drainage system ; the rivers existed before the anticline was upraised, and then maintained their courses by erosion as uplift progressed. There are between sixty and seventy of these *cluses* in the Folded Jura, of which a quarter are in France. The drainage as a result reveals a complex alternation between the longitudinal *vaux* and the transverse *cluses*, with sudden changes of direction, elbow-like bends and frequent river captures (Figs. 129, 131).

(ii) **The Jura Méridional.**[1]—Between the Rhône and its parallel tributary the Ain on the west, the folding is more tightly compressed than in the central Jura, and sheafs of parallel ridges trend southward. The prominent *crêt*-lines culminate in such peaks as the Grand Colombier (5,033 feet), which rises steeply for more than 4,000 feet above the Rhône to the east in its *val* between Seyssel and Culoz. This area is given the name of Bugey, sometimes divided into *Haut-Bugey* to the north of the Albarine-Seran valleys, and *Bas-Bugey* between these valleys and the most southerly elbow of the Rhône.

The low *Plateau de Crémieu*, to the south of the Rhône, is the most southerly manifestation of the Jura proper. Actually the Jurassic limestone, concealed for the most part beneath late Tertiary deposits of the Rhône valley, makes a final brief appearance along the left bank of the Rhône in the Plateau de Balmes.

(iii) **The Plateau Jura.**—The Plateau Jura has been considerably faulted, and there are several distinctive blocks, although the strata for the most part remain horizontal. Three major levels can be distinguished, separated by steps, descending towards the Saône

[1] M. Dubois, *Le Jura méridional : étude morphologique* (1959) ; and M. Dubois and R. Lebeau, 'Le Jura méridional', in *A. de G.* (1962), vol. lxxi, pp. 337-8.

valley. The highest surface, bordering the Folded Jura, and some-times called the Plateau de Noseray, lies at about 2,750 to 3,000 feet, consisting mainly of resistant Upper Jurassic limestones. Then

FIG. 130.—THE RHÔNE NEAR BELLEGARDE.

The upland area, approximately over 1,750 feet, is generalised. Heights are given in feet.

This exemplifies the transverse *cluses* by which the Rhône and other Jura rivers break through a ridge from one *val* to another. The line of the Valserine and the Rhône below Bellegarde indicates a major synclinal valley.

Based on *Carte de France au 50,000^e*, sheets XXXIII/29, 30, with revisions.

comes the second step, the Plateau de Champagnole at 2,000 to 2,500 feet, of Middle Jurassic Oolite, although in places the Oxford Clay has been preserved in depressions, as in the Combe d'Ain. In this hollow is situated Champagnole, a flourishing little town at a height of 1,800 feet, while Mont Rivel on the mountain wall to the north of the valley rises to 2,589 feet. The lowest section of the plateau, developed on the Keuper and flanked by the Muschelkalk, lies at 1,600 to 2,000 feet.

The north-western edge of the Plateau Jura is characterised by boundary-flexures, forming a distinct edge overlooking the Saône valley. In the north the western bounding fault of the Black Forest trends south-westward as a flexure, and forms the Mont Terrible ridge in Switzerland, continued by the Montagnes du Lomont; the highest point on the latter attains 2,746 feet. The northern edge of the Mont Terrible ridge just projects into France as the *Jura alsacien* (the district of Ferrette), which descends northward towards the Sundgau in southern Alsace. To the south-west of the Lomont, from the neighbourhood of Besançon to near Poligny, the edge of the Jura is less sharply defined, but further south it reappears as the Vignoble in the neighbourhood of Lons-le-Saunier, and is continued southward as the Revermont until it reaches the Ain valley (Fig. 128). The edge of the Revermont rises to about 2,100 feet, while a few miles to the west the Plaine de Bresse is at only 750 feet. In places this marginal ridge is remarkably continuous, although scalloped by deeply-cut gullies and hollows; elsewhere, as near Besançon where the Doubs winds along the margin of the plateau, erosion has broken the edge into individual summits and projecting spurs.

(iv) **The Pays de Gex.**—This little unit-area does not belong geographically to the Jura at all, but to the Swiss Plateau. The Franco-Swiss frontier makes a rectangular salient to the east, almost reaching Lake Geneva, and thus enclosing a small portion of the Swiss Plateau between the frontier and the most easterly Jura ridge. The area is covered with glacial material, although the underlying Oligocene clays are revealed in places, and it drains southwards to the Rhône by the river Journan. The *pays* lies in the Geneva region, and has had special customs arrangements with that city since 1815.

Glaciation.—The Quaternary glaciation had quite an appreciable effect on the Jura,[1] and at its maxima several local glaciers were nurtured by tiny snow-fields. More important was the effect of the main Alpine ice moving outwards from the Swiss Plateau; it probably covered the eastern and southern parts of the Jura, and from it tongues projected westward through the cols. Erratics of undoubted Alpine origin have been found in the Jura as high as 5,000 feet on the southern ridges. Boulder-clay lies in sheets and

[1] J. Tricart, 'Quelques Aspects particuliers des glaciations quaternaires du Jura', in *Revue géographique de l'Est* (1965), vol. 5, pp. 499-527.

undulating mounds over some of the higher depressions on the plateau and between the ridges. Many small lakes are dammed-up by crescentic mounds or lie in uneven depressions in the clay; the Lacs de l'Abbaye and de Sylans in the south, and de Chambly and du Val in a tributary valley of the Ain, are examples. On a larger scale some of the main synclinal *vaux*, similarly floored with boulder-clay, contain lakes; the Doubs, for example, flows in succession through the Lacs de Remoray and de St. Point (Fig. 131), five miles above Pontarlier. The Orbe flows through the Lac des Rousses (Fig. 129) and then in Switzerland through the long narrow Lac de Joux. Occasionally the *cluses* contain lakes; the Lac de Nantua lies in a broad *cluse* cut across the Montagne de Chamoise, west of Nantua.

The Drainage Patterns.—The Jura receive a considerable rainfall, and despite the dominance of limestone there is a plentiful supply of surface water. The presence of beds of Jurassic clays and marls among the limestones, of the Cretaceous and Tertiary clays in the synclines, and of the considerable patches of boulder-clay contribute to the permanent character of the rivers. Springs are common, even up in the high *combes*. Of course, intermittent streams appear in the valleys, which may vary from a torrent to a trickle or even dry up altogether, and complex subterranean drainage systems have developed. Some parts of the higher plateaus consist of monotonous expanses of almost bare limestone, reminiscent of the *Causses*, displaying irregular solution hollows, dry valleys,[1] deep chasms known as *emposieux*, water-sinks and resurgences, with irregular steep-sided summits rising above the general level.

The varied nature of the Jurassic rocks, where resistant limestones lie in close juxtaposition to weaker shales and marls, produces remarkable effects both in the cross-profiles of the valleys and in the nature of the stream-beds. In places steep cliffs fall almost to the water's edge, in others the valley-sides open out, with gentle meadow- or tree-covered slopes. Stepped falls, where a river crosses a succession of horizontal resistant strata, are common. The Loue, for example, leaves its cave as a powerful resurgence down such a 'staircase'.

Most of the drainage of the southern Jura finds its way to the Rhône either directly or via its right-bank tributary the Ain. In the extreme west and north-west, short streams flow down through the steep gorges that fret the edge of the Vignoble and Revermont to join the Saône's left-bank tributaries. The waters of the central and northern French Jura are collected by the Doubs.

The Rhône leaves the south-western wing of Lake Geneva (*Lac*

[1] S. Daveau, 'Vallées sèches des plateaux du Jura', in *Revue géographique de l'Est* (1965), vol. 5, pp. 461-72.

Léman), which lies at 1,230 feet above sea-level; the river has already descended 4,750 feet from its glacier-source in central Switzerland. The abrupt checking of the gradient as the river leaves the Alpine tract causes considerable deposition in the lake; the milky colour of the laden current can be traced from the air far out into the clear waters as it extends its lacustrine delta. The lake therefore serves a valuable purpose as a filter-bed, and the Rhône issues as a sediment-free stream through the sluices in the barrage controlling the lake level.

The Rhône negotiates the fold-ridges of the southern Jura by a series of *vaux* alternating with the usual *cluses* through the ridges. Below Pougny, twenty-five miles from Lake Geneva, the turbulent river surges through the well-named Défilé de l'Ecluse (Fig. 130). The valley is so steep-sided that the railway from Geneva to Bellegarde tunnels through the spur to the north rather than attempt to follow the gorge. A few miles further downstream, the river negotiates a lower and less sharply defined ridge by means of a double right-angled bend; Bellegarde stands on the northern abutment of this ridge overlooking the river.

Then the Rhône follows a long synclinal *val*-section, continuing the trend of its tributary the Valserine from the north. Although this is a *val*, it is deep and steep-sided, with limestone hills rising for nearly a thousand feet above the river. This offered a first-rate site for a reservoir, and the huge Génissiat dam, thirty-one miles downstream from Lake Geneva, and rising for 260 feet above its base, has ponded up a narrow lake extending fourteen miles upstream almost as far as Bellegarde.

The river continues southwards, its valley enclosed by the ridges of the Montagne du Grand Colombier to the west and the forested Montagne du Gros Foug to the east. In this flat-floored valley deposition has caused extensive braiding (Fig. 135) among shingle-islands and marshes. The valley opens out southward into the main Sub-Alpine Depression (see p. 631), although the Rhône, hugging its western side, leaves this for another parallel Jura syncline, and the depression itself is occupied by the Lac du Bourget and by extensive marshlands (the Marais de Chautagne); the lake, fed from the south by the Leyesse, is connected to the Rhône by the Canal de Savières. The Rhône proceeds southwards to Yenne, turns abruptly west through another transverse gorge (the Défilé de Pierre-Châtel), follows a further synclinal valley, and then crosses the last main Jura ridge to St. Genix-sur-Guiers. This is in point of fact the most southerly point reached by the river in its mid-section between Geneva and Lyons. It meanders and braids its channel; a few miles downstream from St. Genix its streams extend in width over the flat valley-floor for over a mile, enclosing gravel- and sand-banks such

LXI Mont Blanc and the Vallée de Chamonix, in winter

LXII The Glacier de Leschaux, a tributary of the Mer de Glace, with the Grandes Jorasses in the right background

LXIII The Cirque de Gavarnie in the central Pyrenees

LXIV A Pyrenean valley: the thermal spa of Cauterets, situated on the banks of the Gave de Cauterets as 'les Iles Molottes', 'les Iles des Sables', and 'les Graviers Grand Jean'. The river then crosses the narrow southerly extremity of the Plateau Jura for about twenty miles, swings round the northern abutment of the Plateau de Crémieu, and enters the Plaine de Bresse.

Above Lyons the Rhône has a predominantly Alpine régime, and high-water occurs in late spring and early summer because of snow-melt in the French Alps; the Arve is a major contributor, draining as it does the north-western side of the Mont Blanc massif and the Alps of Haute-Savoie, while the Jura tributaries add their quota. Lake Geneva, however, acts as a stabilising reservoir, damping down the flood-waters of Alpine Switzerland, though the sluice-gates in the controlling barrage are necessarily open in early summer and the river-flow is much increased. A marked low-water period is experienced in late summer, and then a secondary maximum follows the increased rainfall of the autumn months. The winter freeze materially reduces the outflow for several months until the spring snow-melt begins.

The Ain, the major tributary of the middle Rhône, is the chief drainage artery of the southern Jura. Its headstream, the Bienne, rises not far from the Valserine (which flows directly to the Rhône) and the Orbe (which flows in a north-easterly direction to Lake Neuchâtel and so to the Rhine); this is a striking drainage dispersal (Fig. 129). The upper Ain and the Bienne both reveal the rectilinear pattern of Jura rivers. The greater part of the course of the Ain is trenched in a south-westerly direction across the Plateau Jura.

The Doubs, which joins the Saône about twenty miles above Chalon, has a most remarkable course. It rises in the *Hautes Chaînes* of the Folded Jura on the slopes of Mont Risoux, and pursues a north-easterly direction into the Lac de St. Point (Fig. 131), which once extended further to the south-west along the floor of a *val*. The Doubs built up a marshy alluvial flat, which in due course cut the original lake into two, separating St. Point to the north-east from de Remoray to the south-west. Areas of marsh still cover the valley-floor. Below the Lac de St. Point, the Doubs turns abruptly through a magnificent *cluse* to enter a basin in which stands Pontarlier at a height of 2,600 feet. This synclinal depression is drained by the Drugeon, joining the Doubs a few miles below the town. The floor of this basin is so flat that areas of peat-bogs (*tourbières*) have accumulated. After forming the Franco-Swiss frontier for more than thirty miles, the Doubs passes into Switzer-land for a short distance, and then makes a striking reversal of direction by means of an acute bend. It seems that the upper north-easterly section of its course is a legacy of a former continuation to the proto-Rhine. River-capture caused this change of direction; the beheaded trunk flows as a misfit to the Rhine just above Basel as the tiny river Birse (Fig. 128).

R.G.W.E.—X

The Doubs bends northwards yet again, crossing the Plateau Jura, but near Montbéliard it flows south-westwards along the margin of

FIG. 131.—THE VALLEY OF THE UPPER DOUBS.

The edge of the upland is shown by hachures in generalised form, in order to bring out the broad pattern of ridges and valleys. Heights are given in feet.
R, Lac de Remoray.

Based on *Carte de France au 50,000ᵉ*, sheets XXXIV/25, 26.

the Montagnes du Lomont through Baume-les-Dames, Besançon and Dole into the Plaine de Bresse and hence to its junction with the Saône.

Both the Doubs and the Saône receive left-bank tributaries from the Jura, many of them the product of complex underground systems developed in the limestone. The Loue, for example, emerges as a seething resurgence from a cave near Mouthier, only five miles from the Doubs but 1,170 feet below. E. de Martonne describes how the *absinthe* factory at Pontarlier suffered damage from fire; the liqueur from the damaged vats escaped through the limestone joints, and its unmistakable odour was in due course traced far below in the waters of the Loue. The Loue then flows through a magnificent gorge where vertical cliffs of limestone alternate with tree-covered terraces. It approaches within three or four miles of the Doubs below Besançon, but swings away again, and does not make its confluence for another thirty miles, below Dole.

LAND-USE

Many contrasts are evident in the climate of the Jura, as between the northern end where a distinct bleakness is apparent, and the southern part which possesses a certain brightness, almost of a Mediterranean quality. There are contrasts too between the high ranges and the south-facing valley slopes, and altitude ranges from 1,500 feet to over 5,000 feet. The region as a whole lies in the east of France and so is subject to continental influences. The winters are quite severe; at Rousses, near the frontier to the east of Morez, the lake is frozen on an average for 130 days per annum, while frost is experienced on the *Hautes Chaînes* on an average for a hundred days and for about eighty on the plateau.

Precipitation is heavy, averaging 39 inches on the plateau and as much as 65 or 70 inches on the crest-lines. Much falls as snow; at Mouthe, in the upper Doubs valley at an altitude of 3,100 feet, the average accumulated depth of snow is about ten feet, and several high villages have developed as winter-sports' centres, notably Gilley on the eastern slopes of Mont Chaumont, Morteau and Pontarlier. The expectancy of the number of days during which snow may lie around 2,000 feet is about 55, increasing to 125 at 4,000 feet. No road-passes are sufficiently high to suffer regular snow-blocking, although the Col de la Faucille between St. Claude and Geneva may be intermittently closed. On the other hand summer days are sunny, although continental influences may reveal themselves in considerable August-September rain. Mean July temperatures of 66° F. occur in the southern valleys.

The Jura occupy the greater part of the three *départements* of Doubs, Jura and Ain, although the western part of the last extends into the Plaine de Bresse. However, the official returns for these three *départements* are indicative of the land-use in the Jura generally.

Land-Use, 1963

(Percentages of Total Area)

Department	Arable	Pasture	Woodland
Doubs . .	26	34	34
Jura . .	27	26	32
Ain . .	28	29	22

Source: *Ministère de l'Agriculture*, published in *Annuaire statistique de la France, 1964.*

Woodland.—Woodland covers approximately one-third of the Jura. Indeed, the characteristic landscape of the *Hautes Chaînes* comprises steep sides of the *monts* swathed with dark conifers (notably spruce), interrupted by near vertical limestone cliffs too steep to support vegetation, rising from the fresh green meadows in the *vaux*. In some of the gorges, such as the Loue, where the river has cut deeply into horizontal strata of varying resistance, a striking alternation is apparent between tree-clad terraces and precipitous limestone walls. Many parts of the Plateau Jura have been planted with blocks of conifers. Deciduous trees increase on the lower slopes—beech, mountain-ash, plane, maple and (particularly in the south) sweet chestnut and oak. On lower slopes and in the valleys patches of green meadow-land alternate with clumps of trees, forming the pleasant landscape known as the *pré-bois*. The State is not an important owner of forests; in fact only 4 per cent of the woodlands in the *département* of Doubs and 13 per cent in Jura are state owned. It is estimated that 15,000 private proprietors own small 'parcels' of woodland in Jura and nearly as many in Doubs. Most of the remaining woodland is the property of the communes, as much as 68 per cent of the total in Doubs.

Agriculture.—Though there is a varied agricultural life, the emphasis in the Jura is on pastoral activities. Many of the valleys and depressions contain tolerable soils; sometimes Jurassic marls appear in depressions on the plateau, Lower Cretaceous clays in the *vaux*, boulder-clay in the *combes* and recent alluvium along the valley-floors, and these carry a detailed patch-work of cultivation. Along the rivers, stretches of water-meadow afford one and sometimes two crops of hay for winter-feed; some are irrigated by a network of artificial channels. They are succeeded away from the rivers by strips of cultivation, many small scattered 'parcels' growing wheat and oats, potatoes, turnips and other vegetables, and maize and tobacco in the south. Local specialisations include the cultivation of peas near Frasne, cauliflowers around Hautepierre, herbs for the distillation of liqueur at Pontarlier, and flowers for perfume between Culoz and Seyssel. Then on the slopes are orchards of apples, plums, medlars and cherries; fruit is also grown along the sides of the roads. Peaches and even figs are cultivated in favoured places, particularly in the basin of Belley.

Vineyards cover a considerable area of the more favoured south-facing slopes. Admittedly the Jura are not an outstanding wine-producing district, although grapes have been grown since at least the tenth century. The region was badly affected by phylloxera in the late nineteenth century, and the area under vines is now only a sixth of that in 1868. Not much quality wine is produced, though *Château-Chalon, l'Etoile, Salins, Poligny, Menetru, Conliège* and a few others have a more than local reputation. *Arbois* is a rich golden wine of long renown,[1] produced around the little town of that name (where Louis Pasteur lived and died) in the valley of the Cuisance, which flows to the Loue and so to the Doubs. The *département* of Ain has a considerable output of *vin ordinaire* on the north-western slopes of the Revermont, although here large areas of vineyards have been abandoned during the last twenty years.

Most of this Jura agriculture then is of a subsistence character, a *petite culture*, pleasant, comfortable, varied, and in places quite specialised. It is, however, concentrated in the valleys and in the depressions, for on the higher surfaces of the plateaus there is naturally little cultivation, merely rough grazing and plantations of conifers.

The chief agricultural emphasis is on dairying; in the three *départements* in 1963 were 379,000 head of dairy cattle out of a total of 602,000 cattle of all kinds; most of them consist of the red and white '*race tachetée du Jura*'. Before 1914 cattle-rearing was restricted to the high pastures (the *alpages*), often owned in common by members of a valley-commune, for little of the valley-floor could be spared for grazing. These upland pastures are still used, indeed much has been considerably improved by fertilisers, but the pastoral economy is now emphasised in the valleys as well, where about half the arable was converted between the wars into pasture (the *parcs*) lying near each village. Moreover, there has been greater concentration on fodder-crops (oats, beet, trefoil) and on the improvement of hay-meadows. Between the wars, as a result, the output of milk in the Jura doubled. Transhumance is still practised, families taking the animals up to the *alpages* from May to September, but many cattle are now kept permanently in the valleys.

Some of the milk is destined for chocolate factories at Geneva, Pontarlier and Morteau, and much is consumed in liquid form in

[1] R. Dion, 'Le Vin d'Arbois au Moyen-Age', in *A. de G.* (1955), vol. lxiv, pp. 162-9.

towns such as Montbéliard and Besançon or sent further afield to Lyons and even to Paris. But the chief product is cheese, and the term '*Gruyère*' had been applied to Jura produce for centuries. These magnificent cheeses are made in small dairy-chalets, in larger *fromageries*, and in recent years at factories in Pontarlier, Dole and Lons. Some highly organised co-operative societies (*fruitières*) have been developed, which collect the milk, deliver it to the *fromageries*, and then sell cheese to the merchants. Improvements have been effected in technique, as shown by the work of the *Ecoles Nationales d'Industrie Laitière* at Poligny and at Mamirolle. *Gruyère* is not the only Jura cheese, although pre-eminent; there are the delicate blue-veined '*bleu de Jura*' and '*bleu de Gex*', the 'parsley-cheese' ('*fromage persillé*)', and goats'-milk cheeses ('*chevrets*'). Other dairying industries include the production of processed cream-cheeses, cream, butter (notably at two large factories at Loulans-les-Forges and at Arc-et-Senans), and casein for some local industries. Pigs are fed on skim-milk returned from the factories to the farmers, and poultry are bred in huge numbers, particularly in the Ain valley, where these poultry-farms are on a considerable scale, rearing birds for the Paris and other markets. But the production of cheese has been justly called '*la première richesse du Jura*'.

POWER AND INDUSTRY

Power.—The industries of the Jura have long made use of water-power; the tumbling streams were harnessed to drive water-mills to provide power for saw-mills, grain-mills and lathes. But the development of hydro-electric power has gone on apace in France, especially since 1946 under the nationalised *Electricité de France*. Before 1939 only a few small stations were in operation in the Jura, including two on the Ain and several on the Rhône and the Doubs. Since then France's biggest hydro-station has been built on the Rhône below Bellegarde at Génissiat,[1] the famous *Léon Perrier* undertaking (Fig. 130), by the Government-sponsored public corporation, the *Compagnie Nationale du Rhône*, established in 1934 as a multi-purpose planning authority for the development of hydro-electricity, navigation and irrigation along the river. The *val* below Bellegarde offered an obvious site for a reservoir, and work began in 1937. The first task was to drive a tunnel parallel to the river as a temporary by-pass, and a coffer-dam was built at the diversion to enable construction to proceed in the dry bed. In 1939 the Rhône was diverted

[1] A. Blanchard, 'Les Travaux de la Compagnie Nationale du Rhône: Génissiat, Donzère', in *R.G.A.* (1950), vol. 38, pp. 189-92. It must be noted, however, that although the installed capacity of Génissiat is greater than that of Donzère, the output of the latter is usually appreciably higher.

into this tunnel, but in 1940, on the fall of France, the coffer-dam was opened and the site flooded. In 1942 the Germans allowed work to be continued and the immense project went forward until the completion in 1948 of the main barrage. The river was returned to its bed, and water backed-up behind the barrage almost to Bellegarde to form a fourteen-mile long reservoir. The installed capacity of the main power-house is 405,000 kw, with an output of 1·72 milliard kwh out of a French hydro total (1963) of 43·6 milliard kwh. A smaller plant of 45,000 kw capacity was opened in 1952 downstream at Seyssel. The Génissiat plant is linked to the main French grid; a 220 kv line and a more recent 380 kv line run direct to Paris via Vielmoulin and Creneye. It represents a major achievement in the overall Rhône plan; in fact, with the other new stations (see p. 397), the French have already harnessed over half of the Rhône's potential. Apart from the Génissiat and Seyssel stations, plants of smaller capacity are in operation along the Rhône at Chancy-Pougny, Champrion, Culoz, Lucey, La Balme, Brégnier and Sault-Brenaz in order downstream. The station at Cusset, on the Rhône above Lyons, has been enlarged in recent years, and produced 430 million kwh in 1963.

Industry.—What are commonly called '*les petites industries du Jura*' make an appreciable contribution to the economy.[1] They are legacies of long-established 'chalet industries', which occupied winter leisure and still afford on a piece-work basis a useful supplementation of the family incomes. Although still organised in small specialised units, industry is now, however, more concentrated in the many towns and villages, using electric power.

It must be remembered, however, that the distinction between industrial and agricultural employment is difficult to define, indeed, there is much seasonal work in both spheres.

Industry is extremely varied, and includes the activities associated with agricultural products, such as the factory-manufacture of cheese, butter, cream and casein, the distillation of various liqueurs (absinthe, *Pernod*, plum- and cherry-brandy), brewing at Besançon, the production of chocolate, and the processing of tobacco. Several small metallurgical works are still active, which once derived their ores from Liassic strata in the valleys of the Doubs at Laissey, the Loue at Lods and Ornans, and the Ain at Champagnole, their fuel from charcoal, their power from running water; the place-names Ferrière and Forges bear testimony to the antiquity of these iron-works. Today the industry survives in steel-foundries at Pontarlier and Bellegarde, forges at Champagnole, rolling-mills at Syam,

[1] A. Mathieu, 'Les Petites Industries de la montagne dans le Jura français', in *A. de G.* (1929), vol. xxxviii, pp. 439-59.

wire-mills at Lods and Vuillafans, and nail- and bolt-factories at l'Ile-sur-Doubs, Ornans, Jougne and Clerval. Larger-scale engineering is concentrated on the Jura margins, particularly at Montbéliard, which manufactures a variety of engineering products—cars (at the huge *Peugeot* works in the suburbs of Sochaux, employing 12,500 workers), aircraft, cycles, textile machinery, machine-tools and agricultural implements. Besançon too has engineering works. Both these centres derive much labour from rural communes, work-people travelling daily from villages in the Montagnes du Lomont.

The Triassic salt-beds along the north-western flanks of the uplands in the neighbourhood of Salins, Grozon and Montmorot have been the basis of a flourishing salt-trade since the Middle Ages. It has declined in importance, but salt is still extracted by brine pumping at Poligny, from which a pipe-line runs north-west to the *Solvay* works at Dole. About 40,000 tons of salt are produced each year, employing 250 workers. Limestone is quarried at several places for building-stone, notably an attractive free-stone with rose-coloured veins in the Rhône valley between St. Genix and Lagnieu. Cement is manufactured at Villebois and Bellegarde in the Rhône valley, and at Villette and Champagnole in the Ain valley. Lime is worked and crushed for agricultural and other purposes.

Wood-using industries have long been established, now centred at St. Claude in the valley of the Bienne. For centuries workshops in the neighbourhood manufactured buckets, tubs and vats, tool-handles, wooden utensils, clock-cases, cheese-presses and furniture. One specialisation is the carving of rosaries and religious statuettes, for which St. Claude became famous in the eighteenth century, as also for the fashionable carved snuff-boxes. Another item comprises pipes for smokers, originally made from box-wood growing on the Jura slopes, now from cherry wood or heath-roots (*bruyère*) imported from Corsica, Algeria and the eastern Pyrenees; the pipes of St. Claude have a world-wide reputation. In addition to these specialised wood-using industries, larger scale manufactures include butter- and cheese-boxes, furniture, ladders and wine-casks, and a large amount of sawn timber and pit-props is sent away.

The development of these varied industries has led to the introduction of others requiring similar techniques, but with different media. The manufacture of articles in bone and horn in the nineteenth century has developed into similar activities using celluloid, casein and plastics, making combs, toilet articles such as hand-mirror frames, electrical apparatus and fountain-pens. Small centres such as Oyonnax, Moirans, Arinthod, Bois d'Amont, Mouthe, Long-chaumois and La Rixouse contain these specialised factories, employing in all over 7,000 men and women.

Watch- and clock-making, so famous in the Swiss Jura, was introduced into France in the mid-seventeenth century by refugees from Geneva who settled at Morez, Morbier and Perrigny in the valley of the upper Bienne. The small towns of the Pays de Gex manufacture individual watch parts, still sent into Geneva for assembly. In 1793 watch-making was introduced into Besançon, and today this has become the chief individual centre, with a number of factories. About 14,000 workers are engaged in the watch- and clock-industry in the Jura region. Another specialisation is the cutting and polishing of precious stones, both for watches and for jewellery.[1] Workshops are engaged in this industry in the Pays de Gex, in the hills between the rivers Valserine and Bienne (where Septmoncel is the centre), and at St. Claude and Morez. Aspects of the glass industry include the manufacture of spectacles and watch-glasses at Lons-le-Saunier and Morez.

In the extreme south of the Jura, in the district of Bugey, the industrial influence of Lyons makes itself felt, and the electric power available in the Rhône valley is utilised by the textile industry. Thrown-silk and silk thread are made in small factories at Argis, St. Rambert, Ambérieu and Pont-d'Ain, silk cloth is woven at Nantua, Bellegarde and Maillat, linen at Belley, lace and net at Ambérieu and Nantua. Similarly, the influence of Mulhouse has spread into the northern Jura and textile factories are active in Besançon, producing mainly rayon, hosiery and cotton-elastic fabrics.

The Jura therefore is an industrial area of some importance and interest, partly the result of long-established local skills and specialisations and partly the influence of three neighbouring industrial regions—southern Alsace, the Swiss Plateau and the Lyons district, from each of which people and ideas have migrated to the Jura at various times. A few marginal towns—Besançon and Montbéliard in the north-west, Lons-le-Saunier in the west—have grown into larger industrial centres; their factories have drawn workers from both agriculture and from domestic industry, and the development of the grid has enabled power to be utilised on a large scale. The industries which are aptly called '*de luxe ou de demi-luxe*' still employ 40,000 workers, or a quarter of the total industrial personnel.

POPULATION AND SETTLEMENT

Population is remarkably dispersed throughout the Jura, though with concentrations in the valleys and scanty areas on the forested

---

[1] P. Antoine, 'L'Industrie de la pierre précieuse dans le Jura', in *A. de G.* (1949), vol. lviii, pp. 126-31.

plateau and along the *monts*.[1] Much of the plateau has a density of less than fifty per square mile, and the only town there is Pontarlier (16,205 people), lying in a depression crossed by the Doubs. The towns of the western Jura are situated on its margins—in the Doubs valley where stand the industrial centres of Besançon (101,729 people) and Montbéliard (23,374), and at the foot of the Vignoble-Revermont escarpment, notably Lons-le-Saunier (18,757) and Bourg. Besançon formed one of Louis XIV's frontier fortresses, for it lies to the west of one of France's main eastern gateways, the Porte de Bourgogne. The Doubs at that point makes a bend of almost 300 degrees, leaving a meander-spur with a precipitous 'neck' where Vauban built one of his then near-impregnable fortresses ; it was later necessary to tunnel right through this neck to afford passage for the Rhône-Rhine Canal. This tunnel is to be enlarged for the new *Grand Canal du Rhône au Rhin* (see p. 312). Many small villages are situated at considerable altitudes ; the highest are Lajoux (3,871 feet) and Septmoncel (3,855 feet), the latter of which produces a local speciality, a delightful blue cheese.

Although the Folded Jura would seem less propitious for settlement, with its lofty wooded ridges and steep slopes, nevertheless its population is considerably greater than that of the Plateau Jura, over 150 per square mile in many parts. Settlement is concentrated in the valleys where small but prosperous towns and villages have grown up—St. Claude, Oyonnax, Bellegarde, Belley and many more. They have a distinct charm, and many are examples of what the French guide-books call *villes gracieuses*. St. Claude and Oyonnax have populations exceeding 10,000, the others are smaller—Belley with 6,400 and Bellegarde with 6,716 people are typical. The villages are centres of a flourishing and varied agriculture with some local industry, the towns of an equally varied industrial life. Finally, the Jura, with their hills and valleys, forests and meadows, rivers and lakes, and in fact their general charm, attract large numbers of visitors.

The upland arc of the Jura does not attain any great altitude, but its succession of parallel ridges and *vaux* make it quite difficult to cross transversely. In spite of these physical difficulties, the Jura afford major passage-ways between central France and the Swiss Plateau, and beyond to Italy, Austria and the Balkans. Several important trans-continental lines run south-eastward from Basel, Belfort and Dijon. Two lines from Basel traverse the north-eastern wing of the Jura arc to the Aar valley at Brugg and Olten. The Belfort line crosses the frontier at Delle, and negotiates the Folded

---

[1] Some interesting features of the Franco-Swiss frontier region are discussed by S. Daveau, *Les Régions frontalières de la Montagne jurassienne : étude de géographie humaine* (1959).

Jura by means of the Grenchenberg tunnel, thus reaching Solothurn. The Dijon line runs south-east via Dole to Frasne, there diverging; one line continues through Pontarlier to Neuchâtel, the other branch penetrates the main ranges by the Mont d'Or tunnel, built in 1915, and crosses the frontier further south at Vallorbe for Lausanne and Martigny. In the south a line from Bourg follows a difficult route through Haut-Bugey, crossing the Ain by the lofty Viaduc de Cize-Bolozon, so via St. Rambert to Culoz. From there one line continues north along the right bank of the Rhône to Geneva, the other goes south to Aix-les-Bains, the French Alpine resorts, and via the Mont Cenis tunnel to Turin. These lines were expensive to build; tunnels, cuttings, viaducts and avalanche galleries are required, but they are important international route-ways and carry a heavy tourist traffic.

The Jura road-system is remarkably adequate. There are three main-road passes, Les Verrières (2,500 feet) between Pontarlier and Neuchâtel, the Col de St. Cergue (4,051 feet) from Les Rousses to Nyon, and the Col de la Faucille (4,331 feet), between St. Claude and Geneva. These passes may be intermittently blocked by snow in the winter, usually on the Swiss side, but rarely for any length of time. Many minor roads and light railways penetrate the hills to link up the small towns and villages.

CHAPTER 22

THE FRENCH ALPS

The mountainous region of south-eastern France between Lake Geneva and the Mediterranean forms part of the fold-mountain system of the Alps, which sweeps in a curve around the western and northern margins of the North Italian Plain. The frontiers of France, Switzerland and Italy meet at a pinnacle on the summit-ridge of Mont Dolent, in the north-east of the Mont Blanc massif. From this point the Franco-Italian frontier runs away southward, following the main watershed between the tributaries of the Rhône and those of the Po. This leaves four-fifths of this part of the Alps, 120 miles in overall width, within France. Because these uplands receive heavy precipitation on their western slopes they carry extensive snow-fields and numerous glaciers, which are of much more limited extent on the Italian side of the ranges.

GENERAL FEATURES [1]

The Alps are primarily the result of mid-Tertiary earth-movements which upfolded vast thicknesses of Mesozoic and Tertiary sediments; these had accumulated in the geosyncline between the ancient Hercynian foreland of Europe and the plateau-continent of Africa. The direction, nature and degree of this folding depended both on the compressive forces affecting the geosyncline and the positions of the rigid 'outer horsts' of the Hercynian continent—the Central Massif, the Vosges, the Black Forest and the Bohemian Plateau. The outer margins of the folded zone, affected only superficially, are represented by the Jura and further south by the limestone Fore-Alps which lie east of the Rhône valley. Within the main orogenic zone the folding was exceedingly complex, involving the formation of recumbent folds and the carrying forward of several series of *nappes*, that is, overthrust masses that have been forced far away from their 'roots'. One series of these nappes comprises the Pre-Alps, most of which are in Switzerland to the east of Lake Geneva, but one group to the south of the lake lies mostly in France. Of the six major nappes which are developed so well in the Pennine ranges of the Swiss-Italian Alps, one (the Great St. Bernard nappe) is extensively represented in the French Alps.

[1] R. Blanchard, *Les Alpes occidentales* (1944–56), is a monumental work in twelve volumes, dealing in great detail with each part of the French Alps. See also, by the same author, *Les Alpes et leur destin* (1958).

Involved in the folds, which consist mainly of metamorphosed sedimentary rocks, are several blocks of crystalline rock, the so-called 'inner horsts', which represent portions of the 'splintered edge' of the Hercynian continent overwhelmed by and caught up in the folding. Other crystalline masses may represent the deep-seated cores of the folds, or they may be batholithic intrusions over-run by the folds. In either case, these crystalline rocks have been exhumed in places by long-continued denudation.

One other structural complication has affected the southern part of the Alps. The earlier earth-movements which produced the Pyrenees, probably in late Eocene times, induced a west–east direction in these fold-systems, what the French geomorphologists call 'la direction pyrénéenne', in contrast to the predominant north-south trend of the French Alps. The ranges of Lower Provence, although separated from the main Pyrenean region by the Golfe du Lion and the lower Rhône valley, are a structural continuation of the Pyrenees. The same west-east trend is revealed in the Provençal Alps and in the southern sections of the Fore-Alps (Baronnies, Ventoux, Lure, Luberon), spurs of which project into the Rhône valley. The zone of contact in the south-east between the Pyrenean and Alpine trends is therefore complex.

The rocks of which the Alps are composed are thus of great diversity. Granite, gneiss and crystalline schists form the Hercynian massifs; Cretaceous and some Jurassic limestones, together with Tertiary *Flysch* sandstones and marls comprise the outer zone of the Fore-Alps; while in the inner folded zone appear Carboniferous, Permian and a wide range of Mesozoic and Tertiary rocks. What is more, many of these have been metamorphosed into schistose rocks of quite different character; these notably include the *schistes lustrés*, for the most part metamorphosed Secondary rocks. The varied rocks have been intensely modified through long-sustained denudation, for the diverse nature of the rocks has allowed differential weathering full scope in producing the present land-forms.

The prime fact about the major drainage systems (Fig. 133) is that they have developed across the longitudinal structural zones, for the frontier-ridge forms the main watershed between the west-flowing drainage to the Rhône and the east-flowing Po tributaries. In their transverse sections across the structures, the rivers have adjusted their courses wherever possible to belts of less resistant rock, sometimes utilising portions of the various longitudinal zones, and emphasising the more resistant rocks. Two rivers, the Isère and the Durance, have become the master-streams; between them they drain all the French Alps, except for a small part in the north which drains by the Arve, and another area in the south which drains directly to the Mediterranean by way of the Var. Most of the

FIG. 132.—STRUCTURAL DIVISIONS OF THE FRENCH ALPS.

The divisions are described in the text, under the following headings: **I**, The Fore-Alps, together with the Pre-Alps of Chablais; **II**, The Sub-Alpine Furrow, including the '*Pays de la moyenne Durance*'; **III**, The Hercynian Massifs; and **IV**, The Sedimentary Zone of the High Alps, including the upper valleys of the Isère, Arc and Durance.

The abbreviations are as follows: **A.R.**, Aiguilles Rouges; **M.B.**, Mont Blanc; **G.R.**, Grandes Rousses; **T.**, Taillefer.

The extension of the Mont Blanc massif into Italy and Switzerland and that of Mercantour into Italy are indicated.

tributaries of these rivers consist of immature torrents and cascades, frequently flowing in gorges. The steep gradients, heavy precipitation, considerable snow-melt and torrential runoff over the crystalline

FIG. 133.—GENERAL MAP OF THE FRENCH ALPS.

rocks combine to make the rivers powerful agents of sculpture. They bring down loads of rock-waste, most of which ultimately reaches the Rhône valley. The evidence of the ravages of these mountain torrents is everywhere ; hillsides are gashed with gullies and there are rock-slopes from which surface material has been scoured. Deforestation has accelerated this process, particularly in the southern Alps. Considerable areas consist of limestone, notably in the Fore-Alps, and as a result complex underground drainage systems have developed.

A second contribution to the physical landscape is the work of glaciation. In Quaternary times, the High Alps nurtured much more extensive snow-fields and glaciers than exist today (Fig. 134). During the maximum Riss stage the glaciers pushed their way well down into the Rhône valley, probably even to the west of Lyons, for erratics have been found within that city. The whole of Bas-Dauphiné was probably covered by a converging piedmont-glacier. In the later Würm stages, when the ice-covering was thinner and less extensive, differential erosion was more pronounced.

The glaciers left a marked impress on the relief, notably in the form of over-deepened trough-like valleys in which the present rivers are clearly misfits. The *cluses* separating the individual Fore-Alpine massifs were widened and deepened by glaciers which used the narrow pre-glacial gorges as exits. They produced all the other familiar features of upland glaciation—cirques (often known as *combes* in this region), hanging-valleys, rock-steps and valley-benches. These benches, occurring at different heights as the glaciers diminished in size, are given various local names, such as *plans*, *planets*, *replats* and *replatons*. The differing levels of surface of the valley-glaciers are also demonstrated by clear-cut cols which represent glacial exit-channels (*seuils de transfluence*) at different altitudes. Examples include the Col des Montets between the Chamonix and Trient valleys, the Col des Gets between the Dranse and the Giffre (an Arve tributary), the Col de Megève between the Arve and the Arly, the Col de Faverge (or de Tamie) between the Annecy and Isère valleys, and the broad Chambéry valley. Many other cols, particularly in the high frontier-ridges, are the familiar result of 'back to back' cirque recession.

While upland glaciation is primarily erosional in its effects, some boulder-clay was deposited in the valleys. Crescentic moraines are apparent far below the ends of the present glacier-snouts ; in the Chamonix valley, for example, well-defined moraines lie athwart the valley near Les Tines, through which the Arve has cut a gorge in which the boulder-clay is clearly displayed.

In the highest massifs, notably Mont Blanc, the Vanoise and the Pelvoux, snow-fields and glaciers (Fig. 134) still cover an aggregate area of about 200 square miles. Though much shrunken in comparison with those of Quaternary times, they afford attractive ingredients in the Alpine landscape.

The varied rocks present different responses to weathering. The

FIG. 134.—PAST AND PRESENT GLACIATION IN THE FRENCH ALPS.

The major snowfields and glaciers at the present time are found in the Mont Blanc region (M.B.), the Vanoise (V) and the Pelvoux (P).

Based on (i) E. de Martonne, *Les Alpes* (1926), p. 42 ; and (ii) *Atlas de France* (1939), plate 10.

massive granite of Mont Blanc, with its prominent vertical joints, weathers into steep buttresses and clean-cut pinnacles or *aiguilles*. The shales and metamorphosed schists form crumbling ridges, flanked by scree-slopes, the product of potent frost-shattering. Limestone results in a diverse relief of sharp crests, barren plateaus, vertical cliffs, steep-sided gorges and deep chasms. In the south, where the Mediterranean aridity becomes increasingly marked, karstic features are widespread.

The climatic range between the northern and southern ends of the French Alps has resulted in pronounced differences in both landscape and economy. In the north are snow-fields and glaciers, dark pine woods, fresh green Alpine meadows and ribbons of agriculture running along the valleys. In the south are semi-arid limestone plateaus and scarps, with scrub-like vegetation in the higher parts and chestnut woods and olive-groves on the lower slopes. As the shores of the Côte d'Azur are approached there is an almost sub-tropical appearance, with the exotic vegetation of mimosa, oleander, palm and bougainvillaea. A remarkable transition appears southward in the dominant tones of the landscape—a fresh greenness in Savoy, sombre browns in Dauphiny, and harsh greys, dazzling whites and dusty greens in the southern Alps.

Agriculture shows this same contrast. In the north and centre, specialised pastoral industries are based on cattle, utilising both the valley-floors and the seasonal alp-pastures,[1] while forest industries are important, especially in the heavily wooded Fore-Alpine massifs. Further south sheep are kept on the patchy upland pastures of the limestone, although not to the same extent as in the past, and an indication of a near-Mediterranean economy is afforded by the cultivation of small plots of hard wheat, maize, almonds and olives.

Nor is agriculture the sole or even the dominant aspect of the economy. The development of hydro-electricity has not only contributed to France's power supplies, but has helped some of the valleys to become important industrial areas, forming a kind of linear industrialisation. Electro-chemical and electro-metallurgical factories have been established in the upper valleys of the Isère and the Arc, while Grenoble dominates the textile, glove and other industries of the middle Isère valley.

Finally, the whole region from the shores of Lake Geneva to the Riviera forms a popular and prosperous tourist area, both in summer and winter, capitalising the assets of a most attractive mountain landscape. These two extremities are linked by the 375 miles long *Route des Alpes*, one of the finest series of mountain roads in Europe. The high passes are crossed and the lonely valleys are penetrated by motor-

[1] Ph. Arbos, *La Vie pastorale dans les Alpes françaises* (1922) is the classic work on this subject.

roads, and hotels are found in the most remote districts. The mountaineering and winter-sports' centres of Chamonix and La Grave contrast with the pleasant leisurely spas of Evian, Aix and Annecy. The various names bestowed upon different parts of the French Alps are legion. The two old provincial names, Savoy (*Savoie*) and Dauphiny (*Dauphiné*), are still used to designate the northern and central Alps respectively, and the former is perpetuated in the two *départements* of Savoie and Haute-Savoie. Other regional names have been bestowed upon various groups of the mountain ranges, such as the Graian, Cottian, Provençal and Maritime Alps. Individual upland blocks, separated by deep valleys, each have their distinctive names, as marked on Fig. 132. Several of the glacially-widened troughs, where so much of the life of the Alps is concentrated, form valley-*pays*. These include the *Tarentaise*,[1] the *Combe de Savoie* and the *Grésivaudan*, three distinct sections of the upper and middle Isère valley; the *Maurienne*,[1] the long curving valley of the Arc; the *Briançonnais* and the *Embrunais* of the upper Durance; and the *Faucigny* of the Arve valley. Many of these were once administrative units; thus the Maurienne and the Tarentaise were episcopal republics.

It is convenient to describe the French Alps in more detail under their four main structural divisions. These comprise (i) the Fore-Alpine limestone zone to the west (including the small area of Pre-Alps to the south of Lake Geneva); (ii) a longitudinal depression known as the Sub-Alpine Furrow; (iii) a discontinuous series of arcuate crystalline massifs; and (iv) the main sedimentary zone along the Franco-Italian frontier (Fig. 132).

THE FORE-ALPINE LIMESTONE ZONE

A more or less continuous zone of Jurassic and Cretaceous rocks extends from Lake Geneva to the Mediterranean coast near Monaco. This zone of gentle folds follows for the most part the north-south trend of the High Alps. In the south, however, the trend assumes more of a west-east nature as it becomes involved with the mountain-structures of Provence. As a result, this zone, which varies between twelve and twenty miles as far south as the Drôme valley, widens to sixty miles or more in the south.

Both the terms 'fore-Alpine' and 'pre-Alpine' zone are bestowed on this unit as a whole. The latter is, however, unfortunate, since the name 'Pre-Alps' is restricted by L. W. Collet and other geomorphologists to the area of nappes extending from Lake Thun in

[1] H. Onde, *La Maurienne et la Tarentaise: étude de géographie physique* (1938).

Switzerland to Lake Geneva (the Romande Pre-Alps), and continuing south to the Arve valley as the Chablais Pre-Alps. These Pre-Alps involve a varied stratigraphical sequence with a number of thrust-planes, and their origin is far from clear. Since this term Pre-Alps has received general recognition in its geomorphological connotation, it seems desirable to use the alternative form of Fore-Alps for the uplands other than Chablais.

The Chablais Pre-Alps.—The Chablais massif approaches Lake Geneva so closely between Evian and the Swiss frontier that the roadway has been blasted out along the foot of precipitous limestone cliffs, which drop towards the lake from the 7,299-foot summit of the Dent d'Oche. The Chablais consists of a complex series of limestones, sandstones and marls, varying in age from the Upper Triassic to the Oligocene, and much affected by complicated over-thrusts. Even a few exposures of granitic rocks appear in the south of this upland, an indication that the Hercynian basement was involved.

The Chablais has been eroded into a maze of limestone ridges and peaks over 8,000 feet, alternating with narrow valleys cut in the marls and more open basins in the sandstones. The Dranse, rising in the south-east of the upland, flows right across the north-east to south-west grain, so producing a most spectacular valley. Below St. Jean d'Aulph the stream crosses the heart of the Chablais in a series of magnificent gorges, where steep wooded slopes alternate with sheer limestone cliffs—the Défilé des Tines, the Gorges du Diable, the Défilé de la Garde and the Gorges de la Dranse. Then the Dranse suddenly enters the narrow plain bordering Lake Geneva, and the extent of its eroding powers is demonstrated by the lacustrine delta of shingle and sand which it is building out into Lake Geneva. To the west the uplands descend irregularly in a maze of wooded ridges towards the plain which borders the western wing of Lake Geneva.

The Giffre Massif.—The south-western part of the Chablais Pre-Alps is sometimes distinguished (as by R. Blanchard [1]) as the Massif du Giffre. The two are separated by a zone of Flysch rocks in which the Giffre has worn its valley. This upland area is also complex; part at least was carved out of the Nappe de Morcles-Aravis, one of the most westerly nappes of the High Calcareous Alps, forced over the Aiguilles Rouges granite. The upland, dissected by the rivers Giffre and the Diosaz, culminates in the ridge of the Buet (10,200 feet), which runs northward, followed by the frontier, into the Dent

[1] R. Blanchard, *Les Alpes occidentales*, vol. i, *Les Préalpes françaises du nord* (1944), pp. 63-102.

du Midi group on the western side of the Rhône between Martigny and Lake Geneva.

Although the western part of the Giffre massif, overlooking the Arve valley, is densely wooded, much of the central and eastern uplands consist of rather desolate limestone. The Désert de Platé comprises an area of four square miles of fissured limestone plateau, almost bare of vegetation. The impress of past glaciation is shown by the numerous *combes* in which usually lie small lakes, morainic mounds and scattered erratics. The Giffre itself rises in the immense Cirque du Fer-à-Cheval to the north-east of Sixt, surrounded by a thousand-foot half-circle of steep crags, down which fall numerous torrents. The floor of this cirque is an infilled lake-basin, indeed the name Plan du Lac indicates this. A few small permanent snow-fields and glaciers include the Glaciers des Baux, du Mont Ruan, de Prazon and du Cheval Blanc, but they only cover about two square miles.

The Fore-Alpine Massifs.—The zone of the Fore-Alpine massifs has been divided by the river-valleys into several well-defined units. The most northerly is the *Genevois*, overlooking the town of Geneva and the Rhône valley below the lake; the higher central part is known specifically as the Plateau des Bornes, while in the east is the Chaîne des Aravis culminating in Mont Charvin at 7,920 feet. Next to the south is the *Bauges*, to the east of the depression in which lies the Lac du Bourget; this triangular upland is reminiscent of the Jura, though rather higher. The diamond-shaped *Grande Chartreuse* massif is tucked within the angle of the Isère valley to the north of Grenoble, and further to the south-west across that valley lies the *Vercors*, a rugged limestone plateau. The *Dévoluy* massif, crowned by the prominent Obiou (9,164 feet), rises to the south of the Drac, an area of desolate rugged limestone and sandstone; the name of the long serrated crest of the Crêt des Aiguilles is descriptive. Further south the lower course of the Durance lies across the widest extension of the Fore-Alpine zone, and there is a whole series of these limestone uplands—*Diois*[1] and *Ventoux* which flank the Rhône valley, *St. Christol*, *Lure* and *Luberon*. Here are rocky peaks rising to over 6,000 feet, with rugged ridges known as *barres*, precipitous cliffs, stretches of dreary limestone plateau known as *plans*, and deeply-cut gorges here called *clues*. The Durance and its tributaries, as well as shorter torrential streams which flow directly to the Rhône, have dissected these uplands into numerous rugged blocks. Beyond the middle Durance basin the Cretaceous limestone country continues eastward to the

[1] J. Masseport, *Le Diois, les Baronnies et leur avant-pays rhodanien: étude morphologique* (1960).

Mediterranean Sea beyond the Italian frontier, forming a series of upland masses known generally as the *Alpes de Provence*.

The rocks of the Fore-Alps consist mainly of Secondary lime-stones, with surviving patches of Tertiary marls, clays and sands (the *Flysch*). They have been somewhat superficially folded, in much the same manner as the Jura. The degree of complexity decreases southward; the overthrusts of the Bornes and the Bauges are ultimately replaced by a mere gentle flexuring in the Vercors. The steep slopes of the Granier above Chambéry and of the Neyrier above the Lac d'Annecy also reveal a gentle undulation or flexuring of the strata. These folds are clearly autochthonous, that is, they are now more or less in the position in which the sediments which compose them were laid down.

The summits are usually of Lower Cretaceous limestones, some-times (where denudation is less well advanced) of Upper Jurassic limestone. Occasionally the broken limb of an anticline stands out as a prominent rock-peak, or the remains of a syncline forms a saddle-like summit or a flat-topped eminence with precipitous slopes. Thus, for example, in the Chartreuse are the Alpette and the Chamechaude (the latter of 6,834 feet is the highest point in the group), both dis-tinct fragments of synclines. One of the most remarkable peaks is Mont Aiguille (6,880 feet) in the Vercors, overlooking the Drac valley. It has a broad pasture-covered summit, surrounded by 400 feet of steep rocks rising from swathing scree-slopes. Though for long known as 'Mont Inaccessible', its challenge is so obvious that it was first climbed as early as 1492 by a party at the behest of Charles VIII of France, using, so it is related, '*subtilz engins*'. Hun-dreds of other fantastic peaks can be seen in the Fore-Alps—obelisks, spires, pyramids, molars, crests, combs and palisades, the '*hautes ruines*' which are the product of the folding, faulting, jointing and extreme denudation of the limestone strata. Some of the ridges (*crêts*) are, however, remarkably continuous. One of the most striking is the Haut-du-Seuil, which forms the eastern edge of the Chartreuse overlooking the Grésivaudan; it runs uninterruptedly for twelve miles at a uniform height of 6,200 feet, rising but slightly to its highest point, the Dent de Crolles (6,776 feet).

Rainfall is heavy in the northern and western Fore-Alps, and river systems are well developed in spite of the extent of the lime-stone, so most of the plateaus are eroded into a chaos of deeply-cut valleys. One of the most impressive gorges is that of the Fier, a stream which flows westwards from the foot of Lac d'Annecy to the Rhône, thus separating the Genevois from the Bauges. The gorge is a water-fretted fissure, nearly 200 feet deep, the walls of which are so narrow that they can be touched from either side. In the uplands further south, where the summer aridity is more pronounced (thus emphasising their karstic character), the concentrated runoff of the intense but short-lived autumn and winter rains has produced a fantastic chaos of gullies and gorges.

Although the presence of Cretaceous marls and clays, exposed when a stream has cut through the overlying limestone, ensures plentiful surface water in the more northerly valleys and depressions, complex subterranean drainage systems have developed, and many powerful resurgences appear on the valley-sides. The sink-holes and cavern-systems form the haunts of French speleologists, some-times descending for hundreds of feet and extending horizontally for miles. The deepest continuous system yet traced and descended is the Gouffre de Berger. This *gouffre* lies on the Plateau de Sornin in the north-east of the Vercors massif, only five miles from Grenoble. In recent years its ramifications have been explored to a depth from the surface of 3,707 feet, 'the world depth record' for any under-ground system.[1] Its passages are traversed by an underground stream, the Germe, which finally appears in the Isère valley through the fantastic labyrinth of the Cuves de Sassenage at the foot of the limestone cliffs. Another system is in the Chartreuse, the famous Trou de Glaz. Its entry is not far from the summit of the Dent de Crolles, the highest point of the Grande Chartreuse overlooking the Grésivaudan, but the resurgence has been traced to the Grotte de Guiers-Mort in the interior of the Chartreuse massif, ten miles away horizontally and 2,160 feet below vertically.[2] These are but two examples of hundreds of cavern-systems, many of which have been explored and mapped.

The Fore-Alps are not high enough to carry permanent snow-fields and glaciers at the present time, except for some tiny ones on the flanks of the Obiou in the Dévoluy, but the impress of glaciation is clear. There are some superb cirques, known in these parts as *combes*. One of the finest is the Combe-Laval in the Vercors, a vast basin with torrent-scored sides, bounded by vertical cliffs of lime-stone alternating with thickly wooded ledges, with scree-slopes below.

THE SUB-ALPINE FURROW

A distinctly continuous depression can be traced for 110 miles between the limestone Fore-Alps on the west and the crystalline

[1] An account of this system and others in the Vercors is given by J. J. Garbier and C. Pommier, 'Explorations au Vercors', in *Annales de Spéléologie* (1955), vol. x, pp. 5-21; and J. Cadoux et al., *One Thousand Metres Down* (1957), translated by R. L. G. Irving from *Opération-1000* (1955).

[2] See P. Chevalier (translated E. M. Hatt), *Subterranean Climbers* (1951); O. Chevalier, 'Le Dent de Crolles souterrain', in *R.G.A.* (1941), vol. 29, pp. 25-31; and J. Masseport, 'Notes morphologiques sur la Chartreuse Septen-trionale', *ibid.* (1953), vol. 41, pp. 115-33.

massifs on the east. This is given several names by French geo-graphers, such as '*la grande dépression intérieure*', or in the phrase of Raoul Blanchard '*le Sillon alpin*'.[1] Its development has been due to the denudation of sedimentary deposits, mostly of Lower Liassic age, as compared with more resistant crystalline rocks to the east and the Cretaceous limestones of the Fore-Alps to the west. The Lias rocks consist in great part of shales, together with outcrops of other equally soft Jurassic marls. Thus while the main drainage lines were developed in a general direction transversely across the Alpine structures, wherever possible the rivers have taken advantage of this zone of less resistance. The furrow is occupied in succession by portions of the Arve and the Arly, then by the Isère from Albert-ville to Grenoble, where it is most clearly developed (Fig. 132). Further south the floor of the trench, lying at a greater altitude, is occupied by the Drac and so is known as the *pays du Drac*. It fades out in the neighbourhood of the Col Bayard, the watershed between the Drac and the Durance. The result of this furrow has been to concentrate the outflow of the drainage of the central French Alps towards the river Isère below Grenoble, through the Cluse de l'Isère.

This *cluse* is one of the four 'gateways' between the Rhône valley and the French Alps; the others are the Cluses de Chambéry, d'Annecy and de l'Arve. The second and third are broad open troughs which are in effect offshoots of the main Alpine furrow, since they are floored in part with the same Lias shales, but neither has any through drainage; in the descriptive French term, each forms '*une cluse morte*'. A low divide occurs near the town of Chambéry in the narrowest part of the *cluse*, between several streams flowing south into the Isère and others flowing north into the Lac du Bourget, eleven miles in length, lying in a glacially overdeepened hollow between steep walls. This hollow continues northward into the extensive marshes of the Rhône valley below Seyssel (see p. 608), but the lake is linked to the Rhône only by the artificial Canal de Savières (Fig. 135). The charming Lac d'Annecy [2] occupies a curving valley between the Genevois and the Bauges massifs, and likewise drains northwards to the Fier and so to the Rhône. The watershed between the south-western end of the Annecy valley and the Combe de Savoie is much more pronounced than in the case of the Chambéry trough, because of a spur of the Bauges projecting north-eastward.

In the north the Arve, rising in the crystalline Mont Blanc massif, breaks through between the Giffre and the Genevois massifs by means

[1] J. Miège, *La Vie rurale du sillon alpin: étude géographique* (1961).

[2] F. Milon, 'Le Lac d'Annecy', in *A. de G.* (1939), vol. xlviii, pp. 120-37; this describes its origin and form, variations of level, temperature of waters, and surrounding settlement.

Fig. 135.—The River Rhône and the Sub-Alpine Depression
near the Lac du Bourget.

The upland areas are indicated generally by stipple. **T**, Tunnel.

The Rhône flows southwards through the flat-floored marshy valley between
the Montagne du Grand Colombier and the Montagne du Gros Foug. It leaves
the Sub-Alpine Depression to the west of the isolated hill on which stands
Vions, and continues southwards through a parallel syncline towards Lucey and
Yenne. The railway runs on high embankments across the floor of the depression
and then skirts the steep slopes which bound Lac du Bourget on the east.

Based on *Carte de France au 50,000ᵉ*, sheet XXXIII/31.

of a prominent gorge, whose character is indicated by the name of the town (Cluses) situated at its mouth. Below Cluses the valley opens out, wide and flat-floored, and the river is braided, with several channels enclosing shingle-banks (Plate LX).

The Pays de Moyenne Durance.—Although this area is not strictly part of *le Sillon alpin*, the basin of the middle Durance,[1] sometimes known as the *Gapençais* in the west and as the *Embrunais* in the east (after the names of the towns of Gap and Embrun), forms a distinct lowland between the Fore-Alpine massif of Dévoluy and the western margins of the Cottian Alps. Much of this lowland consists of what is called '*la plaine caillouteuse de la Durance*', from the sheets of gravel deposited by the Durance where it leaves its upland course.

THE ZONE OF HERCYNIAN MASSIFS

The crystalline massifs lying within the French Alps are shown on Fig. 132. In the north are the massifs of Mont Blanc and the Aiguilles Rouges, the former containing the highest summit in the Alpine system. These crystalline structures are continued southward, although intermittently, by outcrops of Pre-Cambrian gneisses and Hercynian granites in the Massif de Beaufort. The massifs then become more attenuated, forming the arcuate range of the Chaîne de Belledonne, lying to the east of the valley of the Isère. Two smaller adjoining massifs are structurally continuous with the Belledonne: to the east the Grandes Rousses, to the south across the Romanche valley the Taillefer. Then appears the largest individual crystalline mass, that of Pelvoux, culminating in some magnificent peaks and snow-fields. Further south the Mercantour (or Argentera) upland lies across the Franco-Italian frontier. Finally, in the extreme south are Maures and Esterel, the southern edge of which forms the coast between Cannes and the Rades d'Hyères (see p. 420).

The Aiguilles Rouges.—The Aiguilles Rouges form a narrow upland between the valley of the Giffre on the west and the flat-floored Vallée de Chamonix on the east. The latter is an erosion groove cut by river action in Upper Lias shales preserved within a narrow syncline, and enlarged by glaciation into a pronounced U-profile.[2] Morphologically the Aiguilles Rouges are extremely complex. Although the core is composed of granite (exposed in deeply-cut gorges such as that of the Eau Noire near Vallorcine), most of the higher parts consist of gneiss. Flanking the granites and gneisses are

---

[1] P. Veyret, *Les Pays de la moyenne Durance alpestre* (1944), deals in detail with Gap, Embrun, Digne, etc., and their surrounding *pays*.

[2] G. Conard, 'Morphologie de la vallée de Chamonix et de ses abords', in *A. de G.* (1931), vol. xl, pp. 396-410; this includes a detailed morphological map (pp. 398-9).

crystalline schists, the remnants of the sedimentary rocks which covered the old Hercynian ranges. Flanking these again are some Carboniferous deposits : conglomerates (especially near Vallorcine), sandstones and schists. These Carboniferous schists contain anthracite, which was worked for a few years near Coupeau, on the hill-slopes above Les Houches.

The present form of the Aiguilles Rouges is due to sustained denudation. To the main streams which define the massif (the Arve on the east and south, the Diosaz on the west) flow innumerable torrents, mostly taking their rise in tiny snow-fields and glaciers, or in the little lakes. These torrents have furrowed the upland with deep ravines. The culminating ridge of the Aiguilles Rouges is the Brévent, a well-known viewpoint for the Mont Blanc range opposite, falling towards Chamonix in a bold but broken precipice flanked by scree-slopes, then by pine forests. This summit-ridge, ten miles in length, 7,500 feet in height, rises at intervals to prominent rocky crests, the highest of which is the Aiguille de Belvédère (9,731 feet).

The Mont Blanc Massif.—This magnificent mountain mass extends south-westward from the right angle of the Rhône near Martigny for a distance of twenty-five miles, with a maximum width of ten miles. The north-eastern and northern parts of the massif are in Switzerland, the eastern and south-eastern in Italy, the western and north-western in France. The frontier mostly follows the main ridge on the eastern side of the massif, crossing such peaks as the Grandes Jorasses, though the main summit of Mont Blanc is wholly in France (Plate LXI).

Much of the Mont Blanc massif consists of homogeneous granite ; most of the pinnacled peaks (known as *aiguilles*) are carved from this splendid rock. It is, however, flanked in the Chamonix valley and on the corresponding Italian south-eastern slopes by dark-coloured crystalline schists. Moreover, the very highest rocks visible through the snow near the summit of Mont Blanc itself, known as La Tournette, are also of these same dark schists. It is evident, then, that the Mont Blanc massif is of the nature of a batholith, intruded probably in Permian times ; in places the Carboniferous rocks have been clearly metamorphosed along the line of contact. The patches of crystalline schists on the higher parts of the range are surviving fragments of the overlying cover of the batholith, now largely removed, thus exposing the granite.[1] The granite was involved in the Alpine folding movements, and was broken into a series of wedge-shaped slices trending north-east to south-west, while hosts of minor faults were produced.

[1] Details of this complex structure are summarised, with a full bibliography, by. L. W. Collet, *The Structure of the Alps* (1927), pp. 31-45.

Long-continued denudation, involving glaciation, frost-shattering, and the work of the torrents flowing from the snow-fields and glaciers around the margins, has given the massif its present form. There are three distinct elements : the rock-pinnacles and ridges, the snow-fields, and the glaciers. These elements are shown in generalised form on Fig. 136. Viewed from the Aiguilles Rouges on the opposite side of the Chamonix valley, the main line of the rock pinnacles rises above the 'shelf' of the Plan de l'Aiguille at about 7,000 feet, which marks the upper edge of the crystalline schists. Charmoz, Grépon, Blaitière, Plan and dozens more—they project boldly from the rock or ice ridges like a vast serrated comb. If one goes up the Montenvers rack-railway behind this frontal wall of the Aiguilles, many more peaks are revealed, both on the frontier-ridge and on the spurs projecting westward between the glaciers. The incredible spire of the Dent du Géant, the fantastic twin-peaked obelisk of the Dru, the dominating pyramid of the Aiguille Verte, are all carved from the massive jointed clean-cut granite.

The heart of the massif is occupied by the snow-fields. Mont Blanc itself is a snow-hump, reaching 15,782 feet, with snow-slopes falling away steeply on each side ; it might almost be termed a *glacier de calotte*. From the *névés* filling the hollows between the rock-ridges the glaciers move downwards and outwards ; six major and more than twenty minor ones flow towards the Chamonix valley. The largest is the Mer de Glace, deriving its ice-supply from a dozen large cirques in the heart of the massif, and descending to about 3,750 feet above sea-level. Two others, the Glaciers des Bossons and de Bionnassay, descend with remarkable steepness to within a few hundred feet of the Chamonix valley-floor ; the former falls from 12,000 feet to 3,600 feet in only two miles, and so is fantastically crevassed. These glaciers represent a late stage in the glaciation of the massif, the shrunken remnants of the Quaternary ice-sheets, for the whole Vallée de Chamonix must have been filled with ice at one time. The glaciers are still shrinking, as can be seen by examining topographical maps of a century ago ; during this present century the recession has been quite marked. Indeed, in 1949 the Glacier du Tour had become so poorly supplied with ice from above that the rock-bed was visible through the thin ice above the tongue ; this tongue became completely detached and fell as an avalanche in August, unhappily entombing a camp in the valley below. As a result, the glacier in effect 'retreated' fifty yards or so, since the mass of débris soon melted. Many of the former lengthy glaciers are now left hanging high up on the slopes, barely protruding from the cirques, and frequent ice-avalanches fall from them (Plate LXII).

Frost action is very potent at high altitudes among the well-jointed granites, and scree-slopes stream away from the buttresses to move down on the glaciers as morainic burden. The milky glacier-torrents which emerge from the snouts carry huge quantities of

FIG. 136.—PEAKS AND RIDGES OF THE MONT BLANC MASSIF.

The glaciers and snow-fields are shown by light form-lines, the peaks by black triangles, and the major ridges by heavy lines.

The Franco-Italian frontier runs south-westward from Mont Dolent (where the Swiss frontier also converges) along the ridge through the Grandes Jorasses and the Dent du Géant to Mont Blanc.

Ch., Aiguille de Charmoz; **D.**, Dôme; **Gr.**, Aiguille du Grépon; **G.J.**, Grandes Jorasses.

Based on the *Carte Vallot, Tour du Mont-Blanc, Cartes-itinéraires à l'échelle de 1:60,000*, by Charles Vallot.

rock-flour, the final product of glacial disintegration, down to the Arve and beyond. In 1892 the village of St. Gervais-les-Bains was almost destroyed by the torrent issuing from the Glacier de Bionnassay.

A vast volume of water had become ponded up behind the glacier-tongue, which ultimately collapsed, whereupon the water swept down the valley carrying a huge load of rocks; the results can be seen even now in the rock-cone above the village. A tunnel has been hollowed out under the glacier and is carefully maintained so as to allow melt-water to escape freely. Rock-avalanches are continuous, sometimes on an enormous scale, especially among the schists on the flanks.

Below the permanent snow-line are the *alp*-meadows, while the steep sides of the main valleys are thickly wooded with conifers, maintained to provide timber and to act as avalanche-breaks. In the valleys are the tourist resorts, the hotels and pensions of Chamonix itself, Argentière, Les Houches and other attractive places.

The Massif de Beaufort.—To the south-west of Mont Blanc is the much lower Massif de Beaufort, a triangular upland lying to the north of the Tarentaise valley. Most of the surface consists of Pre-Cambrian rocks, but small exposures of granite appear in the valley of the Doron to the east of the little town of Beaufort. Part of the younger cover survives, forming narrow outcrops of Triassic and even Jurassic rocks parallel to the 'grain' of the structure. The massif is not lofty, the highest peak being Le Rognaix (9,876 feet), with no permanent snow-fields and glaciers, but it is dissected into a chaos of ridges by deeply-cut valleys radiating to the Isère and its tributary the Doron.

The Belledonne, Grandes Rousses and Taillefer Massifs.—To the east of the Grésivaudan rises the elongated massif of the Belledonne, the rocks of which mainly consist of gneisses, with some granite outcrops in the north of the range. The Belledonne is not lofty, and its highest point, the Grand-Pic de Belledonne, rises only to 9,781 feet. No permanent glaciers occur, although occasionally patches of snow survive in north-facing gullies and depressions for several years, and winter snowfall is heavy. It is a wild rugged range, deeply scored by mountain torrents, with many *combes* and craggy peaks separated by deeply notched cols. The northern part of the range consists of a maze of ridges and rock-basins containing seven lakes, and it is given the name of the Massif des Sept-Laux.

To the east of the Belledonne, and separated from it by the valley of the Eau d'Olle (deeply cut into a narrow outcrop of Lias shales), is the small massif of the Grandes Rousses, also composed largely of gneissic rocks with some granite. This massif is nearly two thousand feet higher than the Belledonne, and the Pic de l'Etendard has an altitude of 11,385 feet. As a result it carries several small permanent snow-fields and glaciers, notably the Glacier de St.

Sorlin which flows for about three miles to the north-east.

The Taillefer, south of the Romanche valley, forms a long narrow ridge culminating in a main summit at 9,387 feet. It is much dissected by past glaciation and several rocky cirques containing small lakes such as the Lac de l'Emay. Veins of lead and silver ores occur in these crystalline rocks and were worked sporadically in the past; the ruins and spoil-heaps of the Mines de Brouffier are at a height of over 7,500 feet.

The Pelvoux Massif.—To the east of the southern end of the Belledonne is the extensive Pelvoux massif (Fig. 137), almost surrounded by steep-sided valleys to which torrents flow outwards from the heart of the uplands. On the north is the Romanche, on the west and south the Drac, on the east the headstreams of the Durance. Only on the extreme north, at the 6,752-foot high Col du Lautaret, are the perimeter-valleys interrupted. The massif itself has been dissected into a confusion of peaks and ridges, cirques and radial valleys. There are extensive snow-fields, several glaciers (notably the Glacier Blanc, which flows eastwards from the heart of the massif for about three miles), and some magnificent peaks, the highest of which is the serrated comb-like ridge of the Barre des Ecrins (13,452 feet), with a north face consisting of a superb ice-slope. The main summit in the south is the Pelvoux itself (12,944 feet), a massive mountain flanked by steep buttresses rising to an undulating upper plateau from which rocky summits protrude. The northern part of the massif is dominated by La Meije, overlooking the climbing-centre of La Grave in the Romanche valley to the north. Its culminating point is the Grand-Pic de la Meije (13,065 feet), with its rocky south face and ice-draped northern cliffs.

Ecrins, Meije, Pelvoux—these are the principal summits of Dauphiné, but there are hundreds of other granite *pics*, *aiguilles* and *têtes*, and some snow-peaks too, such as the well-named Dôme de Neige and the shapely Pic des Agneaux. The contribution to the Alpine ranges of France, therefore, by the granitic massif of Pelvoux is indeed second only to that of Mont Blanc.

The Mercantour Massif.—To the south-east of the Pelvoux comes an interruption in this series of crystalline massifs for about forty miles, until the Mercantour (or Argentera) massif is reached. Much of this upland lies in Italy; the highest point is the Punta Argentera (10,827 feet). To the east of the Tinée valley (a headstream of the Var), the frontier follows the crest-line of the Mercantour, crossing in succession a series of prominent granite peaks, notably Mont Tenibrés (9,944 feet), the highest summit of this massif within France.

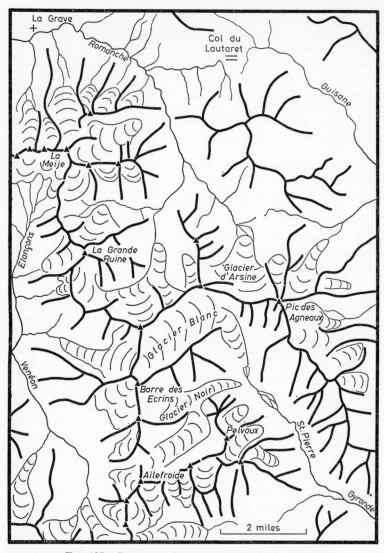

FIG. 137.—PEAKS AND RIDGES OF THE PELVOUX MASSIF.

The glaciers and snowfields are shown by light form-lines, the peaks by black triangles, and the major ridges by heavy lines.

The three main groups of peaks (La Meije, Barre des Ecrins and Pelvoux) are indicated. The complexity of the ridge-lines (*crêts*) and summits (*pics, pointes, aiguilles*) indicates the deep dissection of this crystalline massif.

The Col du Lautaret (one of the celebrated passes for the motorist), at a height of 6,752 feet, is on the watershed between the Romanche (hence to the Isère) and the Durance ; the road links Grenoble in the Isère valley with Briançon in the Durance valley.

Based on *Carte de France au 50,000ᵉ*, sheets XXXIV/35, 36.

THE SEDIMENTARY ZONE OF THE HIGH ALPS

To the east of the crystalline massifs lies the Sedimentary Zone of the High Alps, part of the system of nappes. In the French Alps the Great St. Bernard nappe (number IV in the accepted sequence of the six individuals) is dominant; this is the usual name given by Swiss geomorphologists, although some of the French refer to it as the *nappe du Briançonnais*. It can be traced from the Isère valley near the southern end of the Beaufort massif, through the Vanoise into the Briançon district to the east of the Pelvoux, and then south-eastward on the Italian side of the Mercantour to the Mediterranean Sea near Savona. The nappe is so well developed in the neighbourhood of Briançon in the valley of the upper Durance that this part of the Sedimentary Alps is sometimes referred to as the Briançonnais zone.

A further minor nappe can be distinguished to the west of the Great St. Bernard, known as the *Nappe du Flysch* or *Nappe de l'Embrunais*; it is given the first name because it consists mainly of Tertiary *Flysch* sediments, and the second because it is well developed in the neighbourhood of Embrun. Further south it is known as the *Nappe de l'Ubaye*. Only a narrow vestige of this nappe exists in the north, extending intermittently from the southern end of the Beaufort range southward to the Pelvoux, but it widens out in the Embrunais and the Ubaye and so makes a substantial contribution to the Sedimentary Zone of the Alps.

The rocks in the western part consist for the most part of sandstones, shales and breccias of Eocene age, known collectively as the *Flysch*. Further east appears an outcrop of Upper Carboniferous rocks, which can be traced from the Rhône valley, through the Aosta valley, the Arc valley, and into the Durance valley near Briançon. Some of these Carboniferous strata contain anthracite, worked near La Mure and Avignonnet in the Drac valley, in the Tarentaise and Maurienne valleys, and near Briançon. Mesozoic sediments, especially of Triassic age, include various breccias, dolomitic limestones, and beds of common salt and gypsum. Some narrow outcrops of Jurassic and Cretaceous limestones lie parallel to the 'grain' of the Alpine structures. Finally there are the *Schistes lustrés*, the rocks resulting from sedimentation in the deep parts of the geosyncline, probably of Mesozoic age, but affected by metamorphism since they were so profoundly involved in the folding movements. They overlaid the Great St. Bernard nappe, and so have been largely removed by denudation in the west and centre where the nappe was at its highest, but they still survive in the east. They are found in the French Alps on a large scale only in two districts where the frontier makes distinct bends to the east. These districts form part of the

R.G.W.E.—Y

Graian Alps, in the neighbourhood of the headstreams of the Arc and the Isère, and part of the Cottian Alps in the district of Queyras.

These sedimentary and metamorphic rocks are of great variety, and denudation has had full scope in producing a diversified landscape. Broad valleys have been worn in the clays and marls. The upper Durance valley has been eroded through the very heart of Briançonnais, from the Col du Lautaret southward past Briançon itself. Similarly, the Isère, which derives its head-waters from a group of small glacier-lobes near the Franco-Italian frontier, flows away north-westwards through soft shales and slates in a rather desolate valley, now transformed in appearance by the lake ponded up behind the Tignes barrage. A few miles to the south the Arc, one of the Isère's main tributaries, flows south-westwards.

These major valleys cut the zone into a number of upland groups —the Vanoise, the Graian Alps, the Cottian Alps and the Maritime Alps.

The Vanoise.—This area of mountains lies between the sharply defined valleys of the Tarentaise and the Maurienne. The upper valleys of the Isère and the Arc are so close together in the east, within two or three miles, that the rivers almost completely surround the massif and give it a distinct unity. The Vanoise is a massive group, with the highest peaks (many above 10,000 feet) along its southern edge overlooking the Maurienne. Numerous powerful torrents flow northwards to the Isère, thus dissecting the massif into a series of bold ridges, which are sufficiently high for some considerable snow-fields to accumulate. In the north-east is the group of the Grande-Motte (12,018 feet) and the Grande-Casse (12,668 feet); the latter, the highest peak of the district, has a remarkable arête-like summit, sixty feet long, but less than a yard in width. To the southeast is the group of La Vanoise itself, which has given its name to the whole massif, culminating in the snow-peak of the Dôme de Chasseforêts, and rising to 11,802 feet from the surrounding snow-fields, which cover about forty square miles. This summit forms another example of a *glacier de calotte*, similar to but on a smaller scale than Mont Blanc itself. A few glaciers push their way downwards for a mile or two from these snow-fields. The third prominent group of mountains within the massif is that of the Péclet-Polset further west, culminating in the 11,700 foot Aiguille de Péclet; here also is a small cluster of snow-fields.

The Graian Alps.—The mountain groups which form the main ridge-line of the Alps between the Petit-St. Bernard and the Mont Cenis passes are known collectively as the Graian Alps. The ridge-line though sinuous is continuous, and rarely falls below 10,000 feet.

The highest peak in the Graians, the Gran Paradiso, is not on the main ridge, but rises to over 13,300 feet from a semi-detached mass of uplands well to the east in Italy. The frontier-ridge itself culminates in the Grande-Sassière (12,323 feet), which looks down upon the desolate stony valley of the upper Isère, the scene of recent great hydro-electric developments (see pp. 653–5). Part of this mountain region has now been designated a national park, continuous with the Gran Paradiso park in Italy.

The ridge-line of the Graians is flanked by almost continuous snow-fields and glaciers. These occur on a much greater scale on the western side where the precipitation is heavier. One can stand on a rock-ridge with extensive snow-fields to the west, from which glaciers push down into the lateral valleys towards the Tarentaise and Maurienne, while crumbling rock-buttresses and vast slopes of scree fall away to the east.

The Cottian Alps.—The main ridge-line of the Alps swings away south-eastward from the re-entrant of Italian territory in the Dora Riparia valley towards the Mercantour and the Mediterranean. In the neighbourhood of Briançon the headstreams of the Durance have eroded deep valleys in the clays and marls, and tributaries from the east, such as the Cerveyvette and the Guil, have notched deeply into the uplands. So advanced is this denudation that the frontier-ridges are here at their lowest for hundreds of miles. Indeed, the much higher summits of the Pelvoux to the west testify to the greater resistance of the granites and gneisses as compared with these sedimentary rocks. To the east of Briançon, the Durance headstream on the French side and the Dora Riparia on the Italian have cut back so deeply into the ridge that it falls to a mere 6,083 feet in the grassy Col du Mont Genèvre.

The highest point in the Cottians is the graceful pyramid of Monte Viso (12,602 feet), but it lies wholly in Italy. The parts of the Cottians in France, namely the Queyras massif to the south of the Guil valley and the Parpaillon upland lying between the Durance and its tributary the Ubaye, are much lower. They are, however, dissected by the torrential tributaries of the Durance, and in the south also of the Var. A few peaks in the Parpaillon just exceed 11,000 feet, and carry some tiny permanent snow-fields. This part of the sedimentary Alps is desolate, with crags, shattered ridges and scree-slopes.

The Maritime Alps.—The term Maritime Alps is applied rather generally to the ranges at the southern end of the High Alps. Structurally they are not wholly part of the Briançonnais zone, but can certainly be regarded as part of the High Sedimentary Alps. They include the ranges of Trois-Evêches and of Mont Pélat (10,017 feet), which overlooks the valley of the Var to the east. The former group is interesting in that on the northern slopes is the shrunken Glacier de la Blanche, which has the distinction of being the most southerly glacier in the French Alps.

CLIMATE

The north–south trend of the French Alps lies transverse both to air-masses moving across France from the Atlantic and to the transition zone that separates the central European climatic region from that of the Mediterranean. Indeed, the distinction between the *Alpes du Nord* and the *Alpes du Sud* rests largely on a climatic basis, indicated by a line drawn westward from Briançon to Valence.

It is difficult to generalise about temperatures, for there is an appreciable latitudinal range between north and south. As a general indication, the mean January and July figures for Chamonix (at about 3,300 feet) are 22° F. and 62° F., for Annecy (at 1,460 feet in a deep sheltered valley) 31° F. and 67° F., and for Gap (much further south in a tributary valley of the Durance at 2,400 feet) 31° F. and 66° F. respectively. Aspect, however, is of profound significance. The distinction between south-facing valley-slopes (the *adret* or *endroit*) and the shady sides (the *ubac* or the *envers*) is so profound that it dominates the patterns of settlement and land-use in those narrow valleys orientated from west to east.

Associated with aspect is the degree of exposure to or shelter from winds from particular directions, and some of these winds are so regularly experienced in the Alps that they possess specific names. The *mistral* affects the Provençal Alps, while to the north of Digne a similar cold, dry, blustery wind is referred to as the *bise*. Winds from a southerly direction are known as the *marin* in the south, as the *vente du midi* in the north. From the south-east the *levant* affects the Maritime Alps, and the *lombarde* the Graian Alps. Most of the southerly winds bring mild damp conditions in winter, with rain or snow at higher altitudes. Stormy conditions with mild temperatures and heavy short-lived precipitation are associated with the *traverse* in the northern part of the Fore-Alps and with the *labech* in the south. The *föhn* is rarely experienced in the French Alps, mainly because of the longitudinal structure and the absence of transverse barriers to a southerly air-stream.

Inversion is another common phenomenon; many otherwise sheltered valleys are liable to spells of frost and cold damp fog. It is noticeable that in the Grésivaudan the vines grow on the slopes a hundred feet or so above the valley-floor; the lowest slopes are used for crops less liable to frost-damage.

Altitude causes great variation in temperature; during the few years that an observatory on the summit of Mont Blanc was in operation at the end of last century, the lowest temperature recorded was $-45°$ F. An average diminution of temperature with height is experienced of $3·3°$ F. per 1,000 feet, falling to $2·8°$ F. in winter and rising to $3·9°$ F. in spring, according to E. Bénévent.[1]

The effects of a longitudinal division between the outer (western) ranges and the inner (eastern) ranges is shown by the precipitation figures. Though lower, the windward slopes of the upstanding western Fore-Alps receive more than 60 inches of precipitation. Three stations in the west, centre and east of the Chartreuse (St. Laurent-du-Pont, St. Pierre-de-Chartreuse and St. Pancrasse) have 67, 67 and 59 inches respectively. Thus although the third station is at a height of 3,281 feet, compared with the first at only 1,345 feet, exposure to the prevailing wind means more than mere altitude. Annecy, slightly in the rain-shadow of both the southern Jura and the Fore-Alps, has about 50 inches, and Chamonix, although much higher, is tucked in a deep valley between the Aiguilles Rouges and Mont Blanc and receives about 44 inches.[2] Much of this comes in the form of thunderstorms ; the Mont Blanc massif is particularly subject to violent storms in summer which seem to build up from the heated lowlands of Lombardy and the Valle d'Aosta. The deep interior valleys of the Briançonnais, Haute-Maurienne and Haute-Tarentaise have a lower precipitation, about 35 inches or less annually ; Modane, in the Maurienne, has as little as 24 inches, and Lanslebourg in the upper Arc valley about 31 inches.

The distinction between the central and northern Alps as compared with the southern Alps is marked in respect both of seasonal régime and actual totals of precipitation. The northern part is termed by Bénévent the '*Zone continentale*' ; the months with heaviest precipitation (unfortunately from the climber's point of view) are between June and August. There follows the '*Zone de transition à tendance continentale*', with a more uniform distribution, though still with an appreciable maximum between June and October. To the south again is the complementary '*Zone de transition à tendance méditerranéenne*' ; at Gap, for example, the two wettest months are October and November, while July and August are drier than the period February to June. Finally comes the '*Zone méditerranéenne sublittorale*', with a distinct minimum of almost complete aridity between May and September. Not only then is there a decrease eastward in the total precipitation but also southward, as shown by the figures for Flumet in the Genevois (65

[1] E. Bénévent, *Le Climat des Alpes françaises* (*Mémorial de l'Office National Météorologique de France*) (1926).
[1] J. Steinberg, 'Le Climat estival de la haute vallée de l'Arve', in *A. de G.* (1965), vol. lxxiv, pp. 129-59.

inches) and for Castellane (35 inches) in the Verdon valley among the southern Fore-Alps.

Much of this precipitation falls in the form of snow, and the French Alpine region is covered in most winters down to the lowest valleys. During the early summer the snow-line rapidly recedes, uncovering the *alp*-pastures, to the zone of permanent snow. Some indication of the mean duration of the snow-cover is given:

Days with Snow-Cover

(Altitude in feet)

	2,000	4,000	6,000	8,000
High Alps of Savoy .	55	125	180	240
Cottian Alps . . .	40	100	150	220
Provençal Alps . .	5-10	80	150	240

Source: E. Bénévent, 'La Neige dans les Alpes françaises', in *Recueils de l'Institut de Géographie Alpine* (1917), vol. v, pp. 403-98.

It can be seen from this table that at altitudes exceeding 8,000 feet the latitudinal effects are not marked, although at lower altitudes the difference is quite appreciable. It is emphasised that these are mean figures; they vary enormously between the mild winters, the despair of winter sportsmen, and the severe ones when the snow-cover is long sustained, and subsequent damage from avalanches and flood melt-water may be considerable. Settlements are carefully sited with respect to known avalanche-tracks; a rock-spur may be used as protection and the slopes below obvious gully-lines are avoided. Above most villages dense plantations of conifers are maintained as avalanche-breaks, and critical points on roads and railways are protected by avalanche-galleries. The depth of snow varies according to aspect; north-facing hollows will retain it for weeks after southern slopes have been stripped, and above 8,000 feet drifts may persist throughout the year well below the general snow-line. At Tour (above Chamonix at about 4700 feet) an average of 31 feet of snow is received each year.

A further indication of snow-fall is afforded by the information concerning snow-blocking on the Alpine roads (Fig. 139), supplied by such sources as the invaluable *Guide Michelin*. Below about 3,000 feet interruption is rare, although some of the roads along deep valley-floors may be blocked for a few days. The high passes above 6,500 feet are usually closed from October to May. The 6,083-foot Mont Genèvre, between Briançon and Cesanne in Italy, is always kept clear by snow-ploughs except for brief periods following heavy storms, as is also the Col du Lautaret (6,752 feet) between

Briançon and La Grave. No effort is made to keep open the high passes ; the Col de l'Iseran between Bourg St. Maurice in the upper Val d'Isère and Bonneval near the source of the Arc is invariably blocked from mid-October to late June or even July.

LAND-USE

Administratively the French Alps are covered by seven *départements*. Actually the large unit of Isère extends to the Rhône, and Alpes-Maritimes and Var reach the Mediterranean coast, but broadly the land-use statistics for these *départements* may be taken as representative of the Alpine regions of France.

Land-Use, 1963

(Percentage of Total Area)

	Arable	Permanent Pasture	Land not under Cultivation	Woodland
Northern Alps				
Haute-Savoie . .	22	30	15	32
Savoie . . .	5	27	40	25
Isère. . . .	24	24	22	27
Hautes-Alpes . .	9	33	24	32
Southern Alps				
Basses-Alpes . .	12	32	25	32
Alpes-Maritimes .	3	29	30	30
Var	7	9	20	49

Source: *Ministère de l'Agriculture*, published in *Annuaire statistique de la France, 1964.*

The differences in climatic régime between the northern and southern French Alps are reflected in land-use, and it is necessary therefore to consider them separately. It must be remembered that the transition is gradual ; while as far north as the Grésivaudan agriculture may reveal southern characteristics (such as the cultivation of maize, vine and even figs), conversely the peaks of the Maritime Alps and Mercantour are sufficiently lofty to carry forests [1] and pasture similar to those of the northern mountains.

Agriculture in the Northern Alps.—Within this northern area differences are apparent between the Fore-Alps and the High Alps to the east. The former are more extensively wooded, the result of their copious rainfall and of the presence of clays and marls among the limestone scarps. 51 per cent of the surface of the Chartreuse is

[1] R. Leroy, 'Les Forêts des Alpes françaises', in *R.G.A.* (1957), vol. 45, pp. 441-55.

wooded, and 47 per cent of the Vercors. There is a definite zoning of tree species, with beech, oak and sweet chestnut to about 3,000 feet, succeeded by spruce and fir to the tree-line, with occasional Arolla pine near the upper limits. Further east in the drier High Alps spruce is the commonest tree, particularly in the Haute-Tarentaise, Haute-Maurienne and the Briançonnais. Much is deliberately planted by the State and by the communes for fuel, for the timber industries, to check soil-erosion and as avalanche-breaks; the first State forest was created in 1860. The forest has been cut into both from below to provide arable fields, orchards and vineyards on the gentle slopes above the valleys, and from above to extend the *alp*-pastures. In the Chablais and the Genevois pasture has largely replaced woodland, except on steep mountain-sides.

About a third of the active population in Haute-Savoie, Savoie and Hautes-Alpes, and a fifth in Isère, are occupied with agriculture. Many more primarily industrial workers, and others engaged seasonally in the catering for tourists, take part in some agriculture. The proportion is in fact as low as it is because of the development of industry in the Alpine valleys and in such towns as Grenoble.

The traditional Alpine rural economy is dependent on cattle-rearing with ancillary cultivation. In the four northern *départements* there were in 1963 about 511,000 cattle, of which three-fifths were dairy animals. In the higher eastern areas the animals are of the famous *Tarine* breed, hardy and well suited to the uplands; their agility on steep slopes is of a chamois-like quality. In the Chablais and Genevois, where the pastures appear so rich and green, the dominant breed is known as *Abondance* or the *pie-rouge de l'Est*, akin to those of the Jura and Swiss Plateau. A third type, the heavy milk-yielding *Villard-de-Lans*, is grazed on the limestone pastures of the Chartreuse and the Vercors. The pattern of the pastoral economy has changed little during the years; more milk is sent off to the towns of the Rhône valley and beyond, there are more milk-using industries, more factory-made cheese is produced and less in the farm-houses, but the seasonal rhythm of movement of animals has changed little because it is the best suited to the environment.

This seasonal migration follows a regular pattern. They leave the permanent valley-villages and first move up to a valley-bench (known as the *montagnette* [1] or *petite montagne*) above the first steep slopes, each family with its cattle. There they live for the summer in a chalet-cum-barn, known as a *grangette* in Bauges or a *grange* in Chartreuse. In places this building stands isolatedly among its own *alpages*, elsewhere groups form a hamlet ancillary to the permanent village in the valley below. The cattle are grazed there for a while,

[1] J. Robert, 'Les Montagnettes dans les Alpes françaises du Nord', in *Mélanges géographiques offerts à E. Bénévent, 1954*, pp. 167-82.

but as soon as the higher slopes are clear of snow the herds go up to these *grandes montagnes* for two or three months with a few herdsmen (*montagnards*) who live in primitive chalets. At the *montagnettes* hay is cut and stored, or carried down to the villages, and the *fromager* carries on with his manufacture of cheese. On most of these *alpages* irrigation channels lead water from torrents and even from glaciers over the slopes to stimulate the growth of rich grass in the long hours of summer sunshine. In autumn the animals return to the *montagnettes*, where they graze on the second growth of the mown pastures, and by October they are back in the valleys, where they feed on the valley-pastures until the first snows fall, when they are stall-fed for the winter. Near the rivers irrigated meadows provide perhaps two crops of hay for winter feed. The floor of the Grési-vaudan is irrigated by water taken from the endyked Isère through artificial channels (known as *chantournes*), which flow parallel to the river and rejoin it lower down the main valley. Groups of farmers form *syndicats de drainage*, similar to the *wateringues* of Flanders.

There are, of course, many variations in this pattern. In Bornes the tendency is to keep the cattle permanently in the valleys, and the chief labour is to mow, bring down and store sufficient hay from the *alpages* to last the winter. In Chablais many of the valley farmers rent their cattle to the owner of some high pastures, while they, relieved temporarily of the burden, practise arable cultivation and collect hay until the winter, when they recover their animals and resume the making of butter and cheese.

While some dairying is for subsistence (potatoes, bread, cheese and milk are still the staple diet in more remote valleys), most of it is now organised on a commercial basis.[1] Much milk is sent to the industrial towns in the valleys, to Grenoble and to Lyons, and telpher-lines, lorries and milk-tankers provide speedy transport. Cheese is manu-factured in the *fruitières coopératives*, with factories using electric power for the cream-separators and churns. *Gruyère*, as in the Jura, is the main cheese made, although *Rigotte*, *Roblochon* and *Sassenage* are other varieties.

A certain amount of arable cultivation is practised for subsistence. In the broad flat-floored valleys in the Sub-Alpine Depression—in the Combe de Savoie, the Grésivaudan and the Chambéry valley in particular—the Lias clays and marls afford good soils. Away from the water-meadows but still on the valley-floors flourishes quite an intensive cultivation—wheat and maize, potatoes and other vegetables, growing in strips. In the damper Fore-Alpine valleys, oats becomes the dominant cereal, and in the higher districts rye is still grown. On the lower south-facing slopes are orchards of apples,

[1] M. Allefrosde, 'Les Fabrications fromagères en Haute-Savoie', in *R.G.A.* (1952), vol. 40, pp. 625-41.

plums and black cherries and in favoured 'sun-traps' apricots, peaches and walnuts. Up the slopes climb the vineyards, particularly in the Arve valley, above Annecy, in the Arly valley, and in the Grésivaudan. No quality wine is made (although such wines as *Crépy* have a more than local repute), but Isère produced in 1963 about 294,000 hectolitres of *vin ordinaire*. Honey is produced mostly for local sale, but some is sent to the large towns. A few hives are placed in or near most orchards, but some bee-farms operate on a larger scale; one such is the well-known 'Villa des Abeilles' outside Bonneville in the valley of the Arve.

There is in fact a prosperous cheerful air about Savoy, the valleys seem fresh and fertile, and the houses are attractively built and decorated in the manner of Swiss chalets, with bright gardens.

Agriculture in the Southern Alps.—The marked summer aridity and higher temperatures produce striking contrasts between the vegetation of the northern and southern alps. The proportion of permanent pasture is of course much reduced. The actual area under woodland (if estimated on a *départemental* basis) is oddly enough higher, indeed Var has the highest proportion under wood of any Alpine *département*. Actually the figures include large areas of a thin poor scrub-forest, and really indicate that less clearing for pasture and arable land has been effected than in the north. In point of fact man in the past has cleared too much, and as land was abandoned, the result of poor rewards and rural depopulation, the *maquis* and the *garrigue* have spread. So too have the effects of soil erosion, and there is much bare limestone from which the soil has been scoured, with gashed hill-slopes no longer protected with trees. On some of the limestone plateaus the *Département des Eaux et Forêts* has established plantations of larch and pine, which are found as high as 7,500 feet. The Aleppo pine and the Atlas cedar both grow on the Ventoux, evergreen oaks and box are common, and the Austrian pine has been established on some of the poorest terrain. Sweet chestnut and cork oak grow on favoured lower slopes. Much of the limestone plateaus of the southern Alps between about 2,000 and 5,000 feet has a *maquis*-like aspect. Brushwood and underwood (*broussailles et taillis*) are widespread, consisting of thickets of dwarf evergreen oaks and box, broom, lentiscus, lavender, rosemary, thyme and thorny aromatic shrubs. In other districts are crumbling limestone slopes, gaunt cliffs, fans of gravel choking the valleys of torrents hardly visible in summer, a few prickly tufts of vegetation among the white rock; this is the *garrigue*. Except on the higher summits to the east, where snow-melt nurtures short-lived grasses, pasture is scanty and poor.

The agricultural economy also gradually changes as the Mediterranean coast is approached. Only 22,000 dairy cattle were in Hautes-Alpes in 1963, compared with 152,000 in Isère to the north, while further south Basses-Alpes and Var had still fewer, about 5,000 each. The higher frontier ranges of Alpes-Maritimes were able to support about 6,000 head.

On the limestone pastures sheep become the main feature of the economy; Hautes-Alpes in 1963 had 188,000, Basses-Alpes 210,000 and Var 210,000. The massif of Dévoluy is especially important for sheep-rearing. Large numbers of young lambs are slaughtered to provide skins for the glove industry of Grenoble, and ewes' milk cheese, akin to that of Roquefort in the Causses, is processed. Much seasonal movement of sheep still takes place to the high pastures of Dauphiny and the Maritime Alps in summer, back to the floors of the Durance and its tributaries for the winter, some going even further down to the pastures of the Rhône delta in the Crau and the Camargue. Flocks of the *mérinos d'Arles*, which live in the Crau, likewise move in summer up to the Maritime Alps, the Plateau de Digne, Champsaur and Parpaillon, even as far as Dévoluy.

Arable farming in the south is concentrated in the favoured valleys where a thin layer of soil covers the rocks. The northern parts of the Durance valley, notably the *pays* of Embrunais and Gapençais, although showing a tendency to summer drought, have about 30 inches of precipitation. Wheat, maize, tobacco, almonds, apricots and other fruit are patiently and assiduously cultivated, often in unbelievably small patches. Not much further down the Durance valley, that symbol of Mediterranean agriculture, the olive, makes its appearance; its cultivation further east extends up the Var valley as far as Puget-Théniers.

The limestone plateaus in southern Basses-Alpes and northern Var are of very limited value for agriculture. Basses-Alpes is the most scantily populated *département* in the Alps, with a mere 11,000 agricultural workers; even the *département* of Haute-Savoie, only two-thirds as large and including the high peaks of the Mont Blanc massif, had four times as many. The valley-floors of the Durance and tributaries such as the Verdon, Asse and Bléone, and those of the Var and the Tinée, are cultivated. Thus Digne, in a small embayment floored with Miocene deposits, is the centre of a pleasant fruit-growing area; it is famous for its dried prunes (known as *pistoles*) and its delectable *princesses* almonds. Sisteron is the centre of groves of almond trees, as are neighbouring villages such as Le Bersac.

The agricultural economy of these southern Fore-Alps is therefore Mediterranean in character rather than Alpine. Valleys and small depressions among the *maquis* and *garrigue* grow hard wheat and maize; orchards of almonds and walnuts occur in favoured places; olive groves climb up the limestone slopes; there are vine-yards and in places gardens of lavender. About 43,500 acres in Basses-Alpes and 8,650 acres in Var were under wheat in 1963, but the yield per acre was the lowest in France, less than half that of the Paris Basin. A large amount of *vin ordinaire* is produced, in fact Var is the sixth *département* in order of production, but there is no quality wine. Further south still the agricultural economy becomes quite Provençal.

POWER AND INDUSTRY

Power (Fig. 138).—Industrial activity in the Alpine region has expanded considerably as a result of the development of hydro-electricity. The high precipitation, the snow-fields and glaciers which form natural reservoirs, the deep valleys penetrating far into the mountains, the narrow *cluses* affording sites for barrages, the rock-steps in the main valleys, the moraine-dammed lakes, and the torrents emerging from hanging-valleys, are all favourable factors. The effects of the long winter freeze and the periods of summer drought are partly remediable by the construction of reservoirs.

The French were pioneers in the production of electricity from water-power, for in 1869 the engineer Aristide Bergés used a stream descending 1,590 feet into the Grésivaudan to produce electricity, and utilised the power to drive machinery in his wood pulp and paper-mill at Lancey, ten miles from Grenoble. By 1896 ten stations were in operation (including the *Calypso* plant in the Maurienne), which had increased to fifty-seven by 1914, although these were all small-scale by modern standards.

Development continued in the inter-war years, and by 1939 a large number of small stations had been constructed in the French Alps. The power produced was for the most part used locally by the electro-chemical and electro-metallurgical industries, and by the electrified lines of the *P.L.M.* Company. Most of these units were in the Maurienne, the Tarentaise and the valleys of the Romanche and Arly, though others were built along the valleys of the Arve, Drac and Durance and one or two small ones high up in the Var valley. A few schemes were on a larger scale. One of the earliest large projects, begun in 1904, is the Sept-Laux or *Fond-de-France* installation. Four of the seven lakes on the upland to the north of the Belledonne (Cos, Cottepen, La Motte and Carré) were inter-connected and seven barrages built. This has been steadily extended, the latest developments being completed in 1943. Again, between 1931 and 1935 the Bissorte barrage, 200 feet high and 600 yards in width, was built across the mouth of the hanging-valley of the Riveau de Bissorte above La Praz (a few miles below Modane in the Maurienne). The surface of the lake lies at 6,830 feet, giving a fall of 3,753 feet (the longest single chute in the French Alps) to the power-station at La Praz, which provides power for the largest electro-metallurgical plant in the Maurienne; this incidentally was destroyed by German forces in 1944 but has been rebuilt. In 1935 the Chambon scheme was begun, completed three years later, in the valley of the Romanche; its storage reservoir is in a hanging-valley on the southern side of the Romanche, fed by streams coming from the snow-fields at the western edge of the Meije group. Another impressive scheme, completed in 1935, was the construction of the Barrage de Sautet across the upper Drac, so ponding up a reservoir along the valleys of the main river and its tributary the Souloise. The Sautet power-station did not in fact utilise all the potential head of water thus made available, and in 1946 a second station, the Cordéac, was constructed a few miles away. By the end of the 1939–1945 war no less than 118 power-stations of over 1,000 kw capacity were in operation in the French Alps.

By 1964 about 60 per cent of the hydro- and 32 per cent of the total power generated in France was produced in the Alps, including the Rhône valley.[1] Schemes are being pushed steadily ahead. The tendency is still to carry out a large number of small projects, though within an integrated plan, rather than a few major schemes, as in the Rhône basin. One project, started as long ago as 1921 but interrupted during the depression of the 'thirties, was completed in 1948, the Castillon barrage built across the gorge of the Verdon near Castillon in the Provençal Alps. This remarkable ' Grand-cañon ', as it is known, deeply dissected in the Jurassic limestones, now affords a storage reservoir of 150 million cubic metres and a large power-station has been constructed.

Chief developments at the present time concern the upper Isère basin, and three major projects have so far been undertaken. In the upper Isère valley the Tignes scheme was completed in 1954. Near Tignes the glaciated valley opens out as a broad basin, but narrows again further down to form a gorge, so providing an ideal site for a reservoir. A barrage was built, 587 feet high, creating the largest reservoir in the French Alps, which unfortunately necessitated the submergence of the village of Tignes and the compulsory evacuation of its 800 inhabitants to a new village higher up the valley slopes. The reservoir supplies Les Brévières power-station, with an installed capacity of 32,000 kw, completed in 1952. Some of the water from the Isère below this reservoir was diverted through an aqueduct down the valley to another marked step in the

---

[1] For a full account, illustrated with maps, see G. Kish, 'Hydro-Electric Power in France: Plans and Projects', in G.R. (1955), vol. 45, pp. 81-98. See also J. Ritter, 'L'Aménagement hydroélectrique du bassin de l'Isère', in A. de G. (1959), vol. 68, pp. 34-53.

gradient above Bourg-St. Maurice, where a second bigger station, Malgovert (75,000 kw), was opened in 1954. Another interesting

Fig. 138.—Hydro-Electricity Stations in the Northern French Alps.
Only the larger stations are shown; there is a considerable number of smaller stations along most of the river-valleys.
Based on *Atlas de France*, sheet 46, and various official publications.

development is the Isère-Drac diversion. At Moutiers the Isère makes a right-angled bend and flows north-westwards through the Tarentaise before it swings south again through the Combe de Savoie. The diversion, accomplished by means of a tunnel 6,500 feet long beneath the Vanoise massif, was intended to withdraw water from the Isère valley into the much lower Maurienne, so providing a head of 500 feet of water. The scheme was largely completed in 1954, when four underground power-houses, known as the Randens station, of 32,000 kw each, were opened. The Aussois project, still under development, utilises streams issuing from snow-fields and glaciers on the southern side of the Vanoise, concentrated through aqueducts and tunnels into the Aussois reservoir formed by damming a subsidiary valley of the Arc. The largest hydro-station in the Alps, La Bathie-Roselend (Savoie), was completed in 1961, with an installed capacity of 480,000 kw.

Other developments have been the Pizançon station on the Isère near where it leaves the Fore-Alps for the Rhône valley, the enlarged Passy station on the upper Arve near St. Gervais-les Bains, the Pont-Escoffier station in the upper Romanche, the Ste. Tulle station on the Durance just above its junction with the Verdon, and Le Bancairon station on the Tinée before it joins the Var. Another scheme, begun in 1953 and completed in 1959, is an earth-barrage across the Durance at Serre-Ponçon [1] below the confluence of the Ubaye. Because of the infilling of alluvium to a depth of at least 300 feet, affording no foundations, a concrete dam was impracticable. The barrage is made of clay and marl, 377 feet high and 1,500 feet in length; the resulting lake fills the Durance valley for eleven miles upstream and that of the Ubaye for five miles. This supplies a head of water for a station at the foot of the dam, with an installed capacity of 352,000 kw and for a number of smaller stations downstream, and also supplies irrigation water in summer for the middle Durance valley.

While the industries of the neighbouring valleys are the prime beneficiary of these enterprises, the Alpine stations are useful contributors to the grid. Since the setting-up of *E.D.F.* a close degree of integration has been possible, and several high voltage (380 kv) transmission lines have been erected. From the Tarentaise stations one line runs to Génissiat and then north-westward via Vielmoulin and Creneye to Paris, while another goes west to Lyons. Other lines supply towns such as Grenoble, and one via Grisolle and Ste. Tulle reaches Marseilles. Thus the Alpine *houille blanche* has indeed become a major contributor to the French industrial economy.

Industry. [2]—For several centuries small-scale industry has been active

[1] A. Bertin, 'Le Barrage de Serre-Ponçon', in *R.G.A.* (1960), vol. 48, pp. 625-89.

[2] A full account of industrial development prior to 1948 is given by G. Veyret-Verner, *L'Industrie des Alpes françaises: étude géographique* (1948), for later years by J. Lefebvre, *L'Evolution des localisations industrielles: l'exemple des Alpes françaises* (1960).

in the Alpine valleys. Many small blast-furnaces and foundries used charcoal for fuel and running water to work the bellows. Iron-ore mines were numerous, and two larger groups of mines operated at Allevard (in a tributary valley opening from the east into the Grési-vaudan) and at St. Georges-d'Hurtières in the lower Maurienne. Other metals mined sporadically were copper, gold and silver; argentiferous galena was worked as early as the twelfth century in the upper Durance valley, and the village of Argentière grew up there, while Argentine in the Maurienne had a similar origin. Small textile factories manufacturing wool, silk, hemp and later cotton were widespread; for example, a string of woollen-mills was located along the valley of the Verdon in the south, and the larger towns of Annecy and Chambéry were also important. The glove industry of Grenoble has been highly organised under its *maîtres-gantiers* since the sixteenth century. Watch- and clock-making spread to Cluses from the Geneva district in the eighteenth century. Pottery, tiles, bricks and glass-ware were manufactured in the valleys; glass-making has been important from the mid-eighteenth century at Thorens, Allex and Annecy, using Tertiary sands from the valleys of the Mont Salève, and salt from Trias deposits in the Tarentaise, from the saline springs at Salins near Moûtiers, and from the saline Lac d'Arbonne near Bourg-St. Maurice. Paper was made at ten localities before the nineteenth century—including Moustiers, Sisteron, Die and Romeyer in the south, Vizille in the Drac valley, and Faverges to the south of Annecy. Then there was a wide range of village crafts—the making of agricultural implements, domestic utensils, wooden objects, textiles and leather goods. Many of these activities were supplementary to an agricultural livelihood, most of them indeed winter activities. Thus industry, although small-scale, was surprisingly varied.

In the nineteenth century many of these industries declined, largely because the coming of rail communications brought in cheaply made factory products. Correspondingly, the attraction of urban indus-tries drew off an increasing amount of labour. But the railway, an 'agent destructeur de l'industrie ancienne', as G. Veyret-Verner puts it, then became an 'agent de rénovation'. The coal of the Mure basin was mined, and the resources of limestone provided the raw material for the first modern industrialisation—the manufacture of cement and the production of agricultural lime. By the beginning of the twentieth century about thirty cement-works were in operation, the majority near Grenoble.

The modern development of industry in the Alps is associated with the exploitation of hydro-electric power, and the Alpine valleys, with their focus and 'capital' at Grenoble, now form a distinct industrial region. From adjoining mountains one can look down on a linear industrialisation, a long line of factories and chimneys along the Grésivaudan,[1] Tarentaise, Maurienne and Romanche and on a smaller scale in the upper Arve, the Arly and the middle Durance valleys. Some of the traditional industries such as glove-making, textiles and watch-making have been modernised, but several introductions have resulted from technological developments.

Several large works are engaged in electric steel and alloy production, the most important of which are at Ugine in the Arly valley and at St. Michel-de-Maurienne. Plentiful cheap electricity is essential for the refining of aluminium from its ore, hydrated oxide of aluminium. It was in the French Alps, at Froges in the Grésivaudan a few miles from Grenoble, that Héroult first refined aluminium by electrolysis. The main source of bauxite is in the valley of the Argens in the *département* of Var (see p. 413). The ore is reduced to alumina near the area of production, and then sent to the furnaces in the Arc and Isère valleys. It takes about 25,000 kwh to produce a ton of aluminium, and so the French output of this metal, which totalled 50,200 tons in 1964 (almost all produced in the Alpine valleys but for one or two small refineries in the Pyrenees), consumes a considerable amount of electricity. The largest aluminium factory in France is the *Les Plans* works at St. Jean-de-Maurienne, and others are in the same valley at St. Michel-de-Maurienne, Prémont and La Praz, and a series in the Romanche at Livet, Rioupéroux, Les Clavaux and Pierre-Eybesse, between Bourg d'Oisans and St. Barthélemy. Others are active in the Tarentaise, centred on Moûtiers, though on a smaller scale, and in the valley of the Doron de Bozel, where factories are in operation at Champagny, Ballaudaz, La Perrière and La Rageat.

Many factories specialise in the refining of other metals and in the production of ferro-alloys. The Giffre works in the Arly valley produce ferro-chrome, -tungsten, -molybdenum and -titanium, Chedde produces ferro-vanadium and pure chrome, Ugine a range of ferro-alloys.

Several electro-chemical works are situated in the same valleys, for the production of calcium carbide and of its fertiliser-derivative calcium cyanamide requires the concentrated and controlled heat of electric furnaces. The largest unit is at Argentière in the upper Durance valley eight miles below Briançon. In the Maurienne a series of these electro-chemical factories extends from near Modane as far as Aiguebelle—at St. Gobain, Montricher, St. Martin-sur-la-Chambre, Argentine and La Pouille—and others are in the Romanche, the Tarentaise and the Arly valley. Other chemicals are

[1] D. Bacconnet, 'L'Industrialisation d'une grande vallée alpestre et ses répercussions démographiques et rurales: le Grésivaudan', in *R.G.A.* (1956), vol. 44, pp. 99-166.

made, and an explosives factory is active at Chedde in the Arve valley.

Many small factories, mostly making silk and rayon, are in the Drôme and Aygues valleys, under the influence of Lyons, and small isolated ones are at such towns as Gap, Briançon, Faverges, Ugine, and Annecy. Silk thread and cloth are made at St. Pierre-d'Albigny and La Rochette in the Combe de Savoie. The main textile centre is Grenoble.

The timber-using industries have long been important in the well-wooded northern Fore-Alps. The emphasis is now not so much on small *bric-à-brac* and manufactured articles generally, as in the Jura, but on sawn timber for joinery and pit-props, and each small valley in the Fore-Alpine massifs has its saw-mills and wood-yards. The manufacture of paper, established for centuries, has been developed on modern lines. Ten factories are in operation in the Grésivaudan (the biggest at Lancey in the lower Drac valley), and a few outlying ones at Annecy, Modane, Sisteron and Malaucène; the tendency is to produce high-quality papers.

The focus of this Alpine industrial region is Grenoble, itself an important manufacturing town. Its main industry has for long been the making of gloves, using lamb-skins from the Alpine flocks and also brought from the Central Massif and the Pyrenees; this is still largely a domestic industry, and employs about 15,000 people, mostly women, much the same number as before the war. Grenoble is the centre of a flourishing textile industry, especially of silk and rayon (a large viscose-rayon factory was built in 1926), and also manufactures electro-metallurgical and -chemical products, electrical apparatus (including power-station equipment such as turbines and switch-gear), paper and leather. Cement-, lime- and plaster-works are active both to the south of Grenoble in the lower Drac valley and in the Isère valley below the city, using limestone brought down from the Grande Chartreuse by overhead cable-ways.

In the *département* of Isère almost exactly 50 per cent of the gainfully employed population are engaged in industry. The proportion is less in the other Alpine *départements*, but nevertheless in all about a quarter of a million people are occupied in industry in the French Alps. A large number of these are foreigners, working temporarily in the factories—Italians, Spaniards, Poles and North Africans.

POPULATION AND SETTLEMENT

The Alpine region stands out clearly as an area of low density, for much consists of uninhabited mountains with rock-ridges, snowfields and glaciers, there are considerable areas of merely seasonal occupation by pastoralists, and the forested lands are widespread. Nevertheless, some of the valleys form long narrow strips of surprisingly dense population. At favoured points, particularly where several valleys meet, larger towns have developed; helped by the development of roads and railways (including some international routeways), they have become centres of thriving industry and tourism. Many small towns and villages are situated along the sides of the valleys, on alluvial fans deposited by streams issuing from tributary valleys or higher up on glacially-worn benches, occasionally on the floor of a valley where a transverse resistant rock-bar affords a site above floods and facilities for power development. The dominance of the *adret* (sunny side) is always apparent, but more so in the upper narrow valleys orientated from west to east. Population, therefore, though irregularly distributed, is not inconsiderable.[1]

The Northern Alps.—The *départements* of Savoie and Haute-Savoie contained in 1962 about 596,000 people, with an average density per square mile of 150. This is surprisingly high when one remembers that the Mont Blanc massif, the Graians and the Vanoise are included. One concentration lies along the southern shore of Lake Geneva and in the valleys of the western Chablais. Thonon- and Evian-les-Bains have long been lake-side spas with mineral springs of international repute, and are excellent tourist centres. A second line of settlements extends along the Arve valley to the market-town of Annemasse near the Swiss frontier. The centre for the Mont Blanc area is Chamonix, and with its neighbouring hamlets (Argentière, Les Bossons, Les Houches and St. Gervais) it provides for tourists both in summer and winter; between 100,000 and 150,000 people visit the district annually. The villages and towns of the Arve valley have hotels, they serve the needs of farmers in the more remote side-valleys, and most of them possess industries utilising Arve water-power. These include a large electro-chemical works, wood industries, the making of butter and cheese, and specifically at Cluses (due to the influence of Geneva) the manufacture of watches and clocks. These towns each have from 1,000 to 3,000 inhabitants.

The valleys of the Isère and its tributary the Arc, together with the adjacent 'troughs' of Annecy and Chambéry, account for most of the remaining population of the two Savoyan *départements*, the result of the linear industrialisation of the valleys. Many villages and small towns stand away from the river to avoid flooding, usually in an embayment where a tributary enters the main valley or on the gentle slopes of an alluvial fan. The north side is of course much more favoured than the south. Again there are many tourist centres; Bourg-St. Maurice, for example, the terminus of the Isère valley railway, lies at the foot of the Petit-St. Bernard pass, and the *Route*

[1] An interesting case-study is P. Rambaud, *Economie et sociologie de la montagne* (1962), a study of the commune of Albiez-le-Vieux in the Maurienne.

des Alpes passes southward through the town to the Col de l'Iseran. Other climbing-resorts are La Grave in the Romanche and La Bérarde in the Venéon; these are the centres for the Pelvoux massif as Chamonix is for Mont Blanc, but they are less developed and commercialised. Further to the south Modane is the centre for the Maurienne and the southern Vanoise, and has the advantage of being on the main line to Turin via the Mont Cenis tunnel.

Further west in their side-valleys are Annecy and Chambéry, the 'capitals' of Haute-Savoie and Savoie respectively. Annecy, with a population of 45,715 in 1962, is exceeded in size in the French Alps only by Grenoble and Chambéry. It is the centre of a prosperous agricultural district, it has become a well-known resort helped by its lake-side position and attractive surrounding hills, and is a notable centre for coach tours. Chambéry, in the flat-floored trough to the south of the Lac du Bourget, had a population of 47,447 in 1962. It too is the market-centre for a prosperous agricultural district and for the neighbouring Bauges and Chartreuse uplands, it has a variety of manufactures, and the pleasant surrounding country, together with its mild climate, make it a popular resort. More famous is Aix-les-Bains on the eastern shores of the Lac du Bourget, for long one of the fashionable European spas, where many thousands have 'taken the cure' from its sulphur and alum warm springs, indeed, the first thermal station (*Aquae Gratianae*) was established as long ago as 125 B.C. It has also developed as a centre for winter sports, with the construction of a mountain-railway up Mont Revard to the east.

To the south-west of Savoy lies the *département* of Isère, with its population of 729,789 in 1961 and an average density of 231 per square mile. This is as high as it is, in spite of the scantily populated southern Chartreuse, northern Vercors and western Pelvoux massifs, partly because it is crossed by the broad trench of the Grésivaudan, partly because it includes the 'regional capital' of Dauphiny—Grenoble, and partly because it extends to the Rhône and includes the basin of Vienne. The Grésivaudan contains a series of large villages and small towns—Barraux, La Buissière, Lumbin, Crolles, Bernins and many more—situated on the lower slopes of the north-western side of the valley. The valley is so broad that the south-eastern side of the valley also has several small towns, since the *ubac* effect is not marked; indeed the railway line (the Grenoble-Mont Cenis-Turin route) follows this side and so links these towns.

Grenoble,[1] at the southern end of the Grésivaudan on the left bank of the Isère, has grown up at a commanding position in the French Alps, since it is the focus of all the Isère valley routes. Not only does

[1] J. E. Brush, 'The function of Grenoble as a central place', in *G.R.* (1960), vol. 50, pp. 586-8; and G. Armand and C. Marie, *Les Grandes Villes françaises, La Documentation française*, no. 3288 (1966).

the main railway line via the Mont Cenis pass through the town, but it is the centre of a system of electrified light-railways serving the neighbouring valleys. Grenoble's importance as a road-focus is shown by the fact that from the town a route runs south over the Col de La Croix-Haute (3,858 feet) to Sisteron and Marseilles, north-west via the Voiron depression to Lyons, north-east up the Isère valley to Chambéry, Annecy and Chamonix, and south-east over the Col du Lautaret (6,752 feet) to Briançon, thence via the Mont Genèvre pass to Italy. Its title of 'La Porte des Alpes' is well deserved, for it receives over 100,000 visitors each year, and at the end of every street one sees a wooded hillside or mountain summit. Moreover it is the administrative, judicial, and servicing centre for Dauphiny, and it has a university with a distinguished school of 'Alpine Geography'. The chief importance of modern Grenoble is as a manufacturing town, as described above. As a result its population has grown steadily from 24,000 in 1832 to 162,764 in 1962. If the six neighbouring communes which form part of the official agglomeration are included, the total in 1962 was about 241,359.

The Southern Alps.—Great areas of the Fore-Alps are unpopulated, except for some small fertile basins along the Durance and the lower courses of its tributaries. The general density of population is distinctly low; Hautes-Alpes (which lies partly in the northern Alps) had in 1962 a density of thirty-nine per square mile, while Basses-Alpes had only thirty-one.

Few towns are of any size or importance, for apart from the limited economy even tourism is less developed than in the north; visitors either go north to the High Alps of Savoy and Dauphiny or south to the Mediterranean Riviera coast, and the limestone uplands fall between the two. Gap, the *chef-lieu* of Hautes-Alpes, is the largest town, with a population of 21,935 in 1962. It is situated in the Gapençais, where the river Luye flows south in a pleasant vale to join the middle Durance. Further to the north-east in the upper Durance valley is Briançon at a height of 4,350 feet, a town of great antiquity, for it was once called *Brigantium*, the capital of a Celtic kingdom. It became a mediaeval walled town, and was later fortified by Vauban, for it commands the Mont Genèvre pass into Italy. The town consists of steep narrow streets on the slopes below the citadel, with many old forts on the hills around. It is a busy tourist resort, with the Pelvoux massif to the west and the Cottian Alps to the east, while the *Route des Alpes* comes down the Guisane valley. The only other towns, also in the Durance basin, are Sisteron, an attractive old Provençal town with narrow streets climbing the steep sides of a rock eminence near the gorge-like confluence of the Buech and the Durance, and Digne, the chief town of the *département* of Basses-Alpes; the latter had 13,660 people in 1962, and is a pleasant resort for the Provençal Alps. It has been a spa for a long time, with its warm alkaline and sulphurous springs.

COMMUNICATIONS

The pattern of communications in the French Alps, both of roads and railways, is more dense than might be expected, for two main reasons. One is that the Alps lie across lines of movement between central France and northern Italy, facilitated by several transverse valleys, the other is that the whole region has been opened up to cater both for the annual influx of tourists and for the needs of industry. There are several international passes (Fig. 139)—the *Petit-St. Bernard* (7,178 feet) between Bourg-St. Maurice and Aosta, the *Mont Cenis* (6,834 feet) between Lanslebourg and Susa, the *Mont Genèvre* (6,083 feet) between Briançon and Cesana Torinese, and the *Col de Larche* (6,545 feet) between Barcelonnette and Cuneo.

There are only two main trans-Alpine railways between France and Italy. The more northerly utilises the famous Mont Cenis (or Fréjus) tunnel, eight and a half miles long, constructed during the years 1857–70, the first of the great trans-Alpine tunnels. It penetrates the Massif de Fréjus at a maximum height of 4,246 feet, while the frontier-ridge rises 5,500 feet above. The section between Culoz and Modane was the first line to be electrified in France, an operation completed in the 'twenties of this century. The other trans-Alpine route runs north-eastward from Nice into the southern ranges of the Maritime Alps, and then crosses the Col de Tende into Italy before descending to Cuneo, hence to Turin. In addition, a narrow-gauge railway links Chamonix and Martigny in the extreme north by means of a tunnel under the Col des Montets, then following the valley of the Trient into Switzerland.

The French Alps are quite well served by internal railways and roads. A longitudinal line runs from Geneva via Culoz and Chambéry (a section of the Mont Cenis line) to Grenoble, then south to Veynes; this section provides one of the finest railway journeys in the Alps. Beyond Vif the line leaves the Drac valley and crosses the Dévoluy massif by way of the Col de la Croix-Haute at 3,858 feet; it uses sweeping curves, astonishing loops, long viaducts and several tunnels. At Veynes, where it is crossed by the line between Livron in the Rhône valley and Briançon, the railway continues southward, and from Sisteron it follows the Durance valley into Lower Provence, thence to Marseilles. Other lines run transversely into the French Alps, serving the tourist resorts: from Aix-les-Bains to Annecy, Bonneville and up the Arve valley to Chamonix, up the Isère valley via Albertville and Moûtiers to Bourg-St. Maurice, and up the

FIG. 139.—THE MAIN ROADS OF THE FRENCH ALPS.

The main passes are indicated from north to south by numbers, with altitudes in feet, as follows : (1) Col des Gets (3,815) ; (2) Col du Forclaz (4,996) ; (3) Col des Montets (4,793) ; (4) Col des Aravis (4,914) ; (5) Col du Petit-St. Bernard (7,178) ; (6) Col de l'Iseran (9,085) ; (7) Col du Mont Cenis (6,834) ; (8) Col du Galibier (8,399) ; (9) Col du Lautaret (6,752) ; (10) Col du Glandon (6,401) ; (11) Col de la Croix de Fer (6,847) ; (12) Col du Granier (3,819) ; (13) Col de la Porte (4,347) ; (14) Col de Rousset (4,628) ; (15) Col de la Croix-Haute (3,858) ; (16) Col Bayard (4,077) ; (17) Col de Cabre (3,871) ; (18) Col du Mont Gènevre (6,083) ; (19) Col d'Izoard (7,743) ; (20) Col de Vars (6,926) ; (21) Col de Larche (6,545) ; (22) Col de la Cayolle (7,631) ; (23) Col d'Allos (7,382) ; (24) Col de Maure (4,419) ; (25) Col de Tende (1,873).

Based on (i) the *Michelin* series of road-maps, 1 : 200,000 ; (ii) the annual *Guide Michelin* ; and (iii) *Europe: Strassen Atlas* (*Kümmerly und Frey,* Bern).

Durance valley to Briançon. In addition to the standard-gauge lines, light-railways serve settlements in side valleys. Grenoble is the centre of seven of these lines converging on the town. Two other lengthy narrow-gauge lines penetrate the Provençal Alps, one from Digne to Nice, the other from Aix-en-Provence via Draguignan also to Nice. The mountain-railways and telpher-lines (*téléfériques*) are obvious concomitants of the mountain resorts. The *téléfériques* are numerous, used not only for tourists but also for bringing down milk, cheese, timber and limestone. The highest of the passenger *téléfériques* goes almost to the summit of the Aiguille du Midi, at a height of 11,834 feet, thence over the snowfields to the Col de Géant on the Italian frontier.

The internal road-system is good, and large numbers of cars and an extensive service of *autocars* penetrate in summer far into the upper valleys and over the cols. The famous *Route des Alpes* has been developed from Thonon and Evian on Lake Geneva all the way to Nice, crossing from valley to valley by high inter-connected roads over the cols. The passes are shown on Fig. 139; twenty-five are listed by *Michelin*, all over 3,800 feet. The highest is the Col de l'Iseran (9,085 feet), open only from early July to mid-October, which links the upper Isère valley with that of the Arc, between Bourg-St. Maurice and Lanslebourg. The second highest is the 8,399-foot Col du Galibier, which forms a link between St. Michel in the Maurienne and then either down the Romanche to La Grave and Le Bourg d'Oisans, or down the Lautaret road to Briançon. The top of the col is pierced by a quarter-mile long road tunnel, constructed in 1891 to save the last few hundred feet of steep ascent. The successive crossing of these two cols offers a magnificent stretch of Alpine motoring.

In 1965 a road-tunnel[1] was opened under Mont Blanc between Chamonix and Courmayeur in Italy. It is 7·5 miles long, the longest road-tunnel in the world, entering on the French side at 3,950 feet and leaving on the Italian side at about 4,500 feet.

[1] P. Guichonnet, 'L'Achèvement du tunnel du Mont-Blanc', in *R.G.A.* (1963), vol. 51, pp. 145-54.

CHAPTER 23

THE PYRENEES

The Pyrenees form a mountain barrier more than 250 miles in length between the Bay of Biscay and the Mediterranean. In altitude they do not compare with the Alps, for their highest summit, the Pic d'Aneto in the Maladetta massif (which lies wholly in Spain) attains only 11,169 feet, and the ranges both at the western and eastern ends rarely exceed 3,000 feet. The maximum width of the uplands is only about fifty miles; in the west it is less than twenty miles, and in the east the culminating prong of the Mont d'Albères is little more than five miles across, reaching the coast at Cap Cerbère. The greater part of the Pyrenees, in fact, lies in Spain, forming a complex area of *sierras* and deep valleys drained by the headstreams of the Ebro.

Nevertheless, the Pyrenees are in many ways the most satisfactory of the so-called 'natural frontiers of France'. The effectiveness of the physical barrier is the result partly of the abruptness with which the mountains rise as a long snow-fringed rampart from the foot-hills bordering the plain of Aquitaine; as M. Sorre [1] expresses it, '*l'impression première est, en somme, d'une crête rigide et continue*'. The high-level continuity of this rampart is especially evident in the but slightly serrated central Pyrenees; for a distance of more than a hundred miles the lowest pass is La Plan de Direts (6,165 feet). While many valleys run southward deep into the mountains, they almost all end in *culs-de-sac*, and open longitudinal valleys (as in the Alps), which invite penetration by routeways and settlement, are only slightly developed.

For much of its length the main crest-line demarcates the Franco-Spanish frontier. The two chief exceptions are in the neighbourhood of the Val d'Aran (Fig. 141), where a right-angled bend to the north leaves the whole of the Maladetta massif and the head-waters of the Garonne in Spain, and in the east where the Col de la Perche between the upper valleys of the Têt and the Segre is entirely in France. The Pyrenean frontier, defined by the Treaty of the Pyrenees in 1659, has remained remarkably stable. The effectiveness of the mountains as a physical obstacle must, however, not be exaggerated, for in point of fact sovereign states have straddled the ranges both on the west and the east. Navarre emerged as a unit at the end of the first

---

[1] M. Sorre, *Les Pyrénées* (1922, several editions), is one of the 'classic' French regional monographs. For a further general account, see P. Arque, *Géographie des Pyrénées françaises* (1943). Recent publications are G. Viers, *Les Pyrénées* (1962); and R. Brunet *et al.*, *Les Pyrénées françaises* (1961), *Edsco Documents*.

millennium A.D. and maintained a high degree of independence until 1516, when Spain annexed the southern side; the northern portion survived until its ruler became Henry IV of France in 1594. In the east Roussillon intermittently formed part of a state of Catalonia, which belonged to France and Spain in turn until the Treaty of the Pyrenees. The barrier-quality of the mountain ranges has been due less to the actual physical obstacles (although they are admittedly considerable in the central part) than to the lack of incentive to create trans-Pyrenean routes; the mountains separate no important commercial or industrial regions, as did the Alps lying athwart the route-ways between the Mediterranean and central Europe.

STRUCTURE AND RELIEF

Structure.—The Pyrenees owe their basic structures to the fold-movements of Tertiary times, though of a somewhat earlier date (Eocene and early Oligocene) than the main Alpine systems. The orogeny was one of great complexity, involving masses of granite and of Pre-Cambrian gneissic rocks (fragments of the ancient Hercynian continent), highly metamorphosed Palaeozoic slates, schists and limestones, and flanking Jurassic, Cretaceous and Older Tertiary limestones (Fig. 140). The folding was so intense that numerous large-scale recumbent overfolds were formed; in places metamorphosed Palaeozoic rocks overlie Upper Cretaceous limestones. Denudation has however gone on longer and proceeded further than in the Alps, and much of the complicated rock-structure

FIG. 140.—SIMPLIFIED GEOLOGICAL MAP OF THE PYRENEES.

Based on (i) folding map in L. de Launay, *Géologie de la France* (1921); and (ii) *Carte géologique de la France*, 1 : 1,000,000, published by the *Service de la Carte géologique détaillée de la France* (1933).

overlying the major thrust-planes has been removed.

Faulting was associated both with the main orogenic movements and with late-Tertiary disturbances, involving *en masse* uplift and depression. These resulted in a number of prominent plateaus and lofty basins, especially in the eastern Pyrenees, and were also responsible for the formation of the plain of Roussillon and for the western Mediterranean basin generally, including the Golfe du Lion which separates the Pyrenean ranges from those of Provence.

The net result of these structural processes has been the formation of three more or less longitudinal structural zones in the French Pyrenees, although these are not all everywhere well represented. On the northern flanks occurs what might be called the 'external' or 'frontal' zone (the *Pré-Pyrénées*), where the relatively superficial though closely packed folding involved mainly Upper Cretaceous limestones. Many straight though usually short parallel ridges can be distinguished, now emphasised by erosion which has worn vales in the associated clays and marls. Some French geographers use the name *Petites Pyrénées* for the whole of this zone, although others would restrict this term to the ridges rising to 1,750 or 2,500 feet between the rivers Garonne and Ariège. Another upland within this zone is the Plantaurel. Further west the late-Tertiary fans which spread out over the foothills (Lannemezan, Bigorre, etc., described in Chapter 13) completely mask the structural features of this frontal zone, which only reappears in the extreme west.

The second longitudinal zone is that of *Ariège*. Complex folding has here brought diverse rocks into close juxtaposition, so that subsequent differential denudation has emphasised the long narrow exposures of granites and gneissic rocks, Older Palaeozoic schists, and Mesozoic limestones, clays and marls. These varied rocks and structures make equally varied contributions to the landscape. The granitic and other crystalline rocks form '*noyaux*' elongated from west to east, projecting from the Mesozoic cover: Barousse, Milhas, Castillon, Arize, the curiously named Massif des Trois Seigneurs, St. Barthélemy (sometimes called the Chaîne de Tabe) and Agly. The limestones form long *crêtes* separated by longitudinal valleys worn in the marls and clays, or such plateaus as those of the Pays de Sault in the east and the Pays de Gave further west. To the east the Ariège zone fades out into the broad trench of Fenouillèdes (the upper Agly valley) to the south of the outlying Corbières massif.[1] The last (sometimes referred to as *le Mouthoumet* after the town on its northern flanks) is structurally not a part of the Pyrenees but of the Central Massif, an upstanding mass of Palaeozoic rocks separated from the Montagne Noire by the '*couloir*' of the Aude valley.

[1] P. Brunet, 'Recherches morphologiques sur les Corbières', *Mém. et Document. du Centre* (1958), pp. 59-134.

The high central line of the Pyrenees is known as the *zone axiale* or as the *zone des grands massifs*.[1] In the words of D. Faucher, '*l'axe de la chaîne est formé par un affleurement de terrains primaires*'. The Palaeozoic rocks were vigorously folded during the Hercynian orogeny, as were those of Corbières and the Montagne Noire, and at the same time batholithic masses of granite were intruded into the cores of the folds. All these were heavily denuded and then involved in the Tertiary orogeny. Long continued erosion has now divided the axial zone into '*un chapelet de massifs*' of granite, mica-schists and gneiss: Balaïtous, Vignemale, Néouvielle, Posets, Maladetta, Valira, Campcardos, Carlitte, Puigmal and Canigou; these massifs, elongated more or less from west to east, stand out on Fig. 140. Deeply-cut valleys, mostly trending transversely northward, but with a few short longitudinal sections (the Tourmalet and part of the upper Garonne, for example), define these upland groups of high plateaus from which rise rugged peaks, the *pyramides massives*. A few small intrusions of andesite and kindred rocks have been revealed by denudation; the most notable result is the striking profile of the Pic du Midi de Bigorre (9,465 feet), isolated by the removal of the much less resistant surrounding slates of Carboniferous age.

These then are the three main structural zones of the Pyrenees which are represented in France. Further south are two more, the *zones calcaires espagnoles*, a narrow belt of Upper Cretaceous limestones, succeeded by the *zone de l'Aragon* of Eocene and some Oligocene rocks. The latter is wholly in Spain, but the former constitutes the main crest-line in a number of places; in succession from west to east are the Pic d'Orhy, the Vizaurin, and the Mont Perdu group. The last forms the frontier to the south of the Cirque de Gavarnie; its back-wall rises to a lofty limestone ridge, culminating in the fine summits of Mont Perdu itself (11,007 feet), the summit of which is in Spain, the Tours de Marboré and the Soum de Ramond.

Drainage.—For much of its length the main Pyrenean crest-line forms a remarkably continuous watershed between streams flowing northwards into France, southwards into Spain, consequent upon the slope of the main axial uplift; the streams originally flowed over a now largely vanished cover of Mesozoic and Tertiary rocks. The two master-streams are the Garonne, with its tributary the Ariège draining the central and much of the eastern Pyrenees, and the Adour in the west with its series of tributaries, each known

---

[1] P. Barrère, 'Le Relief des massifs granitiques de Néouvielle, de Cauterets et de Panticosa', in *R.G.P.S.-O.* (1952), vol. xxiii, pp. 69-98; this contains maps of the massifs and some fine air-photographs. For a detailed account, see Ch. Jacob, *Zone axiale, versant sud et versant nord des Pyrénées* (*Livre jubilaire du Centenaire de la Société géologique de France*, 1930).

by its generic name of *gave*, indicating a foaming torrent. Their valleys extend far into the ranges, terminating as steep trough-heads which rise to mere notches forming high-level passes in the ridge-line (Plate LXIV).

Major longitudinal valleys are notably absent in the central and western French Pyrenees; the only prominent examples are the Val d'Aran on the Spanish side of the frontier and the valley of the Ariège near Ax-les-Thermes. In detail, however, the many streams reveal some degree of adaptation to the structure, and in places they follow narrow outcrops of less resistant rocks in a direction parallel to the main Pyrenean crest-line, so that short open west–east valleys alternate with transverse gorge-like sections. In the east the rivers Agly, Têt and Tech occupy prominent west-east valleys of structural origin, as they flow from the uplands of Carlitte and Canigou into the plain of Roussillon (see pp. 441-6).

The Garonne rises in the Val d'Aran in Spain, an open west-east valley developed along a narrow outcrop of slate between crystalline massifs to north and south. It has two head streams (known as *garonas* in the Spanish Pyrenees, hence the name of the main river), one rising at the eastern end of the Val, the other emerging as a strong resurgence from a cavern known as the Goueil de Jouéou (Fig. 141). It was proved by the expert French speleologist, Norbert Casteret, that these waters are derived from a water-sink on the Spanish side of the ridge-line, the Trou de Toro, at a height of 6,500 feet, into which pours a torrent from the snow-fields and glaciers of the Maladetta massif; a remarkable subterranean drainage system passes under the main watershed.[1] The Garonne leaves the Val d'Aran by the gorge of the Pont du Roi, below which the valley opens out again in the basin of Parignac. Beyond this the river leaves the axial zone of the Pyrenees and crosses the open limestone country of the Ariège zone. Near Montréjeau it receives its large headstream, the Neste; this river flows north through the Val d'Aure, receiving many confluents from the Néouvielle massif, then turns abruptly at right-angles to the east into a trench in the frontal zone to the south of the huge fan of the plateau of Lannemezan (see p. 351). The Garonne continues in this direction through the broad basin of St. Gaudens, and after receiving the Salat (which drains the uplands of Couserans) it crosses the Petites Pyrénées below Boussens and so enters the low Tertiary plateaus of Aquitaine.

The main Pyrenean tributary of the Garonne is the Ariège, which rises on the Pic de Nègre, forming for a short distance the boundary of Andorra. It receives many tributaries from the mountains on the eastern margins of Andorra and from the Carlitte massif. From Ax

---

[1] N. Casteret, *Ten Years under the Earth* (English translation by B. Mussey, 1940), pp. 218-35.

to Tarascon the river occupies a broad longitudinal trench separating the frontier ridges from the granitic mass of St. Barthélemy to the north (culminating in a summit just over 7,700 feet), and then the river cuts transversely across the crystalline rocks in a

FIG. 141.—THE SOURCES OF THE GARONNE.

The possible line of the underground connection between the Trou de Toro and Goueil de Jouéou is indicated by a dotted line.

The high peaks of the Maladetta are indicated as follows: **A**, Pic d'Aneto (10,512 feet); **Ma**, Pic Margalide (10,689); **Mo**, Pic Moulières (9,859); **N**, Néthou (11,168).

Based on: (i) *Carte de France à 1:200,000*, sheet 77; and (ii) N. Casteret, *Ten Years under the Earth* (1940), pp. 216-17; this is a translation of two of the distinguished speleologist's works, *Dix Ans sous terre* and *Au fond des gouffres*, translated and edited by B. Mussey.

narrow steep-sided valley to Montgaillard. The Ariège then enters the broad basin in which is situated Foix, succeeded below the town by an almost gorge-like valley through the limestone ridges of the Chaîne du Plantaurel. Finally the river flows across the gently undulating Tertiary plateau to join the Garonne near Portet.

The dissected Massif de Néouvielle forms a remarkable centre of drainage dispersion, for the Neste drains its eastern flanks, the Adour its north-eastern and northern slopes, and the Gave de Pau its western margins. Two streams, the Tourmalet flowing east to the Neste and the Bastan flowing to the west to the Gave de Pau, have cut deep valleys across the massif, separating the Pic du Midi de Bigorre from the Pic d'Aubert-Pic Long group of the Néouvielle massif; their sources are divided only by the Col de Tourmalet (6,939 feet), across which passes a fine motor-road. The Adour itself flows northwards through its broadening valley; near Bagnères-de-Bigorre the extensive flat-floored well cultivated basin contrasts with the wooded slopes on either side. The river continues through Tarbes (see p. 358) across the gravel-fan of Bigorre (Fig. 91). The Gave de Pau, the most easterly of the Pyrenean *gaves*, rises in the Cirque de Gavarnie under the frontier ridge, and flows boldly north through its broad detritus-floored vale towards Lourdes, joined by innumerable torrents from the hanging-valleys on either side. Near Luz, and again lower down near Pierrefitte-Argelès, the valley broadens into quite extensive basins, but the river crosses the limestone country above Lourdes in a prominent gorge. Below the town the river, whose course is blocked by a vast mass of fluvio-glacial material from which streams drain north to the Adour, turns abruptly west and then north-west across the Tertiary fan to Pau.

Two more *gaves*, d'Ossau and d'Aspe, drain the western parts of the High Pyrenees, converging to form the Gave d'Oloron. The Ossau rises among the rugged ridges and basins of the Pic du Midi d'Ossau, the Aspe descends from the frontier ridge in the neighbourhood of the Col du Somport. The latter valley shows well the usual alternation of broad trough and steep-sided gorge; the basin of Bedous-Accous, for example, lies at a height of about 1,500 feet. Further west the Gave de Saison (or de Mauléon), formed by two small streams which drain the basins in which stand the little towns of Larrau and St. Engrâce, flows northwards through a clearly defined valley to join the Oloron. The *pays*-name of *Soule* is given to the valley of the Saison; *Haute-Soule* comprises the valleys and ridges of the two headstreams, *Bas-Soule* the broad valley of the middle Saison eroded through Lower Cretaceous marls, with its centre at Tardets. Finally, in the west the Nive rises in the Cretaceous limestone plateau-country, and flows through the basin of Cize to join the Adour at Bayonne.

Underground Drainage.—The underground section of the course of the upper Garonne already described is one example of a common phenomenon in the Pyrenees, the result of the widespread occurrence of limestones varying in age from Older Palaeozoic to Tertiary.

These are found in close juxtaposition with other impermeable rocks, thus causing water-sinks (*gouffres* or, locally, *lecias*), vast ramifications of cavern-systems, and powerful resurgences (*goueils*). Many hundreds of these cave-systems have been explored and named; as E.-A. Martel puts it, '. . . *la fissuration du sous-sol pyrénéen est formidable*'. On the face of the Mont Perdu group, above the Cirque de Gavarnie near the Brèche de Rolande (a huge rectangular rock-gash in the frontier-ridge), was discovered one of the largest permanently ice-filled caverns in the world (the *Grotte Casteret*), at a height of 8,800 feet, containing a sort of subterranean glacier which occupies the channel worn by an underground river in bygone periods of milder climate. What was for a time the deepest known abyss in France (the *Gouffre Martel*) was discovered opening into the face of the Pyramid de Serre, the steep upper wall of the Cirque du Lez on the French side of the frontier-ridge to the north of the Val d'Aran; it was explored for a vertical depth of 1,566 feet, with a torrent flowing throughout.[1] Adjacent to the Gouffre Martel, the magnificent stalactite-cavern of *La Cigalère* was discovered by Casteret; this had practical results, for the *Union Pyrénéenne Electrique* drove a tunnel through the mountainside into the cavern and tapped an underground stream through pipes, affording a head of water of over 3,000 feet. There are many more of these cave-systems, but the most fantastic is the *Gouffre de Pierre St. Martin*, near the Spanish frontier on the side of the Pic d'Arlas (6,759 feet) in the western Pyrenees; below is the valley of the Licq and the village of St. Engrâce. This *gouffre* has been descended to an overall depth of 2,389 feet. It is entered by an initial vertical shaft no less than 1,135 feet deep; beyond lies an inter-connected series of seven enormous caverns, the last of which, the Salle de la Verna, is large enough to contain a building twice the size of Notre-Dame Cathedral in Paris. Here the underground river finally disappears through a mass of sediment. This cave-system was the scene during the years 1952 to 1955 of incidents of tragedy and remarkable fortitude.[2] Within all these cavern-systems are found large underground lakes, lofty waterfalls and foaming torrents; the water-table fluctuates so violently that many systems can be explored only in August and September. Much information has been derived about this underground water for the benefit of hydro-electric production.

Some of the caverns rival those of the Vezère valley (see p. 342) as the homes of early man, who has left abundant evidence in the shape of wall-paintings, implements and weapons, and the bones of

---

[1] N. Casteret, 'L'Abîme le plus profond de France: le Gouffre Martel', in *La Montagne* (1936), vol. 62, pp. 333-6.

[2] Full accounts are given, translated from the French, by H. Tazieff, *Caves of Adventure* (1953), and N. Casteret, *The Descent of Pierre St. Martin* (1955).

his prey. Many finds have been made at Labastide in the Neste valley ('a salon of Aurignacian and Magdalenian art'), Gargas, Montespan and Marsoulas on the margins of the Garonne valley near St. Gaudens, Mas-d'Azil in the Arize valley, and Niaux and its neighbours in the Ariège valley.[1]

Glaciation.[2]—The present-day permanent snow-fields and glaciers of the Pyrenees are small in extent, with an aggregate area of only about thirteen square miles. They are confined to the higher mountain groups over 10,000 feet in the central Pyrenees, where they form small caps to some of the rounded peaks, or lie in north-facing cirques and on high shelves.[3] Most of the present named glaciers are little more than *névés*. The biggest individual glacier in the French Pyrenees is the Glacier d'Aussoue on the eastern flanks of the Pic de Vignemale; there is also the Glacier Néouvielle in the massif of that name and others on the slopes of Mont Perdu above Gavarnie. Further east a few tiny glaciers exist on the Montvallier and Montcalm massifs, and some *névés* on Carlitte and Canigou. The largest Pyrenean group is on the Maladetta group within Spain, with five individual glaciers and some snow-fields (Fig. 141).

In the Pleistocene, snow-fields and glaciers were of course very much more widespread, though never comparable with those of the Alps. From the high basins and lofty plateaus glacier-tongues pushed northwards along existing river-valleys.[4] The glacier which occupied the valley of the Gave de Pau probably had a maximum length of thirty-four miles, and a thickness of 2,900 feet. The glaciers descended as low as 1,300 and in places 1,100 feet above present sea-level. At least two definite glacial advances can be distinguished, although some authorities claim to have traced three and perhaps four.

This upland glaciation has left its usual stamp on the landscape,[5]

---

[1] N. Casteret, *Ten Years under the Earth* (1940), pp. 218-35.

[2] The most convenient summary of Pyrenean glaciation is F. Taillefer, 'Glaciaire pyrénéen: versant nord et versant sud', in *R.G.P.S.-O.* (1957), vol. xxviii, pp. 221-44; this provides a map of the glaciers and moraines, a table of the glacial chronology, and a detailed bibliography.

[3] The extent and names of the present glaciers are shown by P. Barrère, 'Equilibre glaciaire actuel et quaternaire dans l'ouest des Pyrénées Centrales', in *R.G.P.S.-O.* (1953), vol. xxiv, pp. 116-34; there is a detailed map on p. 118.

[4] See, for example, D. Faucher, 'Le Glacier de l'Ariège dans la basse vallée montagnarde', in *R.G.A.* (1932), vol. 20, pp. 573-89.

[5] For an immensely detailed study of the results of glaciation in the Couserans (the basin of the Salat), see M. Chevalier, 'Le Relief glaciaire des Pyrénées du Couserans', in *R.G.P.S.-O.* (1954), vol. xxv, I, 'Les Cirques' (pp. 97-124), II, 'Les Vallées' (pp. 189-220); this contains detailed maps and some valuable air-photographs. See also H. Awad, 'La Morphologie de la vallée d'Ossau', in *A. de G.* (1939), vol. xlviii, pp. 449-58; this deals with the imposition of ice upon the structural and pre-glacial features, and includes a detailed map of ridges,

in the form of innumerable cirque-basins, lofty arêtes notched by cols, peaks of a distinct pyramidal form, and remarkably over-deepened valleys, with trough-heads, rock-steps and lateral hanging-valleys whose mouths are 1,400 to 1,700 feet above the main valley-floors. Large numbers of tiny rock-basins now contain lakes (the Néouvielle massif is said to have no less than forty-five); some are very deep, notably the Lac Bleu de Lesponne which is 394 feet in depth, and the Lac de Caillaouas which at an altitude of 7,070 feet is 331 feet deep.[1] The best known cirques are those of Gavarnie and Troumouse at the head of the Gave de Pau on the north-western flanks of Mont Perdu in the Tres Sorores massif. Gavarnie is a magnificent amphitheatre nearly two miles across, backed by cliffs rising in a series of enormous steps for 5,000 feet to the rocky crest-line at twice that altitude (Plate LXIII). Several cascades descend this cliff-wall (the longest fall is over 1,500 feet), and huge scree-cones rest against the base of the rocks. Troumouse, at the head of the valley of the Héas (a right-bank tributary of the Gave de Pau), is in some ways finer than Gavarnie, with steep walls rising to a crest-line of such peaks as the Pic de la Munia (10,335 feet).

The upper valleys of the *gaves* are prominently over-deepened, with steep walls and flat floors; several reveal transverse rock-bars which cause falls and rapids on the streams and afford sites for hydro-electric stations. Above the walls are the high valley-benches. Some of the hanging tributaries form spectacular falls; in the Carlitte massif a stream leaves the Etang de Naguilhès and falls in a series of rapids for over 3,000 feet to join the Oriège, a tributary of the Ariège.

Glacial deposition has contributed a swathing cover to the flat valley-floors, and arcs of terminal moraines are present in most of the valleys; these are particularly distinctive near Lourdes in the Gave de Pau and near Arudy in the Gave d'Ossau.[2] Quite large lakes were for a time ponded up behind these *barrages morainiques*, evidence of which can be seen clearly in the valley of the Gave de Pau, but except for the small Lac de Lourdes these lakes have vanished through down-cutting of the outflowing stream and some degree of infilling. Other glacial deposition is shown by lateral moraines high on the valley-sides, as near Campan in the Adour valley and along the valley of the Neste d'Oo. Beyond the morainic lines are great sheets of fluvio-glacial sands and gravels.

Weathering and Post-Glacial Erosion.—The sides of the mountain groups are scored by innumerable gullies, the work of torrents

cirques, moraines, etc. See also G. Viers, 'Le Glaciaire du Massif du Carlit', in *R.G.P.S.-O.* (1961), vol. 32, pp. 6-33, with detailed maps.

[1] L. Gaurier, *Les Lacs des Pyrénées françaises* (1934).

[2] These are plotted on a map in F. Taillefer, *op. cit.*, p. 222.

flowing down into the main valleys, fed particularly by the melt-waters from the heavy winter snowfall. Their load of débris is borne away towards the plain of Aquitaine. Weathering, particu-larly the action of frost, contributes potently to the wastage of the mountains; vast scree-slopes flow away from the foot of each crag. The widespread occurrence of limestone enables chemical erosion to produce karst-like features; the name *causse* is actually used in the western Pyrenees (the Causse d'Ahusky). Large areas of *lapiaz* (*lapiés*) are solution-scarred with 'chasms, oubliettes, trap-holes, fissures, tunnels, funnels, knife-like ridges' (N. Casteret). A vegeta-tion of bracken in the more humid west, of dwarf rhododendron in the centre, and of either *maquis* or *garrigue* in the east only emphasises the rugged character of much of the Pyrenean landscape.

Regional Divisions.—On a structural basis three longitudinal zones have been demarcated. It is, however, more convenient in some ways to divide the Pyrenees into three transverse sections: the western, central and eastern Pyrenees. Some French geographers indeed distinguish a fourth, the broad complex mountains on either side of the Ariège basin, hence their name of *Pyrénées de l'Ariège*. This, however, tends to confuse with the longitudinal Ariège struc-tural zone, and it is better to include their western part within the central Pyrenees, their eastern part within the eastern Pyrenees. This division into three sections is further accentuated by marked contrasts in climate, vegetation and agriculture.

The western Pyrenees (*Pyrénées basques* or *atlantiques*) extend from the Bay of Biscay to the Col du Somport; as has been stressed, these uplands are lower and hummocky, and only two peaks, the Pic d'Anie (8,215 feet) and the Pic d'Orhy (6,517 feet), rise much above the general level of about 3,000 feet. No permanent snow is present. These uplands are crossed by several low passes (although their approaches are indeed steep and strenuous), including the famous Pass of Roncesvalles (3,576 feet) which is within Spain. While the actual crest-line is commonly of Palaeozoic slates and schists, the western Pyrenees consist mainly of Upper Cretaceous limestone plateaus, cut into by the headstreams of the Nive, Saison and Aspe.

The central Pyrenees comprise a series of massifs, eroded into serrated ridges and craggy peaks by the deep valleys of the head-streams of the Adour, Garonne and Ariège. These form the isolated valley-*pays*—the Vallée d'Aspe, the Vallée d'Ossau, the Val d'Aure and many more.

The eastern Pyrenees, to the east of the Col de la Perche, partake of a different character, since they consist fundamentally of a series of easterly trending ridges and massifs—Corbières, Canigou and Albères, penetrated by the longitudinal vales of the Agly (*Fenouil-*

lèdes), the Têt (*Conflent*) and the Tech (*Vallespir*), each opening into the Plaine du Roussillon (see p. 441). The frontier here swings south along the eastern margins of the little state of Andorra, leaving the whole Carlitte massif and the upper part of the Segre valley (known as *Cerdagne*) in France. Thus Cerdagne and Conflent form two high-level *vallées montagnards*. There are also high-level plateaus, the *hautes plaines*, notably those of Quérigut, Sault (sometimes known as the *Pays de Sault*)[1] and Capcir,[2] the upper valley of the Aude on the eastern flanks of Carlitte. Much of this lofty area, covered with glacial and fluvio-glacial débris brought by the Quaternary glaciers from the adjacent mountains, lies above 5,000 feet.

The Corbières massif is not structurally part of the Pyrenees. Culminating in the Pic de Bugarach (4,038 feet), it is a mass of Palaeozoic crystalline rocks similar in character to the Montagne Noire beyond the Aude valley.[3]

CLIMATE

The Pyrenees reveal the usual diversity of climatic features of mountainous areas, with both temperature and humidity modified locally by altitude and aspect. While the French Alps form a broad system trending from north to south, from continental to Mediterranean régimes, the Pyrenees are orientated from west to east, from Atlantic to Mediterranean régimes. The Pyrenees are neither so lofty nor so extensive, but nevertheless their climates reveal very considerable contrasts.

In the eastern Pyrenees conditions partake of the Mediterranean climatic régime, and the features of the plain of Roussillon (see p. 442) are gradually modified towards the west. The mean annual rainfall varies from about 26 to 33 inches; Mont-Louis in the Conflent receives 31 inches, two-thirds of which falls in intense downpours during the autumn months. There is a marked contrast in the precipitation received by places in the deep valleys and on the intervening uplands. The line of the Conflent and Cerdagne valleys, for example, forms in D. Faucher's expressive phrase, '*une sorte de couloir de sécheresse*'; Puigcerda just inside Spain receives only 23 inches, while Canigou further east has a precipitation of 35 to 40 inches. This same contrast is shown in the valley of the upper Ariège; while Tarascon at 1,560 feet receives 31 inches, Saurat ten

---

[1] J.-J. Lagasquie, 'Le Relief calcaire du plateau de Sault', in *R.G.P.S.-O.* (1964) vol. 35, pp. 11-32.

[2] R. Lambert, 'Le Capcir : évolution récente d'un haut bassin des Pyrénées-Orientales', in *R.G.P.S.-O.* (1965), vol. 36, pp. 5-22.

[3] J. Malaurie, 'Le Relief des Corbières Orientales', in *A. de G.* (1950), vol. lix, pp. 259-68, contains a detailed morphological map and sections of the massif.

miles to the west and at twice the altitude has 68 inches. Temperatures too vary strikingly with position and aspect; the valleys extending into the uplands from Roussillon have the same high temperatures in summer, with means of 70° to 75° F. in summer (Amélie-les-Bains in the Tech valley frequently records 85° F.), while on the surrounding plateaus snow lies for several months and can be expected regularly down to about 2,000 feet.

The western Pyrenees reveal, on the other hand, obvious indications of an Atlantic régime, with cloudier skies and an annual precipitation varying from 40 to as much as 60 inches on the west-facing ridges. The distinct autumn-winter maximum is the result of depressions moving eastwards from the Bay of Biscay to the Mediterranean along the northern flanks of the Pyrenees and through the Carcassonne gap. Hendaye, for example, has a mean annual precipitation of 37 inches; the driest month is July with 2·4 inches, the wettest is October with 5·5 inches.[1]

The central Pyrenees naturally form a zone of transition between east and west, though altitude and aspect induce considerable modifications. Thus Arreau at an altitude of 2,300 feet receives 38 inches of rain, compared with twice as much in the lofty Néouvielle massif to the west. The deep valleys of the western *gaves*, open to moist north-westerly air-streams, have an appreciable rainfall; thus Bedous in the valley of the Aspe has 54 inches, Laruns in the Gave d'Ossau about 64 inches. On the other hand, further up the *gaves* the total diminishes as the result of shelter; while Lourdes in the valley of the Gave de Pau at an altitude of 1,312 feet has 51 inches, Argelès further up at 1,500 feet has 44 inches, and Luz at 2,326 feet only 35 inches. However, Gavarnie, higher up still at 4,450 feet in its basin among high peaks, has 48 inches.

It must again be emphasised that locally the Pyrenean climates show great variations. As in all mountain regions, the importance of aspect is reflected in land-use and settlement between the sunny side of a valley (the Alpine *adret*, known in the Pyrenees as the *soulane*, *sola* or *solana*) and the shady side (the *ubac* or *ubaga*).

Snowfall.—As the greater part of the precipitation is received during the winter half-year, much of it falls in the form of snow. The area of permanent snow is small in the Pyrenees, as has already been stressed, the result of their southerly latitude, limited altitude and exposure to mild air-streams from the Mediterranean; during the long warm summer the snow vanishes from all but the highest summits and north-facing cirques. The permanent snow-line there-

[1] Features of the climate and vegetation zones of the western Pyrenees are given by H. Boesch, 'Die Natur im Baskenland', in *Geographica Helvetica* (1955), vol. x, pp. 136-44.

fore lies as high as 9,200 feet even on the north side of the ranges. The winter snowfall is, however, considerable, much greater in the Pyrenees than in many parts of the Alps, and the high massifs wear '*un magnifique manteau hivernal*'. The observatory on the summit of the Pic du Midi de Bigorre usually records a depth of at least twenty feet during most winters; all the passes are blocked for varying lengths of time, many of the high villages are virtually isolated, and winter sports have developed in a number of places. The central Pyrenees are in fact covered on an average for a hundred days above 4,000 feet, for about 170 days above 6,000 feet. This duration of the snow-cover is much shorter on the eastern flanks. The snow-line retreats with amazing rapidity in early summer, and the mountains assume a piebald or striped aspect. Avalanches are widespread and swollen torrents foam down the valleys; many streams are in fact sustained in volume during the summer by snow-melt, especially valuable in the drier eastern valleys, which can use water from the melting snows of Canigou and Carlitte for irrigation.

LAND-USE AND AGRICULTURE

Five *départements* whose southern boundaries coincide with the international frontier cover the French Pyrenees and their foothills. Basses-Pyrénées in the west does, however, include the Basque coastlands and part of the Adour lowlands, while Pyrénées-Orientales contains the plain of Roussillon. Hautes-Pyrénées and Ariège consist almost entirely of the main ranges and foothills. Haute-Garonne is least representative of the Pyrenees, for, as its name would imply, it comprises for the most part the valley of the upper Garonne and includes that part of the Basin of Aquitaine around Toulouse; only a narrow 'peninsula' runs up the valley of the Pique to the frontier. The official returns for the other four *départements* do, however, afford some indication of land-use in the Pyrenees generally.

Land-Use, 1963

(*Percentage of Total Area*)

	Arable	Permanent Pasture	Woodland
Basses-Pyrénées . .	23	15	19
Hautes-Pyrénées . .	17	29	21
Ariège . . .	17	32	25
Pyrénées-Orientales .	5	17	24

Source: *Ministère de l'Agriculture*, quoted by *Annuaire statistique de la France, 1964*.

The Woodlands.—The character of the Pyrenean woodlands emphasises the contrasts between the Atlantic and Mediterranean margins. The more humid western uplands were once covered with magnificent forests of ash, which still clothe the steeper slopes, together with considerable areas of chestnut. The largest forest is that of Irati,[1] which runs up to and beyond the frontier to the west of the Pic d'Orhy ; it occupies about 5,900 acres, of which about 4,700 are still effectively wooded. In the central Pyrenees the beech is dominant on lower slopes, succeeded by spruce, mountain pine, larch and Scotch fir. On the valley floors, where not cleared for agriculture, are copses and lines of planes, poplars, maple, hazel, lime, birch and alder, nurtured by the adequate precipitation. In the east the various Mediterranean oaks (especially kerm- and cork-oaks) gradually become dominant, with pines at higher altitudes.[2]

The story of the gradual past destruction of the forests is much the same as elsewhere in western Europe ; the iron-forges of the Pyrenean valleys required charcoal, trees were felled for timber, especially for shipbuilding, and the *montagnards pyrénéens* attacked the woodland both from above and below to increase their pasture and arable land. Frequently they resorted to burning to produce the cleared lands, the *artigues*. The flocks and herds, especially of goats, prevented regeneration by their close grazing ; in the western Pyrenees constant pollarding of the ash-trees to provide green shoots for fodder ultimately destroyed many trees. Devastation has been worse in the eastern uplands, where much of the former woodland has degenerated into either a *garrigue* of thyme, lavender, dwarf laurel, oleander, aloe and cistus on the limestones, or a *maquis* of dwarf evergreen oak, broom, box and other shrubs on siliceous rocks. Much land in the east and centre is smothered with a dense low scrub of dwarf rhododendron, which, masking the uneven boulder-strewn surface, forms difficult terrain to cross. In the moister west the bracken-fern has spread widely ; it can be cut for litter but it spoils much grazing land.

Some afforestation has been effected during this century, and many of the Pyrenean valleys owe much of their charm to their wooded appearance. The forested area has in fact been increased by almost a fifth during the last fifty years. Some of this is regarded as *forêts de protection*, planted as avalanche-breaks on the hill-sides, or to check landslides and hold the otherwise *terrains mobiles*. Both State- and communally-owned forests have increased appreciably in area.

[1] G. Viers, 'La Forêt d'Irati', in *R.G.P.S.-O.* (1955), vol. xxvi, pp. 5-27 ; this deals with past destruction and present measures of maintenance and afforestation.
[2] See (i) M. Sorre, *Les Pyrénées méditerranéennes. Etude de géographie biologique* (1913) ; (ii) H. Gaussen, *Végétation de la moitié orientale des Pyrénées* (1926) ; and (iii) by the same author, *Géographie botanique et agricole des Pyrénées-Orientales* (1934).

Pastoral Farming.—The table on p. 678 clearly indicates that both *la vie pastorale* and *la vie agricole* contribute to the Pyrenean economy, the former dominating in the high valleys, the latter in the east and on the Aquitaine margins.

In the four *départements* the numbers of sheep (660,000) and of cattle (474,000) are the result of a long steady decline during the last century in the former and a corresponding increase in the latter. Most of the livestock are found in the west and centre, and Basses-Pyrénées had more than a third of each. Several breeds of sheep are represented, some the product of merino crosses; in the high mountains can be seen some attractive long-haired varieties. They are kept for wool, meat and milk; in the central Pyrenees much ewes' milk cheese is made, while from further east 'raw' cheese is sent to Roquefort for final processing. More lamb and mutton is eaten in the towns and villages along the Pyrenean flanks than in any other part of France.

Cattle are also more common in the west and centre; only 12,000 animals, mostly in the high basins, were recorded for Pyrénées-Orientales in 1963. They are kept both for dairying to supply milk to the Pyrenean towns (notably the cream-coloured *race lourdaise*) and for making the various *fromages des Pyrénées*, and also to sell off as stores to the farmers in the plain of Aquitaine and as calves for veal in the markets of Bordeaux and Toulouse. Many are still used as draught-animals, especially in the high valleys. Goats totalled only 10,000 in 1963, more than half of them kept in the *garrigue* country of the east; the herds of silky *chèvres noires* are a familiar sight high up on the mountains. The western Pyrenean valleys have long been famous for horse-rearing; these animals are still widely used for draught purposes. About 17,000 were present in 1961, mainly the agile *cheval navarrais* and the *race ariégeoise*. In some valleys herds of brood-mares are kept from which mules are bred (especially in the head-valleys of the Ariège) for export to Spain.

A pattern of life has evolved which utilises pastures at different altitudes at various times.[1] The water-meadows on the flat valley-floors are crossed by countless runnels fed by the streams descending the steep sides; here the animals graze in spring and autumn, while in summer a crop, sometimes two, of hay is taken. The area devoted to fodder-crops has increased appreciably, notably of lucerne grown under irrigation. In winter the cattle are stall-fed in the *granges-étables*, and many sheep move down to the gravel-covered plateau of

---

[1] Much has been written on this subject. See, for example, H. Cavaillès, *La Vie pastorale et agricole dans les Pyrénées des Gaves, de l'Adour et des Nestes. Etude de géographie humaine* (1931); and M. Chevalier, *La Vie humaine dans les Pyrénées ariégeoises* (1956). The latter is a monumental volume of 1061 pp., with 854 references, many maps and some superb photographs.

Lannemezan, to the lower lands of Armagnac and Comminges, to the Adour lowlands, and in the east to the lowlands of Languedoc. In summer large numbers of animals are taken up to the high pastures (known variously as *plâs*, *plainières*, *coumes* or *comas*), following the receding snow-line. Some are open grass-slopes on the mountain sides, others on valley-benches near the little summer hamlets are carefully surrounded by dry-stone walls and improved by fertilising. The name *estives* or *estibères* is sometimes given to these high pastures, hence the term *estivage* used for the summer-pasturing of animals in the Pyrenees and other mountainous districts. The families looking after the animals live in little summer hamlets (commonly known as *germs*), or in isolated *cabanes* and *bergeries*.[1] For centuries the *montagnards* have jealously guarded their rights of movement and pasturage, frequently held in common by a group of communal proprietors known variously as a *syndicat*, a *vésiau*, a *vehinat* or a *commission*; they could, for example, lay down the exact date of opening a particular pasture to the animals (the '*dévète*', usually in late May) and of its closure to grazing (the '*vète*'). The movement of the animals follows routes delineated by long custom, similar to the *drailles* of the Cévennes (see p. 551), but here known as *camins ramaders*, safeguarded by 'treaties of covenanted entry' (*traités de lie et passerie*, or *paceries* or *faceries*). These rights are especially common and jealously preserved in Canigou and Carlitte, where the sheep come up from the Mediterranean coastlands. Though transhumance and stock-rearing generally has declined during recent decades, as evidenced by the many deserted farms and *cabanes* in the hills, this routine of life still persists in many Pyrenean valleys.[2] One reason for the decline in the movement of cattle is that now many remain on the valley-floors during the summer, when their milk finds a ready market in the popular resorts for which the *estives* are too far distant. Another development has been of co-operation in the handling and processing of milk. For example, the *Société des Fromageries d'Oust* has establish-

---

[1] These are given numerous local names, including *cayolars*, *jasses*, *cujalas*, *orrys*, *orhys*, *bordes* and *pardinas*. The multiplicity of these and other names is due to the fact that in the Pyrenees are spoken Basque, Catalan and the *languedocien*, *gascon* and *béarnais* dialects.

[2] See, for example, in addition to M. Chevalier (*op. cit.*), (i) H. Cavaillès, *La Transhumance pyrénéenne et la circulation des troupeaux dans les plaines de Gascogne* (1931); (ii) M. Chevalier, 'Les Caractères de la vie pastorale dans le bassin supérieur de l'Ariège', in *R.G.P.S.-O.* (1949), vol. xx, pp. 5-84; and (iii) Th. Lefebvre, 'La Transhumance dans les Basses-Pyrénées', in *A. de G.* (1928), vol. xxxviii, pp. 35-60. The last distinguishes five distinct types of movement, and provides two detailed maps (pp. 39 and 53) which show actual routes between the villages and their habitual hill-pastures in summer and the lowland pastures of Aquitaine in winter. See also G. Bertrand, 'Vie pastorale et industrie dans le Val d'Ariège', in *R.G.P.S.-O.* (1961), vol. 32, pp. 63-73.

ments at St. Girons and Massat, and numerous collecting points are served by fleets of lorries. Butter and cheese factories (the *fruitières*) have been established at many towns in the lower parts of the valleys.[1]

Arable Farming.—Within this upland area there is inevitably a scarcity of good soil, and small-scale cultivation is found practised where possible on valley-floors away from the water-meadows, on alluvial fans, and on carefully terraced slopes, usually with the lower edges of the fields protected by dry-stone walls. Some of the high basins, such as that of the upper Adour near Bagnères-de-Bigorre, have flat floors of alluvial soil under a continuous carpet of strip-cultivation. Some land has been improved by fertilising, as evidenced by the replacement of buckwheat (and in parts of rye also) in favour of hard wheat or in the west of maize. Much poor or marginal land has been turned into improved pasture or put under fodder crops. Each of the four *départements* has more than half of its arable area devoted to cereals, except for Pyrénées-Orientales where it falls to a third. Basses-Pyrénées and Ariège have a third of their arable areas under fodder crops, the others about a fifth. The overall pattern is thus generally very similar. But in detail contrasts between the western and eastern uplands are again apparent.

In the west maize rivals wheat, with rye in the higher valleys, and large areas of potatoes, haricots, pumpkins and other vegetables are cultivated. There are some vineyards, but the orchards of apples, cherries and plums are far more extensive. Groves of walnuts and hazel-nuts are succeeded on higher slopes by woods of sweet chestnut. In the lower valleys, market-gardens now cover a large area, supplying the tourist centres during the summer months. In the central Pyrenees wheat increasingly supersedes maize, and rye and potatoes are grown in the higher valleys. Peaches, apricots and vines appear on sunny south-facing slopes.

In the eastern Pyrenees the agricultural systems are really tongue-like extensions of the Mediterranean patterns of the plain of Roussillon, occupying the *vallées montagnardes*[2] and the *hautes plaines*. Among the rock-ridges of the Corbières and the Albères, with their stony wastes, has developed a typical Mediterranean terrace cultivation of vines, olives, almonds, peaches, apricots, even oranges and pomegranates in favoured places, nurtured by streams from the melting snows of Canigou. On the high plains of Capcir and Cer-

---

[1] For example, see M. Bressole and M. Chevalier, 'L'Industrie laitière dans les Pyrénées Ariégeoises', in *R.G.P.S.-O.* (1951), vol. xxii, pp. 71-90; this pays special attention to the Ballongue, where the canton of Castillon is known as '*le pays des fruitières*'.

[2] An attractive study of land-use in an east Pyrenean upland valley, based on intensive field-work, is given by R. Peattie, 'The Conflent: a study in Mountain Geography', in *G.R.* (1930), vol. xx, pp. 245-57.

dagne are orchards of pear, plum and cherry, growing superb dessert-fruit for the Paris markets; the pears of Osseja and the cherries of Céret [1] (the upper Tech valley) are renowned, the former being the first to arrive on the markets of northern France. Elsewhere fields of hard wheat are cultivated in small basins. In some of the higher valleys and basins, such as the Conflent, much of the land is devoted to the cultivation of grass for hay and of fodder-crops by intensive fertilising and irrigating; this provides winter-feed for the cattle coming down from the high pastures. Apples are specially grown in these high valleys.

POWER AND INDUSTRY

Hydro-Electric Power.—The Pyrenees possess a large potential, as yet only partially realised, of hydro-electric power,[2] for they have the advantages of copious precipitation, long yet accessible steep-sided valleys running far into the uplands towards the main crest-line, and a multitude of rock-basin lakes at a high altitude which require only small barrages to increase their storage capacity appreciably. Many of these lakes are at heights exceeding 6,000 feet, and their outflow into the main valley provides a fine natural head. A few larger barrages have been constructed to create new reservoirs, such as Puyvalador at a height of 4,600 feet in Capcir and Bouillouses on the edge of the Carlitte massif. But there has been no major construction of barrages as in the Alps and the Rhône valley.

The emphasis has been on the creation of a large number of small enterprises, rather than of a few major stations. Development started rather later and more slowly in this relatively isolated part of France, to meet local industrial needs and to supply the electrified lines of the former *Midi* railway company. The first high-tension transmission lines in France were in fact built from small stations in the Aude valley to Carcassonne and Narbonne as early as 1901. In 1910 the Orlu station in the valley of the upper Ariège had a head of water supplied by a chute of 3,071 feet, at that time the highest in Europe. After the war of 1914–18 much progress was made, accelerated and co-ordinated by the work of such groups as the *Union des Producteurs d'Electricité des Pyrénées Occidentales* and the *Union Pyrénéenne Electrique*, and stimulated by electrification of the railways carried out by the *Midi* company. By 1939 the Paris-Hendaye

[1] For a detailed study of orchard cultivation in the high valleys, see P. Fénelon, 'La Culture des cerisiers dans la région de Céret', in *R.G.P.S.-O.* (1952), vol. xxiii, pp. 5-28.

[2] A summary of the position before the war of 1939–45, with details of installations, is afforded by L. Babonneau, *L'Energie électrique dans la région pyrénéenne* (1941). A more recent study is R. Brunet, 'L'Equipement électrique des Pyrénées', in *R.G.P.S.-O.* (1962), vol. 33, pp. 123-8.

line had been electrified throughout, together with the transverse line from Bayonne via Toulouse to Béziers and also the two trans-Pyrenean lines. Since the war of 1939–45, *Electricité de France* and the *S.N.C.F.* have pursued a steady policy of development. Several new generating-stations have been constructed, and the considerable activity of the immediate post-war years culminated in the opening of stations at Aston (Ariège valley), Fabrèges (Gave d'Ossau), Bordes (Lez valley), and Cierp (near the confluence of the Pique and the Garonne), followed by the Rouze station in the Aude valley and later at Fabian, Eget-les-Echarts and St. Lary in the Vallée d'Aure (the valley of the river Neste). The latest is the Pragnères station in the valley of the Gave de Pau. Most stations are small in comparison with those of the Alps and Rhône valley, and only four (Miégebat, Pragnères, Aston and Portillon) have an installed capacity exceeding 50,000 kw.

The main transformer stations are at Laruns and Pau for the western group of stations, at Lannemezan for the central group, and at Sabart in the east. While the power-stations mainly supply local industry and the railways, they also make a contribution to the grid. From Lannemezan a 220 kv line runs north-east to Montauban, and 150 kv lines to Pau, Dax and Bordeaux and also to Toulouse. A new 160 kv line has been constructed from the Ariège valley to Narbonne, Béziers and the Rhône valley.

At the beginning of 1964 the total installed capacity of the Pyrenean stations was 1·68 million kw, responsible for an output in 1963 of about one-seventh of the total French hydro-production.

Industry.—The Pyrenean valleys are the scene of two contrasting types of industrial activity, as in the Alps, though developed to a far less degree. On the one hand are the old craft-industries, on the other the new factory industries based on hydro-electricity. The former made use of locally produced wool, flax and hemp, of timber from the mountain-forests both for fabrication and for charcoal-burning, of small deposits of iron- and non-ferrous ores, and of plentiful supplies of fresh water. Many activities grew as the result of isolation and the need for self-sufficiency; these included the spinning and weaving of woollen cloth for clothing. Later the manufacture of cotton and silk developed. These textile industries were widely spread, but were particularly important at Campan and Bagnères-de-Bigorre in the Adour valley, at Nay on the Gave de Pau, at Ancizan and Sarrancolin in the valley of the Aure, and at Lavelanet in one of the side-valleys of the Ariège.[1] Wood-using industries

[1] M. Chevalier, 'L'Industrie textile pyrénéenne et le développement de Lavelanet', in *R.G.P.S.-O.* (1950), vol. xxi, pp. 43-60; this includes a map showing the location of former and contemporary factories (p. 44).

included the manufacture of clogs and *sabots* (especially in the Pays Basque), of furniture, rosaries and religious statuary. Iron-ore has been mined, smelted with charcoal and used at the forges for many centuries, in Canigou since at least the twelfth century. The forges at Baïgorry and Banca in the west, at Louvie and Arthey in the *gave* valleys, at Foix (one of the chief sources of French wrought-iron under the *ancien régime*) and elsewhere made iron objects in great variety, including cannon for the French navy. Nails were produced at Urs and Barguillère.

Many small-scale attempts have been made to mine and refine various non-ferrous ores, including even gold from the river-gravels; the hill-sides reveal here and there the scars of ancient workings but little has been won, and as D. Faucher expresses it, '*quant aux mines, hormis celles de fer, quelle lamentable histoire*'. Some bauxite is worked at Péreille and Roquefixade.

The iron and steel industry has a considerable present-day importance. The ore, mostly haematite of fifty to sixty per cent metal content, is found in the limestones of the Ariège valley near Vicdessos and Rabat, and in Canigou (Fig. 72). While many of the small scattered deposits are now exhausted, the Pyrenean mines still make a useful though fluctuating contribution. In 1913 they produced 370,000 tons and in 1929 about 230,000 tons, but during the economic crisis between 1932 to 1936 output fell to a mere 22,000 tons, though there was some recovery to 109,000 tons in 1939. Since the war the deposits have been vigorously worked, and the yield had been increased to 310,000 tons by 1960, though it had fallen to only 74,000 tons by 1963. The modern Pyrenean steel industry dates from the opening of three blast-furnaces at Tarascon in 1864–7, using Vicdessos ore and coke from Decazeville and Carmaux. Later electric furnaces were installed at Pamiers. These two centres produce about 20,000 tons of steel a year, mostly of high-grade alloys or special quality steels. Some special steels are also made in electric furnaces at Rebouc, various alloys at St. Antoine and ferro-silicates at Mercus.

The availability of power has facilitated some development of the electro-chemical and electro-metallurgical industries.[1] Aluminium is refined at Auzat and Sabart in the Vicdessos valley, at Beyrède in the Aure valley, and at Lannemezan. To the south of Lourdes in the Gave de Pau chemical factories at Soulom and Pierrefitte-Nestalas manufacture nitrogenous and phosphoric fertilisers respectively. A factory at Beyrède near Sarrancolin in the Aure valley makes carborundum abrasives, Boussens in the Garonne valley also has a chemical factory, as has Lannemezan (*Société des Produits Azotes de Lannemezan*), and Marignac near the Garonne-Pique confluence

[1] Y. Doumergue, 'Electro-chimie et électro-métallurgie dans les Hautes-Pyrénées', in *R.G.P.S.-O.* (1965), vol. 36, pp. 373-402.

produces explosives. These factories form small oases of industrial activity in the Pyrenean valleys, contrasting markedly with the predominant *vie pastorale* and *vie agricole*. A rather more extensive area of the industrialisation on the Pyrenean flanks is the triangle between Tarbes, Lourdes and Bagnères-de-Bigorre.[1] Here are located the *Bazet* factory just north of Tarbes which makes insulators, the large electrical and mechanical engineering plant of the *Alsthom* company at Tarbes, an arsenal at Tarbes, two electrical and mechanical engineering plants at Bagnères (one making equipment for the *S.N.C.F.*), and the *Morane* aircraft works at Ossun, between Lourdes and Tarbes.

Quarrying is still active, working limestone for cement in the valley of the Oloron, and marble at St. Béat, Campan, Sarrancolin and Arudy, to be processed at Bagnères; part of Napoleon's tomb in Les Invalides in Paris came from Pyrenean quarries. One large-scale operation is the quarrying of talc (hydrous magnesium silicate), which occurs as large interlaminations within masses of mica-schist, and is worked at the quarry of Trimouns in the St. Barthélemy massif. This, with an annual output of 85,000 tons, is the largest individual talc quarry in the world, and France once had a near monopoly of this material, though today only about ten per cent of the world output is produced.

One further contribution to the economic life of the Pyrenean region is the tourist industry, utilising the attractive scenery of mountain, forest and stream, the heavy winter snowfall which has encouraged winter sports, and the numerous mineral springs. More than fifty places have become spas, based on the mineralised springs which issue either from the margins of igneous intrusions or from the Triassic rocks. Many towns have in their names the elements '*eaux*', '*thermes*' or '*bains*': Eaux-Chaudes and Eaux-Bonnes, Ax-les-Thermes, Amélie-les-Bains and many more.[2] Le Boulou in the valley of the Tech is sometimes known as 'the Vichy of the Pyrenees'.[2] Towns such as Pau and Lourdes (see p. 358) are indeed 'the gateways to the Pyrenees' and the centres of coach excursions, and Cauterets is also a winter-sports' centre (Plate LXIV).

SETTLEMENT AND COMMUNICATIONS

It is obvious that the Pyrenees stand out as one of the sparsely populated parts of France; in 1962 the average density per square mile in Hautes-Pyrénées was 122, in Ariège only 108. Further, the

[1] P. Duchemin, 'L'Industrie moderne à Tarbes et dans sa région', in *R.G.P.S.-O.* (1955), vol. xxvi, pp. 176-89.
[2] Details, with a map, are given by R. Balseinte, 'Les Stations thermales françaises', in *R.G.P.S.-O.* (1955), vol. xxvi, pp. 292-306.

population of the higher valleys is steadily declining, a phenomenon common in many of the mountainous parts of Europe.[1] Large areas on the high frontier ridges, on the dissected plateaus between the north-flowing rivers, and on the steep forested slopes, are quite unpopulated. Between these empty areas long strips of population extend along the valley-floors; at their heads are the temporary summer dwellings of the shepherds and a few permanently inhabited villages such as Gavarnie on the Gave de Pau. Further down are larger settlements—small market-towns, resorts and sometimes centres of small industries. Each valley has one or more such towns —Accous on the Gave d'Aspe, Laruns on the Gave d'Ossau, Luz on the Gave de Pau, Arreau in the Neste valley, Bagnères-de-Luchon in the Pique valley, St. Béat on the upper Garonne, Vicdessos and Ax-les-Thermes [2] in the Ariège valley, and Mont-Louis high up in the Conflent. Longitudinal (west-east) communications were for long difficult or impossible, and so the contacts of each valley have tended to be with the margins of the plain of Aquitaine to the north. Small towns therefore grew up at the mouths of the valleys—St. Jean-Pied-de-Port and Mauléon in the west; Arudy, Lourdes, Bagnères-de-Bigorre and Montréjeau in the centre; Foix in the east. The development of industries in the triangle between Tarbes, Lourdes and Bagnères-de-Bigorre has led to an area of dense population; there are over 60,000 people in Tarbes and its six adjacent communes in what forms an '*agglomération bigourdane*', including 3,500 to 4,000 Spaniards. Towns on the southern edge of the plain of Aquitaine, such as Pau, Tarbes and Pamiers, act as minor regional centres for the uplands to the south, and indeed the spheres of influence of Bayonne, Toulouse and Perpignan extend into the Pyrenees.

In the extreme west lives a group of people, the Basques, whose identity has given rise to the district-name of *Pays Basque*.[3] The Basque tongue (an interesting linguistic problem since it seems to be related to no modern European language) is spoken by about 100,000 people in France, and by five times as many in Spain. Though divided by the frontier, the Basques retain much individuality besides their language (though only those living in remote valleys do not speak French as well), including their customs, folk-dancing, costume and their game of *pelote*.

Communications.—The limited pattern of communications reflects the difficulties of the mountain terrain. The south–north valleys

[1] This problem is discussed by G. Lesenne, 'Le Dépeuplement des vallées d'Argelès, d'Azun et de Cauterets: ses causes et ses conséquences', in *R.G.P.S.-O.* (1956), vol. xxvii, pp. 135-60.

[2] J. Reboul, 'Ax-les-Thermes: étude géographique', in *R.G.P.S.-O.* (1939), vol. x, pp. 117-37.

[3] G. Viers, *Pays Basque français et Barretous* (1961).

contain *cul-de-sac* roads, linked with one main longitudinal route (*N117*) which runs from Bayonne via Pau, Tarbes and Foix to Perpignan, parallel to the frontier but twenty-five to thirty miles away from it. Other links between the Pyrenean valleys are indeed difficult; it is possible to cross from the valley of the Ossau to that of the Pau over the winding Cols de Soulor and d'Aubisque (5,610 feet), or from Pau to the Adour valley by the magnificent road over the Col de Tourmalet (6,939 feet). These and other roads have been considerably improved in recent years to cope with the tourist traffic. But many of the high valleys are linked, if at all, only by mule-tracks. A continuous '*Route des Pyrénées*' can be followed only in the east. Most of the roads in the High Pyrenees are snow-blocked from November to May or even later.

Many tracks lead up to the high *ports* and *brèches* on the frontier-ridge, and five cross into Spain—the Roncesvalles in the west, the Somport and the Pourtalet near the Pic du Midi d'Ossau, the Envalira and the Puymorens. The highest, the Envalira, rises to 7,897 feet, linking Ax-les-Thermes via the little state of Andorra to Lerida; it is blocked until late June. Another road into Spain follows the valley of the Garonne from St. Béat into the Val d'Aran and on to Viella, from where one can proceed to Lerida either via the Col de Bonaigua or by the road-tunnel under the Col de Viella. The easiest routes into Spain are by way of the west flank from Bayonne either to San Sebastian or Pamplona, from the Têt to the Segre valley by the low Col de la Perche, and in the east from Perpignan over the Col du Perthus.

The Pyrenean railway systems are even more limited, although the Hendaye and Cerbère lines around the western and eastern flanks were opened as early as 1864 and 1878 respectively. The Col de la Perche was traversed by a narrow-gauge line to the Spanish frontier at Bourg-Madame in 1911, but a crossing of the main frontier-ridge was not effected until 1928, when the line over the Col de Somport was opened; this required sixteen tunnels, including one at the summit (altitude 3,973 feet) nearly five miles long. In the following year another line was completed from Ax-les-Thermes up the Ariège valley to the Col de Puymorens, under which the line passes in a tunnel nearly 3½ miles long at a height of 5,141 feet, then descending to the frontier-station of La Tour-de-Carol. These two lines are but little used, except for tourist-traffic within France, for the change of gauge at the Spanish frontier prevents any through-traffic. The remaining Pyrenean lines comprise short lengths running southward up the valleys to towns such as Cauterets, Arreau and Luchon.

BIBLIOGRAPHICAL NOTE

Footnotes have been used throughout the text to indicate books and articles to which specific reference has been made. The names of journals quoted frequently are abbreviated, as shown in the following list ; those to which only rare reference is made are quoted in full.

A. de G.	*Annales de Géographie*
B.S. Belge Et. G.	*Bulletin de la Société Belge des Etudes Géographiques*
B.S.R. Belge G.	*Bulletin de la Société Royale Belge de Géographie*
E.G.	*Economic Geography*
G.J.	*Geographical Journal*
G.R.	*Geographical Review*
R.G.A.	*Revue de Géographie Alpine*
R.G.P.S.-O.	*Revue Géographique des Pyrénées et du Sud-Ouest*
T.E.S.G.	*Tijdschrift voor Economische en Sociale Geografie*
T.K. Ned. A.G.	*Tijdschrift van het Koninklijk Nederlandsch Aardrijkskundig Genootschap*
T.P.R.	*Town Planning Review*

References quoted in the footnotes are not repeated below, except where they are of specific interest. It is necessary to summarise here more general sources, including statistical material.

Statistical Sources

Each of the four countries has an active government statistical department. These are (i) for Belgium the *Institut National de Statistique* (44 Rue de Louvain, Bruxelles) ; (ii) for France the *Institut National de la Statistique et des Etudes Economiques* (29 Quai Branly, Paris, 7e) ; (iii) for Luxembourg the *Office de la Statistique Générale* (19 Avenue de la Porte-Neuve, Luxembourg) ; and (iv) for the Netherlands the *Centraal Bureau voor Statistiek* ('s-Gravenhage). Each of these organisations publishes a statistical year-book of immense value : the *Annuaire statistique de la Belgique et du Congo belge*, the *Annuaire statistique de la France*, the *Annuaire statistique (Grand-Duché de Luxembourg)* (though this is actually published quinquennially) and the *Jaarcijfers voor Nederland* (published biennially). Each of these lists as an appendix the considerable number of other more specialised publications which cover every aspect of national life.

General Works : Belgium

1. *Bibliographie géographique de la Belgique*, compiled by M. E. Dumont and L. de Smet (1954 and 1960) ; this is a vast compendium of references.
2. *Atlas de Belgique*, in course of publication by the *Comité National de Géographie* ; this provides a series of beautifully printed maps on the standard scale of 1 : 500,000.

3. A. Demangeon, *Belgique–Pays-Bas–Luxembourg* (1927), which is the second volume of the *Géographie universelle*.
4. M. A. Lefèvre, *Notice sur la carte oro-hydrographique de Belgique à 1 : 500,000* (1937), which provides an admirable summary of the structure and relief of the country.
5. W. Tuckermann, *Länderkunde der Niederlande und Belgiens* (1931).
6. Y. van Wettere-Verhasselt, 'Les Frontières du nord et de l'est de la Belgique', monograph published in the *Revue belge de Géographie* (1965), no. 89, with 400 pp. and a bibliography of 885 references.

Benelux

1. F. Dussart, *Le Benelux* (1958).
2. A. Gamblin, *Géographie du Benelux* (1960).
3. F. Gay and P. Wagret, *Le Benelux* (1965).
4. P. George and R. Sevrin, *Belgique, Pays-Bas, Luxembourg* (1967), a recent survey of 282 pp.

France

1. *Régions géographiques de la France* (1953), produced by a *Commission Centrale* (including E. de Martonne and M. Cholley) for the *Institut National de la Statistique et des Etudes Economiques*, with a most useful folding-map of regions and sub-regions.
2. *Atlas de France*, prepared by the *Comité National de Géographie* founded in 1920, under the sponsorship of the *Académie des Sciences*. Of the eighty-two projected sheets, sixty-nine had been produced before the war. Between 1951 and 1958 a revised edition appeared, with a number of additional sheets.
3. *Atlas aérien*, edited by P. Deffontaines and M.-J. Brunhes-Delamarre, a series of five volumes of magnificent air photographs, with accompanying maps and text, in course of publication. Each of the major regions of France is dealt with in turn.
4. Regional atlases include *Atlas de la France de l'Est* (1960); and *Atlas du Nord* (1961). A vast amount of information is provided by the 46 maps and 200 pp. of accompanying text in *Atlas industriel de la France* (1959).
5. National planning in France is discussed by P. Bauchet, *La Planification française; quinze ans d'expérience* (1962); J. Fourastié and P. Courthéoux, *La Planification économique en France* (1963); and F. Coront-Ducluzeau, *La Formation de l'espace économique nationale* (1964).
6. Ph. Ariès, *Le Peuplement et les migrations intérieures en France métropolitaine* (1961).
7. O. Barré, *L'Architecture du sol de la France* (1903).
8. J. Beaujeu-Garnier, *Le Relief de la France par la carte et le croquis* (1953).
9. L. Bertrand, *Les Grandes Régions géologiques du sol français* (1935).
10. L. Bertrand, *Histoire géologique du sol français* (two volumes, 1944, 1946).
11. P. Vidal de la Blache, *Tableau de la géographie de la France*

(1911); this is *Tome I, première partie*, of *Histoire de France illustrée*.

12. J. Brunhes, *Géographie humaine de la France* (two volumes, 1920) (*tome 1er de l'Histoire de la Nation française*, edited by G. Hanotaux).
13. F. Carrière and Ph. Pinchemel, *Le Fait urbain en France* (1963).
14. J. Chardonnet, *Géographie industrielle*, vol. I, 'Les sources d'énergie' (1962).
15. A Cholley, R. Clazier and J. Dresch, *La France* (n.d.).
16. A. Dauzat, *La Vie rurale en France* (1961).
17. A. Demangeon, *Géographie économique et humaine de la France, 2e et 3e vol. du tome vi de la Géographie universelle* (1946, 1948).
18. R. Dion, *Les Frontières de la France* (1947).
19. D. Faucher, with twenty-five contributors, *La France: géographie-tourisme* (1951-2). This magnificent work published by Larousse, in two volumes, describes France on a regional basis, with a wealth of maps and photographs.
20. J. Fèvre and H. Hauser, *Régions et pays de France* (1909).
21. J. Fourastié and H. Montet, *L'Economie française dans le Monde* (1962).
22. L. Gallois, *Régions naturelles et noms de pays* (1911), a classic exposition of French regional geography.
23. L. Gallouédec and F. Maurette, *Géographie de la France* (n.d.).
24. P. George, *Géographie économique et sociale de la France* (1946).
25. A. Gamblin, *L'Energie en France, étude de géographie* (1961).
26. L. Gorny, *Les Economies régionales en France* (1958).
27. E. Jarry, *Provinces et pays de France: essai de géographie historique* (1950).
28. L. de Launay, *Géologie de la France* (1921); this provides a clear account of the regional geology, with a series of folding maps.
29. P. Mallet, *La Structure économique de la France* (1958).
30. E. de Martonne, *Les Régions géographiques de la France* (1921).
31. E. de Martonne, *Les Grandes Régions de la France* (1926).
32. E. de Martonne, *Géographie physique de la France* (1947), *1er vol. du tome vi de la Géographie universelle*.
33. E. de Martonne, *France physique* (1942).
34. J. Moniez, *L'Industrie charbonnière française depuis 1946* (1959).
35. H. Ormsby, *France: A Regional and Economic Geography* (1931, second edition 1950).
36. P. Pinchemel, *La Géographie de la France* (1964), two volumes, with a detailed bibliography, perhaps the most comprehensive modern text-book on France.
37. C. Précheur, *La Sidérurgie française* (1963).
38. J.-M. Sourdillat, *Géographie agricole de la France* (1959).
39. A. Vigarié, *Les Grands Ports de commerce de la Seine au Rhin* (1964), with an atlas.
40. A most attractive series of texts on the regions of France, entitled *France de Demain*, under the general direction of F.-L. Closon and

P. George, has been published since 1959 by *Presses Universitaires de France* (Paris). The country is covered in eight volumes.

Luxembourg

1. A. Demangeon, *Belgique–Pays-Bas–Luxembourg* (1927), which is the second volume of the *Géographie universelle*.
2. J. Robert, *Geologische Heimatkunde von Luxembourg* (1916).
3. C. Stevens, *Note sur la morphologie du Grand-Duché de Luxembourg interprétée d'après la carte hypsométrique à 1/200,000 de J. Hansen* (1928).

Netherlands

1. A. Demangeon, *Belgique–Pays-Bas–Luxembourg* (1927), which is the second volume of the *Géographie universelle*.
2. *Comptes-Rendus du Congrès International de Géographie, Amsterdam, 1938*; this contains numerous accounts of various aspects of the country.
3. C. H. Edelman, *Soils of the Netherlands* (1950); this includes a most detailed folding-map on a scale of 1/400,000.
4. F. J. Faber, *Geologie van Nederland* (1933).
5. G. J. A. Mulder (edited), *Handboek der Geografie van Nederland* (1949–55); this great work deals with the country both subjectively and by regions.
6. R. Schuiling, *Nederland, Handboek der Ardrijkskunde* (two volumes, 1934, 1936).
7. A. J. Pannekoek (editor), *Geological History of the Netherlands* (1956); this detailed explanation to the Geological Map of the Netherlands on a scale of 1/200,000, in English, is illustrated with a large number of maps and plates, and includes many bibliographical references.
8. The *Atlas van Nederland*, to comprise 101 maps, with a number of smaller plans and explanatory text (with English translation), is in course of publication.

INDEX OF PLACE-NAMES

Note. 1. Strict alphabetical order is maintained, including composite and hyphenated names. The proper name is given first (e.g. Blanc, Mont), except where the generic name has been integrated (e.g. Mont-Louis), and also where Grand-, Petit, Haut- and Bas- are used.

2. References to maps and their captions are indicated by (fig.) after the particular page number. Plate references are given in Roman numerals at the end of each entry.

3. More important page references are given in heavy type.

4. Alternative place-name forms are indexed, and cross-referred to the form actually used in the text.

5. The following abbreviations are used : C. *Canal ;* dept., *département ;* E. *Etang ;* F. *Forêt ;* I. *Ile* or *Iles ;* Pte. *Pointe ;* R. *River.*

2 A 2